AMERICAN GAME BIRDS
of Field and Forest

FRANK C. EDMINSTER

AMERICAN GAME BIRDS

of Field and Forest

THEIR HABITS, ECOLOGY AND MANAGEMENT

⤛⤙ *New York* ⤚⤜

CHARLES SCRIBNER'S SONS

1954

CONTENTS

⊰⊰⟨⟩⟩⟩

CHAPTER 1. *The Ring-necked Pheasant* 1

CHAPTER 2. *The Wild Turkey* 58

CHAPTER 3. *The Sage Grouse* 114

CHAPTER 4.   *The Sharp-tailed Grouse*   **135**

CHAPTER 5.   *The Prairie Chicken*   **168**

CHAPTER 6. *The Ruffed Grouse* 195

CHAPTER 7. *The Bobwhite Quail* 243

CHAPTER 8. *The California Quail*   302

CHAPTER 9. *Gambel's, Mountain, and Scaled Quails*   337

CHAPTER 10.   *The Chukar Partridge*   357

CHAPTER 11.   *The Hungarian Partridge*   368

CHAPTER 12.   *The American Woodcock*   392

CHAPTER 13. *The Band-tailed Pigeon* 415

CHAPTER 14. *The Mourning Dove* 429

CHAPTER 15. *The White-winged Dove* 454

ACKNOWLEDGEMENTS

———————————— ‹‹‹›››———————————

MANY of my colleagues have generously reviewed and criticized one or more chapters of the manuscript. They have helped improve its technical accuracy, completeness, and readability, and I am greatly indebted to them for this help. The following are those who have reviewed portions of the manuscript: Philip F. Allan, U. S. Soil Conservation Service; G. A. Ammann, Michigan Game Division; Wallace Anderson, U. S. Soil Conservation Service; Fred M. Baumgartner, Oklahoma A. & M. College; Glen C. Christensen, Nevada Fish and Game Commission; Verne E. Davison, U. S. Soil Conservation Service; John T. Emlen, University of Wisconsin; Donald S. Galbreath, Washington State Game Department; Ben Glading, California Department of Fish and Game; Gordon W. Gullion, Nevada Fish and Game Commission; Fred M. and Frances Hamerstrom, Wisconsin Conservation Department; Charles O. Handley, West Virginia Conservation Commission; James H. Jenkins, University of Georgia; Wallace Macgregor, California Department of Fish and Game; Robert A. McCabe, University of Wisconsin; H. Elliott McClure, U. S. Army; M. S. McMurtrey, U. S.

Soil Conservation Service; Howard L. Mendell, University of Maine Cooperative Wildlife Research Unit; Johnson A. Neff, U. S. Fish and Wildlife Service; Dan Nelson and Eugene P. Odum, University of Georgia; Robert L. Patterson, Wyoming Game and Fish Commission; George B. Saunders, U. S. Fish and Wildlife Service; Paul M. Scheffer, U. S. Soil Conservation Service; William G. Sheldon, University of Massachusetts Cooperative Wildlife Research Unit; Wendell G. Swank, Arizona Game and Fish Commission; and Charles F. Yocom, Humboldt State College, California.

To W. L. McAtee, formerly of the U. S. Fish and Wildlife Service, I am grateful for help in editing portions of the work.

Credit for use of photographs is due the U. S. Soil Conservation Service, Arizona Game and Fish Commission (O. N. Arrington), California Department of Fish and Game, Delaware Game Commission, Michigan Game Division, Pennsylvania Game Commission, Wisconsin Conservation Department, Wyoming Game and Fish Commission, A. A. Allen, H. Elliott McClure, Johnson A. Neff, and R. J. Niedrach.

PREFACE

IN the preparation of a book on a group of game birds, the problem of organizing the material confronts the author at once. Should each species be covered completely in one place; or, should each phase of the subject be treated for all species in one place? Each approach has its advantages and disadvantages. Some duplication occurs either way. When it is used as a reference, the reader finds some skipping about necessary, either way. If he seeks the sex ratio of all the species, for example, he must jump from one chapter to another to obtain the full story when the book is organized in species chapters. On the other hand, if he wishes the full story of a particular game bird, he must skip from chapter to chapter if the material is organized in chapters devoted to habitat, food habits, management, and so on, with each chapter treating all species. I have chosen to present the subject by species-chapters, since I believe it the better way.

The matter of duplication of material is not easily avoided in species-chapters. Some matters apply equally to several or all species. Should they be repeated in each chapter? I have avoided this as much as possible. Some topics are covered only once, and the reader must seek them in the one chapter where they appear. In particular, the discussion of farm planning methods for improving habitat, land use capabilities in connection with farm conservation planning, and co-operative work in soil conservation districts is given only in Chapter 1. These subjects are treated here because it is the *first* chapter, and because the pheasant is a widely-distributed and very popular bird. The principles that are discussed in these topics are the same throughout the country, and are applicable whatever game birds are involved. The details in the examples used will of course vary from region to region. Hunting co-operatives are discussed only in Chapter 1, water development techniques for arid land species only in Chapter 8, and so on. In each instance, topics of general application treated only once are in the chapter that is most logical.

Duplication of information within a chapter is also a bothersome problem. For example, the number of eggs a bird lays is a part of the story of its nesting *habits*. It is also a phase of its *productivity*. To make the story fluent and complete, some duplication has been necessary. I have tried to keep it to a minimum.

In treating ecological information, one often may give the impression that the facts are completely known, or else forever repeat qualifications to the effect that more data are needed. I hope I have not made it seem that our knowledge of these game birds is thoroughly known. It is not, not even for species such as the bob-white, pheasant, and ruffed grouse that have been studied long and intensively. We are barely over the threshold of learning the ecology of these birds. The fact that much has been learned in the last 25 years does not change the need for continuing research. Our knowledge of some of these birds is so fragmentary that it is difficult even to piece together a full story about them. Much more research is needed on them.

One of the major sources of information on recent and current game research is the *Pittman-Robertson Quarterly,* issued by the United States Fish and Wildlife Service. Its progress summaries of research studies give useful data prior to project completion and final publication. Information from these reports has been used frequently, and the source cited as *"P-R Quarterly"* and the date of issue. These references correspond to the previous quarterly report of the state concerned; e.g. *"P-R Quarterly,* October 1951" would be the same as the April 1951 quarterly report of the state involved. This procedure is followed so that readers may locate all the citations in one series of periodicals and need go to the original report only for further details.

Foreign publications, except those of

Canada, have not been used as sources of scientific data on the exotic species; the book's scope is limited to the stories of birds on this continent. The omission of this literature, especially the English, is in no way a depreciation of its value.

I should make it clear that I do not pretend to be an "expert" on all the species discussed in this book. My own professional work has been mostly in the eastern United States, and my experience with the western species has

been very limited. The treatment of them is largely a job of compilation. Naturally, I have depended heavily on the writings of certain individuals who have pioneered in research on them; in particular, the writings of these men have been of inestimable value: Robert Patterson on the sage grouse; Ben Glading and his associates on the California and mountain quails; Johnson Neff on the band-tailed pigeon; and D. M. Gorsuch on Gambel's quail.

Frank C. Edminster

21 Hale Street,
New Brunswick, New Jersey,
September 19, 1954.

USE OF PLANT NAMES

Plant names used in the text have in general followed the usage of *Standardized Plant Names,* second edition, 1942, but with some exceptions. Where the common name of a plant occurring in a bird's range has a prevalent usage, and differs from that of *Standardized Plant Names,* the colloquial version has been followed. This has resulted in a few instances

in a plant being called by one name in one chapter and by a different name in another. The common names of plants have been used in the text, with a few exceptions where the scientific name was needed for clarity. The scientific names of all plants mentioned in the text are given in a *List of Plant Names,* page 476.

LIST OF FIGURES

⟨⟨⟨⟩⟩⟩

LIST OF TABLES

AMERICAN GAME BIRDS
of Field and Forest

The Ring-necked Pheasant

ORIGIN AND CLASSIFICATION

THE game bird that we know as the "ring-neck," was native in parts of Asia where numerous species of pheasants exist. Three that were very similar in type were the Caucasian pheasant, whose scientific name is *Phasianus colchicus,* the Chinese pheasant (*Phasianus torquatus*), and the green pheasant (*Phasianus versicolor*). The Caucasian pheasant had many variations, or subspecies, that lived in western Asia between the Black Sea and the Caspian Sea, and east of the Caspian Sea as far as western Thibet. The Chinese pheasant also had numerous subspecies in Manchuria, and in eastern and central China. The green pheasant was found in Japan. Some authorities consider these three as one species.

All three of these varieties of pheasants were introduced into the United States, but only the Caucasian and Chinese pheasants have succeeded here. They came by two different routes. The Caucasian species had been successfully established in parts of Europe as early as the 10th century B.C. It reached England over a thousand years ago, possibly brought by the Romans. There it came to be known as the English black-necked pheasant, which is a typical strain of the Caucasian bird. This variety was brought into the Eastern United States around 1790, when fruitless attempts to establish it in New Hampshire and New Jersey were made.

For almost a century after these first trials there were few significant notes about the pheasant in America. Then in 1881, Judge Owen N. Denny, at that time Consul General at Shanghai, arranged for the shipment of a few Chinese pheasants to his native Oregon, where they were liberated in the Willamette Valley. From this nucleus developed the first successful establishment of pheasants in this country. Subsequently, pheasants of various subspecies of both the Chinese and Caucasian species were liberated in great numbers in all states of the United States and all provinces of Canada. Since the species freely cross, as well as the subspecies, the resulting stock of pheasants in America is a mixture. We call it the ring-necked pheasant, and give it the scientific name *Phasianus colchicus*. In the Northwest, the character of our pheasants resembles the Chinese species more than the Caucasian. In the East it is vice versa.

HISTORY OF THE PHEASANT IN AMERICA

THE introduction of pheasants in Oregon succeeded beyond the fondest hopes of its sponsors. The ring-neck expanded its numbers so rapidly that a 2½-month season for hunting was opened in 1892 in Oregon. In the interim, introduction of ring-necks began in Washington State in 1883, and in California in 1889. The California liberations were the first undertaken by a state game agency. But whereas the sportsmen of Washington waited only until 1903 for their first legal hunting season, twenty years after stocking began, California hunters did not enjoy public pheasant hunting until 1933, a delay of 44 years. (Hjersman, 1947.)

After the successful opening of pheasant

hunting in Oregon, most of the Eastern states started new trials with these birds. Success was slow in coming; only scattered areas of thriving pheasant communities were reported before the 1920's. Pennsylvania began stocking pheasants officially in 1915, and had its first open season the same year. Yet, despite continuing open seasons each year, the state game authorities as late as 1919 predicted that "pheasants will never become established in Pennsylvania because they cannot stand hard winters and hard hunting both." It was not many years later that, in numbers shot, it had passed the native ruffed grouse as the most successful game bird of the Commonwealth.

All the other states tried to establish pheasants before World War I. The fabulous pheasant populations of South Dakota resulted from stocking that began in 1912; the first open season was declared in 1919. By the early 1930's, the annual pheasant kill in South Dakota varied from 1 to 2½ millions. The pattern of success and failure over the country soon became sharply defined. The optimum zone proved to be the corn and wheat belts. The area of complete failure was the warm and humid Southeast. Despite the great areas where the pheasant proved to be unsuited, and other large sections where its tenure hangs by a precarious thread, it became in the short space of about 50 years the most popular and most sought after game bird in the United States. An ardent advocate of the ruffed grouse or the bobwhite quail might resent seeing the pheasant termed "most popular." Certainly the ring-neck is not our best game bird from the standpoint of sporting qualities. But the fact is that it furnishes fine upland bird hunting for more hunters over a larger area than does any of our native species. Hence, quantitatively rather than qualitatively, it must be given due laurels.

We can probably look on the present extent of pheasant establishment as about all that can be expected. Only in some newly irrigated sections of the West is it likely to extend its range further, or to prove successful through artificial stocking in new areas. In fact, the greater probability is for some recession to take place in pheasant numbers and distribution. Being an introduced species, it may have over-exploited its initial success, as so often happens with an aggressive animal in a strange environment. Witness the initial surge and subsequent diminution of such introduced creatures as the English sparrow and Japanese beetle—though these may not be proper analogies.

How far such a permanent decrease of pheasants may go can only be guessed. The great decline of the mid-forties was followed by a good recovery, but not to the population levels previously attained. It will depend partly on the changes that take place in our farming systems, as the pheasant is essentially a bird of the crop fields. But there is little doubt that the ring-neck is with us to stay, and will continue to be a most important game bird.

GEOGRAPHIC RANGE IN AMERICA

THE pheasant's range now includes much of our Northern states and the southern edge of Canada (see Figure 1). The bird has an unstable foothold in the southern portions of Maine, New Hampshire, and Vermont. It is found in the farming sections of southern New England, the Connecticut River and Lake Champlain valleys of Vermont, and in northern New York except in the Adirondack Mountains.

Its most significant range, where it furnishes dependable hunting, begins in eastern and central New York and Long Island. From there it extends south through New Jersey and eastern Pennsylvania to the northern edge of Delaware, Maryland, and West Virginia. Westward, the range covers southern Ontario, southern Michigan, Ohio, and thence over a broadening area through the Midwestern states through Iowa, northern Missouri, and western Kansas to northern Oklahoma, eastern Colorado

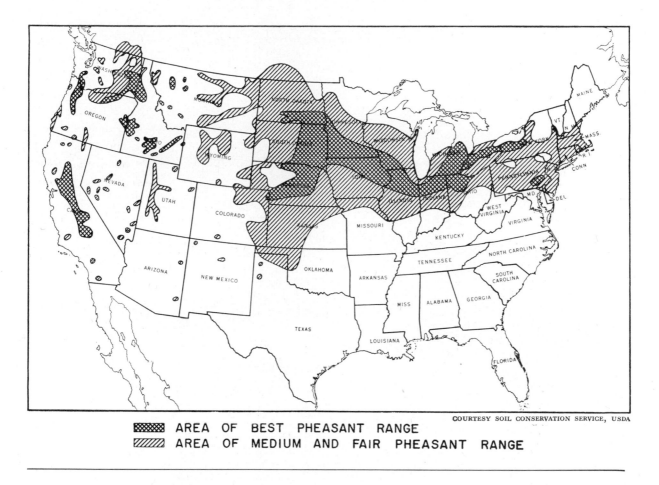

AREA OF BEST PHEASANT RANGE
AREA OF MEDIUM AND FAIR PHEASANT RANGE

COURTESY SOIL CONSERVATION SERVICE, USDA

FIGURE 1. *Geographic range of the ring-necked pheasant in the United States and Canada.*

and Wyoming, central Montana, and southern Saskatchewan. Only the northern forested portions of Wisconsin and Minnesota are excluded from the pheasant range in the Midnorthern states. Its area of successful establishment includes the southern parts of Manitoba, Saskatchewan, and Alberta.

To the west of this great contiguous range, about 2,500 miles across, there is a complete break where the Rockies rise above habitable pheasant country. Then in the intermountain region and in the far West there is another great area of pheasant range. It extends from northern British Columbia southward over much of Washington, Oregon, and Idaho. Thence through many valleys it extends in fingers and in islands into Montana, Wyoming,

Colorado, Utah, and California. Of particular significance are the Palouse Wheat Belt of eastern Washington and northern Idaho, irrigated valleys of eastern Washington and Oregon and Montana, the Willamette Valley of Oregon, the Snake River Valley of southern Idaho, and the Central Valleys of California. Small but notable units of pheasant range lie in southeastern Arizona in high, irrigated valleys, and in New Mexico along the Rio Grande Valley.

Pheasants have not been successfully established in the southeastern quarter of the country. This has not happened for lack of effort on men's part, for they have been tried repeatedly in all these states. Hopeful sportsmen still continue to stock pheasants in this

PLATE 1. *Agriculture is the foundation of pheasant habitat. An aerial view of a part of the Willamette Valley, Oregon, where the pheasant was first introduced successfully into the United States. The pattern of fields of small grains, corn, grass grown for seed, orchards, clover, and pasture, mixed with woodlands and wild lands makes excellent pheasant range.*

area, though the prospects of success are dim indeed. Why the pheasant should not "take" south of a latitude approximating the Mason-Dixon line is not understood. This line that separates the area suitable for pheasants from that which is apparently unsuitable is remarkably sharp. For example, some of the best pheasant hunting in the East is found in Lancaster County in southeastern Pennsylvania. Yet just across the border in Maryland the number of pheasants is insignificant. A distance of less than 50 miles separates good pheasant hunting from practically no pheasant hunting. The baffling thing about this condition is that the ranges are practically identical.

The same soils prevail, and the same kind of farming. The climate is as nearly similar as would be expected in a 50-mile difference of latitude.

This same clear demarcation of the southern limit of the pheasant's range continues all the way across the humid, low-altitude portion of the country to Oklahoma. Many opinions have been expressed about the cause. It is not to be found in the bird's food, cover, natural enemies, diseases, or in man's hunting. Experts generally agree that the solution lies in the climate. But in just what climatic element, or combination of elements, remains a mystery. It is not those most commonly associated with game-bird

COURTESY SOIL CONSERVATION SERVICE, USDA

PLATE 2. *Irrigated valleys of the West produce some of the highest pheasant populations. This is Washington's Kittitas Valley where pheasants abound. Hungarian partridges and California valley quail are also found in the valley and sage grouse in the bordering wild lands.*

losses—cold winters and deep snow. Neither is the cause to be found in humidity or in the amount or distribution of rainfall. Bennitt and Terrill (1940) suggested that the distinction between pheasant range and nonpheasant range may lie in temperatures during the warm months. They point out that the line marking the southern limit of the pheasant range is nearly identical with Thornthwaite's (1931) line between his microthermal and mesothermal climatic provinces. North of this line ". . . the summers are shorter but *relatively* warmer than farther south." It is thought that such a factor might have a direct influence on pheasant embryos on hot days during the nest-

ing period. Yeatter (1950) concluded: "It seems probable that vulnerability of pheasant embryos to air temperature during the laying period has an important influence in limiting the southern distribution of pheasants." Continuous exposure of pheasant eggs to temperatures much over 100° F. is lethal. The probability of this occurring frequently is high in the mesothermal climatic area to the south of the good pheasant range, but is low in the more northern microthermal climate.

The acceptable range of pheasants on this continent comprises areas with a mean annual temperature of from 40° to 74° F. and altitudes ranging from sea level to 7,000 feet.

PLATE 3. *The ring-necked pheasant.*

DESCRIPTION

THE ring-neck is about the size of a trim white leghorn hen. The male birds weigh about 2½ to 3 pounds when full grown, the hens about 2 pounds. The cocks reach a length of 34 inches, of which the tail may be as much as 21 inches when fully developed. The hens are about 24 inches long, half of which is the tail. Their wings are rather short, giving them a wing-spread of only 32 inches.

The male is a brilliantly plumaged bird. The head and neck are a bright, metallic blue-green, casting reflections of purple and bronze. There is a vivid red area of bare skin on the sides of the head, and a conspicuous white ring around the neck below the blue. This ring varies considerably; predominantly Caucasian (or English) birds lack the white ring. The back is brownish-orange with spotting of black and buff. The rump is rufous, tending toward a variegated grayish-blue on the fore part next to the back and extending down the sides. The long, pointed tail is rufous, barred with black and olive. The flanks are buff, spotted with

black and merging into the glossy, coppery breast. The fore part of the wings is a pale bluish color, while the remainder is brown, barred with black and green. The cock is a most difficult bird to describe because of its tremendously variegated pattern of colors, bars, spots, and edgings. But there is no mistaking him for any other bird. He is as distinctive as they come.

The hen is a notable contrast to her consort. She is as somber as he is gaudy. No better description is needed than that she is a mottled blend of browns with some buff and dusky markings. At a quick glance she could be mistaken for a ruffed grouse, prairie chicken, or sharptailed grouse. But her long, pointed tail is one characteristic which easily distinguishes her from both the ruffed grouse and the prairie chicken. The sharp-tail has feathered tarsi, while the pheasant's are bare. The round white spots on the wings, the clear gray throat and abdomen of the sharp-tail are also distinctive.

ITS IMPORTANCE AS A GAME BIRD IN AMERICA

THE annual legal hunting harvest of pheasants in America is between 16 and 18 million birds in good years—truly a phenomenal record for a species of little account only 30 years ago. Of food alone this yield provides 20,000 tons. Even more remarkable is the geographic distribution of this harvest. The northern great plains, stretching from Kansas to Alberta, where the first open hunting season on pheasants took place just shortly after World War I, provides two-thirds of all these birds. Led by the fabulous pheasant lands of South Dakota, where the individual hunter's bag was frequently measured in dozens of birds in the early 1940's, at least three of these states count their annual kill by the million—North and South Dakota and Nebraska. Only Michigan and Minnesota can rank in the same class with them.

Another great pheasant hunting area includes the northern states from Ohio to Minnesota, which, with Iowa, contribute nearly 5 million a year toward the total. From southern Michigan and northwest Ohio through the heartland of America's "breadbasket" to Iowa and southern Minnesota—the corn belt—most of these pheasants are produced. Here too the ring-neck is a Johnny-come-lately. Some of these states did not begin pheasant hunting until well into the 1920's.

It is unlikely that these high pheasant yields in these two best ranges will hold up indefinitely. Apart from temporary declines brought about by changes in annual productivity, a permanent decline to a lower population level is probable. In the eastern and western areas, where the bird first settled, it reached high populations for a few years that could not be maintained. All successful introduced species go through this stage of temporary untenable numbers; finally nature's checks and balances bring them into equilibrium.

Two other divisions of our American pheasant range, the northeastern states and the far West, each harvest up to a million or more birds each good year. In the Northeast, the majority of the birds are grown in New York, Pennsylvania, and New Jersey. Relatively few are harvested in New England, and almost none south of Pennsylvania. The best of these eastern pheasant lands are the fertile limestone valleys of southeastern Pennsylvania and the lake plains of western New York and southern Ontario. In a limited area there the pheasant hunting is as good as in the Midwest range. The far-western pheasant range lies in the semi-humid and irrigated valleys of Washington, Oregon, Idaho, British Columbia, northern and central California, and the intermountain region of Utah and Idaho. The best known of these pheasant hunting areas are the Willamette Valley in Oregon, where the first successful stocking of pheasants was done in the United States, the Yakima Valley in Washington, the Palouse area in Washington and Idaho, the Snake River Valley in Idaho and Oregon, and central California.

It is significant that the good pheasant habitat includes most of the densely populated human areas too. Hunters in New York, Philadelphia, Baltimore, Pittsburgh, Buffalo, Cleveland, Detroit, Chicago, St. Paul, Minneapolis, Omaha, Kansas City, San Francisco, Portland, and Seattle, and dozens of lesser large cities, can reach good pheasant hunting coverts in an hour or two from their homes. Even so, probably most of the hunting is done by rural folks and small-town residents. Altogether, some 70–80% of our licensed hunters, over 10 million, reside in the pheasant range. Many more hunt on their own lands without being licensed. What proportion of these people hunt pheasants is not recorded, but it is a great majority.

The pheasant kill depends on the abundance of the birds, and on the numbers of hunters. Among the four areas of pheasant range, that with the most ring-necks has the fewest hunters; but this makes hunting opportunities even better. In the northern plains area, centering in South Dakota, the average annual bag per hunter is 12 birds in good years. In contrast, the corn belt has many pheasants, but also the most hunters. Its average yearly bag is only 1½ pheasants per hunter. The western area combines good local pheasant populations with large numbers of hunters. There the average year's take per hunter is one to two birds. Finally, in the Northeast, where moderate to low pheasant populations are pursued by large numbers of hunters, the annual yield per man is only a little over half a bird.

The ring-neck has more economic values than merely the hunting he provides; corollary to pheasant hunting is the business it stimulates. Hunting equipment, such as guns, ammunition, and clothing, and the food, hotel, and transportation services for pheasant hunting, cost many millions of dollars annually. In many communities this income is a considerable factor in the local economy.

But not all the gaudy cackler's attributes

are good ones. Unfortunately he frequently gets in trouble with his hosts, the farmers on whose lands he lives. His very popularity gets him in wrong. When the army of pheasant hunting enthusiasts descend upon our northern farmlands on the opening day of the season, a serious social problem arises. For the most part it is an inevitable clash of sincere and just human interests. On the one hand, the farmer desires control over his property; he fears that damage will be done by strangers trespassing. He may or may not be sympathetic to the landless hunter, but to a man, farmers want security from injury to their family, livestock, and equipment. No one can deny the justice of that view. On the other hand, the majority of our hunters do not own farms. If they hunt pheasants, they must do so on the land of others. They *want* to hunt, for hunting is a sport that ranks first among the forms of recreation of American men. As a policy, America wants them to hunt. It is a healthy sport, and one that builds manly virtues. In a way, our American system of hunting is somewhat symbolic of the difference between America and most of the rest of the world. We are free, and in this phase of our freedom we develop those attributes of sagacity and resourcefulness that we think of as superior traits. One can no more criticize a man for wanting to hunt pheasants than he can a landowner for wanting to protect his property.

Thus we have a dilemma. Generally we let it solve itself. There are the laws protecting private property, and those regulating hunting. Within these rules, it becomes a matter to be settled on each farm between owner and visitors. And it would be as simple as that if everyone did stick to the rules. Regrettably, this is not always true; there will always be a few careless folks or wilful violators. Fence gates will be left open, and sometimes fences will even be broken. Domestic animals are sometimes killed inexcusably, but it does happen. People are occasionally hurt, once in a while even killed. Many other things happen

to strain the friendship between country and town cousins, or among farm folks themselves. Much trespassing is done by neighbors.

These real complaints, like taxes, will always be with us. People being what they are, the black sheep will be a social problem in hunting, just as they are in other relations. The only thing we can do is to be vigilant. That's why we have game-law enforcement officers. But all of us have a social responsibility too. We have been too willing to "wink" at conservation law violations and hunting misdemeaners committed on farms. If we all handle these fellows just as we did the food ration cheaters during the war, turn them in as a patriotic duty in guarding our natural resources, then the trouble they cause will be reduced to a minimum.

One more comment on farmer-hunter relations that is often even more important. It concerns the every-day courtesies of folks visiting one another. Too often hunters trespass on unposted property without first calling at the farmer's house and asking for permission. Ask yourself now, did you do that last fall? Place yourself in the landowner's position. He looks out the window and sees several strangers, always rough-looking at a distance, tramping through the corn. He has no idea who they are; maybe they *are* roughnecks. With such thoughts on his mind (and how could it be otherwise?), he curses the trespassers and thinks about his only legal recourse—posting his land against trespass. How much better it would have been to have stopped to say "hello" first. Fine friendships are born that way.

Farm hunting is a social problem, and the ring-neck pheasant has done more to aggravate it than any other single factor. The advent of the pheasant has placed game-bird shooting within the reach of the novice. His numbers have grown accordingly. It is a problem that must be solved if we are to maintain our open hunting system. We hope it can be solved democratically; it would be a great loss to our people if we had to adopt the "preserve" system, limited wholly to a wealthy or privileged class. We think it can be solved.

The hunting problems that came with the ring-neck are not all his sins. Since he is a farm bird it is not surprising that he eats farm crops. Generally these gleanings are not noticeable, but on occasion they become depredations. Corn plants as they first come through the ground, and tomatoes just as they ripen are the crops most affected. We can hardly blame a farmer for objecting to crop losses from this sort of damage. Often the damage is mistakenly blamed on pheasants; they may be charged with raids done by crows, insects, raccoons, or other creatures. And sometimes the real damage is exaggerated through natural "griping." Nevertheless, the ring-neck sometimes really does cause serious crop damage. His other food habits—taking insects, waste grain, and weed seeds—make up for it somewhat, but one doesn't think of that when dollars are lost. One good way to keep down such losses is to harvest the pheasant crop in the fall so that there will not be too many birds around in spring and summer. So, you see, it is to the farmer's interest to have the year's pheasant surplus shot just as other farm crops are harvested annually. That can only be done through permitting hunting.

HABITS OF THE RING-NECK PHEASANT

As the daylight period lengthens in early spring, and the sun's rays become warmer, the bird world awakens from its winter lethargy. A tremendous urge comes upon them. Some it sends migrating northward from their winter homes, returning to the land of their birth. Sedentary birds, like the pheasant, those that do not migrate to the south each year, feel this change too. Ring-necks that have wintered in flocks, with the males and females largely segregated in separate groups, no longer have this gregarious inclination. They suddenly feel the need for isolation from their own sex, and a desire to seek a mate. There is much fighting among flock members, especially of cock birds. This helps to hasten groups' disintegration.

This is not a self-willed change; physiological adjustments in the bird's body forces him to do what he does. In some manner, the changes in the amounts and kinds of rays from the sun cause the gonads—the testes in the male, ovaries in the female—to enlarge. Associated with the changes in the sex glands are corresponding activities in other glands. The cock pheasant, that but a short time before was concerned largely with seeking food and keeping comfortable in the cold winter, now seeks a private sunny spot where he can "crow" and beat his wings in challenge to other males and as an invitation to hens to join his forming harem. Correspondingly, the hen pheasant shifts her attentions to thoughts of dashing suitors and a place to start homemaking.

COURTSHIP

THE courtship period starts some time from late February through March, depending upon weather and latitude. The more sunshine there is in February and March, the sooner will crowing, fighting, mating, and nesting begin.

The crowing territory that a cock selects is his own "property"; he will defend it from the trespass of other male pheasants, just as songbird males defend a "singing" territory. If he loses a territorial battle, he moves on to find another locality. Here too he may be beaten out by another bird already established there, and have to move again. This continues until he finds a crowing area that he can defend successfully. Usually the crowing area is a mixture of open field and woody cover. Grass frequently occupies the larger part, a hay field or the edge of a pasture. The woody cover may be a part of a woodlot, a patch of brush, a hedgerow or ditchbank; or sometimes a swale of coarse herbs may serve. The actual crowing and the rest of the courtship display are carried on mostly on the open ground and in calm, sunny weather; the denser cover is used as shelter from danger and for roosting.

Courtship continues for several weeks, during which the cocks settle their differences and recognize each other's territories. The size of territory used by a single bird depends on the severity of competition. If the birds are not abundant, a single cock may use 25 to 75 acres as his spring territory; but where the competition is intense he must get along with a much smaller area—even as little as three or four acres. The hens gradually decide on their nesting territories, meanwhile "taking in" the displays that the cocks put on.

When the cock has a lady friend visiting, he quits crowing. That was only the "come on!" He then goes through a strutting act, walking around and around the hen, trying to develop her interest. Very often she plays "hard to get," pretending not to be impressed with his antics. He walks in short steps, and keeps his body leaning toward her. Even his plumage is shifted over to place it in the best position for her view. His wing on the close side is held in a drooping position, and the tail may be partly spread.

Ordinarily, actual mating does not take place until after a month or more of courtship. Early April is the usual time. By then each cock may have gathered a harem of two, three, four, or even more hens that have chosen nesting sites in his crowing area and that accept him in mating. This habit of polygamy is natural to the species, but is emphasized by our hunting system of shooting cocks only (in most states). If the sex ratio does not fall below one cock to about five hens, reproduction seems to go ahead efficiently.

NESTING

PHEASANTS nest in grass more than in any other cover although there is some evidence that this is due as much to necessity as to choice. Because most of the good grassland in pheasant range is hay, that is where a quarter to a half of the nests are made. Other favorite kinds of nesting cover are weedy fields (abandoned or fallow), small grains (winter grains like wheat), roadside grass, and fencerows. Few are found in pastures, woods, or tilled fields. The pastures and tilled crops do not provide adequate shelter at nesting time, and woodland just isn't to the pheasant's liking. Where fencerows and roadside ditches are well distributed and have good grass, weeds, and shrubby growth, they are apt to be used for nest locations even more than hayfields. This fact suggests management measures for reducing the high losses from the mowing over of hayfield nests.

Egg-laying starts during the last half of April, sometimes a little earlier, and frequently continues well into the summer—because of the number of nests destroyed. Most hens renest after losing their first nest, and continue to renest until successful in hatching a clutch, until mating fails, or nesting time runs out in July or August. Average clutch size is 11 eggs, which require a two weeks laying period. Some clutches have as few as five or six eggs, and others as many as 23. Very large clutches are apt to be the result of two hens laying in the same nest. They not only double up on their sisters occasionally, but sometimes lay in the nests of other ground birds. Pheasant eggs are rather commonly found in the nests of ruffed grouse, bobwhite quail, mallard duck, Hungarian partridge, and woodcock.

Broods begin hatching in mid-May for those fortunate birds that succeed in incubating the necessary 23 to 25 days without having the nest destroyed. The majority are not that lucky. Nesting studies in Pennsylvania, Ohio, Michigan, Wisconsin, Iowa, and other states have revealed the nesting loss to be very high, rarely under 60%, sometimes as high as 80%. These losses are mostly from farm machinery operations, but some are due to predators. As would be expected, losses vary greatly with the nesting cover. They are greatest, by far, in hayfield nests. The great saving characteristic of the pheasant, in contrast to the habits of some other game birds, particularly the ruffed grouse, is its perseverance in the face of nesting failure. If she has her nest broken up, the hen pheasant simply makes another nest. The renest clutches have fewer eggs than did the first nest, and probably average more infertile eggs. But at least the pheasants keep at it until they hatch a brood, or time runs out on them.

May nests hatch the highest number of eggs. Not only is the clutch size larger than those of later nests, but the proportion of good eggs is higher. The proportion of infertile eggs is about 5%, rarely more. Of the good eggs, another 5% fail to hatch for some reason (other than physical destruction). Thus about 10 chicks hatch from the average 11 egg nest.

THE BROOD PERIOD

THE young pheasant chicks are precocious: they hatch with fully-developed downy plumage, and are able to walk almost at once. They leave the nest, never to return, once dried off.

Both father and mother pheasants are good parents. Father guards the broods of all his harem. They spend most of the summer in his territory. Most of the time father is not actually with any of his families, but he responds at top speed to any note of alarm from one of his wives. Mother and chicks spend their time finding food of insects, seeds, summer fruits, and greens; dusting in dry dirt to help the feathers grow straight; and just loafing. During stormy weather and when danger threatens they seek good hiding cover. Generally they fare well, and mortality of the youngsters is not excessive. In an average year about seven of the chicks will reach adulthood. Thus the loss of young pheasants is normally about 30%.

The newly-hatched pheasant chick weighs a little less than one ounce. Growth starts slowly, and after two weeks the weight is nearly two ounces; at four weeks it is from four to five ounces. Weight increases more rapidly from then on. At eight weeks the young hens weigh almost a pound, and cocks about 1¼ pounds. Rate of growth begins to level off at about 14

weeks, at which time the hens average 2.2 pounds and the cocks 2.7 pounds.

Pheasant broods are very seclusive when young, and are difficult to flush. The youngsters learn to fly at two to three weeks, but make little use of flight until midsummer. They are excellent runners, and frequently resort to a running escape from trouble even when grown up. The father is attentive to the broods in his territory through the summer until he begins to moult; then he becomes more seclusive. This ordinarily starts in August. About that time the youngsters begin to show some independence too, and the mother relaxes her parental authority. In September the birds are pretty much on their own, though the family groups still hold together in a loose way.

Little travelling is done during the summer, except as the birds are forced to shift their activity from one field to the next as crops are harvested; in other words, they tend to remain in the original breeding territory.

THE FALL AND WINTER MONTHS

As the season shifts to autumn, this territorial exclusiveness ceases; birds from any family join up with others to form flocks. Instead of being spread rather evenly over their range, they concentrate in the more restricted cover suitable for fall and winter feeding and escape from hunters and bad weather. Where corn is grown, fields of that crop are prominent in the fall cover. Brush, wet swales, and marshes also are much used. Sometimes the birds travel miles from their summer cover to reach good fall and winter habitat. Often these travels are down from hill farms to nearby valleys.

In good range these flocks number scores of birds; and as winter comes, they tend to separate into groups of males and females. Winter concentrations on the best range in Ohio, Michigan, Nebraska, and South Dakota frequently are counted in many hundreds. This gregarious habit facilitates hunting, as only a portion of the range holds most of the birds. It also facilitates checking pheasant numbers, feeding the birds during stormy weather, and trapping them for transplanting.

The flight of the adult pheasant is strong but cannot be long sustained. The wings are short and rounded, and are moved by thick breast muscles. Wing action is rapid, and the speed of flight may reach 30 to 35 miles an hour. When shot at they often fly up to 200 yards or even more. Generally they keep close to the ground —10 or 15 feet up—but in downhill flights they may reach a height of 50 feet. On long flights, of 100 yards or more, much of the distance is coasted, the sailing being alternated with short bursts of wing action. After the opening of hunting, they resort more to running for escape. Only when "pushed" to the end of good cover and out into the open, or when "cornered" by a dog, will they flush. Under these conditions, it takes a smart dog to stop the bird's running and then keep it from flushing; that is, to hold a good point.

Winter is the critical period for pheasants, as it is with most game birds. Nevertheless, the old ring-neck is a tough fellow. It can take the severe weather in stride if food and shelter are adequate. Only the most severe weather conditions really cause mortality. When food-seeking is made difficult by deep snows, pheasants frequently invade farmyards to pick up waste grain around the barns and in manure piles. They respond quickly to food placed at feeding stations for them, and are adept at taking corn from stalks and shocks.

THE IMPORTANCE OF "EDGES"

THROUGHOUT the year, pheasants frequent cover margins. The cock crows in open grassland, but protective brushy or rank vegetation is close at hand. Most nests are in the margin, not in the center of grass fields. The broods are almost always headquartered in fields where overgrown fencerows, ditch banks, or similar cover is nearby. Every pheasant hunter knows that in autumn there are more birds along the margins of open field and woody cover than elsewhere. In winter the need for having feed-ing cover and protective shelter side by side is greatest. The pheasant is a bird of the "edges," and this fact is very important in its management. Not only are the amount and quality of needed cover types important, but their *arrangement* is equally so. Through good arrangement of the cover types, proper relationships between food and shelter are attained. The length of the edges reflects this arrangement factor.

THE INFLUENCE OF FARMING CHANGES

DESPITE the pheasant's remarkable success in a great variety of agricultural lands in our north temperate climate, it is greatly affected by changes in its environment. It is not very adaptable to many kinds of changes that may take place in farming. There is little doubt that the trend in the northeastern states to more dairying and less grain raising has adversely affected pheasants. Many individual, specific changes in agricultural practices change the pheasant carrying capacity of the land. The requirement in some New England states that cornfields be plowed under in the fall to aid in corn-borer control has greatly reduced the value of winter range. The use of mechanical corn pickers in place of hand-picking leaves more waste grain, but breaks it down so that it may be buried under winter snows. Placing headlights on tractors and cutting hay at night has increased the losses of nesting hens. The greater use of corn for ensilage, which leaves no waste grain, is another example of a change adverse to the welfare of pheasants. The increased adoption of soil conservation farming methods, on the contrary, is benefiting pheasants as well as other wildlife. Interspersion of cover through strip-cropping, stream-bank plantings, terracing, installation of grass waterways, managed hedges, windbreaks, and related practices not only makes a better arrangement of the needed cover types, but adds new and desirable cover. The list of farming changes that affect the pheasant could be extended on and on. The important thing is this: though the ring-neck can take ad-

PLATE 4. *Contour strip-cropping provides many edges between tilled crops, grains and grass. Contour strips in the middle distances are on steep slopes and are planted to conifer trees and shrubs. This adds long shelter areas adjacent to food producing and nesting cover types.*

vantage of improvement in the environment, it does not adapt itself easily to adverse changes; its food and cover needs and its ways of living remain the same.

ADAPTABILITY TO ARTIFICIAL PROPAGATION

ONE point of adaptability has been exceedingly important to the pheasant in this country: its suitability for propagation in captivity. Raising pheasants in domestication is almost as easy as raising chickens. It has been possible to stock them by hundreds of thousands in many states because of this fact. At first these releases were essential if the birds were to become established; but once the ring-neck has been well established in an area, the value of continued stocking of game-farm birds is another matter. We shall discuss this later as a phase of management. Now we wish merely to note that the bird has proved relatively easy to raise under man's care. Equally important is the fact that the pheasant never fully domesticates in captivity; it continues to prefer to live "on its own," and once released does so. Unlike the mallard, which becomes a "puddle duck" when raised in captivity, or the turkey, which behaves like a barnyard gobbler, the pheasant remains a wild bird. If the bird grown in a pen has been properly "hardened," that is, brought up under conditions that develop an ability to take care of itself, its chances of surviving a reasonable time after liberation are good. This depends on many factors, of course, but a vital one is the stamina of the bird. There is abundant evidence that pheasants raised in large-scale production by artificial, indoor brooding methods are lacking in the resourcefulness required for a high percentage of survival.

SHELTER REQUIREMENTS

TYPES OF RANGE

PHEASANT range is delimited first by climatic requirements. They seem to require a microthermal and humid or subhumid climate. "Microthermal" refers to the "temperature efficiency," and covers a temperature efficiency index of 32°–63° where zero is the factor at the northern limit of plant growth and 128° that for the tropical extreme. It occurs in the northern United States and southern Canada, mostly north of the 40th parallel of latitude. "Humid and subhumid conditions" refer to precipitation effectiveness; the ratio of precipitation to evaporation. The humid and subhumid zones have this ratio from 32–127; higher than 127 is "wet" climate, and below 32 is semiarid and arid. In the microthermal temperature zone, the humid and subhumid climatic provinces extend from the Atlantic Ocean to western Iowa and the central Dakotas, and occurs in several of the valleys in the intermountain and northwestern states. (See Thornthwaite, 1931, for details on climatic provinces.)

Within these climatic limits—and they are quite restrictive—pheasant range is determined by land use; and that depends on topography and soils. Generally the best agricultural areas are the better pheasant habitat. Further, those agricultural areas devoted largely to the growing of grain are better for pheasants than those under other forms of farming. And, finally, within the grain-growing areas, those that produce corn are by far the best for ring-necks. In fact, with some exceptions that we may say "prove the rule," pheasants are a by-product of corn-growing. There are many detailed aspects of the environment other than mere cornfields that decide how productive of pheasants an area will be, but these are secondary. They will be discussed later under cover type needs.

The eastern pheasant range is largely centered in dairy districts where corn is grown in a crop rotation with small grain and hay. It is harvested in a variety of ways, each of which is important to pheasant welfare. Where the ears are picked and the plants left standing all winter, the benefit to pheasants is greatest. When the corn is stacked in shocks and left in the field all winter, it is also fairly good for pheasants. But when the crop is taken to the barns, stalks and all, and the fields fall-plowed, there is no cover left to help pheasants in the winter. The fields where the corn is ensilaged (and this method is growing), also leave no winter corn for the birds. The best of this eastern range is in southeastern Pennsylvania in the fertile valleys of Lancaster, Berks, Lehigh, and parts of neighboring counties.

The most productive area of pheasant range is the "corn belt." It extends from western Ohio and southern Michigan, through Indiana, Illinois, Iowa, southern Wisconsin and Minnesota, to eastern Nebraska and the Dakotas. Here the corn is grown largely for feeding to swine and cattle on the farm, or for cash sale. The general habit has been to harvest the corn by picking, and leave the stalks in the field. Even where the fields are "hogged off" by turning swine into them, cover and food for pheasants is usually good. Frequently associated with this corn farming are two cover features of great importance to pheasants. In the famous northwest Ohio pheasant area, and elsewhere through the corn belt, the land is crisscrossed with a network of drainage ditches. The cover of woody plants and rank weeds in these channels provides excellent shelter in winter. Their location adjacent to the food-producing cornfields provides the perfect food and cover combination. These ditches are prevalent in much of the Midwest pheasant range. The other and similarly used cover referred to is marshland. Small cattail sloughs scattered here and there in the poorly drained depressions, or more extensive marshes in the river valleys, provide excellent winter shelter. Where these areas are close to corn, again we have a perfect subsistence combination.

One of the notable exceptions to the dependence of pheasants on grain-raising is in Nebraska. There the ring-neck has thrived in the sandhill region in the north central part of the state. A grassland area broken by shrub thickets and vegetated stream margins, with only small, scattered, cultivated patches, it hardly meets the usual concept of pheasant range. Food habits studies of those pheasants (Sharp and McClure in McAtee, 1945) showed that their subsistence was largely seeds of annual and perennial wild herbs, wild greens, some insects, and a few wild fruits. The same authors found that pheasant numbers varied from none to 100 per section (640 acres), but approached the high numbers only around the fringes of the area where there was considerable cultivation.

In the Northwest and in the intermountain regions of Utah, Idaho, California, and Colorado there are three distinctive types of pheasant range. One is the humid region of western Washington and Oregon, exemplified by the first American home of the pheasant, the Willamette Valley. Here an intensive agriculture of diversified farming and dairying includes a good distribution of shrubby shelter cover. The second type of Western pheasant range is the irrigated lands in the valleys with arid or semi-arid climate. These valleys were formerly desert, or dry range land. Water has made them literally bloom with crops of an intensive agriculture, and it also has enabled them to support pheasants. Some of these valleys extend into a mesothermal climatic zone, which may indicate that the modification of ground temperatures through irrigation offsets that unfavorable part of the natural climate. The agriculture is mostly of a cash crop type. Alfalfa is a common crop, but vegetables, fruit, small grains, and corn are also grown. The pheasants here depend for sustenance on a combination of grains and weed seeds. The irrigation ditches perform much the same shelter functions for the birds as do the drainage ditches in Ohio and the brushy fence rows in the Eastern states. The third type of Western range is the dry land wheat-growing country of eastern Washington and Oregon and northern Idaho. The second of these three types is most productive of pheasants.

COVER TYPES NEEDED

PHEASANTS require three types of cover in their local range. These we may call cropland, grassland, and woody or rank-growing herbaceous vegetation. There are many varieties of each, and they have different values as pheasant cover; they vary in their usefulness to the birds with the seasons, and in different parts of the range. The most important kinds of each of these three cover types are listed in Table 1.

These are the kinds of cover generally found in pheasant range, listed according to the purpose they serve the pheasant. The cropland cover types are primarily valuable for the food they produce, especially in the fall and winter seasons. Grassland cover types are mainly used for nesting, crowing grounds, loafing cover, and good weather shelter. They furnish some food, especially insects for the youngsters. The woody and rank vegetation types are valuable mostly for their protective shelter. They make the travel ways that enable the birds to move about without exposing themselves. They furnish the vegetation most useful in escaping from enemies, whether fox or man. In stormy weather they provide the safest places to avoid discomfort or death from the elements.

Cropland. Of the great variety of tilled and small grain crops grown in this country, corn is incomparably the best for pheasants. It attracts them in late summer, and by fall it becomes of first importance. But, this usefulness lasts only as long as a reasonable amount of the corn field cover remains. This varies immensely in different areas, partly because of the varied uses made of the corn and partly because of local methods of harvesting. Corn used for ensilage, in which the whole stalk and top is chopped up and stored in a silo for fodder, leaves fields of little value to the ring-neck. Sweet corn provides but little food, as the kernels are soft and do not keep well. Where the cornfield is fully harvested and fall-plowed, it is of no value to wildlife. The real merit of corn farming to pheasants lies in the sustained food supply it provides from fall to spring. Where this food source is cut off by the fall harvest, the winter pheasant carrying capacity is at once greatly reduced. Fields grown for seed corn and not plowed in the fall provide food for pheasants, not only in waste corn but also in weed seeds. The amount of such seed available depends on how long the cultivation was carried into the summer. Generally there is ample time left after cultivation ceases for the annual weeds to mature. The foxtail grasses, ragweeds, and smartweeds (*Polygonum*) are the prevalent annual herbs associated with corn that provide the best seeds for pheasants to eat.

Some of the small grains, particularly winter wheat, are good sources of food for pheasants. In this instance too, much of the food comes from weed seeds as well as from waste grain. Ragweed is particularly abundant in harvested fields of winter wheat. All the other grains— oats, barley, rye, buckwheat—are important, but the earlier harvested winter grains are the best; the aftermath of weeds is greater in them and furnishes both weedy shelter and food.

Other cropland types are third rate for pheasants, as a rule. We might make some exceptions. Probably soy beans are as useful as some of the small grains. Tomato fields are frequented by pheasants in the summer, sometimes to the disadvantage of the tomato crop. But here the food is available only in summer, when food is plentiful anyway. Potatoes and most small truck crops are too intensively cultivated to provide weedy cover, and they are generally poor in food for pheasants. Clean-cultivated orchards and vineyards have little to offer pheasants either. Fallow fields are frequently weedy, and may be of considerable use to ring-necks for good-weather shelter and weed seed food.

Grassland. There is wide variation in the usefulness of grasslands for pheasants. At one extreme are the lush fields of alfalfa and clovers grown on good soils. Where such crops are allowed to mature for seed harvest, they provide high-quality and safe nesting areas. Where they are cut for hay the quality of the cover is high, but the hazard from mowing also is high. They are good cover for spring to autumn living. At the other extreme are the arid and semiarid Western lands that support only scanty vegetation; they are of limited value to ring-necks, and then as cover in small areas adjacent to irrigated lands. Between these extremes are a wide variety of grasslands, all of some use as pheasant range. Grass and clover-grass hay fields provide adequate nesting cover, crowing grounds, and general living areas; they are probably the most used of all cover from spring to late summer. Of similar usefulness are fields of mixed wild herbs—frequently called meadows—or wild hay. Their plants include native grasses and legumes and perennial broad-leaved species such as daisy, aster, goldenrod, devil's paintbrush, Queen Anne's lace, and many others. Their value to the birds depends on the lushness of their growth, and when they are mowed. This kind of cover is common on roadsides, between the roadway proper and the adjacent field. Such strips are good nesting cover, generally safer than hay fields.

Orchards of apple and pear trees where it is customary to keep the ground in a permanent sod cover, provide good cover for pheasants. They are similar to hayfields in their usefulness, though the orchard trees also contribute some shelter. Many pheasants successfully nest in them, as the mowing is delayed until other haying is finished. Orchards are of more use to the birds in fall and winter than are most grass fields because of the wind-breaking protection of the trees, and also for the waste fruit that the birds use for food.

Pasture fields are mostly second-rate grass cover for pheasants. They are usually grazed too closely in the spring to conceal nests well. Even if some weedy growth makes some cover later, it is apt to be scattered and disconnected; the better the pasture the more this is likely to be the case. Edges of pastures are commonly used as crowing areas by males when good protective cover adjoins.

A very special sort of grassland, one that is not in as general use now as it will be some day, deserves a particular note: sod strips in cultivated fields used for soil conservation. There are three sorts, called *diversion terraces, grass waterways* or *outlets,* and field border *headlands.* All three are important to pheasants, since they are good grass cover; are mowed last in the haying period; and are often not mowed every year. This makes them the most secure from mowing danger of all the good grass types. They are also well interspersed among other useful cover types.

Diversion terraces are broad, shallow ditches built with a slight grade in the channel. They receive water from the slope above and carry it to a safe outlet in some nearby woodland,

pasture, or waterway. To preserve their water-carrying function they are always kept in a good sod cover. Further, to prevent their being filled with silt, a width of 20 to 40 or more feet above the terrace channel is also kept in sod to serve as a filter strip. Not only do these grass strips provide good nesting cover, but the terrace channel serves as a protected travel way for birds walking across the field.

The grass waterway is a broad strip of thick-growing sod that runs up and down a slight draw on a gentle slope. It may be the outlet for water from terraces, or merely the collecting channel for run-off water from a series of strip-cropped fields. It is mowed either for hay or just for maintenance of the sod, but often late in the season. Because of water gathered in it at times, some nests here may be destroyed by drowning.

Field border headlands are strips of sod, usually from 10 to 25 feet wide, along the margins of fields at the turning ends of plough

TABLE 1

COVER TYPES USED BY PHEASANTS

CROPLAND	GRASSLAND	WOODY OR RANK VEGETATION

CORN:
   seed
   sweet
   ensilage
	HAY:
	   alfalfa, clover
	   grass-clover
	   grass
		WOODLAND:
		
		 CONIFER PLANTATIONS:
		
		 OVERGROWN FENCEROWS, HEDGES,
		   AND WINDBREAKS

SMALL GRAINS:
   winter grains
   spring grains
	MIXED WILD HERBS
	
	 GRAZING LAND:
	   humid pastures
	   semiarid range
	   arid range
		DITCH BANKS:
		   drainage ditches
		   irrigation ditches

TRUCK CROPS, etc:
   potatoes
   tomatoes
   other vegetables
	ORCHARDS (Apple, etc)
	
	 ROADSIDES
		SHRUBBY COVER:
		   dry thickets
		   swales
		   field borders

FALLOW GROUND
 	
 ORCHARDS (cultivated)
   peach, etc.
   vineyard
	CONSERVATION SODLAND:
	   diversion terraces
	   grass waterways
	   headlands
		MARSHES:
		   cattail
		   miscellaneous wet-land herbs

furrows. They make a place for the farming machinery to be turned around without injuring the crop or causing erosion. Where the crop field is next to a woodland, the headland is often combined with shrubs to make a woodland border. The shrub part is developed next to the woods, and the field side is devoted to the herbaceous growth. These headlands are generally mowed only enough to preserve the quality of the sod; that may be only once in each two or three years. This makes them safe for nesting, which combined with the birds' preference for margins, makes the grass headlands specially useful.

Grassland cover can be of great importance to the pheasant, but of the three cover types, it is probably the least essential. At any rate they can thrive with little of it, especially if what there is is well distributed and the other two groups are ideal in quality. But since most of our forms of agriculture do include considerable amounts of hay and pasture, the problem is to make them as safe and useful for pheasants as possible.

Woody or Rank Herbaceous Vegetation. The function of this group of cover types is to afford protective shelter. It therefore assumes its greatest importance from fall to spring, and especially in winter. It is of great value to pheasants only where it is closely associated

COURTESY SOIL CONSERVATION SERVICE, USDA

PLATE 5. *Over-grown fencerows make valuable travel lanes and shelter cover that enable pheasants to reach farm fields safely in their foraging for food.*

COURTESY SOIL CONSERVATION SERVICE, USDA

PLATE 6. *Managed hedges and windbreaks offer many benefits to the farmer. Some make living fences. They aid in insect suppression and in controlling wind and water erosion. This Idaho windbreak is Russian olive.*

with extremely good feeding areas of crop land.

There are two divisions among these protective cover types: those dominated by woody plants; and associations of rank-growing wetland herbaceous plants. Several varieties of both sorts may furnish excellent winter shelter; sometimes the two occur together. There is some evidence that cattail marshes, especially if small (but preferably five acres or more) and well scattered through crop-land areas, may be best of all. Even a good bird dog can't flush a pheasant from a cattail covert if the bird is intent on staying there. These pot-hole cattail areas are an important part of the reason for the high pheasant populations of southwestern Minnesota and eastern South Dakota. One of the reasons the pheasant is able to thrive in the grainless sandhill area of Nebraska is the presence of springy marshes of rushes, smartweeds, wild millet, and associated plants.

In the East, hedgerow cover and conifer plantations seem to provide much of the best protective cover. In Ohio it is the drainage ditch vegetation, a combination of woody plants and aquatic herbs. Open poplar-willow brush provides good cover in Michigan. In the Far West it is the rather similar irrigation-ditch cover. The ditch-bank and hedgerow cover is much of a common type, linear in its distribution, always adjacent to the feeding areas, and

COURTESY SOIL CONSERVATION SERVICE, USDA

PLATE 7. *Even small cattail marshes make valuable protective cover when close to grain fields.*

PLATE 8. *Rank-growing marsh plants provide excellent shelter for pheasants. Large marshes in farming areas are concentration points for pheasant flocks in winter.*

COURTESY SOIL CONSERVATION SERVICE, USDA

apt to be a tangled profusion of shrubs, vines, and rank-growing herbs. The favorable location makes this cover extremely useful to the birds. The same plant composition away from crop lands would be much less usable, as in extensive areas of shrubby cover, woodlands, or large marshes. Small thickets, swales, and woodlands are as valuable as the long, narrow hedges and ditches, provided they are interspersed with good feeding areas. Well-developed shrub borders between woodland and open fields also are good protective shelter. Still, much of the woodland in pheasant range is of little use to the species, because of its great unit size and frequent long distance from corn. Similarly, much of the swale, swamp, and marsh cover is associated with pasture lands, and is to that extent less available to pheasants than if it were allied with crop land.

There is great variety in the quality of these protective shelter types, according to their plant composition and to whatever cultural treatment man may give them. The upland coverts are generally of better quality when composed mostly of shrub species, rather than of trees. An exception is young conifer plantations or natural stands of young evergreens. The presence of vines, such as grape or greenbrier, and of thorny shrubs, such as roses or thorn apples, is an advantage. The prevention or control of fire is necessary for preserving the shelter qualities of both the upland and wetland coverts. Similarly, the exclusion of domestic livestock is important for realizing the best protection from these coverts. Those including shrubs that hold fruit on their branches through the winter have the extra advantage that these fruits serve as emergency foods for the birds.

THE INTERSPERSION OF COVER TYPES

In discussing the components of the pheasant range as separate cover types, we run the risk of depreciating the vital importance of the relationships among them. True, the ring-neck needs crop fields to get food from, grass to nest,

crow, and loaf in, and heavy cover for protection. But the importance of any of these areas depends on its position with respect to the other two. Actually the birds need all three types *every day;* and they must be so located with respect to one another that all are easily reached. To illustrate this principle, let us consider a square mile, 640 acres, which is one-half crop land, one-quarter grass land, and one-quarter woody cover. This area could be made up of three fields, arranged as in Figure 2A. In this arrangement only one area, that circled in the center, could be ideal for pheasants, with all three cover needs handy. But the same square mile with the same amounts of the three kinds of land use *could* be arranged very differently, as in Figure 2B.

Now the fields of grass, woods, and tilled crops, respectively 10, 10, and 20 acres, have 49 places where all three come together, instead of one. By this system, we have a better *arrangement* of the cover types; there are more potential crowing territories, hence more breeding areas as well as winter survival areas. This principle of the relationships of cover types is fundamental. Generally, the greater the *interspersion* of the essential cover types, the larger is the pheasant carrying capacity of the land.

IDEAL LAND USE PATTERN

We may summarize that an ideal land-use pattern for good pheasant range would be about as follows:

(1) More than half of the land devoted to growing grain.

(2) Seed corn grown on about half of the grain land.

(3) Corn cultivation completed early enough in summer to allow a good growth of annual herbs.

(4) Corn harvested by picking from the stalks that are left standing in the field over winter.

(5) Five to 20% of the land in shrubby cover, cattail marshes, and evergreen planta-

tions, including a good network of hedgerows or ditch banks. This cover must be well distributed, and not grazed or burned.

(6) Grass-legume fields well scattered, preferably in a contour strip-cropping arrangement; diversion terraces, grass waterways, and sod headlands present in accordance with the needs of the slopes; some clover fields, preferably those next to woody cover, harvested for seed—that is, late.

(7) Livestock restricted to improved pastures, and their numbers kept within range carrying capacity.

Such a farming system located within the pheasant's established geographical range, on fertile, well-drained soils, should provide large populations of ring-necks and excellent hunting.

FOOD HABITS

PHEASANTS find most of their food in farm-crop fields. Primarily they are grain eaters, with corn the preferred food among the grains. Most good pheasant populations are supported by a grain corn agriculture. In some areas, notably in the Far West, small-grain farming supports considerable numbers of these birds. Any of the grains are acceptable, though winter wheat and barley apparently are best. In a few areas, significant numbers of pheasants are sustained by foods grown on grasslands, woody cover, or in marshes. The sandhill area of Nebraska is an outstanding instance.

Total pheasant food may conveniently be divided into five classes: grains, wild seeds, greens, fruits, insects. Altogether there are hundreds of kinds of plants and small animals that make up this food. For example, Severin (1933) found 118 species of plants and 197 kinds of insects and other animals in the crops and gizzards of 285 pheasants. Nevertheless, there are a rather limited number that furnish a really important share. These are the only ones that need concern us in management.

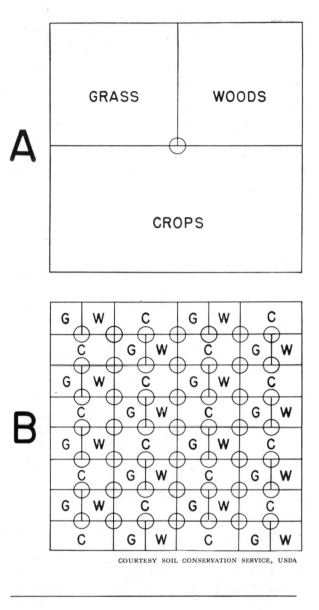

COURTESY SOIL CONSERVATION SERVICE, USDA

FIGURE 2. *Diagram Illustrating Principle of Interspersion of Cover Types.*

A. Square mile, 640 acres: 320 acres of crops, 160 each of grass and woods; one field of each, 3 in all. Only one place (circle) provides ideal pheasant cover type arrangement, where all three needed types meet.

B. Square mile with same total acreage of the three kinds of cover, but arranged in 48 fields of 10 acres each of grass (G) and woods (W), 20 acres each of crops (C). Rearrangement provides 49 places of ideal pheasant cover type relationship (circles).

GRAINS USED FOR FOOD

CULTIVATED grains furnish the bulk of pheasant food in all regions of high population. Studies of their food habits show that as much as 81% of the yearly food may be grain. This high figure was found to be representative in Minnesota (Fried, 1940) and Utah (Rasmussen and McKean in McAtee, 1945). Most of the grain eaten in Minnesota was corn, 50% to 62%. In Utah the grain taken was mostly wheat and barley. In South Dakota the pheasant crops examined in one study averaged 90 kernels of grain per bird, composing most of the volume of food, though only 40% of the number of seeds (Severin, 1933). Corn, wheat, barley, and oats were all used in large

COURTESY SOIL CONSERVATION SERVICE, USDA

quantities. Trautman (1952) examined 1,416 crops of South Dakota pheasants, and reported that kernels of corn and wheat were the staple foods, composing 57.2% and 10.7% respectively of the annual diet. Wheat and barley are the grains most eaten by pheasants in Montana, with corn and oats ranking lower (Hiatt, 1947). In other areas studies have shown grains to have composed various proportions all the way down to as little as 6% of the total food. This low figure was found in the studies of sandhill area of Nebraska pheasants (Sharp and McClure in McAtee, 1945). In Vermont grains and beans made up only 10% of the food (Foote, 1942). In a different part of Nebraska, corn made up 67% of all their food, and in another part of New England— Connecticut—their food included 26% of grain (Pearce in McAtee, 1945). In Rhode Island the fall food was 37% grain (Wright, 1941). Another study in Utah showed that the birds had used grains for 60% of their food, mostly barley and wheat. The two Utah areas compare closely with Michigan (Wight in McAtee, 1945), where pheasant food was 74% grains and beans, of which 33% was corn, 20% wheat, and 8% barley. In Ohio corn furnished 55% of all food (Leedy & Hicks in McAtee, 1945). Then again, in contrast, pheasants in British Columbia ate only 12% grains, these

PLATE 9. *Corn shocks left in field over winter make available food for pheasants. In this field, cultivation was completed early enough to permit good late-season weed growth of ragweed and foxtail.*

COURTESY SOIL CONSERVATION SERVICE, USDA

PLATE 10. *Mechanically-picked corn is so badly broken down in the harvest that it is easily covered with snow when the birds need it most. These fields have an abundance of waste grain.*

being wheat and barley taken mostly in June (Cowan, 1942). Rice is the most important grain in parts of the California range, where in one study its kernels composed 38.5% of the annual food. Barley, oats, and wheat were also important sources of food (Ferrell, Twining and Herkenham, 1949). Grains are eaten more in fall and winter than at other seasons.

It is evident that grains are needed by pheasants for their staple food supply. Fall and winter are the times of greatest use, but spring is also a period of grain-eating. Field corn is superior to other grains, with sweet corn, wheat, rice, and barley the other most important varieties. Oats, rye, buckwheat, and soy beans and other field beans are also of importance. Some grain is gleaned from manure, especially in winter.

WILD SEEDS EATEN BY PHEASANTS

THERE is greater variety among wild seeds used for food by pheasants than any other class of edibles. These wild seeds make up a third or more of the bird's food in the secondary range, and only about a tenth or less of total food in the good grain areas. In British Columbia wild seeds composed 44% of all food, in Connecticut and Vermont the proportion was about 32%, and in the Nebraska sandhills it was 34%. In contrast with these areas, the food records of pheasants

in Michigan and Minnesota showed only 11% and 6%, respectively, of wild seeds; in Montana and South Dakota 7%, proportions typical of the corn and wheat belts.

Among all the wild seeds eaten, there are two that are probably used more than others. These are the ragweeds, especially the lesser ragweed, and the dullseed cornbind and other smartweeds and bindweeds. These annual weed seeds are eaten in all parts of the bird's range. Other important wild seed-food plants include: foxtail grasses in the East, Midwest, and northern plains; common and prairie sunflowers in the northern plains and Far West; lamb's-quarters throughout the range; skunk cabbage in the East and Midwest; jewelweed in the East, Midwest, and plains areas; wild oats and

COURTESY SOIL CONSERVATION SERVICE, USDA

PLATE 11. *Leaving a few rows of grain corn unharvested is the best method of winter feeding pheasants. Field edge rows next to good cover are best.*

PLATE 12. *Placing shocked corn next to protective cover of woods, brush or marsh is another way to make winter food available to the birds.*

COURTESY SOIL CONSERVATION SERVICE, USDA

Russian thistle in the plains and Far West; blue-eyed grass in the plains area; and redroot pigweed throughout the range. Most of these plants—ragweed, smartweed, foxtail, lamb's-quarters, and redroot—are by-products of grain cultivation. They grow in the aftermath of corn and small-grain fields and other tilled crops. The jewelweed and skunk cabbage are perennials found in wet swales. The sunflowers and Russian thistle grow in waste places and grasslands. The periods of greatest consumption of wild plant seeds is during the winter and fall months.

GREENS AS PHEASANT FOOD

Leaves and other succulent vegetative parts of plants furnish the pheasant with a considerable amount of its food. In all likelihood these foods are important in the bird's diet, and furnish needed vitamins, just as they do for people. They seem to be used more in the spring than at other seasons.

The quantities of greens eaten compared with other foods depends on the abundance of grains. Where grains are plentiful, particularly yellow corn, fewer greens are eaten—perhaps 2% to 4% of the year's food. In second-rate range, greens are of considerable importance. In British Columbia (including potatoes), they composed 28% of the year's food; and comparable quantities are eaten in Oregon. In the Nebraska sandhill country greens made up 39% of all pheasant food. In the East, however, only 12% to 14% of the diet is of this sort, and in the better Midwest and northern plains range the proportion of greens used compared with other foods is still smaller.

Some of our commonest wild herbs are among those most frequently eaten by pheasants. The dandelion, clovers, bluegrass, brome grass, alfalfa, chickweed, and dock are of general importance. Waste crop-plants like potatoes and sugar beets are also frequently eaten.

FRUITS USED FOR FOOD

The pheasant eats fruits, particularly wild fruits, mostly as either a dessert or as a starvation ration. They rarely provide the birds with

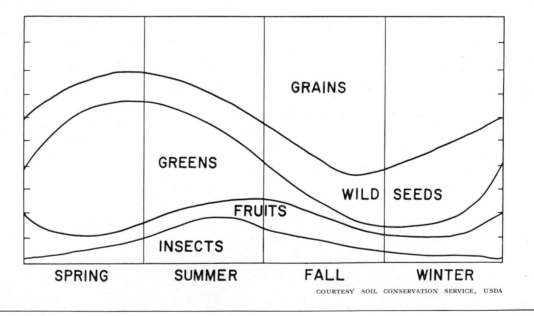

COURTESY SOIL CONSERVATION SERVICE, USDA

FIGURE 3. *Seasonal foods of the pheasant in typical good range according to types of foods and seasons.*

a large share of the year's sustenance. Some cultivated varieties, like tomatoes and apples, may be eaten in large quantities in some localities, but these instances are exceptional. The season of greatest use of fruits is summer and fall, though winter consumption is probably of more significance in actual sustenance value.

Most wild fruits have little food value for a bird like the pheasant, to which they are mainly important as emergency foods. Pheasants fed all they can eat of such fruits as sumac, coralberry, and barberry will lose weight rapidly. Since, however, some of these fruits are available on the bushes above deep snows when other food is unavailable, they often serve to carry the birds through a difficult period until better foods are again available.

Some of the wild fruits commonly eaten by pheasants are grape, sumac, coralberry, multiflora and other roses, nightshade, wolfberry, thorn apple, Thunberg barberry, Russian olive, bayberry, arrowwood, poison ivy, and bittersweet. The year-round consumption of fruit ordinarily amounts to from 4% to 15% of all food. It is highest in the poorer range.

INSECT FOODS

INSECTS are eaten by pheasants in considerable amounts in summer. For the young chicks, they make up about three-fourths of all the food for the first few weeks. With the adults the proportion is smaller, usually totaling less than half of the summer food and from 4% to 20% of the year's supply.

Many varieties are eaten, ease of catching being one of the main factors that determine utilization. Grasshoppers are most commonly taken, followed by ants, caterpillars, flies, beetles, and bugs.

QUANTITY OF FOOD REQUIRED; FEEDING TIME; WATER NEEDS

IN Ohio it was found that adult pheasants ate about 1.4 pounds of corn (almost the whole diet at that time) per bird per week in winter (Leedy and Hicks in McAtee, 1945). In Montana the annual consumption of corn is 1⅕ pounds per bird (Hiatt, 1947). Most of their feeding is done shortly after dawn and just before dusk; very little is done during the middle of the day. They pick and root for food in the ground litter with the beak, but do not use their feet for scratching out food.

Any suitable pheasant range provides enough water for the birds' needs. They are able to get water from dew, insects, and succulent vegetation, as well as from bodies of water.

The proportions of different kinds of foods eaten by pheasants at each season are shown in Figure 3.

ECONOMICS OF PHEASANT FOOD HABITS

PHEASANTS both aid and damage farm crops in their eating; with local exceptions, the net balance is probably somewhat on the beneficial side, though of little economic importance. The birds are insectivorous, especially during the crop-growing months. Many of the insects eaten are crop pests—grasshoppers, cutworms, etc.—but others are neutral or even beneficial. There is no evidence that the pheasant's consumption of harmful insects materially changes insect numbers; but the ring-neck is one of the many birds and other insectivorous animals that collectively do keep insect pests from getting out of hand. They no doubt perform some service to the farmer in this way.

Pheasants eat great quantities of weed seeds; yet the reduction is so small compared with the amount of seed produced that they have no real effect on weed abundance. The tendency is, however, in a useful direction.

The grain eaten is almost all waste from crop harvests, and its consumption is of neither harm nor benefit to the farmer. Sometimes pheasants do harm by taking newly sprouted corn in the late spring. Hiatt (1947) reported that damage to sprouting corn is greatest " . . . in isolated areas near heavy nesting cover." The objections raised over these depredations frequently exaggerate the damage, though it is sometimes enough to require spot reseeding.

The greatest damage caused by pheasants to farm crops results from their pecking at ripe tomatoes in late summer. These raids are very localized, and, like those on sprouted corn, are often overemphasized; still to the individual suffering the loss it may be serious. Sometimes these damages warrant reduction of the numbers of pheasants before the regular hunting season.

EFFECTS OF WEATHER AND CLIMATE ON HABITS AND NUMBERS

DESPITE the fact that the ring-neck is a tough fellow and able to survive in the face of severe weather conditions, climate is a vital factor in its existence. We have already noted that the southern limits of pheasant range in this country is determined by some element in the climate, and not by the habitat. It is not clear what this element is. The evidence indicates that it is effective in preventing successful reproduction rather than in killing off either young or adult birds. Most likely the limiting factor lies in late spring and early summer temperatures, possibly combined with humidity or precipitation, that adversely influence the development and hatching of the eggs.

Throughout the habitable range, and most notably at its northern limits, winter weather affects the survival of the grown birds. It is not that the temperatures are too cold for the birds to withstand, or that the snows are so deep that food is made unavailable; rather, the trouble seems to come from a form of icing during severe storms. Ice forms in the bird's nostrils, eyes, and mouth, and beneath the feather coat, and results in partial or complete asphyxiation as well as body freezing. Even large, healthy birds of good flesh and with plenty of food succumb to this hazard. No doubt this condition is aggravated where the birds are forced to expose themselves away from protective cover in search of food. Yet some of this winter mortality takes place even with good shelter available.

Fortunately the combination of weather conditions that induces these losses does not occur regularly; it is low temperatures, high winds, and drifting snow together that cause the trouble. Freezing rain is another inimical storm condition. The only apparent solution is habitat improvement that will provide better distribution of good protective shelter.

Another weather manifestation that reduces pheasant numbers, or prevents their increase, occurs in late spring at egg-hatching time. A combination of unseasonable cold nights, with rain and lack of sunshine for several days, is sure death to many of the tender young chicks. Under these circumstances the mother hen, after having successfully *hatched* her brood, does not nest again—as she usually does when the nest is destroyed. Instead, she more than likely manages to bring a chick or two through the bad weather period, and that becomes her contribution to the year's pheasant production. In place of the normal 7 to 10 raised she has a much lower number. Poor pheasant hunting the next fall is the inevitable result when this prevails among the majority of pheasant hens.

A slightly different timing of late spring rains may work to the advantage of the pheasant. Wet hay fields delay mowing. When this happens just before hatching time it may delay haying until after the brood comes off. In that way the rain has enabled nests to hatch successfully that otherwise would have been destroyed by farm machinery. Thus adverse weather sometimes may actually benefit the birds.

The pheasant is not limited by altitude or latitude, as such. While the 40th parallel of latitude seems to mark the southern limit of suitable pheasant range in the Eastern states, the birds thrive much farther south in the West where the altitude is greater. In southern Arizona and New Mexico pheasants do well on irrigated lands at altitudes of from 5,000 to 7,000 feet. Here the latitude is only 33°. The cooler climate at the high levels offsets the extreme (for the pheasant) southern latitude. At the northern fringe of the range, at about 44° latitude in the East, 500 feet of elevation seems to be about the limit of acceptable range for the species.

PREDATION; DISEASES AND PARASITES

EGGS, chicks, and adult pheasants make fine eating for predatory or omnivorous animals that can handle them. Despite the ever-present threat of destruction by natural enemies, the numbers and proportions lost through predation are not high. Even more significant, there is abundant evidence that the losses that do occur from flesh and egg eaters is of almost no importance in determining pheasant populations or the numbers of birds present during hunting season. Further, if there is any factor less important than predation in determining pheasant numbers, it is the disease and parasite loss; deaths from either disease or parasitism are so rare as to be negligible in significance. There is not even any appreciable evidence that these organisms so weaken many pheasants that death from predation is thereby increased.

NEST DESTRUCTION BY PREDATORS

NEST destruction is more the rule than the exception with pheasants, but only a small part is due to egg eating. From about 12% to 25% of nests may be rifled; this amounts to from 25% to 40% of all nest losses. Much of this loss is made up through the persistence of the hens renesting.

Most important of the nest predators are skunks, of whatever species may be common in an area. Throughout the pheasant's range, the wood pussy manages to stumble on to more nests than other egg eaters. The crow, too, is an important pheasant egg destroyer. Much of the evident losses from crows is misleading, though, since they most frequently locate nests that have been exposed by mowing. As these nests are already lost, the crow has not thereby contributed to a lower pheasant population. Other than skunk and crow, the significant pheasant nest destroyers are foxes and dogs, and occasionally others. The bull snake is reported to take pheasant eggs from unincubated nests in Nebraska (Sharp and McClure in McAtee, 1945)). Once the hen is setting she manages to drive away any intruding bull snakes, and will even occasionally kill one. In the Far West Douglas's ground squirrel destroys some nests (Einarsen in McAtee, 1945).

LOSSES OF YOUNG

YOUNG pheasants are about as safe from predators as any young game birds can be; the ordinary losses of youngsters from enemy attack are only about 5% to 10%. Compared to losses from other causes, this is almost insignificant; it probably represents only a portion of the predestined loss on good range. Marsh hawks and Cooper's hawks are the most frequent destroyers of pheasant chicks. Shick (1952) found that 45% of the prey at marsh hawk nests on a Michigan area was young pheasants.

PREDATION ON ADULT PHEASANTS

PREDATION on grown pheasants is of little account during the fall and early winter. In late winter and spring it increases, and becomes a prominent part of the mortality. Much of this loss, especially in the spring, is conditioned by activities of the breeding season. The crowing of the cocks in exposed places, and the nesting of the hens, frequently in sparse cover in early spring, both tend to increase deaths from enemy attack.

The proportion of all losses of adult birds caused by predators runs from 10% or even less up to about 25% or a little more. Occasionally these losses may be effective in lowering the breeding population below a fully effective number, but this is exceptional. Most years these losses from predation are secondary to losses from other causes, and have no effect on subsequent production and shooting populations.

The pheasant is well able to care for itself under most circumstances; but there are predators capable of catching pheasants efficiently. Probably most effective are the great horned owl, foxes, Cooper's hawk, the marsh hawk, and domestic dogs and cats. In a few areas of the northernmost range the goshawk might be locally important. Foxes were responsible for over a fourth of all pheasant kills found in a Michigan study (Shick, 1952). Next in rank of destructive predators were the marsh and Cooper's hawks and the great horned owl. Others that will occasionally capture a healthy pheasant include the raccoon, weasel, mink, golden eagle, duck hawk, prairie falcon, and coyote.

DISEASES AND PARASITES

As with all wild creatures, pheasants normally harbor an internal and external flora and fauna of organisms that live on them; but contrary to the way it is with most host animals, these infections and infestations rarely cause the pheasant serious trouble. Death from them as a primary cause is practically unknown among wild birds. Infections following a physical injury are frequent, but the losses from this cause cannot be properly charged to the secondary organism.

Some of the organisms that are known to affect the pheasant are: lice (Mallophaga); caecal worms (*Heterakis gallinae*); tapeworms (*Raillietina*, and *Hymenolepis*); gapeworm (*Syngamus trachealis*); threadworms (*Capillaria*); and eye worm (*Oxyspirura petrowii*).

MAN'S RELATION TO THE PHEASANT

MAN'S interest in the pheasant comes from two widely different yet closely related endeavors: hunting; and farming. For the hunter, the pheasant furnishes more farm game-bird shooting than does any other species. For the farmer,

in addition to hunting (if he is a hunter), the ring-neck brings a social problem of trespass on his land, and occasionally damage to some of his crops. The resolving of the conflicts of these two interests is one of the most important of all problems in game management.

PHEASANT HUNTING

THE time is 8:59 on the morning of November 1. The place is southeastern Pennsylvania, in the rich limestone farming area. It is the moment before the opening of the small-game hunting season. There is nothing else like it in the whole world, save the same scene repeated on corresponding days in northwest Ohio, southern Michigan, northern Iowa, southwestern Minnesota, eastern South Dakota, the Yakima Valley, Washington, and assorted other regions of good pheasant hunting. For it is the pheasant that provides the occasion with its special flavor.

As one drives along the highways, he passes little groups of hunters gathered beside their autos awaiting the fateful moment. Their guns are put together ready for loading, the dogs strain at their leashes. Many of these groups are gathered in a farmyard, and often the landowner is a member of the party. On some posted farms the owner is devoting the day to patrolling his land to prevent illegal trespass. Just before the minute hand gets to even twelve, a shot is heard in the distance. There are remarks about the so-and-so who jumps the mark ahead of time. Then the moment comes.

Dogs are released. Hunters step into the field —usually standing corn or a good swale of rank grass—slipping shells into their guns as they set out. Almost at once all hell breaks loose. Shots sound in every direction. Birds take flight in sudden desperation, frequently heading for the nearest marsh or thicket. Many drop from well-placed shots. The dogs shift from locating birds to retrieving those shot. Many of the winged cocks escape gunners who have no canine retrievers.

The general effect of this scene on the ears is

that of a timed barrage before a big attack, a sort of 3rd battle of the Marne. To one watching the scene from a vantage point on a hill it somewhat resembles an old-fashioned dance. Lines of hunters, usually two to five each (the Pennsylvania law limits farm hunting parties to five), sachay across a corn field, passing each other, one line weaving through the other. As one party leaves the field on one side another group enters on the opposite. And so it goes. It has to be experienced to be believed. The wonder is that more property is not damaged, and that more people are not shot.

The season has opened on all small game, but on opening day few are interested in anything but pheasants. They know that if they want to have much success at bagging pheasants, this is the time. The season is a month long, but the smart hunter knows that nearly a third of the whole season's kill of ring-necks is taken on opening day—most of these in the first two hours. It is that very vulnerability of the pheasant—he's an easy mark for a short time until he gets wise—that makes him so popular. Anyone has a fair chance of bagging him.

As the season proceeds, the hunting intensity drops off. It rises some each Saturday and holiday. The rate of kill drops even faster than the hunters' enthusiasm for the chase. Whereas more than half the total season's kill is taken in the first three days, only about 5% is taken during the last three days.

Hunting takes a heavy toll of pheasants, but since most states permit shooting of cock birds only, it is mostly confined to males. Still the illegal kill of hens is surprisingly large, considering that we are supposed to be law-abiding people. In Pennsylvania the legal kill was estimated at 28% of the fall population (Randall, 1940); in addition, another 14% were lost through crippling, and 4% from illegal killing of hens. The full toll, then, was 46%, mostly cocks, and it included a high proportion of all the cocks. In Iowa the total hunting loss was 50% of the population (Green, 1938), and in the Far West 58% (Einarsen in McAtee,

1945). From 78% to 93% of the cocks on Pelee Island, Ontario, were shot in the hunting seasons from 1947 to 1950 (Stokes, 1952). Other areas report similar hunting season kill figures, generally about half the population killed by gunfire.

The crippling loss was lower in Pennsylvania than in some of the other areas studied. In Vermont it was 19% (Foote, 1942), in Ohio at least 18% of the kill (Leedy and Hicks in McAtee, 1945), in Michigan 60% of the kill, and in the Far West from 30% to 50% of the kill. Crippling losses are only half as high with dogs as without them. The loss of hens from illegal shooting was found to be 40% of the legal kill in Michigan (Wight in McAtee, 1945), and the same in Ohio.

No other kind of upland hunting is as concentrated as pheasant shooting. A gun-hour per acre is hunted in areas of good range near large cities—and much of the best pheasant range is near large cities. In Pennsylvania there is a hunter for every 20 acres of farms; and it seems as though they are all there when the pheasant season opens. In Ohio there are 31 acres per hunter; and the ratio elsewhere though more favorable, indicates plenty of hunting pressure generally.

It takes four to ten hours of hunting on the average to bag a pheasant. Strangely, this success rate seems to apply in second-rate as well as in the best range. The fewer birds in the poorer range are matched by fewer hunters pursuing them. In the very best coverts the hunter's efforts are more amply rewarded.

There are many techniques in pheasant hunting, but most hunters use one of three methods. The best is to hunt with well-trained pointing dogs, either setters or pointers. This is best for two reasons: the extra enjoyment of seeing the dogs perform; and the greater success of finding birds, having their flush under some control, and the assurance of retrieving them when they are shot down. Either reason is ample cause for favoring this style of hunting. But it is also true that it is an expensive system. Bird dogs are costly to buy and maintain, and time-consuming to train, even if you have the skill and the patience to do it. Only a small proportion of pheasant hunters have the facilities or means to keep them. Fortunately one good dog can provide superior hunting for a number of people.

The second method of pheasant hunting is to use flushing dogs. The best breeds are the spaniels, but many will do. These dogs will work close to the hunter if well trained, and scour the nearby cover well. The idea is to keep them close enough so that flushed birds will rise within gunshot. This arrangement requires that the hunter select the coverts and guide the dog's travels in detail. It does not provide the thrills of birds "pinned down" by poised bird dogs awaiting the master's pleasure. The flushing dogs add efficiency in finding pheasants, and help in retrieving cripples—again provided that the dog is trained to retrieve.

The third method is the hunter drive, without dogs. Members of the party line up at convenient distances apart and traverse likely cover systematically. Few birds will be raised in the interior of fields, since the pheasants keep ahead on foot. The opportunities come as the party approaches the end of the field, provided there is an open break in the cover. When the birds are forced out in the open they are apt to flush; but if the sheltering cover continues into the next field the birds simply keep on running. Various circling maneuvers by members of the party may aid in getting birds into the air. Great caution should be exercised in such stratagems to avoid hunting accidents.

This system of hunting is the least effective of the three; hunting with dogs is much better hunting, and much better conservation. Some sportsmen have even recommended making the use of dogs compulsory in hunting pheasants. This would be going a bit far, but use dogs whenever you can.

THE FARMER AND THE PHEASANT

SOME pheasants will be produced on farms despite anything the farmer may do. Even if he were to look upon Mr. Ring-neck as a pest, there would still be some around, just as there are other unwanted animals despite persecution. Fortunately, few farmers look on the pheasant as a pest, though many curse him roundly at times. Withal, it is a basic truth that to a great degree the numbers of pheasants depends on what the farmer does on his land. His attitude is vital; if he wishes more pheasants, he can encourage them with practices that fit well into good farming; if he wishes to discourage them, there are also many ways he can do that. Many of these curbs are not consistent with good farming methods, which is providential for both pheasant and hunter. Some of the cultural operations on the farm that most affect the pheasant's welfare are discussed below.

"Clean farming" is the term frequently applied to the elimination from the farm of all woody or rank-growing plants outside the woodland proper. Most commonly the maligned growth is nature's assortment of trees and shrubs that try to take over field boundaries, fence lines, roadsides, ditch banks, and odd areas of rough ground. The farmer has been led to believe that such vegetation on his farm is a sign of slovenliness, that it harbors pests that damage his crops, and that the plants themselves are undesirable. He has not been told—at least not often until recently, that these woody growths have many positive values. They harbor beneficial insects as well as bad ones: bees, wasps, and others that the farmer needs to help control pest insects and to pollinate crops. These "dirty fence rows" and "waste" areas help conserve soil, break up winds, and make homes for beneficial wildlife. Yet to a considerable extent our farmers still cut down the brush annually, or worse still, burn it. In West Virginia they call this "filthing off," which gives you an idea of the prevailing attitude.

When we discuss the management of the pheasant, we shall see how these destructive practices can be turned to benefits; now we

PLATE 13. *Better understanding between farmer and sportsman is essential for improved pheasant hunting. This Iowa farm is in a cooperative hunting area managed in the interests of both parties. The sign refers hunters to the landowner for a trespass permit.*

only want to recognize their importance. Brushing out the lines of cover between fields and along roads and ditches eliminates the only *secure* shelter in the vicinity. Look at these fields in winter, and see how much protective cover is left for a pheasant. Burning fields, woods, and brush is even worse; it not only destroys the cover, but gradually ruins the soil too.

The drainage of wet spots may take away valuable little marshes and swales needed for shelter. Usually this drainage is sound and provides the farmer with good crop land; but sometimes the soils in a wet area are not productive, and the newly drained land fails to pay its way. Sometimes they prove impossible to drain adequately for crop use, and make only a worthless, sedgy area. In these instances they would be better left undrained, to serve as wildlife cover and for water storage. All proposed drainage should be based on a reliable analysis of the soil and water conditions, so that unwise and unproductive jobs can be avoided.

The time of mowing hayfields, roadsides, and pastures is an important factor in determining pheasant nesting success. Farmers learn where the most pheasants nest, and with good will these areas can be left until all other mowing is completed. Areas mowed for maintenance only—that is, where the cut grass is not harvested—can be worked in July or later. These include roadsides, diversion terraces, grass waterways and outlets, and field border headlands of tilled crops.

The methods of handling the corn crop are exceedingly important in determining pheasant winter carrying capacity. Leaving the plowing of corn stubble until spring, rather than doing it in the fall, saves valuable winter food. On the other hand, the trend toward ensiling corn instead of feeding hard grain loses much potential winter food for the birds. In many other ways the techniques of growing and harvesting corn affect the pheasant's food supplies.

In brief, all the farmer's cultural handling of the land affects the pheasant for better or worse. When he distributes manure on his fields on top of winter snows he often saves many birds hard pressed for food. When he allows his livestock to graze the woodlands, marshes, and odd areas, he reduces the protective cover that pheasants need for their survival. The pheasant responds to changing conditions on the farm, whether for good or bad. Within the general limitations of soil and climate, the number of pheasants depends on what the farmer does with his land and crops.

HIGHWAY TRAFFIC TOLL

PUBLIC highways and railroad rights of ways are prominent land features of good pheasant range; and they take a high toll of pheasant lives. It isn't just that random flights occasionally collide with autos and trains; the traffic arteries themselves affect the distribution and activities of the birds. Pheasants often tend to congregate along roadside fences. Gravel along the road or railroad is an attraction, especially in winter, when grit may be hard to find. So it is not surprising that many are killed when running or flying across traffic lanes.

In Ohio it was found that an average of 5 birds per square mile, or 2.4% of the annual mortality, succumbed to traffic accidents (Leedy and Hicks in McAtee, 1945). Stated another way, they found 21 dead birds per thousand miles of road, when inspected twice weekly. Along railroads they found from 250 to 435 per thousand miles of trackage in a late summer count. About 40% of the total were chicks, and a large majority were females. This probably reflected the preponderance of females in the pheasant population. Other studies have shown similar losses along roads. There is probably little that can be done to change this condition. Further, it is probably true that most of these losses are part of the inevitable mortality of surplus birds in an insecure habitat. Nevertheless the phenomenon is of interest as one of the manifest ways in which man's activities and structures affect the ring-neck pheasant.

MAN'S ROLE AS A CONSERVATIONIST

IN addition to his roles of hunter and farmer, man may affect the pheasant by being a conservationist. He may, of course, be all three rolled into one: that, in fact, is the ideal role—producer, user, and preserver. It is as a conservationist that he reaches his highest ethical standards. The fact that he is able, at least on occasion, to be a conservationist, distinguishes him from most of the rest of the animal world.

As a conservationist he enacts laws that regulate the time when pheasants may be hunted, the number and classes that may be shot, and the weapons that are to be used. In this manner he attempts to adjust the harvest to the size of the crop, and to provide equal opportunity for all who can qualify as hunters.

These game laws are a defensive necessity; only by thus curtailing the individual freedom of our citizens as hunters is it possible to preserve the sport of public hunting at all. But man conserves in positive ways too. Not all his efforts in this direction work as intended, but at least they have commendable objectives. He saves birds from winter hardship by providing them with handouts of food. (But the same person may destroy their natural food by his methods of handling his farm crops). He protects them by creating areas where no hunting is permitted—refuges or sanctuaries. (At the same time he may let his cattle graze off natural shelter that would protect the birds.) He shoots the pheasant's natural enemies in the belief that by so doing he will enable more of them to survive. (Yet he often allows his dogs and cats to roam at will to become serious pred-

PLATE 14. *Farmer and sportsman get together through the game management program of the Shiloh-O 'Fallon Soil Conservation District in Illinois. The local sportsman's club aids cooperating farmers in developing habitat, planting food patches, and by observing hunting regulations.*

COURTESY SOIL CONSERVATION SERVICE, USDA

ators). More and more he is directing his conservation efforts toward improvement of the habitat—the basic need if pheasants are to be produced in greater numbers. But these are matters for discussion when we consider methods of management. Suffice it now to note that, among his other attributes that affect the pheasant, he is something of a conservationist. Only as we strengthen this position can our public pheasant hunting be preserved.

REPRODUCTION AND POPULATIONS

REPRODUCTIVE POTENTIAL

THE pheasant is polygamous, breeds when it is about ten months old, and has only one brood of young a year. Though the sex ratio is even among young birds, in adult populations the females predominate, especially because of the selective hunting of cocks (in most states). The spring ratio of cocks to hens varies greatly, from 1 to 2 to 1 to 6.

The age ratio of birds in the fall is an important indicator of productivity. In good years, with normal success in nesting and brood raising, the young pheasants will compose 65% to 80% of the whole population. When the proportion drops below 65%, it usually indicates poor production for the year. If fewer than half the birds are youngsters, the population is on the down grade, and poor hunting is certain.

Young pheasants may be distinguished from old birds in autumn by several means. The length and shape of the spur of the male is dependable. Spurs of adult cocks measure over three-fourths of an inch from the tip to the front edge of the leg, and the spur is sharp; in young birds it is smaller and the tip blunt. The presence of the bursa of Fabricius, a pouch lying above the intestine at its lower end, is proof that the bird is juvenile. The strength of the lower mandible is indicative of age. By holding the bird in front of you while gripping it by the lower bill between thumb and forefinger, you can test its strength; if the bird is young, the bill will usually break, but if it is adult, the bill remains firm.

The average actual length of life for birds that reach maturity is six to eight months for males (most of which are killed shortly after they reach full size), and 15 to 24 months for females. Almost all the birds die a violent death. Those whose unusual fortune enables them to live out their natural period of longevity will attain eight to ten years.

The size of clutch of pheasant eggs is often difficult to judge, due to high nest losses and subsequent renesting. The average number of eggs per nest for the whole season ranges from nine to eleven. The earliest clutches have more eggs—early April nests 15 or more eggs. As the season progresses, newly laid clutches are smaller and smaller, until late June, when they will have dropped to a mean of eight eggs to a nest.

As with most gallinaceous birds, these attributes of reproduction enable the pheasant to increase its numbers rapidly when environmental conditions are favorable. A single cock and a harem of four hens with ten eggs each *could* become 45 pheasants, 21 males and 24 females, in a single season. Assuming no losses other than legal hunting, this group might decline to 6 males and 24 females by spring, the same ratio of sexes as before. By the end of the second summer, the same perfect production would result in 270 pheasants, 126 males and 144 females. This is a two-season theoretical possibility from an initial 5 birds. Under this imagined process, 15 cocks could have been killed the first year and 90 the second season, and still have maintained the original sex ratio. Thus 105 cocks might be harvested from an original single male (and harem) in two years. Sounds wonderful, doesn't it? But, there is no point in pursuing this hypothesis further; it is obvious that the pheasant's reproductive potential can fully stock any good range quickly. Environmental resistance—the action of the various decimating agencies like adverse weather, predators, and man, and of limiting habitat conditions—prevents the theoretical increase from happening. Only in an understocked range, a habitat that has fewer pheasants than it is capable of supporting, can any increase take place from one year to the next. Once the carrying capacity is reached, the year's full increment of birds must die before another year rolls round. Sometimes even more than the year's increase succumbs before the next spring; then the population temporarily

drops below carrying capacity, and offers the possibility of a net increase the next year.

MORTALITY CAUSES

POPULATIONS that rise each summer and drop back to the same breeding population each spring have losses (mortality) equal to the numbers produced. These losses begin with the egg stage and continue with the chicks and adults. They vary year to year as numbers increase or decrease. The causes of these losses likewise vary. But we can appraise them rather accurately.

Nesting Losses. Most pheasant nests are destroyed before the eggs can be hatched; yet most hen pheasants manage to hatch a clutch of eggs. These seemingly contrary facts are explained by the hen's persistence in renesting when her nest is broken up, and by the cock bird's perseverance in staying with his families throughout the spring and summer seasons.

Normal nest loss is about 60%; under favorable circumstances it may be as low as 40%, and under adverse conditions as high as 80%. In most areas of good range, $\frac{2}{3}$ to $\frac{9}{10}$ of these losses are caused by farm machinery, mainly mowing machines; the rest of the nests lost are mostly robbed by predators. A few are flooded out, destroyed by fire, or deserted by the hen bird. In some of the good range, the proportion of nests lost by hay mowing is lower, owing to more intensive tillage and fewer grass crops. This is often compensated for by an increased number pilfered by natural enemies, so that the net result is about the same in all pheasant range.

Of 241 Minnesota pheasant nests observed by Erickson, *et al.,* (1951), only 29% were successful. Farm machinery and livestock destroyed 41% of those that failed, predators 23%, hail and floods 14%; another 17% were abandoned or used as dump nests by several hens. Shick (1952) checked 87 nests on a 9,000-acre area of good Michigan range, and found that but 30% were successful. Of those that failed, 43% were deserted (some from human disturbance), 18% were destroyed by farm machinery, and 15% by crows.

Hens whose nests are ruined in the spring almost always try again. Even a second or third loss of the nest will not prevent another attempt, as long as the reproductive functions of both sexes remain active. This ends about July, and there are few nests begun later than early July. But by this time, some 60% to 70% or more of pheasant hens will usually have managed to bring off a brood. The longer it takes her to succeed, the smaller the brood will be; but its notable nesting persistence makes it possible for the pheasant to thrive under an adverse agricultural system.

Losses from infertility and poor hatching of the eggs are almost negligible. The proportion of eggs that are infertile averages 2% or 3%, is rare in spring eggs, higher in summer-laid eggs. Death of the embryo before hatching occurs in 2% to 4% of the eggs, rarely more.

Juvenile Mortality. The mother pheasant is a good mother. She usually manages to keep her little family out of harm's way with remarkable success. This is particularly noteworthy in view of the hazardous surroundings—farm fields—in which they are raised. Nevertheless it is normal for a considerable proportion of young pheasants to die before they reach adulthood, that is, about 16 to 18 weeks of age. The losses of these youngsters, especially during the critical period immediately after hatching, is one of the more widely variable of pheasant mortality factors. In fact, it is one of the two periods of the year when losses can become so catastrophic as to make the succeeding hunting season a poor one.

The expected summer reduction in the numbers of chicks is about 30% to 40% of those hatched. Studies in Vermont, Ohio, Iowa, and Utah have shown this amount of loss to be normal. In good years, in some areas, it may be much lower, as it was in Pennsylvania in 1939, where only 12% of the youngsters perished (Randall, 1940). Losses of 30% to 40% mean that from four to six chicks per brood survive

until fall. When the average brood size drops below three by October, then look out—it means poor hunting ahead. Under these conditions the mortality of young birds is up to 65% or 70%, and it can be even higher than that.

In diagnosing the causes of these losses, we do well to separate the normal from the abnormal. The anticipated 30% to 40% loss is largely due to accidents (such as being caught by a mower), inadequate brooding (chilling and soaking when very young), and some predation. There is little disease. The abnormal losses—those that occasionally send the survival rate down to 10% to 30%—are primarily due to climatic causes; a "poor breeding season," they call it. Usually it means cold weather with a long period of rain and little sunshine when the majority of chicks are newly hatched—in late May and early June. Such a combination contributed largely to the decline in pheasant numbers in many areas in 1945 and 1946.

In this connection, a paradoxical relationship between destructive agents—farm machinery and predators—and pheasant survival is worth noting. To illustrate how this works, let us assume that no pheasant nests are destroyed by farm machinery and predatory animals. The birds start nesting at a fairly uniform time, and then all hatch out at about the same time. Now let us suppose that the hatching occurs in the early part of a period of protracted cold, wet, cloudy weather. Then the year's entire production of pheasants is subjected to a very high loss, possibly 80% to 90% or even more. That occasionally occurs with the ruffed grouse, because they almost all hatch at one time.

As a rule, it doesn't work that way with the ring-neck. Usually many of the first nests are destroyed; then the birds renest (which the grouse seldom does). This staggers the hatching times, thus assuring that a period of bad weather cannot catch all the birds vulnerable at once. Thus these destructive agents that force renesting act as a safeguard against near-total destruction in a bad weather year. Odd, isn't it? But it shows that there may be good in even the worst of events.

The period of the highest loss of chicks is immediately after hatching; but the important part played by accidents with machinery somewhat evens the rate of loss through the summer. It becomes a fairly steady decline. Broods of nine on June 1st may drop to an average of 7½ by July 1st, seven on August 1st, 6½ by the first of September, and six by October.

Losses of Adults. The number of full-grown pheasants on the range declines throughout the year, except for the one season, usually accepted as October, when the year's increment of grown-up young birds become adult. From the maximum number in October there is a long and great drop to the small number living through the next year's September.

The greatest decrease usually takes place during the fall hunting season. If perchance there is no hunting, then the high mortality period is apt to be delayed until late winter and early spring. The gross loss during the fall months is usually from 50% to 60% of the October population. This is mostly a result of the legal kill of males, crippling, and the illegal kill of females. Some is caused by predation and accidents; these natural losses may run from 5% to 10% of the population.

The losses in winter are often surprisingly small; at least this is true until late in the winter. Yet winter includes the second critical season, February and March, when extremely high losses occasionally occur. The normal winter losses are mostly the result of predator attack, which is frequently conditioned by the inadequacies of the habitat. This loss ordinarily runs to only 5% to 10% of October populations (or 10% to 20% of the late fall numbers). Under certain combinations of weather—especially if the protective shelter in the habitat is inadequate—predation may skyrocket. Freezing, driving rains with high winds, and sometimes preceded or followed by drifting snow may result in high losses from the birds freezing.

Green (1938) found that 41% of the late fall population of pheasants in Iowa one winter succumbed to this freezing and choking death.

Spring again increases the vulnerability of the birds. The cocks suffer losses from enemy attack, made easy by their courtship activities. The hens suffer some losses from mowing machines during the incubation period. As many as 10% to 15% of all setting hens are killed in this way. Altogether, the spring losses may be 15% to 20% of the numbers surviving the winter, or 6% to 8% of the October population; sometimes they are higher.

Post hunting season losses from November until May on a 9,000-acre area of productive pheasant range in Michigan averaged 56% for three years; the highest loss was 67%, and the lowest 42% (Shick, 1952).

Summer is another period of relative safety. There is no loss from poor weather, or from disease, little predation, and few accidents. At this season the losses will further decrease the adults by only about 2% to 4% of the October count, or around 8% to 10% of the spring survivors.

The annual survival of pheasants on Pelee Island, Ontario, for the four years 1947 to 1950 was from 35% to 63% for hens and 6% to 12% for cocks. The great difference in survival between the two sexes was due to the intensive hunting of the cocks, though some hens were killed (Stokes, 1952).

Adding it all up, of every 100 pheasants present in early October, there will probably be only 20 to 30, sometimes fewer, left by the end of the next September.

LIFE EQUATION

THE summary of the annual gains and losses through the year is the life equation. Actually it is an equation only if the losses and gains balance; then the population is the same at the end of the year as at the beginning. In case the gains exceed the losses, there is a temporary inequation in that direction. If the losses are the greater, a decline occurs that is also a temporary unbalance. Over the years the balance shifts in one direction and then the other, but always tending toward a true balance between gains and losses of pheasant lives— their life equation.

A good perspective of the proportions of these gains and losses can be had if we follow a theoretical population of pheasants through the year. We will assume that 100 pheasants, 20 males and 80 females, have survived the winter on 400 acres of good pheasant range. We will further assume, just to simplify the problem, that no birds leave the 400 acres, and no outsiders enter it. In this particular year the losses balanced the gains, and the population ended as it began with 100 birds. See Table 2.

FLUCTUATIONS IN POPULATIONS

PHEASANT populations are never static; through the year, from October until the next hatching season, they decline. From year to year the net change may be up or down, but it can't continue many years in one direction. If in one year the population is below average, it is most likely to increase the next year; contrarily, if it is high, it will probably decline. These shifts back and forth on either side of a median are to be expected, and they follow no set pattern with respect to time—that is, they are not generally considered to be regularly cyclic. There is some doubt on this point, since the recent pheasant decline paralleled similar declines of other species.

In the years from 1942 to 1947 pheasant numbers declined over much of the American range. This naturally occasioned great howls from the sportsmen, particularly as it included a period when they had just been released from the stringencies of wartime, and earnestly wanted the recreation of good hunting. There has been much debate over what caused this decline, and whether the birds would regain their former numbers. As Kimball (1948) said, "Three-fourths of a pheasant population worth many millions of dollars has disappeared in front of our noses in the short span of four

years, and we don't know why . . . we don't know if it was because the eggs were not laid, the eggs did not hatch, or the young died. . . . It was not because the adults died." It seems clear that the great pheasant decline of the mid-'40's was a failure of production rather than a huge decimation.

A large part of the cause of this decline was adverse weather. Poor hatching seasons in successive years and cold wet weeks in late May and June prevented the hatching and survival of normal crops of young pheasants. But there is more to the story than this.

We are in a period when several agricultural practices in the good pheasant range are undergoing change. Some of these—the ones that are predominantly effective at present—are impairing both the production and the survival of pheasants. This means a lower carrying capacity. Among the more important farmland changes that are influencing the pheasant are: (1) A shift in crops to more grass and fewer tilled crops. In particular, it results in less grain grown, and more hay and pasture, thus reducing pheasant food. (2) An increase in the use of corn as ensilage rather than grain. This means that the corn plant is cut, hauled entire to the barnyard, chopped up, and stored in a silo with a preservative. No grain is left in the field to feed pheasants. (3) The use of more machinery, faster machinery, and round-the-clock operations in growing and harvesting crops. The night mowing of hay with high speed tractors is proving specially destructive to nesting hens and their eggs.

These and other trends in farming are affecting pheasants. Just how much effect they have had is hard to say; but the trends continue, and we do not know when they will end. Fortunately there are other trends that favor the pheasant; the changes are not all bad. The spread of soil conservation programs offers many improvements in pheasant habitat. These will be discussed under management.

There is some reason to believe that the high pheasant populations of the 1930's and early

TABLE 2

LIFE EQUATION OF 100 PHEASANTS FOR A YEAR

TIME	ACTIVITIES	NUMBER OF PHEASANTS	
		young	adult
SPRING	(1) 20 males mate 80 females		100
	(2) Females nest, average 10 eggs 80 × 10 = 800		
	(3) 70% of females hatch nests ultimately, or 560 eggs, of which: 11 are infertile (2%); 22 die in shell (4%); 527 hatch (av. 9.4)	527	
	(4) 15 adults die from predators, machinery, etc. (15% of those over-wintering)		85
SUMMER	(5) 8 adults die from accidents, etc. (8–10% of spring survivors)		77
	(6) 185 chickens die from accidents, inadequate brooding, etc. (35%)	342	
FALL	Surviving young become adults (about 80% of adults are birds of the year)		419
	(7) 231 die from hunting: 30% legal kills of males; 10% crippled males; 15% illegal kill of females		188
	(8) 42 die from predation, accident, etc.		146
WINTER	(9) 46 die from exposure, predation (32% of those surviving the fall)		100
	These 100 birds, which may well again be 20 males and 80 females, survive to the next breeding season.		

1940's were inevitably due for a reduction, possibly a permanent one. The pheasant is an introduced species. It found a niche in a new range, and quickly—over a period of just a few decades—established itself. To all the indigenous organisms in that range the pheasant was a stranger. They did not have the means to cope with the invader—at least not at once. Predatory animals, parasitic organisms, competing species, all "caught unawares," gradually had to accustom themselves to the intruder. At least this is the sort of reasoning the evidence forces us to adopt. It seems that all successful invaders overextend themselves. Consider the English sparrow and the Japanese beetle as examples. In the East, where they first got a foothold in this country, they reached phenomenal numbers; they extended their range westward from these "beachheads." Then after a period the original infestations dropped off to more moderate densities. The whole invasion may be likened to an onrushing wave whose initial crest is followed by an ebb to a lower water level.

The pheasant too has followed this pattern so far. Man established the species in many areas concurrently; from these nuclei the pheasant spread to take over all suitable range. The question is: were the recent high populations of pheasants an untenable condition, comparable to the surge in abundance of other successfully colonized exotics? And are the more recently lowered numbers partly a response to that condition? If the answers are "yes"—and they may very well be—then we may never again see such large numbers of pheasants. The environmental checks will have caught up with the pheasant, to place it in balance with its competitors and enemies.

Despite this gloomy possibility, the ring-neck recovered from its decline of the mid-'40's. Good hatching seasons returned, and better conservation farming methods will continue to improve the habitat. Hunting has been good again in the early '50's, even if not as good as before. And the pheasant will continue to have fluctuations in its numbers, as all wildlife does.

POPULATION DENSITIES AND CARRYING CAPACITY

By dividing the number of birds by the acres of range we obtain their population density in terms of birds per acre. By reversing the division—which provides a more usable figure—we have it in acres per bird. The carrying capacity of the range is the population density it can sustain through the winter to the breeding season. It is a factor of the environment, and primarily of the habitat (within a given climatic area). Thus we know that eastern South Dakota, which is first class range, has a higher pheasant carrying capacity than southeastern Pennsylvania, which is second-class range. In turn, the Pennsylvania range has a higher carrying capacity than that of the Connecticut River valley of Massachusetts, which is third-class range.

The two most useful times for getting population densities are early fall and spring. The first gives us the maximum numbers for gauging hunting probabilities and the need for adjustments in the hunting regulations. The second evaluates the spring breeding stock, which is indicative of the carrying capacity in normal years.

The early fall populations for large areas of range in good years will be approximately one acre per bird in first-class range; three to four acres per bird in second-class range; and five to ten acres or more per bird in third-class (poor) range. Small areas of very favorable habitat within any range may of course have denser

populations. In years of below-normal productivity the fall densities may be far below those cited.

The spring densities of populations, at carrying capacity, are about three to four acres per bird in first-class range; eight to ten acres per bird in second-class range; 15 to 20 acres per bird in third-class range. Again, after a winter with poor survival, the numbers may drop to sparser densities. Also you will hear remarkable stories of ten pheasant nests in a ten-acre hayfield, a half-a-dozen cocks crowing within sight at one point, and so on. These may be true, but they are not indicative of general range carrying capacity or of the average population densities of the range; they merely indicate concentrations in good nesting cover and good crowing territories—at the same time most of the range may be vacant. Such concentrations may even indicate weaknesses in the range—a lack of good nesting and crowing cover, which forces the birds to concentrate.

Another factor in wildlife populations that relates directly to densities is the *saturation point*. This is the greatest density that the species itself will tolerate, and is independent of range conditions. For some species, such as the ruffed grouse, it may set the level of the carrying capacity, and frequently forces a redistribution of the birds. A gregarious species like the pheasant is more tolerant of its kind, and so generally its degree of intolerance is not important in affecting the carrying capacity. About the only way in which this factor influences the pheasant is in connection with the spring competition of males for crowing territories; the females seem to tolerate almost any amount of crowding. Thus it is not possible to define a clear-cut saturation point for ring-necks.

MANAGEMENT OF THE PHEASANT

Management of any game bird can readily be divided into two parts: the production of the crop; and its harvest. The first part, production, deals little with the bird itself; it is mostly a matter of handling the land, for it is the vegetative cover of the land that determines production. Fertile land that lies within the pheasant's range can be handled so as to produce a good crop of birds, but poor land can never be made to grow as many. Such accessories to production as the stocking of game farm birds, and trapping and redistributing surpluses from protected areas to public hunting lands, are a part of this phase. In so far as it can be recommended, predator control comes in here. The harvest part of management begins with the provision of adequate laws, and continues with the establishment of protected areas (refuges). The allowable kill is determined (by taking censuses), and the harvest is controlled by law enforcement and through co-operative arrangements among landowners, sportsmen, and state agencies.

HABITAT DEVELOPMENT

THE improvement of farms will rarely be undertaken just to grow more pheasants; the farmer is in the food-producing business, and the pheasant is at best a secondary interest. What he does with his farm will be done for one or both of two reasons: to grow more or better crops; to improve and preserve his land. Fortunately the ring-neck is a product of good land, and is benefited by most sound land conservation practices. Only through efforts to improve the farm for farming will pheasant habitat be made better. Thus when we discuss developing pheasant cover we are really talking, to a great degree, about a program for soil conservation.

Start with an Inventory of Physical Resources. General recommendations for the improvement of farms are apt not to fit the needs of any one farm, any more than a suit of clothes of the "average" man's size is likely to fit a man chosen at random—clothes must be tailored to the individual's specifications if they are to fit. So a conservation plan should be "tailored" to fit the individual farm. The "measurements" of that farm from which the specifications are determined are the characteristics of its land. To make a physical inventory of the land, four factors must be determined and mapped. These are: (1) The soil type (such as "Hagerstown silt loam"). All the essential physical and chemical nature of a particular soil is set forth when its correct identity is determined. All named soil types are catalogued and described by the soils scientists, just as the plants are by the botanists. (2) The steepness of slope. (3) The amount of erosion (this indicates the amount of topsoil that remains). (4) The present land use. The last shows what kind of cover now exists; it indicates for the whole farm the amounts of the crops grown, hence the nature of the farm business.

This type of the inventorying of farmland resources is done by the U. S. Soil Conservation Service on all farms where it develops soil conservation plans with farmer co-operators of soil conservation districts; it is called a "soil conservation survey." The delineations of the various conditions are made on an aerial photograph of the farm, thus eliminating the need for line and distance measuring of the farm fields. All the important boundaries are clearly shown on the photograph.

Interpreting the Physical Land Inventory. Once the basic physical data are thus set forth for the farm (or other land area) that we wish to develop, we are in position to interpret those conditions in terms of the inherent possibilities of each part of the land for various uses. Here again the U. S. Soil Conservation Service has developed a system by which these data may be translated into recommendations for proper land use—"Land Use Capabilities." Through experience with each combination of soil, slope, and erosion, this determines the most intensive use to which it can be put, and be maintained indefinitely without loss of productivity. Then recommendations are made in the form of tables covering all the conditions found in a

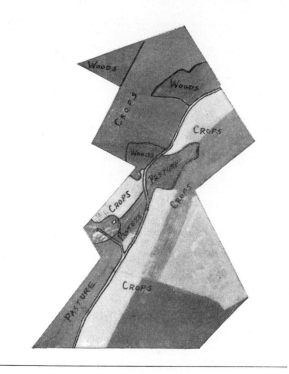

FIGURE 4. *Aerial Photograph Map of Farm of Mr. Good Farmer, York County, Pennsylvania, Showing Land Use before Conservation Planning. Note that the photograph does not show details clearly; this is done so that the writing will stand out, since only field boundaries need be clear. Planning is done with the farmer on the farm and hence the writing is free-hand.*

given area. Thus a conservationist may consult a "Land Use Capability Table" to tell him the possibilities of use for any field or piece of land on a farm that has a soil conservation survey. From that point on his own skills enable him to recommend suitable conservation practices to go with fields devoted to their proper land use.

Let us see how this system works out in a specific case. Figure 4 shows a section of an aerial photograph of an area in York County, Pennsylvania, which is the farm of Mr. Good Farmer. A soil conservation survey is made, and its information is shown on the photograph in Figure 5. (An explanation of the symbols used is given below the aerial photograph.) Now Mr. Trained Conservationist takes this

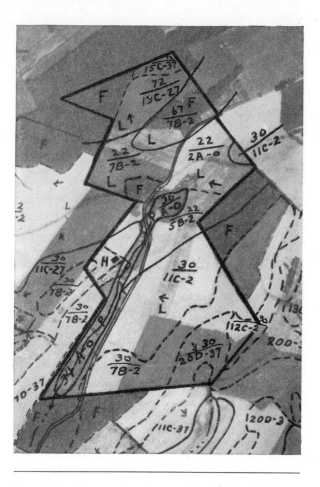

FIGURE 5. *Conservation Survey Map of Good Farmer Farm. Symbols show soil type, slope, erosion, and land use.*

L-cropland; P-pasture; F-woods; H-homestead. Numerator number is soil type (see Land Use Capability table), left denominator is slope (see LUC table), right denominator is degree of erosion where 0 means no soil lost, 1 is 0–25% topsoil gone, 2 is 25–50% topsoil gone, 3 is 50–75% topsoil gone. Numeral 7 added indicates scattered gullies, 8 means frequent gullies.

Mapping is done in blocks and shown on large aerial photos; then farm boundaries are outlined as needed.

information and turns to his Land Use Capability Table, which is shown in Table 4. From there he determines the land use capability class in which each part of the farm belongs—there are eight land use capability classes, defined in Table 3 on page 42.

TABLE 3

LAND USE CAPABILITY CLASSES

(After U.S. Soil Conservation Service)

LAND USE CAPABILITY CLASS I: Very good land, suitable for cultivation with ordinary good farm practices.

II: Good land, suitable for cultivation with the use of simple conservation practices.

III: Moderately good land, suitable for cultivation with more conservation practices than on Class II land, or with practices more intensively applied.

IV: Fairly good land that is best suited for hay and pasture but that can be cultivated occasionally (usually not more than one year in six).

V: Land suited for grazing or woodland with only slight limitations. Not suited to cultivation.

VI: Suited to permanent pasture, or woodland, with the use of appropriate conservation measures.

VII: Suited only for woodland, or wildlife development, with great care. Not usually recommended for pasture.

VIII: Suited only for wildlife and recreation. It is usually very steep, rough, sandy, wet, or extremely erodible.

Having determined the land use capability class for each part of the farm, he labels these on the soil conservation survey photo map (these are also shown on Figure 6). In common practice the different land classes are colored on the map; this makes them stand out clearly, and thus aids in planning for the land's needs. Class I is *light green* (the "go" sign for his best land); class II is *yellow* (caution); class III is *red* (the danger signal when used for tilled crops because of hazards of erosion, wetness, stoniness, or other limiting condition); class IV is *blue;* class V is *dark green;* class VI is *orange;* class VII is *brown;* and class VIII is *purple.*

The land capability class designation for any piece of land may result from one or more of several conditions. For example, a field of capability class III land may be so classed because of its steepness, or erosion hazard, because it is excessively wet and has a water hazard, or because the nature of the soil itself is a hazard to its use. A very drouthy, sandy soil would be a case of the latter sort. In some parts of

the country the climate may place a limit on the use of the land. These matters are indicated on land-use capability maps by subsymbols to the capability class number, "e" for erosion, "s" for soil, "w" for water, and "c" for climate. Thus a steep field might be capability unit IIIe of class III, while a low, flat, wet field would be in unit IIIw if it fitted class III. These subsymbols are also shown in Figure 6.

Adjusting Land Use to Capabilities of the Land. Armed with the information on the LUC map, the planner compares the actual use of each field with its capabilities. Frequently he finds that some parts of the farm are being used more intensively than they can stand. Areas suited only to grassland as the most intensive use may be in tilled crops or grain; other areas that are only suited to woodland may be in pasture or cropland. The indicated changes in land use are basic to attaining a good farm conservation plan. Those fields that are retired to woodland are planned for tree planting. The outer margin of these plantings

TABLE 4

LAND USE CAPABILITIES*

ACCORDING TO SOIL TYPE, SLOPE, AND DEGREE OF EROSION

YORK COUNTY, PENNA.

SOIL TYPE AND NUMBER	"A" SLOPE 0–3%			"B" SLOPE 3%–8%			"C" SLOPE 8%–15%			"D" SLOPE 15%–25%			"E" SLOPE Over 25%		
	erosion			erosion			erosion			erosion			erosion		
	0, 1	2, 27	28, 3, 37	0, 1	2, 27	28. 3, 37	0, 1	2, 27	28, 3, 37	0, 1	2, 27	28, 3, 37	0, 1	2, 27	28, 3, 37
22—CHESTER: gravelly silt loam	I	II	II	II	II	III	II	II	III	III	III	IV	VI	VI	VI
30—MANOR: gravelly loam	I	II	II	II	II	IV	II	III	IV	IV	IV	VI	VI	VI	VII
34—GLENVILLE: silt loam (imperfectly drained)	III	III	III	III	III	III	III	III	IV						
36—WORSHAM: silt loam (poorly drained)	VI	VI	VI	VI	VI	VI	VI	VI	VI						
67—EDGEMONT: gravelly silt loam	I	II	II	II	II	III	III	III	IV	IV	IV	VI	VI	VI	VII
72—CARDIFF: shaly silt loam	I	II	II	II	II	III	III	III	IV	IV	IV	VI	VI	VI	VII

* Only that portion of the table is included that applies to the example used in the text.

is planned for shrubs to provide a transition border, and prevent the new woodland from adversely affecting the adjacent crops. On the farm we are planning, field 10 is designated for reforestation, with "wildlife borders" of shrubs as shown on the farm plan map, Figure 7. This land, formerly cropped, was in land-use capability classes VII and VI.

One small area of land capability class IV (field 4) retired from rotated crops to permanent hay. Two other small areas of land capability class III, fields 5 and 6, are likewise devoted to permanent hay, because of the convenience of their location, size, and shape. All these areas have "e" capability classifications. One other land-use adjustment is made: the development of the poorly drained piece of capability class VI land (field 9) into a pond. Note that this area is capability class VIw because of wetness. The pond surroundings, especially between the pond and the road, are improved by tree and shrub plantings. This completes the land-use changes.

Planning the Conservation Practices. Now all the land is used within its capabilities. For each of the 14 fields into which the farm is divided, the appropriate conservation practices are recommended.

Beginning with the cropland, fields 1 and 3 will be strip-cropped with the crop strips about 100 feet wide. Both edges of each strip are laid out on the contour, to let the short rows come in the middle. The rotation is corn, oats, wheat, and hay. In field 3, a diversion terrace is built in the 6th strip above the road, emptying into the woodland on the adjacent farm (by mutual agreement between the owners). A 40-foot wide filter strip of sod will be maintained above the diversion. A contour hedge of high-bush cranberry is planted on the boundary between strips 3 and 4 in field 3.

Field 2 will be farmed on the contour with a short rotation arranged to balance the crop needs of the farmer. It may be used for cash crops rather intensively, provided winter cover crops are used, or hay turned under once every three years.

Shrub borders are planted or seeded on the crop field margins adjacent to all the woodlands. This involves most of the west side of field 1, the northeast and southeast edges of field 1, the east side of field 2, and the northeast edge of field 3. The border of the tree planting next to the southeast part of field 3 has already been mentioned. These borders will be devoted to four rows of shrubs, consuming a 20-foot width, planted with a low species in the open field side, and progressively higher species toward the woods. Species used (except next to field 2) are bayberry, coralberry, multiflora rose, bicolor lespedeza, hybrid filbert, silky dogwood, high-bush cranberry, and tatarian honeysuckle. The field 2 border is seeded to bicolor lespedeza in the 10 feet next to the woods, and to sericea lespedeza in the adjacent 10 feet on the open field side of the border. On the north property line boundary of fields 2 and 5 a hedge-fence planting of multiflora rose is scheduled.

The permanent hayfields, numbers 4, 5, and 6, are seeded to alfalfa and brome grass, and reseeded as necessary.

Field 7, formerly partly cultivated and partly pastured, and field 8, are devoted to pasture. This adjustment in the boundaries of field 7 is not dictated by land-use necessity but rather by livestock needs, and the convenience of location. Both pastures will be rotated in use, will be limed and treated with superphosphate according to soil test, mowed annually and grazed within carrying capacity. The pasture in field 8 will require a special seed mixture when reseeded, due to its wetness. The newly added pasture in field 7 will be seeded to a short sod grass-legume mixture. Multiflora rose hedge fences will be planted around the two pastures, and along both sides of the stream except at needed watering locations.

The one-acre pond in field 9 will be made with a dam built according to specifications based on the hydraulics of its watershed. It will be stocked with 100 large-mouth bass fingerlings, and 1,000 bluegill sunfish fingerlings. The water is to be fertilized at the rate of 100 pounds of 8-8-4 per application, beginning about April 1 and repeated weekly until the water is so colored by plankton that the hand disappears from view at 12 inches depth; this will be repeated as necessary to maintain this water color density until November 1. All usable fish will be harvested as thoroughly as possible; leafy aquatic plants will be kept out of the pond.

A short grass sod is to be developed for a 20-foot width around the pond, including the dam. Clumps of evergreen trees and fruiting shrubs will be planted at suitable spots around the pond, back of the grass area, and including most of the poorly drained soil area between the dam and the road. Arborvitae, silky dogwood, and high-bush cranberry will be used in the wet soil places.

Field 10 will be planted to a mixture of white and Scotch pines, Norway spruce, Jap larch, black locust, and red oak (using acorns). As aforementioned, a 4-row border surrounds the planting.

The woodland in field 13 will be protected from access by domestic livestock by a fence between field 7 and the shrub border on its north edge. Care will be taken to keep fire from all the woodlands—areas 10, 11, 12, and 13. The marketable trees will be harvested according to sustained yield methods, with due regard for saving hollow trees for use as wildlife dens.

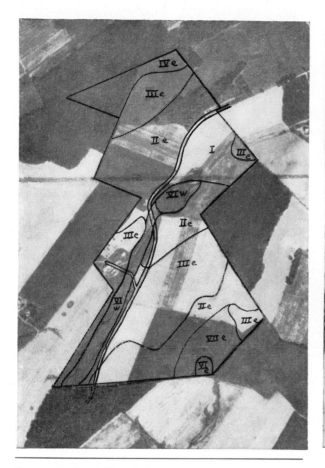

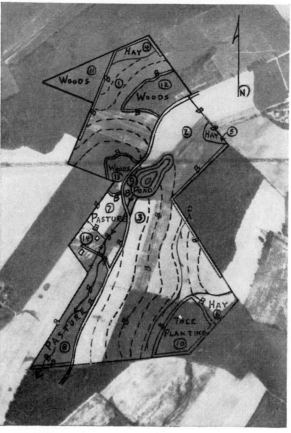

FIGURE 6. *Land Use Cability Map of Good Farmer Farm. The information from the Conservation map is interpreted according to the most intensive use to which each part is adapted. (See definitions of the Land Use Capabilities in Table 3).*

FIGURE 7. *Conservation Plan for Good Farmer Farm. Most of the development practices are indicated by land use designation or symbols.*

- - - - Contour strip crop boundary
– B – Contour hedge planting
– B – Hedge fence planting
= B = Shrub border
Streambank protected and planted
Diversion terrace

Field 14, the homestead, needs no soil conservation treatment.

Such a program of cover development as this example, based on the needs of the farm itself, furnishes the major needs of pheasant habitat in so far as it is practical to achieve them with the physical conditions present, and the type of farming used. Fertile land that lies within the pheasant's range can be handled so as to produce a good crop of birds, but poor land can never be made to grow as many.

Let us see what this program has done to change the cover on this farm.

Quantitatively, the adjustments are as follows:

COVER TYPE	BEFORE		AFTER	
Cultivated land	91 acres		77 acres	
Permanent hay	0 "		4 "	
Pasture	12 "		14 "	
Woodlands	7 "		10 "	
Homestead	3 "		3 "	
Water	0 "		1 "	
Shrub borders, hedges	0 "		4 "	(14,000 feet)

A reduction in acreage devoted to cropland is made up by increases in hay, pasture, woodland, shrub cover, and pond area. This seems at first to be a considerable loss of crop-pro-

PLATE 15. *Proper land use is the basis of sound pheasant habitat development. Planning for conservation practices should be based on the character of the land as revealed by Land Use Capabilities.*

ducing area, but as a matter of fact most of the land lost was unproductive and unprofitable in crops anyway.

Qualitatively, there is even more change. Crops and grass are more lush, owing to conservation treatments; this makes better wildlife cover as well as better crop yields. Protective cover for wildlife is greatly improved by the establishing of travel lanes in hedges, edge cover in borders, winter shelter in the conifer plantings, and lush vegetation around the pond. Food is improved by making the crop fields more accessible, and through use of shrub species in plantings that provide emergency winter fruits.

The most effective changes from the pheasant habitat viewpoint are not, however, in the improved quantity and quality of habitat, great as they are; of still more importance is the vastly benefited *arrangement* of the food and shelter coverts. The widely distributed network of

hedges and shrub borders, and the layout of crop fields in long, narrow strips, make the whole farm more suitable for pheasant use. Whereas cropfield boundaries formerly measured a little less than two miles in length, they now total almost six miles, mostly due to the strip-cropping arrangement. Edges between field and woods, between shrubby cover and woods, and other sorts of edges have been similarly increased in length. All this makes for enlarged pheasant carrying capacity: more food and shelter, of better quality, and arranged so that it can be efficiently used.

This program of land development was based on the character of the land we dealt with, and was tailored to its individual needs. The same procedures can be followed on every farm in America. In the range of the ring-neck, it can result in a marked improvement in the character of its habitat. Its effectiveness will be limited most by the crops grown, and by the methods of harvesting them. Where grains, especially corn, are grown for seed, and harvested by methods that leave considerable waste grain available over winter, results will be best. Where grains are not grown in abundance, or harvest methods leave little winter residue, the quality of the range for pheasants will still be only fair, or poor. If it is to be improved further under such circumstances, supplementary measures must be taken for the special benefit of the pheasant.

Summary of Habitat Development Measures. It may be well to summarize the things that may be done with the land cover to improve habitat.

ON CROPLAND

1. *Contour strip-cropping* of the rotated crops.
2. Use of *diversion terraces* to control water run-off.
3. Manage *ditch-bank* and *stream-bank* cover for erosion control and wildlife shelter.
4. Manage *hedgerow* cover.
5. *Protect stream banks* from livestock and re-vegetate eroding areas.
6. Plant managed *contour hedges* where needed for erosion control and other purposes.
7. Plant *living fences.*
8. Plant field and homestead *windbreaks.*
9. Plant or seed *shrub borders* between crop or pasture land and woods.
10. Retire lands unsuited to permanent use as cropland to grass, woodland, or wildlife coverts in accordance with Land Use Capabilities.

IN PASTURES

1. Retire lands unsuited to permanent use for grazing to woodland, or wildlife coverts.
2. *Confine grazing to good grassland,* excluding woodlands, stream banks, marshes, and wildlife coverts.
3. *Defer grazing* in spring until grass is 3" high, *rotate pastures,* and *graze within carrying capacity.*

IN WOODLANDS

1. Follow a *woodland cutting plan,* using a group selection system to create scattered, small openings.
2. *Interplant conifers* in glades in hardwood stands.
3. *Plant* areas retired from open land to woodland to a mixture of *trees,* including conifers.

ON WILDLIFE AREAS

1. *Maintain and improve marshes* by controlling water levels, excluding livestock, using only properly controlled burning, and planning a sustained fur harvest.
2. By planting and cutting, *develop* all areas suited best for *wildlife cover,* including kettle holes, rock outcrops, odd corners, pond surroundings, etc.
3. *Build ponds* and develop them and their surroundings for wildlife cover.

SUPPLEMENTARY PHEASANT HABITAT IMPROVEMENTS

Food Patches of Annual Seeds. It must be recognized that the foods provided by perennial plants—the fruits, nuts, and seeds of the shrubs and trees established in woodlands, borders, hedges, and so on—are of only secondary use to the pheasant; these birds must have grains and weed seeds in quantity to survive in large numbers. Thus, if the agriculture in an area does not furnish this food supply all year long, then a substitute must be found. The substitute is essentially the same thing: grain. When we set out small fields of grain especially for wildlife we call them "food patches." This can be done successfully for the pheasant. It is warranted only in the second-class range, and where the hunting pressure is such that the cost can be paid. It also will depend on successful co-operative arrangements with landowners, for they will have to do the actual work.

Pheasant food patches should be grown only

in good crop soils. They will consume some of the farm's regular grain land. The job requires everything that grain farming requires, except the harvest. Instead of reaping the crop, it is simply left standing through the fall and winter. The best crops for pheasant food patches are corn, corn and corn! But since corn requires cultivation through the growing season, at a considerable expense, it may be expedient to use others. Wheat, oats, barley, soybeans, or even plowed ground left fallow for its ragweed, smartweed, and foxtail grass seed crops, all may be used. It should be recognized, though, that all the seeds of the latter group are apt to be unavailable when most needed, under deep winter snow. Corn stands up even in the worst weather.

Frequently other mixtures are recommended for food patches, "shotgun" conglomerations of all sorts of things—millets, sorghums, cowpeas, sunflower, Sudan grass, hemp, rape, buckwheat, flax, lespedeza, and so on. Most of these make good songbird food, but contribute little to the pheasant.

Food patches should be placed at the edge of crop fields. They should be adjacent to good shelter—a swale, woods, or brush patch. It is better to have them long and narrow rather than squarish. The best of all are simply the edges of regular grain fields left unharvested.

The number and size of these patches needed depends on the inadequacy of the food supply; generally it is hard to justify more than two or three per farm, totaling one-half to one acre of land. When they are planted separately from a regular crop, the usual cultural methods for the grains used should be followed.

Winter Feeding. Where the winter food supply is known to be inadequate, food patches may likewise be insufficient to carry the birds through to spring. The only way left to prevent heavy winter losses is to provide grain at feeding stations. To be successful, a feeding program should begin early in the winter, in December, so that the birds may learn where to expect food. Until a storm emergency occurs, or until

late winter after food becomes scarce, the feeding should be light—just enough to keep the birds coming. When the food is desperately needed it should be provided in quantity. The best food to use is corn, either as shelled grain or on the cob; any other grains also will help. Once begun, feeding should be continued until the snows are gone.

Feeding stations should be located in protected spots where winter storms will not cover them with snow. They ought to be adjacent to good escape cover (swale, evergreens, marsh, or thicket), so that predators, that also learn where food is concentrated, will not harass and kill the birds. It is also desirable to have them conveniently close to the farm yard, or a road, so that they can be easily serviced through the winter.

The form of the feeding station makes little difference provided it is fully open on one side, and does not let the snow cover the feed; a lean-to made of evergreen boughs is a good type. Spikes on which cobs of corn can be impaled may be nailed through the lean-to supports. If desired, an automatic hopper feeder may be installed beneath the shelter; otherwise the grain can be scattered on the ground.

A secondary use of feeding stations is in counting pheasants for a spring census; they provide concentration points that make counting the birds relatively simple.

Adjusted Farm Practices. There are many ways that pheasant survival is affected by farming techniques. Most of these influence the bird's habitat, though some cause direct losses of the birds. Some of these farming methods can be adjusted to favor the pheasant without seriously detracting from crop production. Others are inevitably a part of our farming system, and their effects on pheasants must be accepted as part of the framework of environment that cannot be changed. Some things that can be changed to advantage are discussed below.

Plowing corn fields for the next crop can be *deferred until spring*, except where a winter grain is being sown. This permits leaving the corn residues in the field over the winter to furnish food for the birds. This is recommended where it does not upset the plowing schedule on the farm. It is good soil conservation, since the corn aftermath is better cover than newly plowed ground.

Proper pasture management preserves needed food and cover. This includes: rotated grazing; exclusion of streams, woods, and thickets from the pasture (except that essential watering facilities and shade must be kept in each pasture); deferring of spring grazing until the sod is three inches high; taking animals off pasture in the fall early enough to permit grass to start new growth; keeping livestock in feed lots in the winter and not permitting the grazing of corn or grain aftermath. All these practices are good land management.

The *small grain* fields can be *cut* with the combine blade set *high;* this leaves a taller stubble and more lush aftermath. Better cover is available for the birds when they seek waste grain and weed seeds for food.

Hay mowing can be *adjusted* to favor nesting success. Most nests are placed in the outer parts of hay fields. When fields are mowed from the center outward, so as to leave the outer edges unmowed as long as possible, some nests may have the extra undisturbed days needed for hatching. Grasslands mowed only once annually can be left unmowed until other early season mowing is done; some can be left until late June or July if mowing is primarily for sod maintenance. Roadsides, headlands, and diversion terraces are in this class.

In connection with mowing operations, and the desire to reduce pheasant nest destruction from machinery operation, it must be said that *"flushing bars"* cannot be recommended. It had been hoped that many nests could be saved from destruction by attaching flushing devices on to mowers; this would enable the operator to raise the blade and leave the nest undisturbed in a small island of uncut hay. In practice none of the various types of flushers have

worked well enough to make their general use worth while. Even the nests thus avoided—and with fast-traveling power mowers they were few—were mostly found by predators in their exposed situation. It's too bad, but we may as well face the facts; a fond hope has not proved valid.

Cover crops in orchards and in tilled fields help to provide some winter cover on fields that might otherwise be left barren. This is also needed for soil conserving purposes. Orchard cover crops can be composed of perennial plants, or seeded early enough in the season to develop a good high stand by winter. They can be of particular value to pheasants when they are next to grain fields.

Corn picking methods greatly affect the amount and availability of winter food. Machine-picked corn leaves a lot of waste grain, but the stalks are apt to be so leveled as to become unavailable for cover during deep winter snows. When a few outer rows of corn next to good cover are hand-picked this condition can be much improved. Some farmers are willing to do this to help hold the pheasants through the difficult winter period.

STOCKING OF GAME-FARM PHEASANTS; TRANSPLANTING

The Need for Stocking. One of the most widespread methods of pheasant management throughout our pheasant range has been the production of pen-reared birds and their subsequent release in farm coverts. Most sportsmen fervently believe that this is sound practice and essential to continued good hunting. Actually this opinion is a great illusion. True, it took stocking to establish the species in its American range, because it had no other way of getting here. Their maintenance, however, is a different matter.

All studies of the survival of stocked birds, and the proportion of stocked birds to natives in the hunters' bag (and there have been plenty of such studies), have shown clearly that the hunting is produced by the natural reproduction of "native" birds. Very few stocked birds are taken by hunters; stocked birds form almost a negligible part of the kill. The better the range, the more this is true. Except in poor range, stocking is mostly wasted effort, a sop to sportsman pressure on the state game agency. In poor range, stocked birds may provide a considerable part of the take. It won't be high in numbers, but it may be justified—if it can be afforded.

The Time for Stocking. There is a great controversy among game breeders, managers, and sportsmen over the best time to stock the birds—assuming you are bound to it. This arises partly from real doubt as to when stocking can be done to be most effective. It is also partly due to the difference in cost of the birds held in captivity for various periods.

As to results, the best time for stocking depends on whether you wish to enlarge the immediate kill or increase the breeding stock. For increasing the kill it is best to stock the birds at the beginning of and during the hunting season. This provides the best possible chance for hunters to get the birds before they die from some other cause. If the birds are on a controlled hunting area, it may even be possible to shoot hens as well as cocks. Only thus can a very significant portion of the stocked birds be brought to bag. If your purpose is to increase the breeding stock in the hope that it will increase the next year's shootable crop, then the best time to stock is early spring—say late March.

The stocking of immature pheasants in summer, or of adult birds in the fall after the hunting season is least effective of all. It can be justified only on the basis of getting rid of the birds because you can't afford to hold them longer.

The Method of Releasing Birds. The birds should be stocked in mild weather. Release is best made in a rather secluded spot of good protective shelter; a swale, thicket, or woodland edge. Food should be immediately available, either naturally or provided; corn is best.

The boxes containing the birds should be placed on the ground, and left there for a few minutes of quiet. Then the apertures may be slowly opened. The operators should then leave, and return later to pick up the crates. This allows the birds to leave at their own time and without undue excitement; thus they may more likely stay in the vicinity.

Numbers to Stock. For "put and take" stocking during the hunting season, the only rule for deciding how many birds to stock is the number desired to be shot. This usually is limited by finances; it has little relation to the carrying capacity of the land, or the need for augmenting breeding stock.

On lands open to the public for "free" shooting, the state agency simply stocks all the birds it can afford. If that's the way the sportsmen want their money spent, then so be it; there's no more comment needed. Under this system, only cocks are shot, and a 20% return can be considered exceptionally good. Since few of the missed birds survive till the next season, each pheasant shot costs five times the expense of raising one bird. How many fifteen-dollar pheasants can you afford? Considering the low license fee paid by the hunter, one is inclined to answer, "None."

Stocking controlled hunting lands, whether private preserve or regulated public shooting, offers more chance for a higher recovery of the birds. In some states the laws permit taking both sexes. Up to 50%, occasionally more, of the stocked birds may be shot. Stocking can be done daily in numbers to meet anticipated daily needs.

Spring stocking is done to augment the native breeding stock. Here again it is largely academic to discuss the proper number to stock. You generally release what your game farms have left, except for those needed for breeders, or what you can afford to buy. It is just an accident if the numbers stocked have any relation to actual range needs. It is a bigger piece of luck if enough survive to fill the need. Still, there can be some logic to this type of stocking. In poor range, or in range temporarily depleted of pheasants, one may stock to bring the number of breeders up to the theoretical carrying capacity. A male and five females per section (640 acres of land) is about the most that can generally be justified, even if the range could carry more. Such a stocking, if successful, would certainly augment the native birds enough to make possible a good fall population.

Trapping and Transplanting. Unshot areas of good pheasant range present a problem of pheasant control. Large numbers of pheasants without an annual shooting harvest are apt to cause damage to farm crops. Furthermore, the harvestable surplus from such areas is wasted, since the annual increase is disposed of by natural causes anyway.

Such areas include posted estates and blocks of farms, parks, refuges, suburban areas, etc. Surplus pheasants in such places should be live-trapped and transplanted to open hunting areas. These wild birds are better for stocking than are game-farm birds, and frequently cost less to trap than to raise or purchase.

Since successful live-trapping depends on baiting the birds into traps, it usually must await early winter. Then the birds have flocked together and can easily be attracted by food stations. The program can be continued as long through the winter as the need for transplanting remains.

PROTECTIVE MEASURES AGAINST OVER-SHOOTING

The tremendous demand for pheasant hunting, combined with the rather limited area of productive range, makes it imperative that the species receive some measure of protection from guns. The hunting has to be rationed, and there must be insurance against complete loss of breeding stock even within the limits of hunting restrictions. Two methods are used: (1) laws that limit the time, methods, and amount of hunting; and (2) taking land out of hunting by the establishment of refuges or sanctuaries.

Laws to Conserve the Pheasant Supply. The pheasant is an easy bird to hunt and its coverts are easily reached by great numbers of hunters. Thus it can stand only a rather short hunting season. Yet, despite this seeming truth, the species owes its survival more to its own cunning than to short hunting seasons. Actually there seems to be little difference in the hunting take with a season a week long compared with one a month long; in either case most of the bag is taken in the first few days. As a long season progresses the hunting success is poorer and poorer, with a resulting loss of enthusiasm by the hunters; and this is combined with greater wariness of the birds that have survived. Thus it is rare to have any sizable area of good range seriously overshot in a hunting season up to a month long. Equally useful are daily and seasonal bag limits in restricting the kill. These laws serve, however, as much to spread the harvest among more hunters as to hold down the total kill.

The question of whether to shoot both sexes of pheasants, or only cocks, is more complicated. The fact that the sexes are easily differentiated makes it possible to limit shooting to cocks. Since it is a polygamous species, it seems logical that special protection for the females might pay off in larger production of young birds. This might work—up to the carrying capacity of the land. Beyond that it is futile to save any more hens, since they will die from other causes anyway. Did you ever stop to wonder what has happened to all the hen pheasants we have been "saving" all these years? Well, they're dead—almost as many of them as if they had been legal game. Therefore it is wasteful not to permit some harvest of the crop of hens; but it should be carefully watched, and if need be, controlled.

Refuges from Hunting. Pheasants respond well to the protection offered by refuges; they soon learn where safety lies, and are "smart" enough to take advantage of sanctuary. Thus the establishment of judiciously located refuges in poor pheasant range offers a means of insuring that all the birds in an area will not be killed in a hunting season; it assures that some will survive for the next year's breeding stock. *Refuges are not needed in good pheasant range.*

The organizational problems of setting up refuges will be discussed later. Here we will consider their size, location, and cover composition.

A refuge should be able to sustain a nucleus group of pheasants for several weeks; it should therefore contain both good protective shelter and good feeding coverts. Small cattail marshes, rank-grown swales, or young conifer and shrub thickets provide the best shelter, and should be made the center of the refuge. Woodlands are also good shelter areas if not grazed by domestic livestock. The feeding area of the refuge should be primarily corn and small grain fields.

The size can be as small as 20 or 30 acres, and be effective if the balance and quality of the cover is good; even smaller areas will serve a few birds. The size may be increased up to 100 acres or more if desired. Some authorities even recommend pheasant refuges of 200 to 3,000 acres, but I doubt their efficiency; it would be better to use smaller units and more of them. A 50–50 balance of food and shelter cover types in the refuge is a good proportion to seek.

Refuges are most effective when located in the center of territories known to be inhabited by sizable numbers of birds. One per farm, well located, is usually ample. In co-operative game management ventures their location may disregard farm boundaries; when leased by a state game agency, they may be placed strategically within the project area, more or less irrespective of farm property lines. Sometimes a state game-lands purchase program can fit into a pheasant refuge system; the refuges then would be units of public land surrounded by private farms. Only poor ("submarginal") farms could be afforded, or should be used for this purpose. Since the combination of small areas of poor land surrounded by good farms is not prevalent, most refuges will have to be located on private land. A well-planned pheasant refuge system in marginal range could well include from 10% to 15% of the total management area.

PREDATOR CONTROL

SINCE predation is not the limiting factor for pheasants under most circumstances, even the theoretical possibilities of reducing predator numbers has little promise of benefit for the birds; the actual good that can be accomplished for pheasants through killing predators is so negligible that it is hardly worth discussing. Still, there are a few sound forms of predator control (not necessarily killing them) that can be recommended for use in the pheasant range; this program may even help to increase the survival of pheasants in some years. Since its benefits are broader, it should be followed anyway.

First comes the control of dogs and cats. Stray animals should be disposed of humanely; those owned should be kept at home. This is especially true from April through July, when the ring-necks have nests or small youngsters. It is not easy to keep the felines tethered, but at least they should be housed at night. Some farm folks keep too many cats, mostly for sentimental reasons. A more realistic view of the number of cats needed to control rodents and serve as pets would give a better "break" to some of our wild friends.

Many of the most efficient predators are valuable furbearers. This group includes foxes, raccoons, weasels, skunks, minks and others. All furbearers should be trapped during the prime pelt season; this is a proper and needed harvest of the surplus animals of a useful wildlife crop. Where this is done, their numbers will rarely become so great as to be a grave threat to other game. The "control" pays for itself, and there need be no fuss over "vermin" campaigns to save the pheasants.

The predatory hawks and owls do take some pheasants. The only ones that frequently eat pheasant dinners are the great horned owl, the

Cooper's hawk, and the goshawk. If selective killing of these species were practicable, it might be recommended; but in fact it isn't practical, and attempts to do it usually result in more harm than good through the mistaken killing of beneficial species. Fortunately these predators act as checks on each other and are rarely abundant, especially in the pheasant range. As an unsentimental and coolly thought-out matter, we may as well forget about the control of hawks and owls and concentrate on more productive ventures.

THE USE OF HUNTING DOGS

ONE of the best things that can be done to improve pheasant hunting is the greater use of dogs in pursuing them, especially trained bird dogs. We have seen that the loss from crippling is tremendous; most of this could be avoided by using retrieving dogs. They don't have to be blue-blooded setters and pointers; any good gun- and game-loving pooch that can be trained to behave and retrieve will be a big help; breed isn't as important as his skill in trailing a pheasant scent and in nailing the wounded, running bird. If possible, use a dog that locates pheasants for you too. Better still, of course, is a pointing dog that both finds *and holds them.* In any case, use a dog, but keep him out of pheasant land in the nesting season.

CENSUSING PHEASANT POPULATIONS

MANY methods have been used to count wild pheasants. By concentrating them at a series of feeding stations in the winter, a reasonably accurate check can be made on their numbers in a restricted locality. The crowing of the cocks in the spring offers a means of gauging their numbers through early morning sound counts. Combined with an estimate of the sex ratio obtained at winter feeding stations, or by flush counts in the spring, the population can be computed. The use of hunter-bag figures and flush counts can similarly be used to estimate fall populations. Any of these figures are valu-

able for use in research work, though they are of little use in game management.

The primary purpose of censusing pheasants in management is to estimate fall populations ahead of time so that judicious seasons and bag limits may be set. It must be done early enough in the season to issue the legal notices on time; this would usually be about September 1. It must be done late enough in the summer so that the estimates of chick survival are reliable. There is just a short time when this is possible: from about mid-July to mid-August.

Before suggesting methods for making this summer census, two points should be clear. First, it is the production of young birds that is the key to the population level; second, absolute accuracy is not important. It is the trend, or change, from the previous year that is important.

The census will be based on a sampling of the range. For a small area, such as a game co-operative, or a preserve, a census of a 1% to 5% sample is enough. Several units should compose the sample rather than a single portion. On a state-wide basis, the census sample may be from .1 to .5 of 1% of the total pheasant range. Here the sampling should include portions of each type of range, in rough proportion to the share they make of the entire range. A sampling unit of range for a single census should be at least 50 to 100 acres.

Ideal conditions for the summer census are met when the grains and hay are cut and the corn is not yet so high as to provide difficult cover in which to locate the birds. The young pheasants should mostly be four weeks old or older, so that the period of high juvenile mortality is past.

Balmy weather should be chosen for the work, avoid extremes of heat and wind, and all rainy weather.

An important point in handling the census work is consistency of method. The cover may be traversed on foot or on horseback. Bird dogs may be used or not, but they usually wilt badly in summer workouts. The census takers may traverse the cover in twos, threes, or fours, and work at distances of from 25 to 100 feet or more apart. They may drag rope lines between them over the open field cover, or not. The data on observations may be recorded in many ways; similiarly, there are many methods of making the interpretations of the data. But whatever system you use, follow it consistently. That applies to the various areas worked, to the days worked in one season, and from one season to another. Be consistent. That makes your data comparable, and the trends evident.

As the census area is traversed records are kept of the number of adult pheasants seen, the number of broods, and the number of chicks in the broods. These data are averaged for two or more surveys of each census unit. They have significance in themselves, and they show trends by comparison with comparable figures for the previous year. The most useful figures are three: (1) the average acres per pheasant, counting all classes of birds; (2) the average number of chicks per brood; and (3) the productivity ratio, that is, the proportion of young birds to adults.

As I said before, trends are more important than absolute numbers. Pheasant populations are exceedingly variable in different parts of its range; densities of birds that would be thought excellent in Massachusetts would be ranked as very low in Minnesota, for example. Thus if last year's pheasant hunting was fair, and this year's census shows a considerable increase in population density, productivity ratio, and chicks-per-brood compared with last year, then a proportionately better hunting season can safely be predicted. To be specific, let us assume that in a certain area in 1946 the summer census revealed an average of five acres per pheasant, a productivity ratio of 70% (chicks to adults), and an average of four chicks per brood; the hunting that fall was poor. In the 1947 census, the figures are three acres per pheasant, 120% productivity ratio, and six chicks per brood; obviously a better hunting season can be predicted. The kill should be nearly double that of the previous year, and liberalization of the hunting restrictions is accordingly warranted. In this way the census contributes to sound game management.

A census method that has been used with some success in the plains states in recent years is based on roadside counts (Mohler, 1948). The open country makes observations from automobiles dependable there as a census technique, whereas in the East this procedure is not valid. As used in Nebraska, early morning counts are made on pleasant days in late July on prescribed 20-mile stretches of rural roads. The car is driven 15 to 20 miles an hour, and the observer records all cocks, hens, and young seen. Three replications on different days are made for each unit. All units censused, when considered together, should be representative of the state's pheasant habitat. Population level is gauged either by the birds seen per mile, or by the ratio of young per adult female. Several years of data are needed to provide a basis for comparisons in order to determine accurately the population level.

The New York Conservation Department uses a farmer questionnaire survey to follow pheasant population trends (Perry, 1946). By obtaining a representative sample of farmer observations on the number of nests seen, the number of nests destroyed by farm machinery, and the number of broods seen, it can derive from the averages a dependable trend. The usefulness of the procedure depends on the adequacy of the sample and on the uniformity with which the data is gathered. It becomes valuable for determining trends only after several years of use.

CONTROLLED HUNTING SYSTEMS

THE regulation of the hunting harvest so that the annual surplus of birds, and no more, is taken is the ultimate function of game management. Such regulation frequently includes other objectives too, as for example the providing of public hunting areas, and the prevention of property damage on private land.

Most of the control of pheasant hunting, as with most other upland hunting, is in the form of state laws enforced by a corps of police officers, variously known as game wardens, conservation officers, field agents, etc. In areas of concentrated hunting—and this includes much of the good pheasant range—this is far from an adequate system. The landowner is dissatisfied because he is imposed on by hordes of strangers trespassing on his farm and often doing considerable damage. In an effort to prevent this, many landowners "post" their land against trespass. In doing so they may lose what little protection the game law enforcement system had provided. Worse, though posting is effective against the law-abiding sportsman, it doesn't keep off the real troublemakers; it just makes things easier for them. Hence the farmer generally desires a better method of hunting control than just land posting.

The sportsman is not pleased either. Much of the land, including the best pheasant land, is posted against him. In actuality this should not of itself be serious, for he should ask permission to hunt on farms anyway. It is no more difficult to call at the house on posted farms to get permission to hunt than it is on unposted farms; and it is surprising how many owners of posted farms will grant that permission. Still, there is an important psychological reaction by many hunters to posting. They assume that they are not wanted on posted land, and hence refrain from asking for a permit. But there are other reasons, too, why the hunter is not pleased with the general system of hunting control. It does not stimulate the landowner to encourage game on his farm; if anything, it tends to have the opposite effect. Thus the hunting provided is the poorest possible instead of the best. This is a major reason why the state wildlife agencies have also been dissatisfied with the degree of hunting control set up merely by the state laws. Their main job is to provide good hunting for the rank and file of sportsmen, and they are frustrated right at the start with farm game because there is no incentive for the farmer to improve conditions for game.

For these reasons—and others associated with them—there have been many attempts in this country to set up a more adequate system of hunting control. The majority have been in pheasant country, and with pheasant hunting the main objective. It is regrettable that most of these efforts have not been successful; but some have been partly successful, and have thereby pointed the way to better arrangements in the future.

Essentials for Success. Some of the things a successful hunting system must do and be to succeed, and avoid to prevent failure, are summarized below.

(1) There must be aggressive and intelligent leadership *by local people*—landowners. Any system depending on professional leadership by a wildlife agency cannot be a real success.

(2) Control of the system must rest with the landowners. They will need a constructive, forward-looking program of conservation in which each member takes pride.

(3) The conservation program should be based on proper land use. Good pheasant management must dovetail with good farmland management. The farm conservation program should include sound wildlife habitat improvements, along with all other needed land development practices.

(4) Overhead costs must be very low—all costs that do not directly pay off in improved game conditions. The returns from a controlled hunting system cannot justify the costs of an expensive sales-promotion campaign, the drawing up of legal contracts, and similar overhead expenses.

(5) The system should give the landowner adequate protection against illegal trespass and property damage. The game crop may then be an asset to the farmer instead of a liability.

(6) The total crop of pheasants should be greater than formerly. This will depend not only on the restriction of the kill to the surplus birds, but on an actual increase in the production of pheasants. Cover improvements,

refuges, and farming methods should be made to favor the pheasant wherever practicable.

(7) Where hunting pressure is very high the arrangements should limit hunters to the desired number by some sort of permit system. The landowners should receive more income from hunting privileges as a result of the hunting system than without it. The income may be in cash or materials and services, may come from the hunter directly or through his hunting license money via state expenditures. There are advantages to both ways, and a combination is probably best.

(8) The hunting co-operative should be associated with some substantial farmer organization. It is highly desirable that this organization have the conservation of natural resources as one of its main objectives; then game management naturally becomes a sound part of their program. A good organization for this purpose that is generally available is the soil conservation district. In these districts all the interested groups—the landowners, sportsmen's clubs, and state game agency—can merge their efforts in a single co-ordinated program of mutual interest.

The Wood County, Ohio, System. One of the best examples of a successful hunting control association is the Wood County, Ohio, Controlled Hunting System (Leedy and Hicks, in McAtee, 1945). Here the farmer group that served as the nucleus for the hunting co-operative was the Plain Church. In addition to the desire of the group to control hunting trespass, they also had the common purpose of paying off the mortgage on their church.

It has been in operation now for over twenty years (since 1930). It permits hunting by members only. Resident members hunt on their own lands without permit, elsewhere on the managed area for a small fee. Nonresidents may become members by paying the hunting permit fee. The amount of hunting is limited by the sale of only about one nonresident permit for each 50 acres. The plan substitutes a "Welcome, Members of ———— Game Protective Association" notice for "No Hunting" signs. It is essentially democratic. Better hunting is provided than is available on uncontrolled lands, and for more hunters than were permitted to hunt there before. It fills most if not all the requirements for a permanently successful co-operative. Other good features, such as cover improvements, can easily be worked into such a plan. Outside aid, as from organized sportsman groups, or conservation agencies, can be arranged without losing the invaluable assets of local initiative and control.

There is little doubt that farmers are interested in controlled hunting systems. In Utah 93% of the farmers in one controlled hunting area were in favor of the plan, whereas only 5% felt it had not improved conditions (Rasmussen and McKean, in McAtee, 1945). This was in a state-sponsored but landowner-operated arrangement, under which hunters paid landowners a fee for a hunting permit.

Opportunity for Controlled Hunting in Conservation Districts. A few more words are in order concerning the opportunity for developing hunting control systems as a phase of the work of soil conservation districts. Many of these districts, which are farmer-operated, legal subdivisions of the state, are doing game management work now. Mostly this is habitat development, but the conditions are admirable for an extension of their interests into the field of hunting control. A number of state wildlife agencies and sportsmen's groups have developed working arrangements with many of these districts. As their operations grow through the years, it will be logical to include management work as well as cover development. Only the newness of this program has kept such plans from evolving before now.

Some of the advantages of the conservation district that makes this development logical are: (1) It is a democratically organized and operated local unit, set up for the specific purpose of doing farm conservation work. (2) The state laws under which it is organized give it wide authority for developing facilities to get conservation work done. (3) The farmers select their own leaders to run the district, and they develop their own program. (4) Facilities of professional and semiprofessional agencies and groups co-operating with the district are co-ordinated into a single program on the farms. (5) The district develops a complete conservation plan for co-operating farms into which all measures are incorporated; this obviates the need for the overhead expenses of selling and contracting for game management alone, since the basic contract is already made.

The amazing development of soil conservation districts in the United States is evidence of their popularity. In ten years after the movement began in 1937, all 48 states as well as our three territories had passed laws to provide for their organization and operation. More than 2,500 of them, including within their boundaries about four-fifths of all our farms, have been organized up to 1953. It may not be a revolution in our agricultural conservation work, but at least it is a rapid evolution which bids fair to set a pattern for the permanent preservation of our land resources.

The above discussion of soil conservation districts as a medium for pheasant management applies equally well to work with other farm game birds; in a less intensive way it may also apply to the management of forest and range game birds on private lands. Through the conservation district all interested agencies may carry out their functions in an efficient and co-ordinated manner. State wildlife agencies help improve habitat and provide for an orderly game harvest. The Soil Conservation Service and Agricultural Conservation Program of the United States Department of Agriculture plan land and water use and development, and provide needed financial help for establishing certain practices. The Extension Service paves the way for farmer participation through educational and publicity work. The state forestry agency offers a woodland management service. Public lands under the care of the Federal Forest Service, Fish and Wildlife Service, state forestry and wildlife agencies, and others, frequently co-ordinate their wildlife management with private land programs in the area. Thus teamwork in conservation is growing.

CHAPTER 2

The Wild Turkey

ORIGIN AND CLASSIFICATION

As American as Thanksgiving, and inseparably associated with its origin, is the wild turkey. It is not only a native of the New World, its like is exclusively of North America. The genus *Meleagris* Linnaeus to which the turkey belongs is one of only two genera in its family Meleagridae.[1] And its species, *M. gallopavo* Linn., is the lone member of that genus. The turkey is thus a unique bird, unlike any other in creation, and with its only close relative forms a whole scientific family.

In its full range, from northeastern United States to Mexico, it is found in six geographic variations, or subspecies. They are named: Eastern wild turkey (*M. gallopavo silvestris* Vieillot); Merriam's wild turkey (*M. g. merriami* Nelson); Florida wild turkey (*M. g. osceola* Scott); Rio Grande wild turkey (*M. g. intermedia* Sennett); and Mexican wild turkey (*M. g. gallopavo* Linnaeus). The sixth subspecies, also from Mexico, *M. g. onusta* Moore, recently described, has no common name and has not yet received official recognition.

Other species of turkeys formerly inhabited America. Along with the modern species, five others have been found in the fossil state in the Pleistocene and Oligocene periods of the Cenozoic era—twenty thousand to some millions of years ago. These remains have been found in numerous places from New Jersey to Florida and California, indicating continent-wide development of the family.

---

[1] The other species, the Yucatan turkey (*Agriocharis ocellata*), is found in parts of Central America.

HISTORY OF THE WILD TURKEY

SPANIARDS were the first white men to see the wild turkey; explorers reaching eastern Mexico early in the 16th century found it both in the wild state and domesticated by the Aztecs. Cortez was probably the first to make specific record of the Mexican turkey, and it is most likely that he also was the first to bring the turkey to Europe. During Coronado's expedition into New Mexico in 1540 was apparently the first time that the wild turkey (Merriam's) was observed by Europeans in what later became the United States.

It was nearly a century later before Englishmen, arriving in Virginia, and a bit later in Massachusetts, first saw the wild turkey. But oddly enough, long before the landings at Jamestown or Plymouth Rock, Englishmen as well as other Europeans had become familiar with the domesticated bird. The speed with which the tame turkey was carried through Europe after its introduction about 1519 into Spain was indeed remarkable, considering the modes of transportation of that era. It was known in Germany by 1530 and in England shortly after that. Then, most anomalously of all, it was introduced into eastern North America from England. Native in the East but never domesticated by the Indians there, it was carried from Mexico to Spain, to England, and then back to America again, to provide a domestic turkey for the settlers along the Atlantic seaboard.

As with other native gallinaceous birds, the turkey was not man-wary when the first white settlers came; the Indians had not hunted it intensively enough to develop in it a fear of man.

In fact, the Indians in some areas actually avoided turkey hunting as a social taboo. Others considered it suitable for hunting only by the children of the tribe. Most of the Eastern tribes, however, used turkeys for food, particularly in the winter months. Other than for food, parts of the turkey were frequently employed for different purposes; the feathers were used on arrows, in the hair, and in making a sort of cloak; spurs from old gobblers were used as arrow points, and parts of the bird were employed in various tribal ceremonies.

The Indians had many ways of hunting the turkey. A common method was to disturb the birds by chasing after them afoot, yelling loudly, and causing them to fly up into trees. Then they would be easily shot down, one at a time, until as many as were wanted were taken. Indian lads would decoy turkeys to them by use of a stuffed bird and imitation of the gobbling of the male. Some Southwestern tribes used a blow gun, which was said to be effective up to about 30 feet. In the winter time, baiting was often practiced with wild roots, and the birds taken in snares. Calling the turkeys close for better shooting was developed to a high art; even in summer, the cries of the poults were imitated to lure in the whole family. Some of the calls were made with the aid of a hollow bone from a turkey wing; hunters skilled in its use could call up mother hens by imitating the piping of the hen calling her brood.

The turkey, like other gallinaceous birds, is built for fast, short flights. It is also capable of rapid speed on foot, but again for but short distances. In semiopen country with good visibility, it was actually possible to run a bird down by repeatedly flushing it before its wing and leg muscles could fully recuperate; two or three flights in quick succession could exhaust a bird. On horseback, or with dogs, this was an easy method of capture as long as the bird could be kept in sight. Fortunately for the turkey, it generally had enough shelter to enable it to get out of sight quickly.

Trapping became a standard method of taking turkeys in the Eastern states in the 17th and 18th centuries. These traps were of various forms, but generally depended on baiting to lure the turkeys in, and on an arrangement of bars or netting to prevent their escape. The pen entrance was often placed in a depression or trench, and the entrance hole made low. Grain enticed the birds in through the low entrance, their heads bent low in feeding. Once in, forgetting the open entrance hole, they attempted to escape only in an upright position, or by flying upward, either of which was futile.

Even if the Indians considered the turkey rather second-rate as food, the white man felt differently; it was considered by many to be the finest tasting of all the native game birds. And, as with the ruffed grouse, the "fool hen" habits of the turkey gradually disappeared and it became a most wary adversary for the hunter. Its large size (hence quite a trophy) combined with its sporty hunting to make the wild turkey one of the most highly prized of American game species.

The numbers of wild turkeys that once existed seem incredible today. Even allowing for the fabulous abundance of game in the American wilderness—much of which was less real than legend—the stories of huge flocks of turkeys seen by competent observers are remarkable. Flocks of fifty to one hundred birds, and a dozen or more flocks in a day's travels, were noted in some of the early journals.[2] A thousand birds in a day seen by two hunters in New England was recorded by Morton (1632). Following the period when the turkey served as an important food for the early pioneers, it was hunted commercially for sale in Eastern cities. In the early 19th century turkeys brought from six to twenty-five cents each, which was less than for domestic fowls; by the 1880's the price had increased to about a dollar a bird. Soon thereafter the turkey became too scarce for profitable hunting, and the increasingly restrictive laws finally banned its sale altogether.

---

[2] See Wright, A. H., *Early Records of the Wild Turkey,* for a summary of many of these early notes.

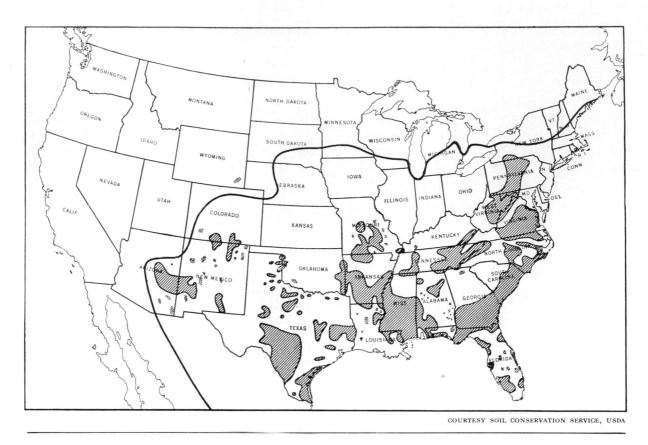

FIGURE 8. *Geographic range of the wild turkey in the United States. Shaded area represents present occupied range. Heavy line is northern and western limits of former range.*

Since the turn of the century, turkey hunting has been entirely a sporting venture. Even though the birds have been greatly restricted in their range, and are generally scarce where they still remain, their pursuit continues to be a very popular form of hunting. Turkey bagging has become to the upland bird shooter what killing a moose is to the big-game hunter: the event of a lifetime for a lucky few; no more than a dream for most sportsmen.

GEOGRAPHIC RANGE

THE original range of the wild turkey covered all or parts of 39 states, southern Ontario, and eastern Mexico to Yucatan (see Figure 8).

Beginning in the northeast extremity, the northern limits of its range ran from southern Maine across southern New Hampshire and Vermont, central New York, southern Ontario, the lower half of the southern peninsula of Michigan, the southern counties of Wisconsin and Minnesota, and on into south-central South Dakota. From there the range boundary turned south through west-central Nebraska and thence westward again across northern Colorado. In western Colorado the western extremity of the range ran southward again, crossing the northwest corner of New Mexico into Arizona. Thence it turned to the west and then again south to include east-central and southeastern Arizona, and then on southeast through Mexico to the coast at Yucatan.

The eastern, southeastern, and south-central portions of this range were almost solidly occupied. They were predominantly forested. The North Central states, and the western and southwestern portions of the range, were largely open country, plains or desertlike, with forests confined largely to the river valleys and mountains. The turkey too was limited to these forested sections, and hence these parts of its range always were broken into "islands" and long, narrow strips. Thus the area south and east of the former range line on Figure 8 depicts only roughly the range that was actually occupied by the turkey.

The occupied turkey range today is but a small fraction of the original area. This constriction was an inevitable result of the white man's occupancy of the country, since the turkey requires semiwilderness conditions. Nineteen of the states originally included wholly or in part within the turkey's range no longer have any wild turkeys. To this group must be added southern Ontario, most of Pennsylvania, Kentucky, Oklahoma, West Virginia, and Colorado, and smaller portions of all the other states in its range.

The approximate present range is shown by the shading in Figure 8. The accuracy of this map is not uniform, since the amount of information available varies in different states. A number of state game commissions have made careful studies of their wild turkey populations; these include Virginia, Pennsylvania, West Virginia, North Carolina, Florida, Alabama, Louisiana, and New Mexico. For these areas the map is reasonably correct; for others it is only a rough approximation.

In general the present-day range covers the extensive forest areas from central Pennsylvania southward through the Appalachian Mountains; along the coast from Virginia to Florida, and thence along the Gulf through Texas and into Mexico; the Ozark Mountains and lower Mississippi Valley; and the high forested mountains of southern Colorado, New Mexico, and eastern Arizona.

COURTESY PENNA. GAME COMMISSION

PLATE 16. *Eastern wild turkey.*

DESCRIPTION

THE Eastern wild turkey is a large, heavy bird, 3 to 4 feet in length, and weighing from 5 to 35 pounds. The great variation in weight is partly because the hens are much lighter than the gobblers. Few gobblers, however, exceed 20 pounds, so that the larger specimens are rare exceptions. Median weight for hens is 8 to 10 pounds, for gobblers 13 to 15 pounds. Old records greatly in excess of these figures are fabulous.

The turkey is a stocky bird, with heavy, medium-long legs, a long, somewhat snakelike neck, and a rather small, sparsely-feathered, long and narrow head. Wings are rather short and rounded, tail medium long and wide. The head of the male has a prominent caruncle that hangs forward over the beak. A "pectoral tuft" or beard hangs from the mid-breast, very prominent in the male, less so in females. Only hens over a year old develop this beard, and then it is usually only about 3 inches long. On the gobbler it reaches 1½ or 2 inches the first year, 3 to 4 inches the second year, and up to 10 inches or more later. The gobblers also develop sharp spurs, which in old birds may become an inch long.

There is no difficulty in describing the turkey so as to distinguish it from other birds; even without mentioning any colors we have already set him apart. Paradoxically, the coloration of the bird is just as difficult to describe as its identity is simple. To a considerable extent the colors do not "stay put." Much of the feather coloring is iridescent and reflects various hues, depending on how the light strikes. Then, too, the skin color of the head varies greatly with the emotions of the bird. But most folks know what the domestic turkey looks like, and the wild one is essentially only a streamlined version.

The general appearance of the turkey is a rich golden-chocolate brown bird with grayish wings and bluish head. Closer inspection reveals that the feathers of the back, breast, wing coverts, and tail coverts are iridescent brown with reflections of red, bronze, green, and purple. The tips of these feathers are mostly dark brown in the hen and black in the gobbler. Tail feathers are brown with black mottling, with a subterminal dark band and a terminal edge of light brown. The primaries are barred black and white; the greater wing coverts make a prominent, very iridescent purplish-bronze patch.

The head is bare and the skin bluish; but the head color of an undisturbed strutting turkey is a brilliant red, and the bluish cast comes only when the birds are disturbed (Mosby and Handley, 1943). Since most wild turkeys are seen only when alarmed, the head is usually observed to be blue.

The unfeathered part of the legs is also variable in color, depending on age; reddish when the bird is young, it becomes grayer with age, finally becoming silvery.

The hen's coloration resembles that of the gobbler but is generally duller and somewhat lighter.

The newly-hatched turkey poult is downy yellowish-brown, with the wing feathers prominent from the beginning. As the days pass, the colors darken and the primaries develop fast. At six weeks the tail and wings are well-grown, and the birds are capable fliers for short dis-tances. The juvenile moult begins with the fourth month, starting with the back feathers. The change to adult plumage results in darker colors, and during the transition the birds have a mottled appearance. After five months the sexes are distinguishable, and the poult resembles the adults, but with its extremities rather large in proportion to its body.

The eggs of the wild turkey measure about 2½ inches by 1⅞ inches, are ovate and pointed, buff or whitish-buff, or a pinkish-buff ground color with a sprinkling of small brownish spots.

The six subspecies of the wild turkeys are distinguished largely by variations in the markings and color of the tail, upper tail coverts, and wing feathers. Compared to the eastern wild turkey, described above, some of these distinguishing marks are given below.

Merriam's turkey has less cinnamon-brown on the upper tail coverts, and the tips of the tail and tail coverts are whitish or buff instead of brown; the rectrices are barred; the rump is velvety black.

Florida turkeys have the white bars on the primaries less prominent, and sometimes broken. The inner secondaries are a uniform dusky brown rather than barred and medium brown. The upper tail coverts are tipped with chocolate-brown.

The Rio Grande turkey has the tail and upper and lower tail coverts tipped with dusky brown; the primaries have wider black bars and narrower white bars; the lower back is bluish-black, with less metallic iridescence.

The Mexican turkey has less cinnamon on the upper tail coverts, and the tips are white or buff instead of brown; the rectrices are mottled rather than even brown; it has more iridescent green on the rump. The bird is smaller than the other subspecies.

M. g. onusta is described as having less cinnamon on the upper tail coverts, and the tips of the tail and upper tail coverts are pure white; there is no cinnamon subterminal bar on the tail; and finally, the wing feathers have less cinnamon.

IMPORTANCE AS A GAME BIRD

THE wild turkey's importance as a sporting bird in the United States rests more on the quality than on the quantity of hunting provided. The total legal kill in the 21 states of its range—of which only 12 permitted hunting in 1947—is only about 30,000 birds a year. Almost all these turkeys were taken in 9 of the states, where the kill averages more than a thousand birds annually: Virginia, Pennsylvania, Texas, Florida, Alabama, North Carolina, Georgia, Arizona, and New Mexico—listed in the approximate order of the size of the kill.

What the turkey lacks in numbers it makes up in the importance attached to the individual quarry. As long as there are even a few hundred turkeys killed in a state each year—enough to maintain the sportsman's interest—the species will rank as an important game bird; the average hunter looks forward to bagging a turkey as one of the highlights of his hunting career.

There is every reason to expect that the three main turkey hunting areas—Pennsylvania-Maryland-West Virginia-Virginia; Georgia-Alabama-Florida; and Texas-New Mexico-Arizona—will continue to provide good sport. Sound conservation measures should increase the turkey population in the future, and therefore its importance in these areas. Turkey hunting is not likely to become of more importance in other parts of its range than at present.

HABITS OF THE WILD TURKEY

COURTSHIP

As spring approaches, the winter turkey flocks—whether families or other groups—break up, and the birds stay by themselves much of the time. The young toms are an exception; they usually stay in groups of their own kind or individually associate themselves with an old tom. This segregation of the young toms happens as a result of their lack of interest in breeding. I say it this way because there is good evidence that they are physiologically capable of breeding as yearlings,

yet rarely do so; hence courtship for the tom usually begins in his second year.

The hens also tend to regroup in the spring, gathering among themselves, sometimes with the yearlings separated from the old hens, sometimes in mixed age groups. These gatherings continue for a part of each day well into the breeding season, but gradually slacken and finally discontinue when incubation consumes their time.

The turkey is polygamous; each breeding tom tries to get a "harem" of hens all his own. Apparently the more hens that join his harem the better; frequently a single tom will have five or six hens in his group. He is quite capable of serving a much larger number, but among wild birds there are few "great lovers" who can command more than a six-hen harem.

Each tom does his gobbling in one area; not necessarily an exact spot as with the ruffed grouse's drumming, but usually in an opening like a glade or field. The purpose of gobbling is primarily to attract hens, but it also seems to serve as a sort of competitive call with other gobblers. At least it is true that each gobbler feels the need for gobbling back at every other gobbler he hears.

Gobbling is mostly done during a few hours just after daybreak. The frequency and amount of gobbling depends on the success it brings. When a hen bird has been attracted to him—and the hens always come to the toms, not *vice versa*—he forgets about gobbling and turns to more urgent matters: intimate courtship and breeding. If he has little success in calling in females, his gobbling tempo increases. This happens more frequently as the season advances and the hens are beginning to incubate. After a peak of activity in midspring gobbling drops off rapidly, and is seldom heard after mid-June.

Frequently there is competition among gobblers for the favors of the hens, and this invariably leads to physical battle. The tom that wins then rules the harem, though a defeated tom may hang around for a while after he has been beaten. He is able, however, only to "pick up the leavings," so to speak, and mate with the hens only when the dominant male is absent. Usually a tom turkey once beaten by another does not challenge that rival again; if he does not leave the area at once after the fight, he usually does so after a short time, or joins the other in a subordinate role.

Fighting among gobblers is most frequent during the breeding season in the spring, though it may occur at any meeting of two or more stray males. The fighting is spirited, but rarely results in severe injury or death. Once a tom knows he's beaten, he usually acknowledges his adversary's superiority by retreating. In captivity, a group of toms penned together will fight until the relative superiority of each is established; this phenomenon has been called the "pecking order." As long as each bird "keeps his place" with respect to the others, harmony prevails; but should one challenge another higher in the pecking order, a fight ensues and the challenger is put back in his place—or, should he win, attains a higher standing in the community.

When a gobbling tom does succeed in attracting a hen bird to his place, the scene changes abruptly. No longer is he interested in gobbling; rather, he goes into his *strutting* routine. The performance he goes through to impress his lady visitor is wondrous to behold. He poses stiffly with wings drooping to the ground, neck and head arched inward against his body, back feathers erect, and tail arched upward and spread full width. Then he takes slow, careful steps forward, parading as it were, in front of the hen, finally taking a few quick, running steps, often with a somewhat sidewise motion, as in a dance. In the movement the wing tips drag rigidly along the ground, and he is apt to utter a deep, throaty sound that has been likened to "humump" (Mosby and Handley, 1943).

It may be noteworthy to draw a parallel between the courtship performances of the male turkey and the ruffed grouse. The gobbling corresponds to the drumming of the grouse, both in its objective and in the general circumstances under which it is done. Then, with the objective of attracting a hen bird to them accomplished,

the cocks of the two species pursue a remarkably similar strutting and noise-making technique that leads up to the mating.

The hen turkey seeks out the gobbling male of her choice in solitude, although occasionally two or more hens will approach a gobbler together. She often assumes an attitude of indifference to the tom's vigorous demonstrations, pretending to be unimpressed by looking the other way, picking at plants or insects, and walking about the clearing, a trait that seems to characterize many of the gallinaceous birds. But in due time, after a satisfying performance by her host, she concedes her interest in him which was her intent all the time and mating follows.

These visits by the hens to the toms are almost a daily occurrence just before and during egg-laying. As soon as incubation starts usually sometime in May the visits cease, and the hen devotes all of her time to the care of the nest. As the members of his harem desert him, the tom gobbles more intently than ever, trying, it seems, to lure them back. When the futility of his efforts is finally convincing, he gives up, and seeks the company of other males for the rest of the spring and summer period.

NESTING

THE hen turkey makes her nest on the ground, a crude hollow in the ground litter; it is almost always well obscured with some form of thick, low-growing vegetation close around it. It is also almost always in or close to an opening: a woodland clearing, a woods road, a brush patch, or in a field beneath a bush, small tree or fallen treetop. In its Southwestern range, where its habitat is a more open type of forest, the nest is often exposed, frequently at the base of a sapling or tree (Ligon, 1946).

Egg-laying begins early in the spring, often before snow is entirely gone. In its northernmost range, the first egg is laid about mid-April, and egg-laying is through after the first week in May; farther south, the clutch may be finished even before the first of April. The number of eggs laid varies from about five to seventeen, averages

PLATE 17. *Wild turkey hen approaching her nest.*

PLATE 17. *Wild turkey hen approaching her nest.*

COURTESY SOIL CONSERVATION SERVICE, USDA

ten or eleven. The usual clutch takes about two weeks or a day or two longer to lay. The hen is exceedingly shy during egg-laying and incubation, and takes great care to avoid the discovery of her nest either by the gobbler or enemies. Some hens cover their eggs with leaves when she leaves the nest for the occasional feeding and toilet.

The eggs require 28 days of incubation to hatch. During the setting period the birds do their feeding, watering, and dusting close by. While she is incubating, large black fluid caecal discharges are made as well as regular droppings, which themselves are larger than usual; their presence usually indicates that a nest is not far away.

For a week or more after the start of incubation, the female will readily desert her nest if disturbed; but as the eggs develop she becomes more broody and attached to her nest. Toward the end of incubation she will rarely desert, unless the eggs are actually destroyed.

Most nests hatch in late May or June, although those in the Southeastern part of the range may come off as early as April. In Pennsylvania, at the other end of the scale, most turkey nests hatch in late June. The time required for actual hatching and drying off of the poults

is short—rarely over 24 hours. As with other gallinaceous birds, the newly created family leaves its home as soon as the poults are dried off and the weather is suitable for their exposure.

The nesting period is one of great danger to both the hen and her eggs. Wild predators, dogs, and man are frequent destroyers of turkey nests, either through intent or accident; the chance of destruction increases as the incubation period progresses. More intensive hunting by predators, which then have their own young to feed as well as themselves, combined with the willingness of the hen turkey to remain on the nest and defend it in case of danger, make the time one of the most dangerous of the year. Once a turkey has had her nest destroyed she is unlikely to make another, unless the loss happened before or early in incubation. These infrequent renests are apt to have some infertile eggs, whereas an infertile egg is rare in a first clutch. Turkeys never hatch more than one laying a year.

BROOD PERIOD

As soon as the newly hatched chicks are dried off, daylight comes, and the ground is dry, the hen takes them off into their new world. Progress is slow at first; but whether it takes a few hours or a few days they usually go straight to the nearest brushy area. There the shelter is good and insects and berries are plentiful.

The poults soon learn to forage for themselves, and to conceal themselves when an attack is threatened—if indeed they did not already possess these abilities through instinct. The old hen is a very conscientious mother. Whenever danger is near she first orders the poults to "freeze" in the ground cover, and does so herself. For most occasions this is enough; their remarkably good protective coloration, especially of the poults, and the lack of motion, obscures them from the potential attacker. Occasionally the hen or a poult is discovered and the attack is on. She then avoids the intruder by running, feigning injury to draw it away from the location of the poults. All the while she is diverting the enemy's attention from her young ones, she is giving them orders and "morale support" by a continuous, quiet clucking.

It is noteworthy that the "broken wing stunt" as performed by the turkey is not carried out as impressively as by the mother woodcock or ruffed grouse under the same circumstances; still, it is effective.

The obedience the mother turkey gets from her youngsters when they are very young is absolute. Regardless of any intruding enemies or confusion from excitement, the poults stay motionless where they have frozen. As long as they are motionless, they are almost impossible to find, even if you know within a few inches of where they are, so well are they protected by their color and markings.

Young turkeys are slower in developing flight than most gallinaceous birds, even though feather development is equally rapid. It is four to five weeks after birth before they are able to fly an appreciable distance. As soon as they are able to fly, they begin roosting in trees. By this time their feathers are well enough developed so that brooding is no longer needed. During periods of inclement weather, though, the hen may shelter the poults with her wings even after they have begun tree-roosting.

The poults begin dust-bathing when they are very young. It is believed that this habit aids in proper development of the feathers; it probably has other uses too. Some have contended that the scratching and rolling in dry dirt is to allay irritation from ectoparasites, just as a dog scratches for fleas. Though this is possible, it is not likely to be the main reason for dusting; to a considerable extent it is probably done just because it feels good.

As the young poults develop, their appearance and habits become more and more like those of the adults. When they are about three months old, they are fairly independent; they forage for food about as they wish, wander considerably, but still remain under some family care even into autumn.

During all the time from hatching through the growing period to adulthood, the poults have no attention from the tom turkeys, father or others. The union of family groups of two or more hens and their broods is not infrequent when their ranges overlap.

FALL AND WINTER MONTHS

By early autumn, when the young turkeys are from three to four months old, they have grown to resemble their parents in most respects. Secondary sexual characters have developed that distinguish the young toms from their sisters. The back and breast contour feathers of the toms are tipped with black, whereas the hens have these feathers brown-tipped. The toms are larger, especially in the head and legs; the hens may average about eight pounds and the toms about ten pounds. The toms have fewer feathers on neck and head. By hunting season the toms usually have at least a rudimentary beard, even though it may not be evident without parting the breast feathers. The hens have none at this age.

As the autumn months pass the young turkeys are increasingly difficult to distinguish from their yearling elders. This is more true of the hens, for the beard growth of yearling toms is usually enough to set them apart from the youngsters. For those individuals whose age—less than a year or between one and two years—is in doubt, there is a sure method of age determination. A structure known as the *bursa of Fabricius* is present in birds in their first year before their first breeding season; but it then disappears, and is never found in birds after the first breeding season. This bursa is a glandlike sac appendage located in the dorsal surface of the intestine just inside the vent. Though it is not a pleasant experience for the bird, the presence or absence of the bursa can be detected in live turkeys and some other game birds by probing (Petrides, 1942). It is readily found in newly killed birds.

Another age determinant that is fairly dependable is the shape and color pattern of the outer primary feather. In the young birds this first wing feather has a pointed tip and no light bars near the tip. After the first year, this feather is rounded at the tip and has light color bars all the way to the tip. These characteristics, together with beard development, serve to distinguish first-year birds and, to some degree, second-year birds, from older ones.

The wild turkey family—mother and youngsters—remain together as a flock through the fall and winter; this family association is not always held, but prevails with the turkey more than with other gallinaceous birds. The fall shuffle that takes place among quail, grouse, and pheasants—the breakup of the family through fighting among the youngsters—is not so apt to happen with turkeys; their tendency is more the other way. Two or more families may band together, with possibly one or more additional hens that had no broods. Sometimes yearling toms will join them, but rarely old toms. Thus the winter flocks are associated. The relations among the birds within a flock change some as winter progresses. Young turkeys do considerable fighting. The individual members of families may regroup within the flock, and in a sense do somewhat of a "shuffle"; but it hardly compares with the antagonisms and dispersals of other species.

Winter flocks vary greatly in size, depending on the number of turkeys inhabiting the range.

Mostly they contain from 3 to 15 or 16 birds. Mosby and Handley (1943) found that the average number for about a thousand flocks observed in Virginia was 11 birds. They noted one flock of over 70, and added that it " . . . probably was an accidental meeting of the majority of turkeys in that locality. . . . " Dalke, Leopold, and Spencer (1946) observed the size of 36 flocks of Missouri turkeys to be from 3 to 34 birds each. Nine of these contained birds of one sex only, 7 of them being of gobblers and 2 of hens. This segregation of the winter flocks by sexes is usually restricted to old birds, and most commonly to old gobblers.

The flocking together of two or more turkey families is stimulated by the gradual losses; some fall victim to hunters or predators, and some succumb to accidents, disease, or starvation. As the number in the brood is reduced, the gregarious instinct of the remaining birds leads them to join with others to make a flock sufficiently large to satisfy their social needs.

In late winter the turkey flocks again begin to regroup, this time according to sex. The two sexes split off from the winter groups to make their separate hen and "stag" parties. As the breeding season approaches in February, March, or April, a further division takes place. Many males take up a solitary life. Some young toms tag after an old gobbler. Some gobblers live through the spring in groups of two or three. The hens keep their small flocks well together until egg-laying time.

ADAPTABILITY TO ARTIFICIAL PROPAGATION

THE true wild turkey is not easily bred and grown in captivity. Yet the domestic turkey is still like its wild progenitor in appearance, and half-wild birds can be raised at game farms. But much more is implied in *successful* artificial propagation for restocking in wild coverts than merely the adaptability of the bird to rearing in captivity. The reared birds must be of a type that can successfully make the change from penned to wild living; they must also be *wild* in character as well as in name. Unfortunately most turkeys raised by the conventional game-farm methods fail in both of these respects. After liberation they either succumb quickly to some predator, or else find their way to the nearest barnyard; they are not able to care for themselves in the forest; they would not provide wary game targets if a hunter should find them before they reach a farm again.

Because of these facts, game commissions interested in stocking wild turkeys began experimenting with new methods of growing them. In the late 1920's and early 1930's Missouri, Virginia, and Pennsylvania, among others, developed a system of mating game-farm hens and wild gobblers. The eggs were run through the usual incubator-brooder routine. The results were far superior to those previously obtained from game-farm birds; but they were also still far short of what was wanted. Stocked hybrids behaved like real wild turkeys, but still retained some of the taint of domesticity that hampered them in getting along on their own. As Dalke, Leopold, and Spencer (1946) summarized it: "Hybrid populations were successfully established on several state refuges, but even under the best of management and protection they no more than held their own. Populations of native birds on other refuges always attained much higher densities. In no case did the hybrids become established on open range when they were subjected to poaching, yet native populations still persist in many parts of the Ozarks under the most severe poaching pressure." As a result of these conclusions, Missouri abandoned its program of the artificial restocking of wild turkeys.

The quality of turkeys grown on game farms today is often relatively good, but even so the turkey has only very limited adaptability for useful artificial propagation. Under ideal conditions of range and protection in areas where the species has been extirpated (and the cause of that extirpation eliminated), the restocking of artificially reared hybrid birds is justified. As a means of building up low native populations it is of little value. For their release before the guns

for immediate harvest, the problem becomes one of economics, and of the willingness of the hunters to be satisfied with only half-wild birds. In Maryland, for example, the annual kill is greater than the whole native population, the kill being made up mostly of recently stocked birds. It is costly business, but under some conditions is thought to be worth the cost.

SHELTER REQUIREMENTS

TYPES OF RANGE [3]

IN its original distribution, the turkey occupied all the forested country from southeastern Canada to the Gulf and from the Atlantic to the southern Rockies. We do not have enough data on populations in colonial days to say for certain just which parts of the range were superior and which parts inferior; such variations in range type as then existed were merged into one another. Today, after agriculture and lumbering have made drastic inroads into the habitable turkey range, the remaining portions divide rather easily into types. These scattered lands still suitable for the turkey are for the most part sections of its former range that were of medium or poor grade. Many of the better parts of the original range have long since been usurped by farming; for the wild turkey, as with most game species, thrived best on the best soils —that is, the soils that produced the most vigorous plant growth. All these productive soils have been put to farming with but two exceptions: those that were too rough and stony, even though fertile; and some areas that have remained in large private estates, not intensely farmed. Other than on these two remnants of the original range, the turkey must now live in habitats with low-grade soils.

The essentials for habitable turkey range are: (1) climate from warm temperate to cold temperate; (2) contiguous forest of 10,000 to 20,-000 acres or more, with openings of all types that

---

[3] Range is here used in its meaning of *general habitat*, rather than geographical distribution.

PLATE 18. *Eastern mountain forest range of the turkey. A view of the Appalachians in western North Carolina.*

constitute less than half the area and are scattered in small units throughout the forest; (3) little molestation from man or his associated domestic animals; (4) age classes of the forest that provide a preponderance of mature trees and a rather open undergrowth; and (5) forest composition such as to provide a plentiful food supply all year long, and adequate winter shelter.

Considering these basic needs, it is easy to understand why the turkey is now living on only about 1% of its original range. It is also easy to see why improvement of the turkey range is so difficult. Working against the interests of the turkey are several fundamental trends: the continuation of intensive farming and lumbering; the increasing human populations, including the growing recreational use of the remaining turkey range; the pressure of domestic livestock on forest lands; the loss of the native chestnut as a food producer, probably forever, and reduced supplies of other mast-producing trees through short-cycle lumbering; the continuing lack of sympathy with or understanding of the need for conserving the remaining stocks of turkeys within conservation laws.

Such turkey range as we have left may be divided into four types, which are described below.

Eastern Mountain Forest. This is probably the most extensive of the types inhabited by the eastern wild turkey (*M. g. sylvestris*). It ranges from central Pennsylvania southward through western Maryland and Virginia; eastern West

PLATE 19. *Coastal flatwoods turkey range extends from Virginia southward to Florida and west to Texas.*

Virginia and Kentucky; western North Carolina; Tennessee; southern Missouri and northern Arkansas. It is predominantly an oak-hickory kind of forest, though some sections are of the beech-birch-maple classification. Its topography is rugged, and the altitude is from a few hundred feet up to more than 3,000 feet. Rainfall is ample, usually 40 inches per year or more. Though its soils are generally poor, most of the areas that support good numbers of turkeys have productive soils even when they are too rough for farming. Dalke, Leopold, and Spencer (1946) who demonstrated the influence of soils on turkeys in the Missouri range, stated: "Within the forested regions of the state, a closer relationship seems to exist between the distribution of turkeys and that of certain soil types than between turkeys and woodland as such. Clarksville stony loam, a widespread residual limestone soil associated with the roughest topography in the Ozark region, was found to support 79% of the turkey population. All of the more dense populations occur here . . . Only 40% of this land is farmed. . . . Ashe stony loam and Hanceville loam together support only 3% of the turkeys. The Ashe stony loam, whose source is the red granite of the eastern Ozarks, is limited in extent, but like the Clarksville stony loam is associated with very rough topography mostly covered by mixed oak-hickory forest. . . . Superficially the areas of Ashe and Clarksville stony loam look very much alike, and their land use

COURTESY U. S. FOREST SERVICE

PLATE 20. *The southwestern mountain range of the wild turkey is characterized by open, park-like forest. Overgrazing by domestic livestock has seriously reduced the value of much of this range to the turkey.*

patterns are similar; yet turkeys occur on Ashe soil only as isolated 'islands' of low population density (1–20 birds per township), and apparently the numbers are still declining." Similar correlations of turkey populations with soils may be found throughout this range type. Latham (1939) concluded that in Pennsylvania " . . . the great majority of the wild turkey range is composed of certain types of sandstone overlaid by limestone soils."

Eastern Piedmont Woodlands. This is a rather narrow band of turkey range that parallels the Appalachian Mountains from Virginia to Georgia. The fact that it remains as turkey range at all is an accident of social history. Under normal development this area would have been farmed to a degree that would have extirpated the wild turkey; instead it is producing the highest turkey populations in Virginia. As explained by Mosby and Handley (1943), "Slavery made agriculture the dominant factor in the development of these regions (coastal areas included) and it became economically desirable to make each plantation large and self-sufficient. . . . With the rise of this economic system, it became practical to operate large holdings of which agriculture required only a portion of the land, thus only the choice sites were cleared and worked. Consequently a considerable area on each plantation remained in forest growth. This condition resulted in a dispersion of the forest which . . . continues to the present time."

PLATE 21. *Turkey range in the famed Edwards Plateau region of Texas. Oaks predominate in the tree cover.*

The Piedmont type is an area of rolling hills and valleys with gentle slopes. Altitudes are moderate, but higher than those of the coastal plain. It does not have the severe winter weather of the mountains to the west. Its forest cover is largely an oak-pine mixture, with scattered farms providing openings that cover about 25% of the land. Rainfall is about 40 inches. The soil of the Piedmont was very productive in its original condition; much of it has now been impoverished through soil erosion.

Eastern and Southern Coastal Woods. A belt of coastal flatwoods extending from Virginia south to Florida along the Atlantic coast and from Florida to south Texas along the Gulf of Mexico constitutes this range type of the wild turkey. Three subspecies of the turkey inhabit it. From Virginia to Georgia and from Alabama to Louisiana and east Texas there is the eastern subspecies (*M. g. silvestris*); in Florida it is the Florida wild turkey (*M. g. osceola*); and in southern Texas the Rio Grande turkey (*M. g. intermedia*).

The coastal range type is characterized by low altitude flat lands, much of which is poorly drained, sandy soils that are generally rather unproductive agriculturally, and woodlands in large blocks broken up by farms scattered over the better drained soils. The woodland is mostly a bottom land hardwood association—oaks, gums, cypress—with pines on the knolls.

The Edwards plateau of Texas is a granitic hill section covered with an open oak forest. Common species in this forest are live, post, blackjack, shinnery, and southern red oaks. This area has one of the highest concentrations of turkeys anywhere.

Southwestern Mountains. The westernmost

and southernmost portions of the turkey range are of a type very different from the other three. It occurs in numerous widely-separated areas of mountains extending from southern Colorado south through New Mexico and eastern Arizona into Mexico. The subspecies occupying the northern or United States part of this range type is Merriam's turkey (*M. g. merriami*). In the Mexican mountains the type subspecies, the Mexican wild turkey (*M. g. gallopavo*), occupies most of the range, except for a small area in the northwest part of the Mexican range, where is found the newly named subspecies *M. g. onusta*.

The southwestern mountain range type is distinguished by high altitudes (6,000 to 10,000 feet), rugged terrain, poor soils, low rainfall, and open forests composed of ponderosa pine and associated species. Each occupied portion of this range type is surrounded by desert or treeless semiarid lands.

COVER TYPES NEEDED

THE wild turkey is a bird of the forest; tree-covered land is the keystone of its habitat. Yet, as is true with most forest wildlife, it urgently needs some range that lacks a tree canopy. Thus good turkey range is forest interspersed with numerous small, well-scattered openings.

It should be emphasized that the cover type composition of the range does not exclusively determine its quality for turkey use; size is also a vital consideration. Contiguous forest of 10,000 to 20,000 acres is a minimum size requirement; 50,000 or more acres in a unit are better. Water is important to turkeys, thus a well developed pattern of streams and swamps is important. Good turkey habitat requires a high degree of protection from man's influences. This protection may result from sparse human populations; natural refuges like precipitous mountains or ravines, or large swamps; or legally segregated areas like game refuges or sanctuaries.

Turkeys use four major types of cover for their habitat. These are listed in Table 5, together with the more important varieties of each, the seasons of use, and the functions they serve.

None of these four cover types is absolutely indispensable; some turkeys can live on range lacking one, two, or even three of them. Two of them present in adequate quantity within the cruising range of a flock of turkeys is better than one alone, and three is better than two; the availability of all four is best. Turkeys can live best in the mixed forest if that is the only type available. Openings are probably the second most important type to go with one of the others. If both hardwoods and coniferous stands are well distributed through the range, the mixed forest type is less important.

Hardwood Forest. The most extensive type of cover in the eastern mountain and eastern Piedmont ranges is the hardwood forest. The oaks are the most important group of trees in this association; the white oak is the most valuable species, with the post, blackjack, red, scarlet, chestnut, pin, willow, northern red, bear, and black oaks also important. Hickories, black walnut, persimmon, black locust, and flowering dogwood are valuable tree components of the lower altitudes of this range. Beech, sugar and red maples, black cherry, serviceberry, white ash, and yellow and black birches are of importance in the higher altitudes.

Shrubs of the understory and some herbaceous plants are also worthy components of this cover type. Wild grapes, dogwoods, poison ivy, greenbrier, and associated shrubs furnish food as well as part of the cover. Some of the ground cover plants, like mosses and ferns, are also used as food.

The bottomland hardwoods are such as the sweet gum, several of the oaks, including white, willow, post, blackjack, swamp white, black, red, swamp chestnut, water, bur, overcup, laurel, turkey, and live oaks, cypress, sassafras, flowering dogwood, and associated trees. Notable among the useful understory plants are greenbrier, dogwoods, wild grape, Hall's honeysuckle, wax myrtle, and hawthorns.

The southern Rocky Mountain hardwoods are distinguished by a number of oaks, including the

Gambel oak, which is of especial importance to turkeys, Fendler, Rocky Mountain white, New Mexican shinnery, Rocky Mountain shin, and other oaks. Associated with them are numerous shrubs and herbs, among which may be noted the bearberry, pointleaf manzanita, lemonade sumac, alligator juniper, Rocky Mountain bee-plant, and numerous grasses.

In all areas the hardwood forest is mostly useful to the turkey in its mature stage. The mast-producing species are then in bearing, the trees afford good roosting sites, and the understory is desirably sparse because of the high, full tree canopy.

The hardwood forest is used throughout the year but somewhat more in spring and fall. It provides preferred nesting cover. Food production is generally high in the mature age class of these woodlands, especially mast for fall and winter.

Coniferous Forest. Evergreens that compose most of the canopy of the coniferous forest are important to the turkey for the protective shelter they afford. Some of them also offer staple food.

The coniferous type of forest makes up a large part of the habitat in the coastal woods and the Southwestern mountain range types. In both areas these forests are rather open, at least in the

---

TABLE 5

COVER TYPES NEEDED BY THE WILD TURKEY

COVER TYPE	SEASONS OF USE	FUNCTIONS SERVED

(*with major varieties*)
 HARDWOOD FOREST
   Northern Hardwoods (beech-birch-maple)
   Appalachian-Ozark Hardwoods (oaks-hickory)
   Bottomland Hardwoods (oaks-gum-cypress)
   Rocky Mountain Hardwoods (oaks-shrubs)
	Spring and fall, less in winter and summer	Nesting, feeding, roosting, brood-raising

MIXED FOREST
   Northern Conifers and Hardwoods (hemlock-white pine-beech-birch-maple)
   Hard Pines and Appalachian Hardwoods (pitch, Virginia, shortleaf pines-oaks-hickory)
   Bottomland Pines and Hardwoods (Loblolly, slash, longleaf pines-cypress-oaks-gum)
   Rocky Mountain Conifers and Hardwoods (ponderosa and piñon pines-juniper-oaks)
	All year cover, but used least in summer. Has good food and shelter	Protective shelter, roosting, feeding, nesting, brood-raising

CONIFEROUS FOREST
   Northern Conifers (hemlock-white pine)
   Hard Pines (Virginia, shortleaf-pitch pines)
   Bottomland Pines (longleaf-loblolly-slash pines)
   Rocky Mountain Conifers (ponderosa, piñon pines-alligator juniper)
	Most used in winter, least in summer. Used all year in Rockies	Protective shelter, roosting, feeding

FOREST OPENINGS
   Farm crop fields
   Grasslands
   Brushland
	Mostly used in summer, least in winter	Feeding, brood-raising, dusting, sunning, nesting, courting

portions that make good turkey cover. The pines are tall and rather widely spaced, with a generally sparse understory.

The conifer stands of the Eastern mountains and Piedmont ranges are very different from the others. They have been more thoroughly lumbered in the past, so that there are rather few mature stands. The prevalent evergreen species tend to develop thick stands rather than open ones. In the higher mountains the hemlock and white pine are most common, whereas in the lower hills and in the Piedmont the common species are the pitch, Virginia, and shortleaf pines.

The bottomland pines of the coastal woods occur on the well-drained soils that lie just above the swamp hardwoods; frequently they make evergreen islands on knolls in the swamps. Along the northern section of this range, in Virginia and the Carolinas, the loblolly pines furnish the cover; farther south and in the Gulf Coast states the longleaf and slash pines are prevalent.

In the Southwestern mountains two species of pines are most important in the conifer forests of the turkey range, ponderosa pine and piñon; ponderosa provides the better roosting sites; piñon furnishes important food as well as shelter.

In coniferous forests as in the deciduous types, a mature stand is the best age class for the turkey. Probably young conifers are of less use to them than young hardwoods. Their density, excluding light necessary to food plants, and the lack of good roosting places, make immature evergreens of little value as turkey habitat.

Understory plants in coniferous forest types are apt to be fewer and different from those found under the hardwoods canopies; this is most true in the Eastern mountains and Piedmont, less true along the coast and in the Western mountains. In the Eastern highlands such plants as viburnums, partridgeberries, blueberries, blackberries, deciduous hollies, ferns, and club mosses are found. In the coastal pine stands there are greenbriers, evergreen hollies, wild legumes, and grasses. The ground cover of the Western highland pine forests is not greatly different from that of the hardwoods of the same region.

The pines serve the turkey as protective shelter; they prefer to roost in tall, sturdy pines or hemlocks most of the time. Here they are best able to escape from their enemies and survive the hazards of stormy weather. They obtain more food from conifers than do most game birds; pine seeds make up a significant part of their diet, but these are mostly gleaned from the ground. A number of the understory and forest floor plants under the pines also provide food.

Mixed Forest. There is doubtless no need to describe the mixed forest in detail; it is merely a combination of the hardwood and conifer stands. It may result from natural plant succession, as with the hemlock-beech-birch-maple climax association of the Eastern mountains, or from lumbering methods or land treatment. The longleaf pine stands of the South, for example, result from burning the deciduous undergrowth.

The mixed forest obviously combines the attributes of the hardwoods and conifer types; to a degree, then, it makes a sort of all-purpose cover. It adds no values that the two component types do not have separately, but fully provides them where both types are present, amply represented, and well distributed. It usually has more species of trees and shrubs in the stand than either of its two constituents alone, but this may or may not make it better cover; that depends on the species and their distribution.

Forest Openings. Breaks in the forest canopy that permit a low-growing plant association to persist over an appreciable area are of tremendous importance to the turkey. It makes less difference what the character of the openings is than that they exist. The better they are interspersed, the more useful they are. They do not need to be very large; an acre or two is enough if there are plenty of them. When they are very large, only the outer portions close to the forest will be used; turkeys do not expose themselves very far out in the open, away from the edge of protective woodland, except in places remote from people, or where they are unmolested.

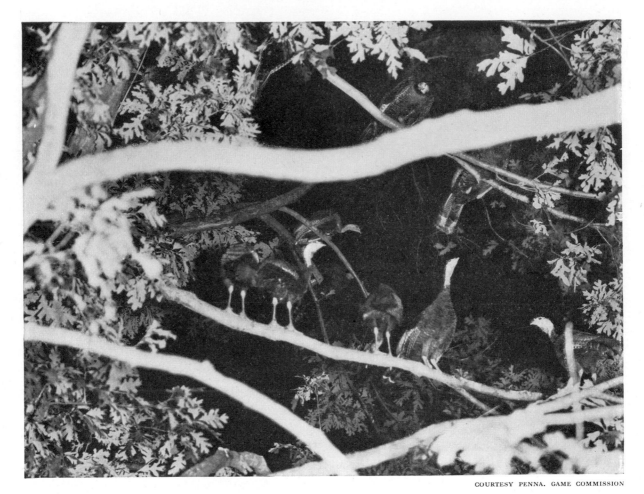

PLATE 22. *Turkey flock roosting in a large white oak tree.*

Slashings that follow clear-cut lumbering are one type of forest opening that occurs independently of farming. Their cover is made up of sprouts of the hardwood trees that have been cut, understory plants of the previous woodland stand, and pioneer species like pin cherry, aspen, brambles, blueberries, and others that come in after exposure of the forest floor to sun and fire.

Shrub associations of a semiclimax nature occur in many sections of turkey range; these may be the bear oak "barrens" found in the Appalachians and along the Atlantic coast, or the manzanita thickets of the Rockies. Abandoned farmlands in turkey range grow up into a transitional brushland stage that serves the same habitat purpose, though composed of different species, usually pioneers.

Grassland margins of the forest are a common type of opening used by turkeys. In the West these are range lands interspersed through the forest; in the East and South they are mostly pastures, and are usually confined to valleys in the mountains or to the medium good agricultural soils elsewhere. The plant cover is a mixture of wild grasses with legumes, perennial forbs,[4] and sedges. Many of these furnish food for the turkeys either as greens or seeds.

Farm crop fields occur in turkey range, and may be used by the birds provided they are close to cover but not to buildings. Turkeys are not averse to feeding on some of man's farm crops either; peanuts, corn, and the small grains are readily taken when accessible.

[4] Herbs other than grasses.

Forest openings are used by the turkeys in a number of ways; they are important as feeding grounds, and are essential for courtship, sunning, and dusting. During the spring they frequently provide nesting sites, and in the summer are preferred cover for raising broods.

INTERSPERSION OF COVER TYPES

ARRANGEMENT of essential cover types is as important as their quality and quantity. The relationship of each cover type to others makes the cover pattern. The more this pattern is broken up, the greater is the *interspersion* of the cover types. The degree to which interspersion is advantageous to a species is related to its daily and seasonal *cruising ranges*—the distance that the turkeys habitually will move in a day to find their daily cover and food requirements, and the distance they will travel within a year to come by their seasonal cover essentials.

The daily cruising range of the turkey during fall, winter, and early spring is about two miles. This is a considerably longer distance than is traveled daily by most gallinaceous birds. The area involved in these movements varies with the nature of the topography; if the birds are restricted by steep mountain slopes to a narrow valley, it may be a thousand acres or less. Without topographic limitations it is more likely to be from 3,000 to 8,000 acres. When the turkey ranges widely, as for an example over an area of 8,000 acres in a day, there is probably poor interspersion of the essential cover types. It simply has to go a long way to get what it needs. If a flock ranges over a much smaller area, good interspersion is indicated; the birds are able to satisfy their needs with relatively little travelling.

Good turkey range should have usable openings in the forest at intervals of a mile or less; at the other extreme, when the openings are more than four miles apart, the birds cannot readily cover the range in a day.

The distribution of the openings is equally important at all seasons. Turkeys will range over much greater areas in a year than they will in a day. For example, in the winter a flock may inhabit coniferous forest with openings available within the daily travel limit—one to four miles. When spring comes they may shift their center of activity to a hardwood stand ten miles away—but still one with or near openings. In summer another general shift may well take place, this time to an area with more brushy cover but also having good forest cover within flying distance.

To meet these seasonal needs for coniferous forest and hardwood forest, both should be available within each 10,000 acres for good range, or in each 25,000 acres for fairly habitable range. To the extent that a mixed forest is present, both these needs are met together.

PLATE 23. *A small, clear-cut opening in the forest cover made for turkeys and other game. Part of the brush is piled and part burned to induce germination of desirable plants that follow fire.*

TABLE 6

LAND USE PATTERN FOR GOOD WILD TURKEY RANGE

COVER TYPE	PROPORTION OF TOTAL COVER	BEST UNIT SIZE (ACRES)	GREATEST DISTANCE IN MILES TO:			REMARKS
			Opening	Conifers	Hardwoods	
HARDWOOD FOREST	15%–75%	500–2,000	2	4		Should contain a good proportion of mast-producing species of mature age
CONIFEROUS FOREST	15%–60%	200–1,000	2		4	Should be mostly of mature age
MIXED FOREST	0%–90%	500–3,000	2			Needed most if either of above components is inadequate
FOREST OPENINGS	10%–25%	5–100		2	2	Should include units of both field and brushland types

IDEAL LAND USE PATTERN

EXACTLY what proportions of the major cover types constitute ideal turkey range, the size of each unit, and their location with respect to one another, is impossible to say; there has not been enough opportunity for scientists to study turkeys under optimum conditions to get at these facts. Nevertheless we know fairly well what a good land use pattern for turkey range should be (see Table 6).

FOODS OF THE WILD TURKEY

THE wild turkey is an omnivorous feeder. Still, it has very marked food preferences, and given free choice would make up a large share of its diet from a rather limited number of plants and animals. It rarely has such choice, and consequently partakes of a great diversity of foods.

Turkey food items may conveniently be grouped into four types: mast; fruits; greens and seeds; and animals. The greens and dry seeds might well be kept distinct, but since they frequently come from the same plants they are conveniently lumped together. During the fall and winter, mast (nuts and seeds of forest trees) makes up a large part of their diet, with the acorns from various oaks the most important. In years when the acorn crop is poor, other foods replace acorns, so that fruits or seeds may bulk largest in the fall and winter diet. The greater share of spring and summer foods come from the greens and dry seeds. The availability of these types of foods year after year is fairly consistent, hence there is less variability in the diet during spring and summer.

Fruits are used most in summer and fall, the seasons of their greatest abundance. There is a wide variation in the use of fruits in different years. This is partly due to the varying abundance of favorite fruits, and partly a reflection of the substitution under pressure of fruit for mast when only a short supply of the latter is on hand.

The animals eaten are mostly insects, though a

rather surprising number of snails and other invertebrates also are taken. The season of greatest animal food consumption is the summer and early fall.

The general proportions of these types of foods used by turkeys in the four seasons of the year are shown diagrammatically in Figure 9. It should be noted that even the general proportions of these foods vary not only in different years but in different parts of the birds' range. Particularly in the Southwestern range, the Rio Grande and Merriam turkeys use more dry seeds and less mast in their diet than turkeys do elsewhere. Then, too, the diet of the young turkeys in the summer is somewhat different from that of their parents; the poults consume more insects, succulent greens, and fruits, and less mast and seeds,

than the old birds. The younger the poults are, the greater is the difference in their diet compared to that of the parents.

MAST IN THE TURKEY'S DIET

THE turkey would almost certainly use more acorns, nuts, and tree seeds than it does if they were available. As it is, the bird frequently makes half or more of its food from acorns alone, up to 65% or more in the fall and winter, less as the year advances into spring and the supply of mast dwindles.

The pre-eminent importance of the acorns to the turkey has not always been true; the American chestnut once served as the most dependable source of mast in its Eastern range. The loss of the chestnut through blight was a terrible

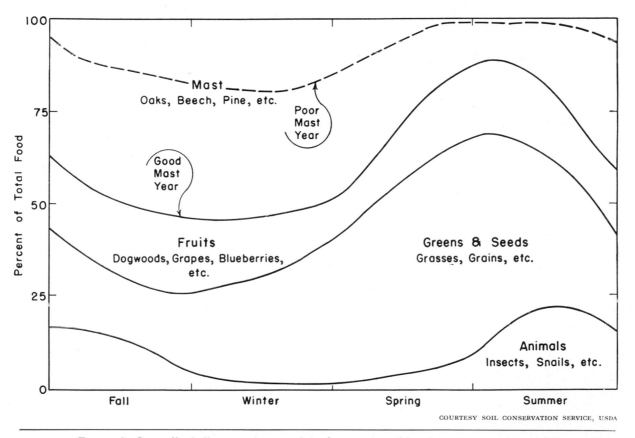

FIGURE 9. *Generalized diagram of seasonal foods eaten by wild turkeys. Proportions vary in different parts of its range and in different years. In years of poor mast crops, the proportions of greens and seeds used is greater than shown.*

tragedy, and one of the worst sufferers has been the turkey. Never again will the Eastern range have the turkey-carrying capacity it had when the chestnut thrived.

The most important mast producers for the wild turkey are the oaks. All of them contribute some to the turkey's diet, but some are vastly more important than others. In the Eastern and Central sections the white, northern red, chestnut, pin, post, and black oaks are best. In the South the same species are important except for the northern red oak, and the live oak also is an important mast producer. In the Southwest, Gambel's oak is one of the most substantial mast plants for the turkey.

The beech, hickories, and pecan produce valuable mast for the turkey when they have a crop, but they are less dependable than the oaks. Seeds and nuts of the pines also vary from year to year; but especially in the Southwest the nuts of the piñon and seeds of the ponderosa pines are valuable turkey food. The seeds of ash trees at times are of considerable importance in the East.

Locally other varieties of mast are used in considerable quantities; among these are maple keys, hazelnuts, bald cypress balls, and elm and birch seeds.

FRUITS EATEN BY THE TURKEY

MANY of the fruits of the forest are important turkey foods. In the summer the huckleberries, blueberries, cherries, and fruits of brambles and black gum are avidly eaten. When fall comes, those of the dogwoods (especially the flowering dogwood), grapes, wild black cherry, pawpaws, haws, persimmon, sumacs, poison ivy, and greenbriers are much relished in the East, South, and Central parts of the bird's range. In the Southwest the fruits of some of the manzanitas and the alligator juniper are eaten in quantity.

Locally other fruits are important too. These may include, wherever they are common, those of the may apple, arum, hackberry, strawberry, teaberry, hollies, Hall's honeysuckle, wax myrtle, prickly pear, ground cherry, pokeberry, roses, and viburnums.

GREENS, DRY SEEDS, AND OTHER PLANT PARTS AS TURKEY FOOD

THE greens, seeds, and other vegetation eaten by turkeys come from a wide variety of plants. Many are grasses, including the grains; some are ferns or legumes; many are farm weeds, or woodland forbs.

Grasses provide much forage for the wild turkey throughout its range, but probably most in the Southwest. The grasses are eaten both as greens and seeds. Up to 30% or more of summer food and 20% or more in the spring and fall diet may come from this family of plants. Food studies of the turkey's diet frequently identify these grasses only to the genus, but listing them thus, those most eaten appear to be: oatgrass, crabgrass, the muhly's, panic grasses, bluegrasses, wild rye, blue grama, fescues, hairy dropseed, paspalums, and six-weeks dropseed. Among the grains, corn and wheat are most important, though their prominence in some food habits records is due partly to collection of birds or droppings at winter feeding stations. Many other grasses are eaten, and no doubt some are used in some areas fully as much as the various grasses noted above.

Even a mere listing of the miscellaneous plants whose leaves, tubers, flowers, or seeds are eaten in quantity by turkeys would require a lengthy statement. Several are worthy of special mention, however, like the ragweeds, whose seeds are a favorite food of so many birds, and are relished by turkeys during the fall and winter. The nutgrass, or chufa, provides tubers much sought after in the turkey's Southern range. The leaves of buttonweed are eaten all year long in the Central region. Some of the sunflowers of the Central and Southwestern ranges are important to turkeys in the fall and winter for their seeds. Ferns and some of the club mosses furnish greens all year long. Certain legumes are relished both for their foliage and seeds, the lespedezas and vetches being most commonly taken in large amounts. Many other plants that offer the turkey tasty greens and seeds are listed in Table 7. Any

PLATE 24. *Turkeys feeding in a farm field next to hardwood swamp habitat along the Canadian River in the Texas Panhandle.*

of these, at times and in some areas, may be of prime importance as food sources.

ANIMAL FOODS OF THE TURKEY

YOUNG turkeys are about as carnivorous as the availability of animal food permits them to be; the old turks, too, have a great fondness for some types of flesh food. Most notable, perhaps, is their taste for grasshoppers; mainly in the summer and early fall, but also in the spring, when available, grasshoppers are consumed in great quantities. As much as 5% or more of their autumn diet may be made up of these insects; and through the summer the proportion may be even higher. Availability is the main factor that limits the amounts of orthopterous insects taken.

Another group of insects that seems to be especially relished is the flies, especially the larval forms. Beyond these two insect orders, almost all other forms of available insects are taken in smaller amounts. Of related forms, the spiders and daddy longlegs are eaten in some numbers. Snails, too, frequently are taken, and a variety of other small invertebrates to a lesser extent.

SUMMARY OF TURKEY FOODS

THE important and more commonly used plants and animals that contribute to the turkey's diet are listed in Table 7. The various foods—species, genera, or other groups—are classified as "preferred," "staple," or "incidental." Both preferred and staple foods are important, in that they furnish the turkey with considerable quantities of nutritious food for a long season, year after year, and over a larger part of the bird's range. The preferred foods are those that the turkey takes whenever it can get them; presumably they are the best, and their use is limited only by their

TABLE 7

FOODS OF THE WILD TURKEY

PREFERRED FOODS

Kinds of Food	Parts Eaten	Proportion of Diet	Fa	Wi	Spr	Su	Area of Use[1]
MAST		Up to 65% or more in fall and winter					
Oaks (*Quercus alba; borealis; gambeli; montana; palustris; stellata; velutina*)	acorns	Up to 30% or more in winter, 20% in spring	1	1	1	1[2]	Entire range
Beech	nuts, buds	Up to 10% or more in fall	1	2	3		East, South
Piñon pine	nuts	High	1	1	2	3	Southwest
FRUITS							
Flowering dogwood	fruits	Up to 15% in fall	1	2	3	3	East, South, Central
Wild grapes	fruits	Up to 20% or more in fall and winter	1	2	2	3	Entire range
Huckleberry and blueberry	fruits	Up to 15% in summer	2	3		1	East, South, Central
GREENS AND SEEDS							
Grasses *Digitaria*, incl. *D. spicata; Muhlenbergia*, incl. *M. texana, phleoides, schreberi; Panicum; Poa; Zea mays*	leaves seeds	Up to 30% in summer, 20% in spring & fall, 5% in winter	1	2	1	1	Entire range
INSECTS							
Grasshoppers (Locustidae)	adults nymphs	High in summer, 5% or more in fall	2		3	1	East, South, Central,

STAPLE FOODS

			Fa	Wi	Spr	Su	
MAST							
Hickories, pecan	nuts	Fairly high	1	2	2		East, South, Central
Ash	seeds	Up to 5% in fall	2	3			East
Pines (*Pinus* incl. *ponderosa*)	seeds needles	Fairly high in fall and winter	2	2	3		Entire range
Oaks (*Quercus coccinea; falcata; ilicifolia; marilandica; nigra; phellos; prinus; virginiana*)	acorns	Fairly high	2	2	2	3	Entire range
FRUIT							
Manzanitas (*Arctostaphylos pungens; uva-ursi*)	fruit	Fairly high	2	2			Central and Southwest
Pawpaw	fruit	Fairly high	2	2	2		South
Dogwoods (*Cornus*) *C. amomum; foemina; paniculata*	fruit	Fairly high	2	3	3	3	East, South, Central
Haws	fruit	Fairly high	2	3	3		East, South, Central

[1] Based on published records. The schedule is unquestionably incomplete.
[2] Symbols for use intensity: 1, high; 2, medium; 3, low.

TABLE 7 (Continued)

Kinds of Food	Parts Eaten	Proportion of Diet	Fa	Wi	Spr	Su	Area of Use
Persimmon	fruit	Up to 2% in fall	2				East
Alligator juniper	fruit	High in fall and winter	1	1	2	3	Southwest
Black gum	fruit	Up to 2% or more in fall	2	3	2	2	East, South, Central
Cherries (*Prunus* incl. *serotina*)	fruit	Up to 4% in summer, 2% in fall	2	3	3	2	East, Central
Sumacs (*Rhus copallina; glabra; toxicodendron; trilobata; typhina vernix*)	fruit	Up to 2% in fall, 1% in spring	1	2	2	3	Entire range
Brambles	fruit leaves	Up to 2% or more in summer	3	3	3	2	East, South, Central
Greenbrier (*Smilax glauca; hispida*)	fruit	Up to 2% from fall to spring	2	2	2	3	East, South, Central
GREENS AND SEEDS							
Ragweed (*Ambrosia* incl. *psilostachya*)	seeds	High	2	2			East, Southwest
Birthwort	seeds	Over 1%	2				East
Beeplant	seeds						Central
Nutgrass	tubers	High	2	2			South, Central
Buttonweed	leaves	High	2	2	3	3	Central
Buckwheat	seeds	Up to 1% in fall	2				East
Grasses	all	Generally high	2	3	2	2	Entire range
Blepharoneuron tricholepis	florets stems						Southwest
Bouteloua gracilis	florets stems leaves						Central, Southwest
Elymus	leaves seeds						Central, Southwest
Festuca	seeds						East, Central, Southwest
Panicum incl. *agrostoides, anceps, boscii, capillare, flexile, sphaerocarpon*	seeds						Entire range
Paspalum	leaves						Central
Sporobolus microspermus	seeds florets						Southwest
Triticum aestivum	grain leaves						East, Central
Sunflower (*Helianthus* incl. *annus*)	seeds	High	2	2			Central, Southwest
Lespedeza	seeds		2	2	3	3	Central
Ferns and Club Mosses	fronds	Up to 10% in fall	1	2	2		East
Hemlock	leaves	Up to 4% in winter		2			East
Vetch (*Vicia* incl. *americana, angustifolia, carolineana*)	leaves	About 1%	2				East
Goldeneye	seeds		2	2			Southwest
INSECTS							
Flies (Diptera)	adults		3		3	2	Entire range

TABLE 7 (Continued)

INCIDENTAL FOODS

Kinds of Food	Parts Eaten	Area of Use
MAST AND FRUITS		
Maple (*Acer* incl. *pennsylvanicum*)	seeds	East
Custard apple	fruit	East
Arum	fruit	East
Peanut	nut	East
Chokeberry	fruit	East
Asparagus	fruit	East
Birch	seed, bud, catkin	East
Bittersweet	fruit	East
Hackberry	fruit	East, South, Central
Hazel	nut	East, Central
Strawberry	fruit, leaves	East
Teaberry	fruit	East
Holly (*Ilex* incl. *opaca, monticola*)	fruit	East, South
Sweet gum	fruit	South
Hall's honeysuckle	fruit, leaves	East
Magnolia	fruit	South
Wild cucumber	fruit	South
Partridgeberry	fruit	East
Mulberry	fruit	Central
Wax myrtle	fruit	East, South
Prickly pear	fruit	Southwest
Virginia creeper	fruit	East
Ground cherry	fruit	South
Pokeberry	fruit	East, Central
Solomon's seal	fruit, leaves	East
Rose	fruit	East, Central
Sassafras	fruit	East
False Solomon's seal	fruit	East
Snowberry	fruit	Central
Bald cypress	seeds	South
Elm	seeds	South
Viburnum	fruit	East
SEEDS, GREENS, AND FLOWERS		
Agoseris	leaves, heads	Southwest
Hog peanut	seeds	Central
Burdock	seeds	Central
Aster	flowers, seed, leaves	East
Milk vetch	seedhead	Southwest
Wild indigo	seeds	East
Beggar ticks	seeds	East
Shepherd's-purse	seed	Central
New Jersey tea	seed	East
Partridge pea	seed	South
Goosefoot	seed	Central
Golden aster	seed	East
Cancerroot	plant	East

TABLE 7 (Continued)

Kinds of Food	Parts Eaten	Area of Use
Doveweed	seed	South
Cuphea		Central
Sedges		
sedge	seed, leaf	East, Central
nutrush	leaf	Central
Tick clover	seed	East, Central, Southwest
Filaree (*Erodium* incl. *cicutarium*)	seed	Southwest
Boneset	seed, bud, flower	East
Bedstraw (*Galium* incl. *aparine*)		East, Central
Wright's silk-tassel	seed	Southwest
Geranium	leaf	Central
Grasses		
bentgrass	leaf	Central
bluestem	leaf	Central
oats	leaf, seed	East, Central, Southwest
brome	leaf, seed	Central, Southwest
pine grass	seed	Southwest
goose grass	leaf	Central
love grass	seed	Southwest
manna grass	leaf	Central
barley	leaf, seed	Central
cut-grass	leaf	Central
rye	leaf, seed	East
foxtail	leaf, seed	Entire range
wedgescale	leaf	Central
triodia	leaf	Central
Witchhazel	seed	East, Central
Jewelweed	seed	East
Rush	leaf	East, Central
Wild pea	leaf	Southwest
Pinweed		Central
Pepperweed		Central
Lily	buds	Southwest
Loosestrife	seed	East
Tobacco	seed	East
Orchis	leaf	East
Oxalis	leaf	Central
Red spruce	leaf	East
Plantain	leaf, seed	East, Central
Sycamore	seed	Central
Knotweed	seed	East, Central
Purslane	tuber	East
Primrose	seed	East
Mosses	leaf	East, Central
Buttercup	leaf, seed, flower	East, Central
Black locust	seed	East
Sorrel	leaf	Central
Figwort	seed	East

TABLE 7 (Continued)		
Kinds of Foods	*Parts Eaten*	*Area of Use*
Sleepy catchfly	seedhead	Southwest
Soybean	seed	East
Nightshade	seed	East
Potato	tuber	East
Goldenrod	leaf	Central
Dandelion	leaf	Southwest
Mushrooms	all	East
Clover (*Trifolium* incl. *pratense*)	leaf	East, Central
Nettle	leaf	East
Cornsalad		Central
Vervain		East, Central
Cowpea	seed	East
ANIMAL FOODS		
INSECTS		Entire range
Beetles (Coleoptera)	adult, larva	East
Bugs (Hemiptera)	adult, nymph	East
Leaf hoppers, etc. (Homoptera)	adult, nymph	East
Wasps, ants (Hymenoptera)	adult, larva	East
Butterflies, moths (Lepidoptera)	adult, pupa	East
Spiders, ticks, etc. (Arachnida)	adult, larva	East, Central
Centipedes, millipedes (Chilopoda and Diplopoda)	adult	East
Crayfish (Crustacea)	adult	East, South
Snails, slugs, etc. (Mollusca)		East
Salamanders (Amphibia)	adult	East

availability. Where they are plentiful and the supply dependable, the number of turkeys may well be high too, if no other factor seriously limits them. Staple foods are those used in large quantity, but evidently with only casual relish; they are the "potatoes" of the turkey's diet when there isn't enough "steak." The third group of "incidental" foods includes those eaten more or less regularly in a part of the range but usually not in large amounts. Added together, however, these incidental foods make up a considerable share of the diet. Entirely omitted from Table 7 are a large number of plant products known to have been eaten by the turkey but not known to have significance in its welfare.

THE QUANTITY OF FOOD EATEN; FEEDING HABITS

THE turkey's crop holds about a half pint of food when comfortably filled; it can be stretched to hold a bit more on occasion. It may seem well-filled, however, with only a small fraction of a pint of food in it; it is about as near to rubber as flesh can be.

How much food the turkey requires for good sustenance cannot be stated categorically. More is needed in cold weather than when the weather is warm. More food in proportion to size is required by the growing young birds than by the adults. When the turkeys can get highly nutritious and energy-producing food, less is needed than when they are forced to accept poorer foods. As a general rule, the turkey should be able to fill it's crop twice daily with palatable and nutritious foods. Otherwise it cannot maintain full vigor.

Turkeys usually partake of a variety of foods at each meal; the number of food items that a single bird will have in its crop at one time may be as high as 50, but usually is from 10 to 20. The number of individual pieces of food gathered for one meal may be many hundreds. Ligon (1946) describes a turkey crop that contained 30 piñon nuts and 215 alligator juniper berries. Mosby and Handley (1943) tell of a Virginia turkey killed in November whose crop contained the following food items: corn, 16 kernels; beard grass, 5 seeds; crabgrass (2 species), 22 seeds; paspalum grass, 34 seeds; witch grass, 12 seeds; white grass, 23 seeds; rice cut-grass, 3 seeds; nimblewill, 30 seeds; dropseed, 19 seeds; tall redtop, 80 seeds; *Uniola laxa,* 8 seeds; beak rush, 34 seeds; chestnut oak, 1 acorn; beggarweed (2 species), 396 seeds; touch-me-not, 1 seed; dwarf sumac, 80 seeds and 1 fruiting stem; wild grape, 13 fruits; sassafras, 24 fruits; flowering dogwood, 160 fruits and seed fragments and 17 fruiting stems; persimmon, 1 seed coat; viburnum, 5 fruits; golden aster, 1,475 seeds and 4 flower heads; grass, 2 blades; clover, 1 leaf; unidentified, 1 leaf; and 1 skipper butterfly. This is a total of 2,469 pieces of food consumed in one meal.

Turkeys are wandering feeders; they are on the move continuously, and cover miles in a day's foraging. The flocks tend to move as a group, and seldom get very widely separated. They are always on the alert, and combine watchfulness for enemies with their searching for food. They are mostly ground feeders, scratching in the ground litter and picking seeds, fruits, and insects off low-growing plants.

Turkey scratchings are easily seen until plant growth or leaf litter obscures them. The scratchings are forward, a foot or more long, and frequently like radii of circles. The birds often feed in one place for a half hour or so, scratch up the ground over a favorable acre or two, then quickly travel a half-mile or more to another likely feeding spot.

The seasons alter their feeding habits. As different foods become available, the birds shift to the coverts supplying them. Winter snows frequently force them to seek food on sheltered south slopes, and along streams and spring runs. When they are hard pressed they will scratch through a foot of snow to get at edibles on the ground.

Feeding times are normally in early morning just after dawn, and again for a short time in late afternoon. When their regular program is upset by bad weather or by the intrusions of enemies they may feed at any hour. At all times they browse a little as they move about.

The organization of the flock during feeding periods is loose and without evident leadership. As an exception, the family group, parents and young, is held rigidly together in summer by parental authority.

WATER NEEDS; GRIT

GOOD turkey range is well watered; the birds need a dependable moisture supply to go with their food. Open water is available in streams, spring heads, and wooded swamps. Moisture is supplied at some seasons in their food—succulent vegetation, fruits, and insects. During dry seasons, especially in fall and winter, their travels are frequently limited to the ravines and swamps where water remains available.

Turkeys strive to keep grit in their gizzards at all times, as do gallinaceous birds in general. Occasionally they run out of stones, and some of the hard seeds help serve the same purpose. Having grit available is exceedingly important, for without it their digestion would be impaired. Mosby and Handley (1943) found the average quantity of grit in turkey gizzards to be 27 cc., and in the crops 7 cc. There are about 3 cc. to a teaspoonful.

THE ECONOMICS OF WILD TURKEY FOOD HABITS

THE significance to man of the turkey's food habits is negligible. The grains, fruits, and nuts that they eat are rarely obtained by depredation on farm crops. The weed seeds eaten have no appreciable beneficial effect on weed abundance. As to insects, their preference for grasshoppers is all to the good but the total quantity consumed is too small to have any measurable effect on grasshopper damage to crops. The turkey's eating habits are therefore neutral.

THE INFLUENCE OF WEATHER AND CLIMATE ON TURKEYS

THE turkey is affected by weather conditions both directly and indirectly. During stormy weather—rain, sleet, snow, high winds, and very cold temperatures, in various combinations—the birds seek the shelter of coniferous cover, of sunny slopes, ravines, and the lee side of mountains. At such times their activity is usually much reduced, and they are apt to remain in one place unless disturbed. Little food is taken, and in specially severe weather they may go for several days without feeding at all. When snow is deep and soft they frequently do their travelling by flying rather than walking.

The effect of weather on the activities of turkeys may lead to secondary and more serious results. Rarely does a turkey die of exposure, though severe winters are no doubt part of the reason for the northern limits of its range; but the birds may well be made vulnerable to predation while facing storms. This is particularly true if cover is inadequate. They may be weakened by not having enough good food because of the snow and ice, then are easy prey for natural enemies. Floods sometimes force lowland turkeys to take refuge on dry knolls or on river levees; here they can be attacked by man or beast with little chance for escape.

Sometimes, however, the weather itself strikes them down. Direct losses from weather usually involve the eggs or very young poults. Nests may be flooded by high spring waters. Cold rains soon after hatching are deadly to young turkeys, as with most precocial birds; they become overchilled, soaked, and lose feeding time when they cannot afford to do so. Though accurate information on these losses is scarce, it seems quite probable that they are among the more serious causes of local declines in turkey populations. This is especially true in good turkey habitat, where losses of eggs and young are likely to be due to adverse weather.

PREDATION, DISEASES, AND PARASITES

NEST DESTRUCTION BY PREDATORS

TURKEY eggs, since they are on the ground and often only moderately well concealed, are vulnerable to egg-eating creatures. Yet, common as it is for turkeys to lose their clutches of eggs to natural enemies, other sources of nest destruction are usually more important. Man's lumbering and farming activities, especially trampling by domestic livestock, frequently cause hen turkeys to lose their eggs or desert them. Weather conditions and fire cause more nest losses in some years than do predators.

In Virginia Mosby and Handley (1943) reported two nests destroyed by crows and two by skunks among forty they observed to fail; in addition, they had reports of nests broken up by foxes, dogs, opossums, and black snakes. Substantially this same group of species has been reported as turkey nest destroyers in Pennsylvania, West Virginia, and Maryland. The raccoon was also in the group important in Pennsylvania. In Missouri various writers have named the hog, dog, fox, opossum, and the black timber rattler, and copperhead snakes as pilferers of turkey nests. Ligon (1946) reported observations on eleven Merriam turkey nests in the Southwest. Five were destroyed by animals; two by bobcats killing the hen, one by a golden eagle killing the hen, one by a badger, and one probably by a raven. He notes that there is considerable evidence that bears and porcupines also eat turkey eggs.

Because of the small amount of information available on this subject it is impossible to appraise accurately the significance of predation on turkey nests in determining population levels. It seems very unlikely that nest predation is generally a limiting factor on the increase of the bird.

PREDATION ON YOUNG TURKEYS

THERE are scattered records of a number of predators eating turkey poults; these are almost entirely the same creatures that prey on the adults, though there are some exceptions. Bent (1938) tells of two-week-old poults being devoured by rock squirrels in Texas. Some of the lesser birds of prey, and mammals that could not successfully attack an adult turkey, may occasionally take a partly grown one. These losses, and in fact all the losses of young turkeys to predators, do not amount to a large proportion of the annual hatch of the birds. Summer is a season of plentiful food for predators, and at the same time one of difficult hunting for such elusive prey as turkeys. As with most other gallinaceous birds, the losses of young from other causes far outweigh those from predation.

ENEMIES OF ADULT TURKEYS

A FULL-GROWN turkey is a big, strong bird, wary in habit, speedy afoot and in flight. It is not an easy mark for carnivorous animals under most circumstances. Despite this, the old turks have many natural enemies, and numbers of them succumb each year to tooth or talon.

The most effective turkey predators are naturally the larger ones. Among the predaceous birds the great horned owl most often succeeds in "bagging" a turkey. It is an important enemy throughout the turkey's range, East, South, and West. In the Southwest the golden eagle and occasionally the bald eagle is known to kill some turkeys. In the East the goshawk is supposed to get an occasional turk, and the other accipitrine hawks—Cooper's and sharp-shinned—may take a poult now and then.

Among the mammals the coyote, bobcat, and the red and gray foxes are most destructive of turkeys. Of these the coyote is limited to the Central and Western parts of the range, the gray fox covers all but the Southwest, the red fox is found mostly in the East, and the bobcat over the whole range.

In addition to these the wolf (formerly), lynx, cougar, black bear, stray dog, raccoon, and occasionally others kill some turkeys where they are common in good turkey range.

Predation apparently does not play a really big part in limiting turkey populations except locally. Though Ligon (1946) says: "Turkeys apparently are an irresistible attraction to coyotes, and the question as to whether the white man or the coyote has had the most adverse effect on the Mountain turkey is debatable," many turkey populations in the Southwest thrive in the face of high numbers of coyotes, as near Canadian, Texas (letter, P. Allan). Dalke, Leopold, and Spencer (1946) say that " . . . in Missouri, man still causes a larger drain on the wild turkey population than all its natural enemies combined." And that in spite of there being no legal hunting! Studies of the turkey in the Eastern states have uniformly concluded that predation is a secondary factor in influencing turkey populations.

DISEASES AND PARASITES OF THE WILD TURKEY

THE turkey, as a species, is known to be susceptible to a large number of diseases and parasites. The majority of these infections and infestations are known to occur only in birds in captivity, though there is no question that it is *possible* for wild birds to have all of them too. Since many of these troubles are primarily correlated with the concentration of penned birds and the poor circumstances under which they live in domesticity, they are unlikely to be important to wild turkey flocks. We shall deal here only with the organisms known to occur in and on the wild birds, and shall merely mention the others known to occur only in captives.

Probably the greatest potential disease scourge of wild turkeys is blackhead, or enterohepatitis. It is caused by a protozoan (*Histomonas meleagridis*), and quickly becomes epidemic when it strikes birds in confinement, especially those living on the ground; it evidently spreads readily within a wild flock too; Stoddard (1935) reported three cases found on heavily stocked Georgia range in 1934. It has also been identified in three wild birds in Virginia (Mosby and Handley, 1943) and in several in Missouri (Dalke, Leopold, and Spencer, 1946). In all instances it was noted that the infection probably came about by the turkeys traversing ground infected by domestic fowls. Birds affected with this disease rarely recover; it is the one disease that seems most likely to affect wild turkey populations seriously in occasional areas and years.

Another protozoan that has been reported from wild birds in Virginia is a species of *Leucocytozoon* (Mosby and Handley, 1943). These blood parasites are similar to the malarial parasite. No significance has been ascribed to their presence in wild turkeys, but they have caused serious mortality among domestic turkeys and are common in game-farm turkeys. Conceivably they could be a threat to wild flocks.

Several other diseases of wild turkeys were reported by Shillinger and Morley (1937), including coccidiosis (causative agent, *Eimeria*), tuberculosis (cause: *Mycobacterium avium*), ulcerative enteritis (probable cause: *Corynebacterium perdicum*), and thrush (caused by *Oidium albicans*). It was not clear whether these cases were wild or captive wild turkeys, but presumably they were wild collected birds. Mosby and Handley (1943) also reported a wild bird with an intestinal tumor that would have been fatal in time.

Endoparasites are common in turkeys, as in most wild game birds. Both intestinal round worms (*Ascaridia*) and tapeworms (*Metroliasthes* and *Raillietina*) are common in wild specimens, but rarely cause serious illness.

External parasites also are frequent on turkeys. Ticks, chiggers, fleas, lice, and louse flies are all known to occur naturally. If present in great numbers any of them might so sap the bird's strength as to weaken it, but apparently this does not happen very often.

The list of infecting disease organisms and infesting parasites enlarges when game-farm birds are taken into consideration; any of these afflictions could conceivably strike a wild bird too. Among these pathological conditions known so far only on game farms are: pullorum disease; paratyphoid; perosis; pendulous crop; aspergillosis; cholera; botulism; tracheitis; edematous

roup; fowl typhoid; trichomoniasis; fowl diphtheria; gizzard worm (*Cheilospirura*); gapeworm (*Syngamus*); and cropworm (*Capillaria*).

Despite the number of organisms that may afflict the wild turkey, few are of appreciable significance in determining the level of turkey abundance. Even those few—blackhead, perhaps leucocytozoon, possibly others—rarely become epidemic among wild birds. Disease is a minor factor of wild-turkey ecology today.

MAN'S RELATIONS TO THE TURKEY

MAN has been the wild turkey's greatest enemy; directly as a hunter, but—of vastly greater importance—indirectly as a farmer and lumberman, he has reduced this fine game bird to a pitiable remnant of its once great numbers. To some degree this has been an inevitable by-product of the progress of man's occupancy of this continent. It is equally true that it has been the result of wanton wastefulness—burning of the land, cut-out and get-out lumbering, overgrazing of the land by domestic livestock, and poaching.

There is just a little hope for man in this sorry picture; what man destroys he can sometimes rebuild; he may still make reparation. By reversing his arbitrary excesses he can—at least theoretically—enable the turkey to make a partial comeback. Whether he will or not remains to be seen; the odds for it just now seem not very good.

MAN'S HUNTING

TURKEY hunting by the white man has the longest history among all American game birds. The Spaniards first encountered the turkey early in the 16th century. Not only has turkey hunting had a long chronicle, but it has probably had more variations than any other kind of game-bird shooting. From the Indian's blowgun to the modern repeating shotgun and high-powered rifle, all manner of hand weapons have been employed and ingenious traps and snares have been substituted for direct pursuit. Pointing bird dogs have been used as well as just plain dogs. The turks are stalked and still-hunted, pursued by organized drives, and enticed to blinds. But the most interesting of the techniques of turkey hunting are the "calling up" practices. By various calls the turkey is lured close to the hunter, the easier to seal its doom. Skills developed in turkey-calling have contributed greatly to the art of hunting this grand bird.

Of hunting in the "good old days" there is an ample literature, and it will not serve our purpose to repeat much of it here. There is little doubt that turkeys were once abundant in many parts of the range, and that there was a great hunting slaughter of them. This indiscriminate killing would unquestionably have exterminated the species in time, even if the ruination of its habitat had not occurred. Early in the 19th century the species had been eliminated from much of New England, even though it was still possible to purchase them in Boston for three-pence as late as 1823. By the middle of the last century the free and easy days of turkey slaughter were over. Audubon wrote of their threatened extermination. Hunting restrictions were imposed by the states, and the modern era of limited hunting began.

In many parts of the turkey range its numbers are continuing to decrease, despite stringent hunting restrictions. Of 21 states that have a significant number of turkeys, nine have now stopped legal hunting altogether; four of these have ordered their closed seasons in the last few years—since 1940. In other sections the turkeys are holding their own or are actually increasing. It is a favorable commentary that a densely populated and heavily hunted state like Pennsylvania still kills an average of 3,800 turkeys a year—considerably more than would have been possible a couple of decades ago; in 1951 the Pennsylvania turkey harvest was 8,962. There is a nucleus of 500 to 600 Merriam turkeys colonized in southeastern Wyoming (Ligon, 1946), an area entirely out of the species original range.

It is evidence that judicious stocking still has a place in game management, albeit a limited one.

There are now 12 states that have open hunting seasons for wild turkeys; the annual kill is roughly 30,000. Texas and Virginia lead with about 7,000 and 6,800 birds bagged annually. Pennsylvania and Maryland, however, have by far the highest kill per unit of occupied range, hunters in each of them getting more than a bird per square mile. These high-kill ratios are maintained to a considerable degree with game-farm birds. Mr. Ernest Vaughn, State Game Warden for Maryland, tells me (1948) that the population of real, native-stock wild turkeys in that state is only about 300. The known and estimated bags of turkeys and data on their populations are given in Table 8. The figures in this table are taken from all accurate sources available, as noted in the reference column. Other figures are the author's own estimates, which may be in considerable error; lacking better data, I have computed these on the basis of whatever pertinent information I could find. No claim is made for their accuracy, except that I believe they are better than nothing at all.

The proportion of the population of turkeys brought to the hunters' bag varies greatly. In the more heavily populated states—Pennsylvania, Maryland, Virginia, and Florida—it runs high, from 25% to 30%. In the more sparsely settled areas of the Southwest it is low, often less than 10%; the general average is about 14%. This figure is roughly the same as for the ruffed grouse, another woodland species. In addition there is some loss from crippling; Mosby and Handley (1943) place the crippling loss at 3% of the population, or about 10% of the legal kill. Then there is always illegal killing; in some areas this may even exceed the legal take. In Virginia it was estimated as one-third as much as the legal kill, making a total hunting loss of 43%. Applying the same ratios to the average hunting losses in all states, the total reduction of birds from man's hunting would be about 21%.

As long as reasonable populations can be maintained—that is, the range kept in condition

TABLE 8

POPULATION AND ANNUAL KILL OF WILD TURKEY, BY STATES

(WITH OCCUPIED RANGE AREA AND AVERAGE POPULATION DENSITIES)

STATE	TURKEY POPULA-TION	ANNUAL KILL	% KILL	OCCUPIED RANGE (SQ. MI.)	POPULATION DENSITY (BIRDS/ SQ. MI.)	REFERENCES
ALABAMA	13,487	2,100	15	19,059	0.7	Dalke, *et. al.*, '46 Mosby, Handley '43
ARIZONA	25,000	1,200†	6	10,000**	2.5**	Ligon '46
ARKANSAS	3,000**	300†	10**	6,000**	0.5**	Gresh '46
COLORADO	3,400			2,500**	1.4**	Ligon '46
FLORIDA	12,300	3,150	25	14,535	0.8	Mosby, Handley '43
GEORGIA	6,000**	1,200	20**	7,500**	0.8**	Gresh '46
KENTUCKY	1,000**			1,000**	1.0**	
LOUISIANA	1,738	100	6	1,320	1.3	Bick '47
MARYLAND	1,200**‡	856	30**	800**	1.5**	Wilson '47
MISSISSIPPI	6,000	400*	7	7,500**	0.8**	Gresh '46, Blakey '37
MISSOURI	4,340	200*	5	7,000	0.6	Dalke, *et al.*, '46
NEW MEXICO	16,000	1,000	6	12,000**	1.3**	Ligon '46
NORTH CAROLINA	10,050**	2,000**	20**	10,050	1.0**	Mosby, Handley '43
OKLAHOMA	1,000**			1,000**	1.0**	
PENNSYLVANIA	8,000**‡	3,800	30**	3,125	2.6**	Latham '39 Mosby, Handley '43
SOUTH CAROLINA	2,500**	500	20**	3,100**	0.8**	Gresh '46
TENNESSEE	1,000**			2,000**	0.5**	
TEXAS	70,000**	7,000**	10**	50,000**	1.4**	
VIRGINIA	23,237	6,808	29	13,765	1.7	Mosby, Handley '43
WEST VIRGINIA	5,988	467	8	4,725	1.3	Glover, Bailey '47
WYOMING*	600			600**	1.0**	Ligon '46
Total	215,840**	31,081**	Av. 14**	177,579**	Av. 1.2**	

* An introduction outside its original range.
† Hunting season closed in recent years.
** Figures estimated by the the author or computed from estimates.
‡ Population is low relative to the kill, as the kill is largely game-farm birds.

to support them—this degree of hunting will not seriously hurt them. Only when the range itself deteriorates so that the stock of birds dwindles —as it has in the Central range in Arkansas and Missouri—is it necessary to call a halt to hunting in an effort to protect the last remnants.

The state-wide kill figures are averages of hunting mortality; the kill in some areas is lower, in others higher, than the average. Glover and Bailey (1947) report the 1946 turkey population in Hampshire County, West Virginia, to

have been reduced by 70% during the hunting season—obviously an excessive loss. Ligon (1946) notes that "Hunting in connection with logging and lumbering operations west of the Rio Grande . . . in Colorado was no doubt largely responsible for the almost total extermination of turkeys in that region . . . " This is in a part of the bird's range where the average kill is low. Where hunting results in this high a kill, more protection in some form is essential.

Excessive hunting-bag is not always reflected

in official aboveboard records such as the last; illegal hunting is a prime factor that reduces the turkey in some areas, especially in marginal range. "Turkey shooting is a tradition as deeply ingrained in the Ozark people [of Missouri] as burning the woods," comment Dalke, Leopold, and Spencer (1946); " . . . we must conclude that in spite of a closed season hunting losses are still severe . . . " McIlhenny (1914), who hunted the turkey extensively in the South, concluded long ago: "I have ample evidence that wild turkeys will not shrink from civilization. It is the trapping, snaring, baiting, and killing of all old gobblers that decimates their numbers, not the legitimate hunting by sportsmen."

The legal limitations on turkey hunting have been more and more restricting as the years passed. Most open seasons are in the fall or winter, though two states, Alabama and Louisiana, still have April hunting. The time of legal hunting spreads over a period of from 12 days (New Mexico) up to 95 days (South Carolina), with the others in between. Four states limit the kill to gobblers (Alabama, Louisiana, South Carolina, Texas). Daily limits are either one or two birds; seasonal limits range from one to four, except for South Carolina, which permits taking twenty. Five of the twelve turkey-hunting states have a one-bird seasonal limit.

FARMING AND LUMBERING AFFECTING THE TURKEY

THE overkilling of turkeys in years gone by is an obvious reason for the bird's present rather sad plight. There is no doubt that hunting, both the legal and illegal varieties, has been an important factor in *reducing* their numbers. But great as it was, it was small compared to the destruction wrought by man's operations as farmer and lumberman.

When our forefathers cleared the wilderness, plowed the new lands, and hacked over the forests that could not be cleared for farming, they had no malicious intent to hurt the turkey; nevertheless, that was the insidious result. Chopping down trees and plowing up soil did not *kill*

turkeys; it just prevented any more from being produced. The result is the same, whether turkeys are all killed in an area or merely prevented from reproducing, namely, fewer and fewer turkeys. The disastrous effects on the turkey of our inhabiting the land are no less vital because they were accidental.

Much of this destruction was inevitable; good lands had to be made to produce food. But much of this destruction was wasteful and unnecessary; we did not *have* to skin the mountains for every last log; we did not *have* to burn the slashed woodlands as the lumbermen moved on; we did not *have* to turn swine into the woods to destroy the understory and ground litter after the canopy was gone. But that's what was generally done. And the turkey was squeezed more and more into isolated remnants of the more inaccessible portions of its original range.

The reduction of the extensive mature forest to open fields and small patches of woodland, the invasion of the remaining forest by roads and camps, have limited the wild turkey to a small fraction of its former range. In Pennsylvania the occupied area was only about 2 million acres in the mid-1930's (Latham, 1939), or about 7% of its former extent. (It has increased some since then.) Over the whole species range it has probably been reduced even more than this, such has been the effect of man's farming and lumbering activities on this game species.

The impact of farmer and woodcutter on the turkey is more than historical; it continues today. It can still force the turkey from much of its remaining home if the trend continues unchecked. On the other hand, it is theoretically possible to halt, and even to reverse, this trend; there is evidence that this has actually happened in some places. Pennsylvania, Maryland, and West Virginia have more turkeys today than twenty to thirty years ago; the expansion of farmland has about stopped. In some of the older, hillier farming sections of the East farm abandonment has progressed rapidly in the last three decades; even some of the back roads are gone, and some sections are now freer of man's habitations than

PLATE 25. *Wild turkeys crossing a Pennsylvania mountain road to forage in a farm field.*

they once were. There is some progress being made in sustained-yield forestry in place of the quick exploitation system. All these trends are in favor of the wild turkey.

Even with these signs of hope for the future, it is still true today that man—primarily in his role as a farm, ranch, or forest operator—is the turkey's worst enemy; only by man's controlling his own activities more favorably to the welfare of the land can the turkey be saved from virtual extinction. Consequently, man is the turkey's only possible savior.

The disastrous influence of domestic livestock on the turkey is a problem on public lands as well as private. The National Forests in the East, South, and Southwest, and other federal grazing lands in the Southwest, permit large numbers of sheep, hogs, goats, and cattle on their semiopen forests. These are frequently turkey range, or

could be good turkey range except for the unfavorable effects of the livestock. These animals compete with the turkey for its primary foods—mast and grass. Unfortunately the private uses of the public domain are too often settled as a political matter rather than in the interests of the land and of all the people. Hence the outlook for the improvement of the turkey range on public lands by curtailing the grazing of domestic stock does not appear rosy.

The grazing problem may be either better or worse on privately owned turkey range than on public lands. Tracts held by lumber interests, and game preserves and large estates owned by wealthy individuals and groups, are apt to have less livestock on them than private farms and ranches. These landowners often restrict the numbers of domestic stock in order to favor game. There is also a real chance for improvement of the turkey cover on farms and ranches in turkey range by the encouragement of the sound practice of limiting livestock to *good quality* pastures and range land. Woodlands and Eastern low-quality grasslands can profitably be excluded from grazing and be developed for game and timber. But on public lands the old urge to get something for nothing usually spoils any chance of having constructive limitation of grazing.

Despoilation of the forest by man-caused fires is another scourge that has impoverished much of our wild turkey cover. A serious problem throughout the bird's range, it is worst in the Ozark region of Arkansas and Missouri. This burning of the forest is frequently associated with the grazing problem. As Dalke, Leopold, and Spencer (1946) say, "Most Ozark fires stem from the activities of the stock owners, who burn deliberately to 'bring green grass' or kill ticks, or inadvertently while clearing more pasture." Change will come about only through a combination of education, together with land-use regulations applied locally as a part of organized conservation programs. Fortunately there is no real benefit from this burning; the folks who do it are only hurting their own interests through incorrect beliefs. Sometime we shall overcome this folly; but when?

The overcutting of forests, frequently followed by fire, has destroyed much fine turkey range. The lumbering of the virgin stands was also accompanied by meat hunting of the turkeys and other game to provide food for the camps. Ligon (1946) expresses the opinion that "Hunting in connection with logging and lumbering operations west of the Rio Grande . . . in Colorado was no doubt largely responsible for the almost total extermination of turkeys in that region, and extensive mining operations had equally disastrous effects east of the Rio Grande. . . ." Even without the hunting or fire added to its troubles, the turkey found the logged-off forests unsuitable; food supplies from the mast-producing trees were gone; so was much of its shelter. Some of these forests are now improving as tur-

key range under public ownership. Sustained-yield lumbering can keep them all productive of turkeys—other factors being favorable—if man becomes wise enough to handle the woods that way.

The drainage of swamp forests, with the ensuing invasion of agriculture, has taken its toll of once good turkey range. Blakey (1941) cites the case of the exploitation of the basin of the Great Pee Dee River in South Carolina by drainage and lumbering, followed by agriculture, as having reduced the turkeys to a few remnants that would probably soon disappear. The threat of drainage is greatest in the coastal plain range of the turkey from Virginia to Louisiana. Much has already been lost; still more of the shrinking range is threatened. In so far as these lands are actually suitable for high-grade agricultural production we must accept their loss. It is in areas where the resulting farmland is marginal or poorer that drainage should be vigorously opposed. The potential value of undrained lands for agricultural use can be determined by expert soil conservationists if those interested will but consult them ahead of time.

As Glover and Bailey (1947) said, "Man is the wild turkey's worst enemy . . . the turkey population . . . is inversely proportional to the number of people living in that area."

MAN AS A TURKEY CONSERVATIONIST

MAN would *like* to save the turkey from extermination; he would like to have the turkey prosper in great abundance. No one hates the turkey (as some game birds are disliked for the occasional troubles they cause). Yet it is one of the scarcest of our important game birds.

This ineffectiveness in conserving the turkey comes partly from inadequate knowledge of the species. This is rapidly being rectified; in the past two years (1947–48) eleven states have been studying the bird under Pittman-Robertson projects, and other studies have been under way as well. Much is now known of its needs and the ways of providing them. The far greater cause of failure to help the turkey more has been our inability to do the fundamental things that we know are necessary for its welfare.

Mostly the efforts deliberately to conserve the turkey have merely flirted with the more superficial techniques that are only stopgaps. We provide grain for them in the winter because the habitat is in such poor condition that it cannot grow the food they need. We restock inferior game-farm birds in range that is too poor to grow turkeys naturally. We trap birds from the few remnants of good range left, and leave them to almost certain doom in some other area that is too far depleted to have maintained its own stock. We make a big to-do about "controlling" predators to save turkeys, when it is we, not the predators, that have caused the turkey's sad plight. We pass more and more restrictive laws on man the hunter while we merrily continue to let the real culprit—man the farmer (and his dogs and livestock), rancher, and lumberman—go on in his destructive ways.

So the story of man the turkey conservationist is a bit pathetic. Theoretically, he could "come down to earth" and become a farmer-, rancher-, or lumberman-conservationist. The forests and grasslands *could* be cared for on a sustained-yield basis for trees, livestock *and* turkeys for the greater welfare of all. Will this come to pass? Only time can tell. This much we can say: if man does it, he can be a true conservationist, and the turkey will prosper as much as such a species can prosper in our modern times. If he fails to do it, the forests and ranges will go with the turkey. The old gobbler will have served as a symbol of man's own impending disaster.

PRODUCTIVITY AND POPULATIONS
REPRODUCTIVE CHARACTERISTICS

WILD turkey hens usually breed as yearlings, but some have their first eggs as two-year-olds. The gobblers almost always take two years to mature sexually. Turkeys have only one brood a year. The number of eggs laid averages about 11, but may range from 8 to 17. Clutches below 8 are probably due to some mishap; those above 17 are likely to be the product of two hens.

The sex ratio at the breeding season is apt to be unbalanced; there are frequently from two to four hens for every mature gobbler, sometimes more. This is mainly due to the variation in the breeding age of the sexes. A corollary of this condition is the habit of the old gobbler to have a "harem," a group of hens that regularly come to him for breeding. And the bird seems naturally polygamous.

There is very little infertility of first clutch eggs. When nests are destroyed another clutch may be laid, but renesting is usual only when the first nest is broken up early in the incubation period. Second clutches are smaller than the first ones, and infertility is often high.

The average clutch requires about 16 days to lay; incubation then takes 28 days.

The reproductive potential of the wild turkey is moderately high; not as high as that of most gallinaceous birds, but considerably higher than that of some of the game birds (such as the woodcock and the mouring dove). Given reasonable success with its breeding, the turkey can maintain good populations and provide a lot of hunting. The turkey scarcity is due to the environment and bad management, not to the bird.

MORTALITY CAUSES

THE determination of causes and degrees of mortality is difficult with any wild species, but it is specially so with the turkey. Its generally sparse numbers, shy habits, and the difficult terrain of its habitat combine to make turkey studies generally unproductive of accurately measurable data; yet a fair idea of what happens to turkeys can be pieced together from information available from the many studies of the bird that have been carried on in recent years.

Half or more of the clutches fail to hatch, according to observers in Alabama, Virginia, Missouri, and the Southwest. It is probable that these losses are actually higher than the true average for wild nests, because many of those recorded were lost due to disturbances by the observers themselves. For example, of 40 nests noted by

Mosby and Handley (1943), 21 were lost, and 12 of these by desertion after the hen had been flushed. Similarly, of 29 nests studied by Dalke, Leopold, and Spencer (1946), 18 were lost, six of them by desertion. Half of all the nests studied by Glover and Bailey (1947) in West Virginia were abandoned. So it is clear that the turkey hen is very intolerant of disturbance while she is incubating. Mosby and Handley (1943) turned up an interesting sidelight on this point; they found that "native" birds deserted much more readily than did captivity-reared hens that had been stocked. This is natural, since the game-farm birds were somewhat accustomed to man, and were not as easily upset by having a man discover their nest. On the other hand the game-farm setting hens (in the wild) suffered greater nest loss from predation than did the native birds, which indicated a greater resourcefulness on the part of the truly wild birds in dealing with natural enemies.

Man appears to be the worst nest destroyer of all. Not only are many nests abandoned after discovery, but others are lost by the trampling of domestic livestock, being run over by mowing machinery, burned, and disturbed by lumbering; in most parts of its range man is generally responsible for more than half the loss of turkey nests. Natural enemies of many kinds combine to take the next largest toll. Rarely is any one species very destructive, but all taken together may do significant damage. A few nests are lost from flooding, lightning fires, and cold weather.

The survival of the hatched poults follows about the same course as with the young of other gallinaceous game birds. About half of them— or usually slightly less—reach maturity in autumn in the normal years, and far fewer in occasional bad years. The major cause of death seems to be exposure to the elements, especially during the first few weeks after hatching. Ligon (1946) notes that this is particularly true at high altitudes, where rain is apt to be accompanied by low temperatures. A few are taken by predators, but not enough to be of any account.

Analysis of the losses of adult turkeys is complicated by the fact that in much of the range game-farm birds are added to the population each year by stocking. These birds are far less secure than the native stock, and their mortality is exceedingly high. It is therefore difficult to evaluate the evidence for *real* wild turkeys.

In observing turkeys through the winter in eastern West Virginia, Glover (1948) found that their losses amounted to from 30% to 80% of the fall population in the six areas he studied. These areas were all either refuges or controlled hunting areas where turkeys were protected though some of the losses were probably from legal hunting around the areas. Glover attributed most of the decline to starvation; only a few instances of predation were found, even when the flocks were in poor condition from lack of food. Food supplies were exceptionally poor during this period, hence the high losses on some of the areas may have been abnormal. It is entirely likely, though, that the normal losses of turkeys from fall to spring that come about from hunting, predation, and starvation will be over half the fall population. This will be more true of areas where many game-farm birds are stocked, for they succumb to both enemies and starvation more readily than do the natives.

LIFE EQUATION

A BALANCE sheet of gains and losses through the year—the "life equation"—of such an erratic bird as the turkey is bound to be merely an example of what a turkey population might be expected to do under imagined conditions. Table 9 exhibits such an example, accounting for one hundred turkeys and their progeny from one spring to the next, over a year in which they exactly maintained their numbers. In other years all details of this accounting might be very different.

FLUCTUATIONS IN POPULATIONS

THE long-time trend in turkey populations has been downward. In the last decade this downward trend has been stopped in many areas, and in a few places has actually been reversed. This

		NUMBER OF TURKEYS	
TIME	ACTIVITIES	young	adults
SPRING	(1) 33 males mate 67 females		100
	(2) Two-thirds of females nest, av. 11 eggs 50 × 11 = 550 eggs laid		
	(3) Half of first nests hatch or 275 eggs; of which 6 are infertile (2%); 12 die in shell (4%); 257 hatch (av. 10.3)	257	
	(4) One-fifth of females losing first nests renest, laying 35 eggs, of which half are destroyed, or 18 eggs; 6 are infertile; 3 die in shell; 9 hatch	266	
	(5) 15 adults die from predation, etc. (15% of over-wintering birds)		85
SUMMER	(6) 4 adults die from accidents, etc. (5% of spring survivors)		81
	(7) 133 poults die from exposure, etc. (50%), and 133 survivors become adults (about 60% of adults are birds of the year)		214
FALL	(8) 45 die from hunting: 31 legal kill (14%); 4 cripples (2%); 10 illegal kill (5%)		169
WINTER	(9) 69 die from starvation, predation, etc. over fall and winter (32% of adult fall population), leaving		100

TABLE 9
LIFE EQUATION OF 100 TURKEYS FOR A YEAR (AN EXAMPLE)

These 100 birds, which may again be 33 males and 67 females, survive to begin another breeding season.

gives rise to some hope that the species need not be exterminated or reduced to mere remnants throughout most of its range. Apart from the gradual decline since colonial times, there have no doubt been times when the drop in numbers was much more rapid than in others. The loss of the chestnut in the Eastern states may have speeded up the reduction in turkey numbers in some areas, though the turkey decline generally came first.

The annual changes in population make a jagged up-and-down line that runs along the gradual decline curve when represented graphically. The life line jumps up steeply with each new hatch of young birds, then drops more gradually—but still rather steeply—through the year until reproduction provides another in-crement. In a good breeding and brooding year the peak of that year's graph will go very high compared to the average; and years of mast failure and hard winters will correspondingly show lower than average troughs in the line as it passes the winter period. These annual changes are to be expected, but the gradual lowering of the peak points illustrates the growing danger.

These annual changes reflect the yearly variations of weather and food conditions more than anything else. But the long-time trend toward decline is a measure of the lowering carrying capacity of the habitat due to lumbering, farming, and other man's activities. There is no evidence that the turkey follows any regular cycles of abundance.

It is difficult to estimate the numbers of turkeys per square mile that lived on good range back in the 18th and early 19th centuries; the accounts of great numbers by early writers did not measure them in relation to the area of land that they occupied. They were more likely to express the great abundance of the birds by comments such as " . . . at the beginning of the 19th century turkeys were so abundant that they sold for six cents apiece, though the largest ones, weighing from twenty-five to thirty pounds, sometimes brought a quarter of a dollar" (Judd, 1905). Still, there is no doubt that turkeys were abundant then compared with now. One could well believe that there may have been a turkey per ten acres on optimum range in good years—ten times the numbers present on good range today in the best years.

Examination of available information on present-day turkey populations over their whole remaining range indicates an average of about a bird per square mile or slightly more—say one for about every 500 acres. This of course includes much poor range. On the best portions of their habitat, the present populations may run from about 2 to 8 birds per square mile.

There have been a number of reasonably accurate censuses made in recent years. For example, Ligon (1946) reports an average of 2.6 turkeys per square mile in the White River and San Carlos Indian reservations in Arizona, where the birds have been well treated in late years. On 2,460 square miles of the White River reservation, which he considers to have something like a "normal" population, there are about 6 per square mile. In Missouri, where the range has been very badly treated, Dalke, Leopold, and Spencer (1946) gave the average density of turkeys as 0.6 bird per square mile, with about double that number on the best sixth of the range and 1.6 birds per square mile in the best township. On one 4,600-acre refuge the turkeys numbered 20.4 per square mile in the spring of 1945.

In Virginia the average for the entire range of over 13,000 square miles was given by Mosby and Handley (1943) as 1.7 per square mile. In the best segment (58 square miles) it was 2.9 birds for each square mile. On four managed areas of 10,000 to 15,000 acres they numbered 12 to 16 per square mile. These figures are fairly typical for the nearby states of West Virginia, Maryland, and Pennsylvania too, though some fairly large sections have as many as 4 birds to the square mile. This latter figure is probably augmented somewhat by liberations of game-farm turkeys.

The Southeastern range from Florida to Louisiana seems to have somewhat lower average populations than the Eastern area, being more nearly comparable in that respect with the Missouri-Arkansas area. The numbers of turkeys on the Texas range, particularly in the Edwards plateau area, are larger than farther east, in some instances running up to about 8 birds per square mile over areas of 15,000 to 20,000 acres.

All these population density estimates are for fall or winter periods; they are therefore at the medium-high to the highest part of the annual population cycle. The breeding populations will average from 25% to 50% lower in most years.

It seems likely that these densities of turkey numbers which are certainly not anything to be exuberant about nevertheless reflect rather accurately the actual carrying capacities of the turkey habitat as it is today. The best of it can support only a bird for each ten to fifteen acres; the average comes closer to holding only a turkey for each square mile. The poor portions are so bad that the carrying capacity is down to a bird to a thousand or more acres. That's approaching extermination.

MANAGEMENT OF THE WILD TURKEY

The opportunity to manage the wild turkey is essentially a simple matter that calls for proper use of the land and proper behavior of the people. At the same time it is undoubtedly a most difficult thing actually to accomplish. The probability of our really doing the good things that should be done that would restore the turkey is, sad to say, very poor. Still, the fact that it is possible, and also practicable from the viewpoint of the welfare of all the people, offers some hope.

The rift between what is proper and what is actually done in handling turkey range arises from the selfishness and shortsightedness of farmers, stockmen, and lumbermen. The urge of private citizens to grab whatever quick benefits they can get from public lands "while the getting is good" and with little or no cost to themselves has caused tremendous harm to turkey range on National Forests and other public grazing lands. This easy-money fever has not lessened appreciably today, though it must be said that the conservation agencies and interests are fighting it more successfully than formerly. The "open range" grazing system that is still practiced to a considerable extent in the South and West— whether it involves public or private lands—is more of the same; it is manifestly impossible to have proper management of land when everybody can let his domestic stock run loose on it. The record of forest owners or operators has been equally exploitive; why should an individual or even a corporation, owning a large tract of mature timber, harvest it on a sustained-yield basis for years when he can cash in and get rich quick right now by clear-cutting? Of course there is a good answer to that one; but it isn't heeded unless the owner's family or the corporation plans on operating the land for a long time; only on a long-term basis does it "pay" to handle the forest by sustained-yield principles. It is exactly such permanency of management that must come about if our forests are to be productive in private ownership. An individual has got to be willing to take his "cut" out of the woods a little at a time throughout his active career, and pass them along to the next fellow in equally productive condition.

To bring about these changes requires a great change in the attitudes and habits of people. Only by having leaders who preach this gospel can it gain a foothold. These leaders should come from every field of human activity—political, economic, social, religious. The preacher from his pulpit and the labor leader in his union meetings must show their flock the way of permanent security in natural resources just as does the conservationist. When the people understand the problem and its significance to them well enough, then they will demand and get the needed changes. Our attitudes toward the land and our habits of grazing the range and cutting the forest will evolve into a social system that will make possible a sustained yield not only of forest products and livestock forage but of wild turkeys and other indigenous wildlife as well.

The vital function of education in this development cannot be overemphasized. In the developing of a new generation of citizens fully aware of the importance of these natural resources to all the people lies the great hope of bringing with them the changes in land-use practices that will make a firm foundation of resource conservation. At this point it may be well to mention the functions of the professional conservation agencies. For education alone, however vital it is, is only half the contribution that society must make to the citizen if he is to be able to manage the resources in his care for the best benefit to himself and his community. Experience has shown consistently that if we are to get conservation on the land and keep it on the land there is need for what have been called the "action agencies" of government. These agencies of professional conservationists operate at the state and Federal levels. They work in such agencies as the state game and fish commissions and forestry departments, and the National Forest Service, Soil Conservation Service, Fish and Wildlife Service, and others. Very frequently these agencies, which help landowners to work out good conservation plans and to get these plans into operation, make their aid available through the medium of locally organized and controlled conservation districts. Over 2,600 soil conservation districts are in operation in the United States today (1954), covering about four-fifths of our farm and ranch lands, as well as numerous grazing districts, drainage districts, and other forms of local self-help groups in the conservation field. Most of these public conservation agencies also administer public lands—state forests and game lands, National Forests, National Wildlife Refuges, Taylor grazing lands, and so on. In their staffs is the know-how to do these conservation jobs. Before the land is predominantly well cared for by sustained yield management, our citizens will have to learn how to get the most help from these professionals.

The management of turkey range involves large areas of lands that are low grade from the agricultural view, especially as regards the growing of cultivated crops. Most of the turkey habitat is poor even for the grazing of domestic stock—that is, poor by comparison with highly productive pastures and range land. Much of the turkey range is either good or potentially good forest land. But even though so much of this land is marginal or worse for growing crops or livestock, much of it is now subjected to overuse for these purposes; overcropping and overgrazing are two of the basic faults in our handling of much of this land today. How are we to tell which land is suitable for growing crops, which is naturally adapted only to growing grass as its most intensive agricultural use, and which should be used only to grow trees and not for farm crops or livestock at all? The physical nature of the land itself is the essential determinant. The type of soil it has, its topography, and the amount of good soil that is left after erosion and soil-mining —these are the elements of its physical capability for sustaining agriculture. An analysis of these factors is the only sound basis on which proper land-use determinations can be made.

Inventorying land as to its capabilities for use has been pioneered by the U. S. Soil Conservation Service. The procedure is to map the distinguishing features of the land on aerial photographs by means of field surveys made by "conservation surveyors" trained for this purpose. The soil type, as recognized by the soils scientists, which gives basic origin, nature, depth, structure, and inherent productiveness of the soil, is the first item mapped. Then the character of the topography, the erosion condition, and the present land use are shown. Finally, interpretations of all the combinations of the soil, topography, and erosion condition are made; these are based on experience in dealing with these conditions under various kinds of land use. These interpretations are called "land use capabilities," and are classified in eight major divisions; on the maps they are colored to facilitate their use. Classes I to IV are lands capable of use for growing crops, with more and more intensive need for conservation practices in Classes II, III, and IV respectively. Classes V and VI are suitable for use as pasture or range grassland but not for cultivation. Class VI requires more intensive conservation treatment than Class V. Class VII is adapted best for growing forests, but is sometimes suited for grazing on a limited basis. Finally, Class VIII is composed of areas often suited to use for wildlife habitat but not good for producing forests, crops, or grass. (See Table 3, page 42.)

The crux of our problem with turkey range will largely concern the land-use Classes VI and VII. One can be used for grazing domestic stock with proper conservation practices—Class VI land. The other should not generally be used for grazing, but for the growing of trees and the accompanying wildlife crops. By means of a physical inventory of the land, which depicts the location and extent of these different kinds of land, the right determination can be made for their use. Turkey range, by and large, will be made up of Class VII land with a considerable interspersion of Class VI land. Small amounts of Classes I to V will be found in fertile valleys. The problem then is to get the crop areas confined to the lands to which they are really suited, the livestock limited to Class VI lands (or better) and *off* the Class VII and VIII lands. When this is done we shall have a proper land-use pattern, and one that is conducive to producing turkeys as a by-product of the major kinds of land use.

The next step is to apply the adapted and needed conservation practices to each kind of land. The combination—proper land use and needed conservation practices—will provide the best possible habitat.

A general limiting factor in developing turkey range—one that is over and above the questions of land use and conservation practices—is the limited tolerance of the bird for interference by man. Hence areas that are smaller than 10,000 acres of contiguous cover with relatively little human activity are not suitable for developing as turkey range, even though the land itself is right; 20,000 acres or more are better.

LAND-USE PRACTICES

WE have now discussed the first essential for developing satisfactory turkey populations: having all the different kinds of land in the range devoted to a major use consistent with its inherent capabilities. We have noted that the opportunities for developing good turkey numbers will be limited to areas having a minimum of 10,000 to 20,000 acres of contiguous cover of the type they need with little interference in the area by man. These conditions met, the next step is to assure several general conditions on the land that may be termed land-use practices.

The first of these concerns *fire*. The need here is a negative one: the land should *not* be burned. This applies especially to forests and grasslands in turkey range. None of the reasons why people burn the woods or range grasslands are valid. Whether their idea is to control ticks, stimulate new green growth, or just for the heck of it, it is wrong; it does not accomplish any beneficial objectives they may have in mind. It destroys game cover and forest reproduction, and reduces the valuable vegetative litter on the soil that is needed to maintain the soil and to hold water in it. The elimination of grass and forest fires will come about mainly through successful education. It must be backed up by adequate fire-control laws, and also by a fire-fighting system that will keep the damage from fires to a reasonable minimum. This castigation of burning the land does not of course apply to the proper use of fire as a tool in land management; there are some situations, mainly in certain forest types in the Southeastern states, where prescribed and controlled burning is a practice good both for game and forestry.

Controlled grazing is the next necessary land-use practice. Not only should domestic stock be confined to grazing areas that are suitable for this use, but they should be limited in numbers to the number of head ("animal units" is the more precise term, one cow being one animal unit, smaller animals less) per acre that the condition of the range can well support. This will vary at different seasons of the year, and the numbers of stock on pasture or range should be adjusted accordingly. The development of stock water facilities to distribute grazing intensity evenly is often needed. If the grazing intensity by domestic animals is within the "carrying capacity" of the range, then the grassland will be maintained in a continually productive condition—which includes the growth of the grasses, legumes, and forbs that make grassland suitable feeding areas for wild turkeys.

The harvesting of forest trees on a sustained-yield schedule is the next essential land-use practice, if a framework is to exist within which we can expect to maintain reasonable turkey numbers. Only through systematic, long-term, small-unit-per-year rotation of cuttings can the needed turkey habitat types be maintained with anything like dependability. Not only will this assure that the different needed forest types can exist, but that they will probably be arranged with good interspersion—a matter of great importance to the quality of turkey habitat. Regardless of the details of the silviculture of the forest harvest—which we shall discuss later—this pattern of sustained yield of the wood products is the only system that can offer continuously good turkey cover.

Proportions of major land uses in a section of turkey range will determine to a considerable extent its carrying capacity for the birds. Ten thousand acres of continuous hardwood forest, or of grassland, or of coniferous forest, will be poor turkey range even though it is high quality habitat of that one type. All three types (hardwoods, conifers, grasses) must be available within the movement area of individual turkey flocks. This distribution of grassland and forest can hardly be decided for the benefit of wild turkeys except on areas of refuges or game preserves where the turkey is the primary crop. It is well, however, to recognize the importance of interspersion in order to decide what areas of potential turkey range are most suitable for management. As a general rule, good turkey range should consist of from 50–70% of oak hardwood forest, from 15–30% of coniferous forest, and about 15–20% of grassland. Interspersion of these three types so that these proportions apply within most 10,000-acre units is important. Some water is needed, scattered throughout the range, and a small amount of cropland is tolerable. When the land-use pattern fits this scheme, when all the land is being properly used, it is apt to be suited to good turkey management. To the extent that it diverges from this pattern, to that degree is it likely to be less suited for turkeys.

HABITAT DEVELOPMENT

Providing Food for the Turkey. The turkey obtains its food from all three of its essential cover types: hardwood forest, coniferous forest, and forest openings that are usually grasslands. (The mixed forest cover type is a hybrid between two of these, and provides the same vegetation as they do but in different combination.) Of these, the coniferous forest is relatively unimportant as a source of food compared to the other two. Thus the development of turkey food supplies will involve, first, the silviculture of the hardwood forest, and second, the care of the forest openings, whether grassland or other.

All three levels of the hardwood forest include food plants that contribute products eaten by turkeys. Trees ripen mast and fruits in the crown canopy, the shrubs and vines of the understory add more fruit to the food supply, and the ground-cover plants provide greens and seeds. The understory and ground cover are managed by protection—excluding domestic livestock from the forest—and by manipulating light filtering through the crown by cutting. Thus the cutting system used will not only determine the character of the crown canopy of the forest but also that of the understory and ground cover.

The most vital food supply from the trees is the mast crop, largely acorns from the oaks. The acorn yield is at best an erratic crop, depending much on the weather, about which we can do nothing. But there are two other almost equally important determinants: the age of the trees, and the variety of species. Young oaks produce few acorns; the forest must have a good proportion of mature trees if it is to yield ample mast for turkeys. Since the age of trees in the stand depends on the cutting cycle, it is by the lumbering plan that provision can be made for the needed amount and distribution of mature oak stands. As an example, a 1,000-acre lumbering unit handled on a 100-year cycle with a 50-acre cutting every five years would give a stand half over 50 years old, one-quarter over 75 years old, and half of the younger trees all the time, once it was in full swing. It would be easy to arrange this cutting sequence so as to have excellent interspersion of the age classes. Of course, whether a cutting is ready or not in a 100-year-old stand depends on the growing capacities of the site; actually the length of the full cutting cycle must be varied according to the time required to grow a marketable log. What, then, is the diameter of this stem? It should be 18 inches or more in diameter at breast height; a minimum for expedient cutting would be at least 14 inches. It is unfortunate that too much cutting of secondgrowth forests today is below these limits of efficiency, which is one of the reasons so much of our woodland is in bad shape. Any qualified forester can prove the sound economics of the longer cycle—but too often mere man will not wait. On our ability to evolve a system whereby the owner can operate on a long cutting cycle depends not only the welfare of the forest but of some of its valuable by-products like the turkey.

To sum up this matter of the age class of the

oak forest: probably at least one-quarter of the stand should be of a diameter class of 14 inches or larger; and half of this should be above 18 inches. On such a basis the forest would have the trees that can produce mast for turkeys and other forest game.

The oak-mast crop varies also according to the species of oak; rarely do all species have a good crop at once; it is also seldom that they all fail at once. To the extent that the forest has a good mixture of the better oaks—white, northern red, gambel (West), chestnut, pin, post, and black—it has the best possible chance of producing a good crop of mast every year. Here we have another instance of the wisdom of not "placing all our eggs in one basket"—of having a variety of sources of acorns so that one or more is sure to be productive each year. Developing an oak forest ideally constituted with this variety is not easy. But we can choose areas for intensive turkey management that already have the necessary diversity. On game management areas we can also affect the composition of the stand over a period of years by leaving the kinds we want and removing the others.

Along with the oaks there are other valuable mast and fruit trees that may also be favored to advantage. The Western piñon and ponderosa pines will be found mostly in the coniferous forest, but the majority of the food producers will be in the hardwoods. Some of them, like the ash, black cherry, and hickories, may also be valuable lumber trees. Others may be "fillers" or low grade lumber species, like the beech, gums, and flowering dogwood. They all have a place in a well-managed forest, and can be given particular attention in the planning of cuttings on public lands and game preserves. As with the oaks, these trees must be mature to produce their mast and fruit crops. The fruit species will be most useful where they can get the most sunlight, preferably along the forest edge or in a stand of younger trees.

The forest openings will likely be of two widely different kinds. We have given a good deal of attention to grasslands as a type of forest open-ing or component of turkey range, but we must also give due attention to the brushy type of opening. This may be a natural shrub association like an alder thicket, or it may be an early stage in woody plant succession resulting from a forest clear-cutting or the abandonment of farmland. Both are much needed by turkeys, and are used for somewhat the same purposes.

Many of the elements of brushy cover are valuable food sources. Wild grapes, blueberries, huckleberries, brambles, sumacs, greenbriers, dogwoods, haws, and others are producers of fruit much sought by turkeys. Most of these are natural components of this stage of plant succession; and can be induced simply by cutting openings in the forest to let sunlight hit the forest floor without interruption. The blueberries, huckleberries, and some others are stimulated by burns. Patch-burning of the slash from lumbering will aid these shrubs. Rarely will planting of shrub seedlings be justified for turkey food, and rarely will it be successful anyway. The development of brush cover along woodland edges of farm fields on game preserves might be an exception to this general rule; here some species of shrubs can be planted to good advantage for turkeys and other kinds of game as well.

Greens and seeds eaten by turkeys come largely from grasslands and other open fields. Some of these are the produce of good pasture or range plants, and will be available to turkeys if the grass is kept in good condition and not overgrazed. Thus the bluegrass, blue grama, and some of the muhlenbergias and panicums are examples of species useful to both the turkey and domestic stock. Certain other open field foods are weeds that are either evidence of poor sod on the range or are a by-product of tillage; examples are crabgrass, ragweed, and sunflower. Still other sources of turkey food are crop plants, including corn, wheat, and buckwheat.

The best management of grasslands for turkeys is also the best way to handle it for domestic stock. Develop good range by limiting the number of livestock to its carrying capacity at all seasons; rotate the use of the range so that it will have adequate "rest" periods; reseed when needed with the best grass-legume seed mixtures for the area; and fertilize where the natural mineral elements are leached out. Providing water at scattered places on the range will help distribute grazing evenly. Some Eastern pastures require only lime and fertilizer treatments to bring in wild white clover and other desirable plants. The turkeys inhabiting an area that includes such well-managed grassland will take advantage of it for feeding and other purposes.

The provision of food for turkeys on public lands or game preserves may be made by plantings in crop fields adjacent to forest cover; the grains mentioned above—corn, wheat, and buckwheat—are among the best. Nutgrass (chufa) is also useful for turkey-food plantings in the Southeastern states (planted by tubers). Clovers, Korean lespedeza, vetch, and tall oat grass are desirable species to establish as "hay" type feeding areas for the turks. These foods are adequate and probably as good as any; but it should be noted that a good many other kinds have been recommended for turkey-food plantings by various competent authorities. These include soybeans, cowpeas, winter oats, velvet beans, peanuts, German millet, and sorghums. Food patches should be a mixture of a few suitable food plants; they are more useful in several small plots—about one to five acres is ideal—than in one large one. Both winter cover-crop types for greens and annual seed or tuber producers should be used. Proximity to good protective cover is very important in selecting sites. Good soils only should be used for this purpose, and all the usual cultural practices, like seedbed preparation, liming, fertilization, and cultivation, should be followed just as though the food patch were a farm crop.

Providing Good Shelter for Turkeys. Having good shelter in the turkey's habitat presupposes the same general conditions of proper land-use practices that have been discussed. The restriction of the grazing of domestic stock to good grassland, the prevention of fires on the land—

particularly the forest in so far as shelter is concerned—and the policy of a sustained-yield harvest of forest crops—these are the essential framework for having good cover, both as to its food and shelter aspects.

Protective shelter—the vegetation that enables the turkey to escape from its enemies and comfortably to survive bad weather—is mainly in the coniferous forest and brushy openings; to the extent that the lumbering system provides good distribution of enough of these cover types of high quality will the turkey have the shelter it needs. Other cover needs, as for nesting, courtship, sunning, and so on, we may presume will be adequate if the more exacting requirements of protective cover are met.

Much of the pure hardwood forest that now composes the turkey's range contained in its original condition a considerable mixture of conifers. The conifers have been eliminated from much of these forests through lumbering, and because of their natural inability to succeed themselves under many forest conditions. It is difficult to get them back, especially if no seed trees are left. In forests that still have a good mixture of conifers, lumbering methods should provide for the leaving of a suitable number of seed trees rather than taking them all out. On game preserves, where effort may be justified for improving the cover, conifer seedlings may be planted in prepared plots in forest clearings and along natural edges; in the Eastern states the white pine and the spruces are best adapted for this purpose. Such plantings must be protected from close hardwood competition for a number of years after planting, by means of scarifying the planting site or by releasing the conifers through cutting or poisoning the competing hardwoods.

When land use is adjusted to the natural adaptabilities of the land, there are frequently many areas retired from farming or grazing to woodland use. Sometimes the mere protection of such areas from domestic stock will be sufficient to enable nature to reforest them with a good mixture of trees and shrub species. Where good seed trees of desirable species are not at hand, or where for psychological reasons it is desirable to have the landowner plant trees, reforestation is recommended. Such tree plantings are made up mostly of coniferous species, especially in the Eastern states. The species used and the establishment techniques will be those in standard use in the area; but in so far as there is choice of conifers to favor the turkey the hemlock, white pine, loblolly pine, piñon pine, ponderosa pine, and the spruces are preferred.

In the planning for the development of coniferous forest in the turkey habitat, a general objective of between 15% and 30% of the total forest in this type is about the best. Distribution of the conifer units is equally important; it is far better to have small units of conifer woods, or a good mixed conifer-hardwood stand, in every square mile, than to have many thousands of acres on one unit and no more for many miles. But coniferous cover will almost always contain *some* hardwoods; it will not usually be *pure* conifers. Thus the mixed stand serves this same purpose, provided that the conifer portion is well represented—say one-quarter or more of the whole, and with both mature and young trees in sufficient numbers to offer both roosting shelter and near-the-ground shelter.

Openings in the forest (except grasslands or farm fields, previously discussed) that serve the turkeys' needs can be made as a by-product of the lumbering system. These brushy areas will be small and well scattered if single-tree or group-selection cutting is followed. They will be of relatively little use to the turkey unless the group system is used, and the groups of trees harvested leave a slashing of half an acre or more; larger unit cuttings will offer still better brushy cover if they are well distributed. These units should not take on the nature of large-scale clear-cutting operations, however; and should not exceed 40 or 50 acres even on very large areas of operation.

On game preserves and public forests managed for a high game crop, cuttings can be made deliberately for the purpose of creating openings.

They will serve all the forest-game species, especially deer, grouse, and rabbits, hence can be justified on a broader base than just turkey management. Such cuttings, generally made in units of one or two acres, should be planned on a rotation that will provide a good distribution of them at all times. The rotation should be long enough so that at least low-grade wood products can be obtained from them on recuttings; this would be a minimum of 25 years. The number and extent of management clearings will depend partly on the natural deficiency of such openings; if they are entirely lacking, up to 5% or more of the woods may be used in these cuttings; otherwise they should be placed where the deficiency is greatest. Spacing should be at least a tenth of a mile from other cuttings or from natural openings. The shape may be varied to take advantage of conditions of cover or topography, to retain valuable food-tree stands, cover patches, avoid steep slopes, etc. Part of the slash should be piled over a few high stumps and left; the rest should be burned on scattered spots to help induce the germination of such plants as blueberry, pin cherry, blackberry, and others that follow such burns.

Improvements in the distribution of openings in the forest can be made by taking advantage of the natural breaks that man has made for various purposes. Roads and trails should be kept well brushed out, both to maintain the passageway and to keep the best possible opening for game use. Old orchards, sawmill sites, log landings, and abandoned camps can be prevented from returning to continuous forest if the invading trees are kept cut back. In some cases the maintenance of some of these openings will be easier, and the turkey food furnished may be increased, if the clearings are seeded to an adaptable grass-legume mixture that will maintain itself with only occasional reseeding.

WATER SOURCES NEEDED BY TURKEYS

THE turkey's need for water all the year cannot be met merely by the succulence of its foods; the soft fruits, tender greens, and soft-bodied insects that it eats will help give it the moisture needed, but drinking water is essential too. After rains and on dewy mornings water is everywhere and there is no difficulty at all; at other times, especially during periods of drouth, the turkeys have to go for water to springs, water holes, streams, or ponds. To the extent that the bird's range is well watered all is well. If there is no water for a mile from any place the birds would otherwise frequent, water may limit the use of the cover. From the management standpoint there are ways of developing these water supplies. It is generally good policy to "improve" springs anywhere in a forest or on the range. Such improvement may involve fencing to keep livestock away (and possibly piping some of the water to a tank to water the animals), avoidance of cutting trees close to the spring to keep it shaded and protected, or cleaning out to make an adequate water pool. Water holes—which are different from springs, being holes dug to expose the ground water—are valuable to forest managers for use in fire-fighting as well as for game-watering places. Low places with the ground water close to the surface are not always available at desirable intervals through a forest, but to the extent that

they are they should be dug out and cleaned annually. It is usually well to place a wood fence around these holes if they are deep or obscured by vegetation; this helps in finding them and guards against accidents.

Stream improvement that would make more dependable watering places, and the building of ponds that would add new ones, are both complicated; neither can be justified for turkey management alone. If existing streams have capabilities for improvement for trout fishing or other uses, then the need for watering places for turkeys can be added as part of the justification for this work. Similarly, if there are good locations for the building of ponds or lakes for recreation, fishing, waterfowl use, water storage, flood alleviation, or other purposes, the fact that they may help to provide needed watering places for wild turkeys and other game species may add to the justification for their construction.

WINTER FEEDING

WHILE the practice of providing grain to turkeys for emergency feeding during starvation periods is hardly a matter of habitat improvement, it is a result of habitat deficiencies, and is an effort

PLATE 26. *Winter feeding station for turkeys with corn in a wire basket.*

COURTESY PENNA. GAME COMMISSION

to give the birds the food that the habitat does not have.

At best the business of setting up and caring for winter feeding stations is a stopgap. It rarely solves any problem—the possible exception being in the *unusual* year when the mast crop fails completely even in good habitat. Under this condition it can be presumed that the reduced carrying capacity of the range is temporary, and that we are justified in trying to carry through the winter more birds than the food supplies will naturally support; if the range can support them in most years, saving some of the birds for the next breeding season may be wise. I say "may" because, even under these extreme conditions, it is doubtful if winter feeding is a practical thing to do over most of the range; it can be done only on managed areas, and on places that can be conveniently reached, and where significant numbers of turkeys will use the feed.

Game-preserve owners who want to carry more turkeys—usually game-farm birds—than their range will support, can use winter feeding to some advantage. They are dealing with semi-domesticated birds that come readily to feeding stations, and also with abnormal economic factors. They can afford it even though it is costly.

One of the troubles with winter feeding even where it can be justified is that to be effective it must be planned ahead; it has to be planned whether or not starvation emergencies do ultimately arise. It has to be carried on in token form throughout the winter, in order to have the birds accustomed to coming to the station for food, so that they will find it when the going gets tough. This means that the operation must be performed whether it is needed or not, even though the amount of feed may be rather low until emergencies arise. Here again this whole business becomes more realistic on a game preserve where more birds are being carried than natural food will support, and where the feeding program is sure to be needed all winter long.

Where winter feeding is to be undertaken, the stations should be selected and baiting started early in the winter. The sites should be close to good protective cover, preferably under conifers that will shelter the feed from the snow. The turkeys should have good visibility from the feeding place. Small amounts of feed should be placed at intervals of one or two weeks to keep them coming. Then when a starvation condition comes the amount of feed in the station should be increased to meet their needs.

Deer and squirrels may make it difficult to feed turkeys economically; but this can be overcome to some extent by feeding ear corn in wire baskets or on trays so hung that deer can't reach them, and so enclosed that squirrels can't carry the ears away. Corn is the most suitable feed.

STOCKING GAME FARM AND TRANSPLANTED TURKEYS

RESTOCKING wild turkeys to improve the population for public hunting has a small but definite place in turkey management; on game preserves where shooting just-stocked birds can be afforded, that place is bigger. Where there are existing stocks of wild turkeys, however small, there stocking is undesirable; the need is to build up these wild populations. Areas of suitable range that have been entirely depleted of turkeys, and where the cause of that depletion has been removed, are the places where turkey stocking can be profitable. The recommendations for restocking made here are limited to those conditions.

Where a vacant range is to be restocked, enough birds should be used so that even a high mortality rate will still give them some chance of getting established. At least twenty birds to a flock, and with at least five flocks placed in an area where the survivors can get together for breeding and re-flocking later, is suggested. This should be continued for at least five years. Only the best quality of birds should be used; preferably wild birds that have been trapped on some sections of range where they are abundant enough to justify their removal. If wild-trapped turkeys are not available, game-farm birds that have been grown from eggs laid by high quality hens mated with wild toms can be used. More harm than good will come of stocking inferior turkeys raised in captivity.

For management purposes, turkey trapping has been done mostly in the South and Southwest. A log pole or a pole and wire trap may be used; in West Virginia a cage made of poles and wire with a drop front has been most effective (Handley, letter). Regardless of the type of trap, the trapping site should be in a place where food is scarce but where turkeys are near enough to be baited to the place. It is best done in late winter, when baiting is most effective. After the flock is accustomed to feeding at the selected spot, the trap is set up there. A standard pole trap is described by Ligon (1946a) as 10 feet wide, 12 feet long, 3½ feet high, and made of poles and posts from three to six inches in diameter. Openings three feet square are placed in each end, and an underpass dug under each about 12 inches wide and 16 inches deep. The openings may be closed by manually operated drop- or pull-gates, or provided with funnel entrances. Such traps are time-consuming to build, their use tends to injure captured birds, and they are not very portable. They are effective in catching a few turkeys at a time, but not for getting a whole flock at once.

Sylvester and Lane (1946) describe a box-shaped net trap about 15 by 20 feet and 6 feet high with drop-door ends. Netting traps are likely to be badly damaged by deer. If wire netting is used the turkeys often suffer injury. But, since it is generally best to operate any of these traps from a blind, the skill of the operator is most important in making the trap work satisfactorily. Trapped turkeys should be disturbed as little as possible when being caught by hand nets and placed in crates for transporting; they should be caught as quickly as possible after the springing of the trap.

No time should be lost in transferring the trapped birds to new territory. They can be carried in crates lined with burlap. Liberation should be made quietly in a forest clearing, and early in the morning if at all possible.

Game-farm turkeys of the highest possible quality may be used for stocking vacant range where transplanting of wild birds cannot be done. Even at best these birds are a poor substitute for really wild turkeys, but some are worth using. Game-farm hens should be wild birds, or at least the pedigreed progeny of truly wild turkeys. They are placed in a large wild-land enclosure in the spring, where they can be mated by wild toms flying in through the open top of the enclosures. The eggs are collected, and raised in incubators and brooders until the poults are able to stand the weather; then they are transferred to hardening pens of considerable size located in woodland. The young toms may well be stocked when they are 12 to 16 weeks old; the hens are better kept until early spring, for release just ahead of the breeding season.

PREDATOR CONTROL

SINCE predation is a minor factor in determining turkey numbers, special efforts to reduce the populations of any predatory species to favor the turkey are unnecessary. This conclusion is apart from the practical impossibility of really "controlling" the potentially destructive kinds anyway. But this does not at all mean that certain predators should not be reduced by practical means. Most of the animals that can take turkeys are fur bearers, and should be trapped during the prime-pelt season. Some, like the coyote, that have furs so poor that trapping does not pay, will usually be trapped anyway to reduce damage to domestic stock (whether or not it really does reduce this damage is doubtful, but that is beside the present point). Crows that occasionally take turkey eggs should be hunted for sport to the greatest extent that the sportsmen will undertake. Not that it will certainly help the turkey; but at least it will furnish good shooting, and it will not hurt the crow population enough to measure. Hawks and owls are too insignificant in turkey ecology to be concerned about, except the great horned owl; special efforts may be needed to reduce horned owls on areas of vacant turkey range prior to stocking.

For the most part you can add it all up, and

there is only one sensible answer to the problem of turkey predators: that is, forget it. If you have energy or money to spend on behalf of the turkey it will be much better spent on some other form of aid.

PROTECTION AGAINST OVERSHOOTING

IT would not be a fair appraisal to say that hunting has been the most serious limiting factor on turkey numbers. On the other hand, the turkey is one species of upland game bird that is so vulnerable to man's weapons under present-day conditions that we cannot pass off hunting problems as being secondary; there is little doubt that in many areas hunting, both legal and poaching, is effective in reducing fall turkey numbers below what should be allowed. How then can we control this hunting?

Laws Relating to the Turkey. A good framework of laws is the first essential to limiting the kill of turkeys. Areas that contain only remnant populations should have no open hunting season at all; and newly stocked range where you are trying to re-establish the turkey should also be protected from hunting. It is best that they be refuges for a time. On the rest of the range the restrictions on hunting should be gauged to the ability of the population to "take" the anticipated hunting pressure. Fortunately, hunting restrictions on turkeys are popularly acceptable. An individual bird is enough of a prize so that the limit can be cut to one a day—or even one a season, if needed—with the acquiescence of most hunters. The sexes are distinguishable; hence the law can protect the females (and young males too), if that is desirable. The turkey is a big enough target to warrant the use of rifle-shooting in terrain in which rifle-shooting may be permitted. Thus a minimum of hunting could be provided by a short season in the fall for one turkey a day and a limit of one also for the season, to be taken only with a rifle. Where the abundance of turkeys permits, the season may be lengthened up to as much as a month, the permissible weapons can include shotguns, and the daily and seasonal limit can be increased. As a

general rule, restrictions should be directed toward the continued prospering of the turkey.

The laws that govern the hunting of the turkey in any state in any year should be based on the advice of qualified game managers in the game commission, and should be set by the administrative action of the agency rather than by legislation. The advice given by the game experts should be based on a census of the turkey population, made by whatever means they have available to obtain an estimate of the numbers of the birds. In Virginia and Missouri this has been done by questionnaires (Dalke, 1943). The system followed is to obtain estimates of the numbers of turkeys in a given unit of range from natives who know that country intimately. By the cross-checking of these figures untruths can be spotted and dropped. This method would be worthless with most game species, but because of the large size of the turkey and the special interest in the bird it seems feasible.

The Poaching Problem. The illegal hunting of turkeys is a very serious problem in some parts of its range, and it is a very difficult one to combat. Poaching is practiced mostly by natives—folks who live in scattered houses in the semi-wilderness areas inhabited by turkeys. For this reason it is almost impossible to enforce the laws by apprehending them. The answer usually given to this dilemma is "education"—the idea being that if the youngsters are taught conservation they will become law-abiding. It is also hoped—rather piously, to be sure—that this education will somehow reach the adults, and that it will win out over their long ingrained habits.

To begin with, it should be recognized that these people by and large do not consider it wrong to take these game birds (or other game either), even though they may be aware that it is against the law; they simply think the law is wrong, or does not apply to them. In any case, they consider it right to do as they think best in such matters. Thus strict law enforcement will not solve the trouble, even if the violators could be apprehended. It is doubtful if the ordinary educational methods will be effective for a long time either. These people are strong leader followers; they get their guidance from the advice and example of these natural leaders, those who, through their lifetimes, develop those qualities that cause others to follow them. Though they hold no titled or elective office, they still set the habit pattern for the community. Only by reaching those leaders and selling them on the wisdom of the game laws can we bring about a quick change in local attitudes. This is not easy, but the social scientists do have techniques for tackling such problems. If the conservationists who deal with this matter will utilize the methods of social science to influence these indigenous leaders, they have some chance of reducing the illegal kill of turkeys, and thus enable the birds to make a better showing in those sections of its range.

Refuges. The turkey responds well to the protection afforded by refuges—that is, areas of good range set aside where no hunting or other molestation is permitted. We have already noted that it is almost essential to create an effective sanctuary in any area of unoccupied range where it is desired to re-establish the turkey. The setting aside refuges in any public forests where turkeys are an important game species is expedient and recommended.

Because of the wide-ranging habits of the turkey, it is necessary that refuges to be effective be very large. Whereas a few acres will be helpful to rabbits and quail, and a few hundred will often suffice for waterfowl, it takes thousands of acres in a block to provide a suitable protected area for the turk. The authorities have varied in their opinions on the desirable size for turkey refuges, which reflected in part the differences in the types of range with which they were dealing. Mosby and Handley (1943) recommended areas of " . . . a few hundred to several thousand acres . . . " in Virginia, and Kozicky and Metz (1948) subscribe to the same for Pennsylvania, adding that several 500-acre refuges are better than a single one of 3,000. I subscribe to this view too; but I believe that units as small as 500 acres must be very well placed to be effective. In contrast to these small Eastern refuges, recom-

mendations for turkey refuges in the South and West are much larger. Stoddard (1936) called for "Sanctuaries of 20,000 acres to a hundred thousand and upward . . . in the early stages of a restoration program." Glover and Bailey (1947) say that at least 10,000 acres in a unit is needed in West Virginia. Blakey (1937) recommends at least a township for Missouri, which is about 23,000 acres. The highest population of the Merriam's turkey in Arizona is on a reservation of some two million acres (Ligon, 1946).

It is evident that the turkey needs a lot of room to prosper. Large reserved areas of this type present many problems of administration. Generally they should be confined to public lands, which somewhat limits their placement, since all large areas of public land are interspersed with private holdings. Just the job of labeling such areas so that the public can conveniently obey the rules is quite a job. But there is another angle to this refuge matter that cannot properly be neglected—a biological one. The turkey is not alone among the game species on most of its range; there will be grouse and other game birds, and deer and other game mammals. If we protect the turkey and keep the hunters out of the refuge, then we lose all the possible hunting that the other game birds and mammals could provide. The others—at least the ruffed grouse and white-tailed deer—do not need the protection of the refuge. If any of the other game species do benefit from some hunting elimination, they certainly don't need such large areas set aside for them. But maybe we can just write off this lost hunting as part of the payment for protecting the turkey. If it were as easy as that it would indeed be simple. But we have not reckoned with the troubles that come with the protection of the white-tail. With his natural enemies (panthers, bobcats, wolves) largely gone, there is nothing left but the food supply to limit his increase; and that's just what happens. The deer increase until they are checked by starvation, accompanied by disease. The well-known problem of overpopulation of a browsing animal sets in, and the forest itself then begins to suffer; a "deer line" shows up, and tree and shrub reproduction is clipped off. The very species we set out to benefit now suffers, because its habitat is impaired. So what to do? We simply *have* to harvest the deer crop one way or another. Periodic controlled hunts is one way. Distributing the turkey refuges in smaller and more widely scattered units, like those recommended in Virginia and Pennsylvania, is another help. Most of the deer in the area of a 500- to 1,000-acre refuge can be got at by hunters using the surrounding lands. This seems to be the best compromise. And when very large turkey refuges are set up, controlled deer hunts for both sexes should be held often enough to keep the animals in check. As an example, West Virginia opens all its turkey refuges to deer hunting, which comes *after* the turkey season.

When refuges for turkeys are set up, several things should be kept in mind in deciding on their location. They should be placed where they will protect as many turkeys as possible—that is, where there are many known flocks. Private land holdings should be left out. The boundaries should be well marked, and the law prohibiting trespass strictly enforced. Qualified game managers should take an annual census of the turkeys so that changes can be made when they become advisable, such as adjustments in the refuge boundaries, the trapping of turkeys to stock new areas, deciding when controlled deer hunts are necessary. There should come a time on many turkey refuges where it may even be possible to drop the protection and permit controlled hunting.

Controlled Turkey Hunts. Since unrestricted public hunting can be so damaging to the turkey, any way that the kill can be limited to a safe figure is worth consideration. On public lands where there is local administration, and on private game preserves, carefully controlled hunts are feasible. Public-land hunts must be handled without favoritism among those who wish to participate. Since the number of those who desire such hunting always far exceeds that which can safely be authorized, the participants must be selected by

drawing lots. The game manager must estimate the probable proportion of hunters who will be successful, and base his number of permittees on that figure, related to the number of turkeys that are to be taken. Thus, if half the hunters may be expected to bag a turkey, and 500 birds can safely be taken, then 1,000 permits can be issued. Since there are always a few permittees who fail to show up, a few additional permits can be issued if the experience of the managers warrants. These hunts are managed most easily on areas that have few entrance roads; controls can then be set up at a few points with road blocks. The special permits issued for such hunts, and charged for, should clearly set forth the rules of the occasion, so that no excuses of not knowing the regulations can reasonably be offered.

A most commendable arrangement between the U. S. Forest Service and the West Virginia Conservation Commission has been set up to provide teamwork in the handling of game management and public hunting in the national forests in that state. A similar plan is in effect in Virginia in the state forests. A special hunting fee is charged for hunting in these managed forests, which goes into a fund used jointly by the two agencies to improve the habitat in the forests. It is a fine example of realistic teamwork between conservation agencies (each handling the functions that are its proper province) that makes for better game management. We could do with a lot more of it.

So we come to the end of the discussion on managing the wild turkey. And even though it is a great and difficult problem, it is fitting that we end on an encouraging note—for it *is* possible to manage the wild turkey so that its numbers may greatly increase. Mosby and Handley (1943) estimate that the habitable turkey range in Virginia can be increased by 16%—not to mention the improved numbers of birds possible over the whole range. Dalke, Leopold, and Spencer (1946) estimate that the range in Missouri *could* support 70,000 turkeys, though it now has fewer than 5,000. And Ligon (1946) says: "It is not unreasonable to assume that, with proper management, populations of the Merriam's turkey can be restored to something like former abundance on most of the natural range of this strain, and maintained at high levels." Let us encourage every citizen and group of citizens, and every public agency that can favorably influence the wild turkey and its environment, to do everything possible to bring about this management, so that this magnificent game bird may always be with us in good numbers.

CHAPTER 3

The Sage Grouse

THE family Tetraonidae, the grouses, spruce partridges, and ptarmigans, is widely represented in the United States; there are seven genera and eleven species. Of these five will be covered in this book—sage grouse, sharp-tailed grouse, greater and lesser prairie chickens, and ruffed grouse. The other six, which are omitted because of their relatively small importance as game birds in this country, are as follows: the "blue" grouses—the dusky grouse (*Dendragapus obscurus*) and sooty grouse (*D. fuliginosis*), which are by some considered to be a single species; the spruce grouses—Canadian spruce grouse (*Canachites canadensis*) and Franklin's grouse (*C. franklini*); and the ptarmigans—willow ptarmigan (*Lagopus lagopus*) and white-tailed ptarmigan (*L. leucurus*).

CLASSIFICATION

THE sage grouse is named *Centrocercus urophasianus* Bonaparte, which in Latin means "spiny-tailed pheasant." It is the only member of its genus.

DESCRIPTION

THE largest of North American grouse—the sage hen or sage chicken as it is also called—is from 21 to 30 inches long and weighs from three to seven pounds, depending on the sex. In general appearance it is a grayish-brown bird with a dark belly and long, pointed tail feathers. The sexes are similar, but the male is almost twice the size of the female.

The male bird is predominantly black on the upper body, with spots and bars of lighter colors; the wings are grayish-brown above, white beneath; the 20 tail feathers are black and gray, with brownish spots; the breast is white, with thin black streaks, and the belly is black; the top of the head is finely mottled with gray, black, and tan, which merges into gray at the back of the head; the chin is mottled black and white, with a narrow white band between it and the black throat, which has light feather tips; the neck is grayish, with long filoplumes at the side, which are white at the base, and with loose skin in front covered with scale-like white feathers. These odd feathers surround a pair of bare olive patches; the legs and tarsi are gray, and feathered to the toes, which are black; the bill is short and black; the eye has a brown iris and black pupil.

The female has the same general color pattern as the male, but is much smaller, and its colors are duller and more mottled. She lacks the neck air sacs, the scaly fore-neck feathers, and the lateral neck filoplumes. The rectrices are much shorter than in the male, averaging 7 to 8 inches, in comparison with 11 to 12 inches on the cock.

The male does not acquire full breeding plumage until his second winter. Then all colors are brighter than at other times, especially the white nuptial neck and breast feathers. He is much heavier at this time than at other seasons—a characteristic more prominent in this species than in other grouse.

The downy chicks are mottled grayish-black. The juvenile plumage is similar to that of the

COURTESY WYOMING GAME AND FISH COMMISSION

PLATE 27. *Sage grouse.*

adult hen, but is more brownish and less whitish.

GEOGRAPHICAL RANGE AND DISTRIBUTION

THE sage grouse was originally found wherever sagebrush was plentiful. This semiarid area extended from the southern edge of the prairie provinces of Canada south to the northern parts of New Mexico and Arizona, west to the eastern parts of the Pacific states, and east to western Kansas and Nebraska. The range occupied today is much more restricted, since it has been limited by livestock grazing and agriculture. According to Patterson (1952), the bird now occupies over 130 million acres of intermountain country, centering in Wyoming, Montana, southern Idaho, eastern Oregon, Nevada, western Colorado, and northern Utah. Fringes of the present range occur in southern Alberta, the southwestern corners of the Dakotas, east-central Washington, northwestern California, southern Utah, and northern New Mexico. (See Figure 10 for map.)

HISTORY OF THE SAGE GROUSE

FROM the time of the Lewis and Clark expedition in the early 19th century the settlers of the Western United States were acquainted with the sage hen. It was abundant in pioneer times, and accounts of early western writers tell of flocks of thousands of the birds being common, especially at water holes. The sage chickens were an important part of the diet of the Indians of the West, and were used to some extent by the white settlers.

The bird maintained its abundance fairly well through most of the 19th century, but toward its end there were definite signs of serious decline; the encroachment of the white man on its range became critical soon after 1900. Observers noted the dwindling of sage hen numbers, and there were predictions of impending extermination. The complete elimination of the species did happen in much of the fringe of its range, and throughout the more completely settled portions.

COURTESY SOIL CONSERVATION SERVICE, USDA

FIGURE 10. *Geographic range of the sage grouse.*

PLATE 28. *High deserts and mountain foothills are the home of the sage grouse. Wyoming's Teton Mountains are in the background.*

Human interference was the major difficulty that beset the birds. Overgrazing and burning severely damaged their cover and water holes. They were excluded from extensive areas of cultivation. Hunting contributed to the problem, but was not a very serious factor; and predation was only a secondary consideration. The drouth period in the 1930's added another major influence that resulted in the depletion of the range—for grouse and domestic stock alike. The decline in sage hens was so serious at that time that most observers thought they were in danger of early extinction, or at least reduction in numbers to the extent that the species would no longer provide hunting.

Legal hunting was stopped or very greatly reduced throughout its range. Many of the state wildlife agencies began projects to see if anything could be done for this fine bird, which up to that time had had little scientific study.

The most comprehensive of these resulted in the most definitive work on the species ever made, *The Sage Grouse in Wyoming*, by Robert L. Patterson (1952).

In the early 1940's the birds increased somewhat in numbers, but there soon followed another period of decline to an all-time low, about 1944–46. This change was short-lived, and in the last years of the decade a general increase in sage hens occurred throughout the range. These two periods of increase were not only a definite reversal of the long downward trend, but gave real hope that the species was not doomed after all; it also provided substantial evidence that the sage grouse may be cyclic, like all other American grouse. The recovery of the sage hen was aided by its protection from hunting, but it came about primarily from improved range conditions and favorable weather. The end of the era of the unrestricted grazing of public lands helped make it possible for the habitat once again to support the birds in good numbers.

The status of the species was so improved by 1949–50 that seven states had open hunting seasons. It seems quite probable that sage grouse numbers reached a peak from 1949 to 1951, and—if past evidence is confirmed—will decline again soon. Now the question is, how severe will future declines be, and will huntable populations return for a few years of each decade?

IMPORTANCE AS A GAME BIRD

SINCE 1940 all or portions of nine states have been open to sage grouse hunting in some years; seven of them had hunting seasons in 1951, as shown in Table 10; the other two, Colorado and Montana, have not permitted hunting since 1945 and 1943 respectively.

The period of hunting varied from mid-August in Nevada and Wyoming to early October in Washington. Hunters were generally very successful; the average daily bag ranged from a little over one bird per hunter in Idaho to 3½ in Nevada. The average bag in other recent years has exceeded four birds per hunter in both Nevada and Wyoming.

The number of people now participating in sage grouse hunting is almost 50,000, and they take a harvest of 70,000 to 80,000 birds in years of good populations. The opportunity for this sport is limited, and its total significance in upland game-bird hunting is rather small. Yet it is a very important game bird in Wyoming, Nevada, and Idaho, and the annual kill approaches in many counties the take of pheasants. What it lacks in volume it makes up for in distinctiveness, for there is no other game bird quite like this one. The cover in which it is hunted is also unique, for it is the only native game bird in the sage brush habitat. (The introduced chukar partridge is rapidly assuming importance in the sage lands of Nevada, Washington, and Wyoming.)

HABITS OF THE SAGE GROUSE

COURTSHIP

THE breeding season behavior of the sage grouse is among the most unusual and spectacular of all game birds. The activity centers in a *strutting ground,* which varies in size from a few hun-

TABLE 10

SAGE GROUSE HUNTING SEASONS, 1951*

STATE	LENGTH	AREA	DAILY BAG LIMIT	HARVEST
California	2 days	1 county	2	3,000
Idaho	1 "	25 counties	2	17,500
Nevada	1 "	5 "	5	18,000
Oregon	9 "	4 "	4	5,000
Utah	2 "	permits on 14 units	4	2,500
Washington	2 "	3 counties	1 per season	1,200
Wyoming	2 "	4 "	3	25,000

* Adapted from Patterson (1952).

PLATE 29. *Courtship of the sage grouse takes place on a strutting ground that may be a few hundred square feet or several acres in size. Note the hens in the center of the picture paying no attention to the performing cocks.*

dred square feet to several acres. The area is usually an exposed one, common locations being open knolls and ridges in sagebrush, open spots on level land, and alkali flats. All the cock birds from an area of several square miles gather here in the late winter and early spring. The height of the courtship period begins in mid-April and lasts three or four weeks. The full season of activity may extend up to three months, ending in late May or early June. The number of cocks using a single strutting ground may be just a few or up to 300 or 400. Late arrivals are usually immature males.

Daily activity varies with the weather and time of day; most strutting is done in the morning on clear quiet days; cold and snow have little influence on it. The mature cocks each have their individual areas on the strutting ground, while the immature males hang around the margin.

As the male starts the strutting performance, he arches his tail erect and in full spread; the rectrices form a sort of half-circle of pointed rays. He raises the filoplumes over the back of his head in a sort of open umbrella, holds his head high, inflates the air sacs part way, and carries the wings low with tips nearly on the ground. He then inhales air in gulps to complete the inflation of the air sacs, and makes a short, quick run forward. On this run the wings are moved up and down, so that the wing edges scrape the scale-like cape feathers and make a swishing noise. This action is repeated three times rapidly, and at the finish the whole air sac region of the neck is bouncing on the bird's breast. There is an accompanying resonant "plopping" sound made by the contraction of the distended neck muscles that cause the barc membranes to vibrate (Honess and Allred, 1942). According to Patterson (1952) this performance may be repeated at the height of activity 12 to 15 times per minute.

Hen birds visit the strutting grounds in the early morning when they are ready to mate, and select spots that they favor for receiving the chosen male. The more dominant males are chosen most commonly, with the result that a few cock birds do most of the mating.

NESTING

MOST females have retired to their nesting site well before the strutting season is over. Most nests are placed close to low sagebrush plants that are 10 to 20 inches in height, and in areas where the vegetation covers about half the ground surface. While nests are usually built on dry sites, they are commonly close to water courses. Nesting areas are frequently used year after year, with some exact nesting cavities occasionally reused. In favored areas nests may be only a few hundred feet apart.

The usual clutch of first eggs is seven or eight; late nests, which are not common, have usually five to six eggs. Incubation takes about 25 days, and hatching is from mid-May to mid-June.

THE BROOD PERIOD

THE hen takes complete care of the young chicks; cock birds have no association with the youngsters until the flocks begin to gather in late summer preparatory to moving to the winter range. The mother teaches her babes feeding habits, and how to escape danger when she calls a warning. When danger threatens the chicks depend more on running than flying for escape, while the mother feigns injury to draw away intruders. When this fails she attacks by flying at the enemy with loud cackling and hissing.

The family association of the sage grouse is looser than with most game birds; it is common for a chick to stray from its own group and join another brood. Some mothers thus bring up more young than they hatched.

The core of the brood habitat is sagebrush range combined with water. The latter may be streams, irrigation channels, ponds, or marshes. Irrigated or wild hay meadows are used for feeding when available. Areas having all three—sagebrush, water, and hay—often have concentrations of sage grouse broods. The water does not seem to be an absolute requirement for young broods, since some are raised with none available other than dew and succulent vegetation; but water does help to make superior brood cover.

Mortality is low during the early brood

PLATE 30. *Sage hen beside her nest. Nests are often located next to a small shrub. This species lays the smallest number of eggs of any of our grouses.*

COURTESY WYOMING GAME AND FISH COMMISSION

period, unless weather conditions are very bad; later there are losses from predation and accidents which take a considerable toll. This is partly because the family begins to disintegrate when the chicks are about eight weeks old. By early September the shuffle is complete, and the young grouse are independent of the mother. At the end of the juvenile period the contribution of the average brood to the fall flock is about 2½ birds.

The young birds do not attain full physical growth until November. The young hens become sexually mature the following spring, but the males do not reach breeding condition until very late in the spring. They do not ordinarily participate in courtship the first year.

FALL AND WINTER ACTIVITIES

Sage grouse are notably gregarious. Only during the incubation period in the spring are the hens solitary; even then they tend somewhat to nest in colonies. After the families break up in the summer, flocking begins in earnest; by midautumn the birds are gathered in groups of dozens or hundreds, and sometimes thousands. The hens and immature cocks form the biggest flocks, the adult males usually in separate groups.

The hunting of sage hens has customarily been a summer activity; even now most hunting seasons are scheduled in August and early September. This is unfortunate for both hunter and grouse. The sage grouse is typically an unwary bird in summer, and the hunter does not have as sporting a target as if hunting were in October. By then the birds are over the summer family period and have become much more sensitive to man's presence. In areas close to farms and roads the hunter kill is considerable, but in remote areas the grouse seldom see a man, and tend to keep the "fool hen" behavior all the time.

The sage grouse is among the least sedentary of all the grouse. It is not migratory in the usual sense, but most of them do travel considerable distances at certain seasons. These movements are as much altitudinal as geographical. The summer is spent at rather high elevations, where there is water available, and often ranches. As winter approaches the birds drift downward toward the valleys; winter snows force them to seek the lower elevations, where their food is not covered. These are often arid regions that would be untenable in summer. Snow makes up for the water deficiency in winter.

The adult males keep to themselves throughout the winter, and often remain at higher altitudes than the others, closer to their breeding areas.

The extent of seasonal flock movements depends on the weather. Deep snows cause the birds to make more extensive travels in winter than are made in seasons of light snow; they may move as much as a hundred miles or more in some years. Other factors that also affect their movements are the distribution of sagebrush and—except in winter—water.

Daily movements also are considerable for a gallinaceous bird. After roosting on the ground of the sagebrush prairie, the birds seek food and water in the early morning; this takes them to streams, marshes, springs, and hayfields as well as to the ever-present sagebrush. The midday is spent loafing in the high-growing sagebrush. Toward evening the birds feed again before going to roost. These daily travels may cover several hundred yards, or several miles. In summer they prefer to walk rather than fly, but at other times they make flights easily and often for great distances. Girard (1937) says they may make flights of several miles at a time at speeds up to 45 or 50 miles per hour.

ADAPTABILITY TO CHANGING ENVIRONMENT

When a species is so closely associated with a single habitat type as the sage hen is with the sagebrush prairie, and is dependent so completely on a single food source, the sagebrush, it is not surprising that it is intolerant of environmental changes. Despite the fact that the sage grouse is unable to alter its ways very much, it has made out rather well since its home was taken over by the white man. For many decades the conversion of land to agriculture was spotty, and the result not very different from the native cover; ranchers converted wild meadows into domestic hayfields, which the birds found useful as feeding grounds. Water diversion was not yet widespread. Finally the extensive overgrazing of the range caused the carrying capacity to drop for grouse, and for cattle and sheep as well. When this was corrected by law the range returned to habitable conditions. To all of these changes the birds adapted successfully.

In recent years this picture has changed greatly. Since large-scale irrigation has enabled the conversion of extensive areas to agriculture, much sagebrush has disappeared. Modern machinery has speeded this change; industrial and urban development in some places has added to it. As a result the sage hen has disappeared from hundreds of thousands of acres that it once occupied in abundance. No doubt this trend will continue, and, as Patterson (1952) says, the birds will not be able to adjust to such changes in the future any more than they have in the past. In all probability the only range that will remain for them outside of game preserves will be those areas that are not suited for conversion to agriculture.

TOLERANCE OF OTHER GAME BIRDS

SEVERAL species of game birds occupy to some degree the same range as the sage hen; yet in no instance is there any evident conflict. For the most part there is little actual competition for food, shelter, nesting sites, or other specific needs. A number of kinds of waterfowl nest in habitat used by the grouse. The ring-necked pheasant is found in irrigated farming areas, but they use little of the sagebrush land, except during nesting season and hunting seasons. Mourning doves are common in the farming areas too. Other species that may live near sage

grouse are the sharp-tailed grouse, ruffed grouse, wild turkey, chukar partridge, and Hungarian partridge. There is no evidence that any of these birds have any influence on sage grouse welfare.

ADAPTABILITY TO ARTIFICIAL PROPAGATION

THOUGH there have been small-scale trials of raising sage hens in captivity (Batterson and Morse, 1948), there is no evidence that it can be done on a practical scale. Neither is there any need for stocking game farm-reared sage hens, since the species is easily wild-trapped for transplanting.

HABITAT OF THE SAGE GROUSE

THE sage grouse is found in two types of range: about 70% of the occupied range is the sagebrush-grass prairie type; the rest is the salt-desert shrub type. Generally they are separate; but in many areas they are intermixed, particularly in western Wyoming, and Utah and Nevada.

SAGEBRUSH-GRASS HABITAT

THE sagebrush-grass range is semiarid country varying from 2,000 feet altitude in east-central Washington to over 8,000 feet in Wyoming. It includes arid lowland prairies, and fairly well-watered basins broken up by high mountains. The higher altitudes, forested mountains, are not used by the sage grouse; thus its usable habitat is not contiguous. Precipitation varies from a mere five inches on the desert fringes to thirty inches in the mountain foothills. It is windy country, and both daily and seasonal temperature ranges are great. The sagebrush-grass range extends from southwestern Saskatchewan south through Montana and Wyoming and southwest through southern Idaho. Another portion of this range occurs in the central Columbia River valley of Washington.

The vegetative cover in its original state was

COURTESY WYOMING GAME AND FISH COMMISSION

COURTESY WYOMING GAME AND FISH COMMISSION

Sage grouse habitat is chiefly of two types.
PLATE 31. Top. *Sagebrush-grass habitat in Eden Valley, Wyoming.*
PLATE 32. Bottom. *Salt-desert shrub habitat on an alkali flat.*

pre-eminently the ubiquitous sagebrush, the key plant in this wilderness climax association. Other shrubs associated with it in less abundance include more species of sagebrush (silver and bud sagebrush particularly), salt sage, shad scale, rabbit brush, greasewood, and winter fat. Several bunch grasses make up the more prominent herbs, including Western wheat grass, bluebunch wheat grass, giant wild rye, sand dropseed, needle and thread grass, and Indian rice grass.

These plants do not ordinarily occur as a uniform mixture, but rather in pure species stands, or a variety of mixtures. They make many different cover types, of which the sagebrush type and the grass-meadow are most significant to the sage hen.

Since the advent of agriculture, two changes of great significance have taken place. Overgrazing has damaged much of the grass cover, with a resultant spread of sagebrush; and a lot of grass and sagebrush lands have been converted to domesticated crops such as alfalfa and clover. Where these changes have not been too extensive, the habitat is still good for the sage grouse. With the domesticated crops have come other plant invaders, such as Russian thistle and other weeds.

Sagebrush is generally a good soil indicator; it thrives best on deep, rather moist, well-drained soils. It exists on many sites, however, and as a result is found in varied form and size. On poor dry sites it may be a prostrate shrub, while on well-watered, fertile soils it becomes a large shrub. These different growths of sagebrush are used for different purposes by sage grouse. The low, sparse cover is best for strutting grounds, medium low and rather open cover for nesting, that of medium height and density for feeding, and the tallest and thickest stands for loafing and roosting. The latter are generally close to water courses.

SALT-DESERT SHRUB HABITAT

THE salt-desert shrub habitat type may best be described by comparing it with the sagebrush-grass type just discussed. It is more arid than the sagebrush-grass range, for the precipitation rarely exceeds 10 inches a year. The soils are saline, and generally poor from the agricultural viewpoint. Plant cover is generally more sparse and lower growing. The variety of plants is poorer, though most of the same species are found. There is a larger proportion of shrubs, fewer grasses, and little of cultivated crops.

This habitat is not as ideal for the sage grouse as is the sagebrush-grass type, and much of it is fringe range for the species. Geographically it extends from southwestern Wyoming and eastern Oregon south through much of Nevada, parts of Utah, and western Colorado.

FOOD HABITS

FEW game animals, and no other game birds, obtain so much of their food from so few sources as does the sage hen; only during the warm months from late spring until early fall is the bird's diet made up of a wide variety of foods. At this season the predominantly vegetable diet is varied by the addition of considerable animal food; also many kinds of plant materials. See Figure 11 for a graphical presentation of the kinds of foods used at different seasons.

The winter diet is most exceptional, composed almost entirely of sagebrush leaves. The common big sagebrush is the most used of the several species of this group, and is the one intended when just *sagebrush* is named. These plants make an ideal source of food; they are evergreen, large enough to stand above the snow of the winter range, and highly nutritious.

When spring arrives the birds broaden their fare by adding a number of other greens besides sagebrush. These may conveniently be divided into two groups: legumes, and weeds and grasses. Among the legumes whose leaves are commonly eaten are alfalfa, white clover, sweet clover, and milk vetch; these legumes furnish considerable food in the spring and much more in the summer. Among the other plants whose leaves are eaten in spring are rabbit brush, rush (*Juncus*), dandelion, and a variety of grasses; both leaves and fruits of round-leaf snowberry are eaten. A number of kinds of insects are also taken in late spring but they make up a very small part of the food consumed.

The summer diet is more omnivorous than at other seasons; sagebrush leaves and flowers then compose less than half the food. Legumes and some of the weed plants are the source of about as much food as sagebrush. Some products of weed plants eaten in addition to those noted above come from salsify, wild mustard, and prickly lettuce. A large variety of animal foods are eaten; they make up 10%, more or less, of the summer fare. Among those commonly taken are ants, beetles, grasshoppers, and insect galls.

Juvenile sage grouse eat insects almost exclusively for a week or two after birth. They soon add succulent greens to their fare, and before they are a month old their diet is about the same as that of the adults. The rapidity with which the young sage hens accustom themselves to the diet of their elders is a contrast to the much slower adaptation of most other gallinaceous species.

Toward the end of the summer and throughout the fall the diet is progressively one of more sagebrush and less of the other foods. By winter they are subsisting on sagebrush alone—by choice if not entirely by necessity.

The food habits of the sage grouse are substantially neutral economically. The amount of legume forage taken from fields of alfalfa and clover is rarely enough to constitute serious damage. The occasional foraging of buckwheat, bean, potato, and truck crop fields is of no economic significance. The consumption of insects is too small to be of much help or harm to man's interests. Most of the bird's food, the sagebrush, is also forage for domestic stock and other game, notably the prong-horned antelope; the volume taken by the chickens is not enough

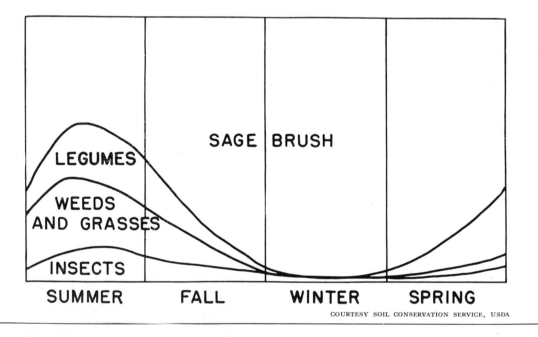

FIGURE 11. *Types of food used by sage grouse by seasons. (After: Patterson, 1952; Martin, Zim and Nelson, 1951; Batterson and Morse, 1948; Griner, 1939).*

to affect appreciably the welfare of the grazing mammals.

WATER NEEDS

WATER is used by the birds throughout the year when and where available. Despite this desire and need for water, there is clear evidence that at times the grouse, young and old, can go many days without free water, and even without dew. Despite this ability to get along for periods without water, good populations occur only in habitat that has a good water supply.

The usual daily routine is to drink water at feeding times—early morning and evening; if open water is not available, dew is used. Snow furnishes the water needs in winter. A considerable part of the daily travels of sage grouse are made to reach the water areas in their territory.

EFFECTS OF WEATHER AND CLIMATE

IN a general sense the climate makes sage grouse range what it is; this is true in a much closer sense than with the range of most species of game birds. The low annual rainfall, which varies within rather narrow limits, sets the character of the vegetative cover; just a little less rainfall and the range would be a desert uninhabitable for sage grouse. If the rainfall averaged very much more than it does, it would result in vegetation entirely different from the sagebrush complex, this would also be wholly unsuited to the sage hen. The temperature range also plays a part in determining the character of the plant growth, as evidenced by the northern and southern limits of sagebrush growth.

Ordinary weather that prevails in sage grouse country causes these birds no trouble; they adjust to seasonal changes by shifting to new ground. As the early winter snows deepen in the high altitudes they move to lower levels, where the sagebrush still stands above the snow. Late winter snows do not even dampen the ardor of the strutting ground behavior of the adult males. As the summer range dries up, the birds move to locations where adequate water exists. Ordinary rains and temperatures bother them not at all.

But extremes of weather are another matter; any extreme condition of drouth, rain, snow, or temperature of a severity order of ten years or more that lasts very long can cause the birds real trouble. Yet even under most of these circumstances the mortality is not exceptionally high. Air temperatures as low as 8° F. during the egg-laying period cause no egg loss (Patterson, 1952). The most dangerous time for bad weather to strike is the hatching and early brood period. Patterson recounts finding several normal-looking chicks dead within 25 feet of their nest after temperatures down to 34° F. and concurrent rain of 1.4 inches. It seems clear that periodic occurrences of protracted temperatures around freezing and heavy rains at this critical time can result in large juvenile losses of sage grouse, as with most other game birds. Adults are able to survive under almost all weather extremes, though high losses from predation may at times be conditioned by bad weather.

PREDATION; DISEASES AND PARASITES; ACCIDENTS

PREDATION is the largest direct cause of mortality of sage grouse. A variety of predators take their toll of eggs, young, and adults throughout the year. In no case is the sage grouse a major source of food for the predator, though the total effect of predation on sage grouse numbers is considerable.

NEST PREDATION

SAGE hen nest predators are mostly mammals; the badger, coyote, and some of the ground squirrels are the species that pilfer the most eggs over most of the bird's range. The magpie and American raven are the only birds that are important as egg destroyers. Hawks and owls may occasionally cause the loss of a nest by killing the hen, but this does not happen often enough to be an important source of nest mortality. Some other mammals that are occasional nest predators include dogs, cats, skunks, weasels, bobcats, and minks.

The causes of predation of 47 Wyoming sage hen nests was summarized by Patterson (1952). Ground squirrels were responsible for 42% of the losses, badgers 36%, and coyotes and magpies 11% each. The ground squirrels involved were mostly the Wyoming ground squirrel (*Citellus richardsoni elegans*) and the small striped ground squirrel (*C. tridecemlineatus parvus*).

PREDATION OF YOUNG AND ADULT SAGE HENS

SOME loss of young sage grouse from predation is normally to be expected. Though accurate figures are not available on the degree of this mortality, it seems clear that it is rarely a dominant factor in determining hunting season populations. A variety of hawks take most of the chicks that are eaten by predators; the ferruginous rough-legged hawk, Cooper's hawk, and the redtail are the three that most commonly take juvenile sage hens. Prairie falcons, golden eagles, marsh hawks, and horned owls take some chicks, as do coyotes, bobcats, and some of the other mammalian predators found in the range.

Presnall and Ward (1953) report digging out a coyote den in Jackson County, Colorado, from which an adult coyote was taken. Examination of the stomach showed she had eaten one adult and six young sage hens; the ground at the den was littered with bones and feathers of sage hens.

Predation on adult sage grouse is most intense during winter and spring. The courtship activities of the males make them particularly vulnerable for several months. The golden eagle, coyote, and horned owl are the species that most commonly prey on adult sage hens; bobcats, the larger hawks, and some of the other mammalian predators may occasionally take a few birds. These losses are seldom large enough to prevent successful recovery in the succeeding breeding season.

DISEASES AND PARASITES

AT least eight species of internal parasites and four of ectoparasites are known to infect and infest the sage grouse (Simon, 1940); but only two of these have been shown to cause serious disease resulting in small epizootics. These are two species of coccidia of the genus *Eimeria*, that together have caused scattered outbreaks of coccidiosis that resulted in considerable local losses. There is no evidence that this disease or any other is connected with major sage grouse declines.

The endoparasites of the sage grouse are of three types: three protozoans, a species of *Tritrichomonas*, and the two species of coccidia, *E. angusta* and *E. centrocerci*. Two are cestodes (tapeworms), *Raillietina centrocerci* and *Rhabdometra nullicollis*. The other three are nematodes (round worms): *Habronema urophasiana*, *Cheilospirura centrocerci* and *Heterakis gallinae*. Any of these parasites may be common in sage grouse, and almost all birds will have a considerable internal fauna of them. Juvenile sage hens seem to have more parasites than adults. These conditions are normal and are not commonly associated with mortality. The condition under which the coccidia *Eimeria* became very populous and toxic was suspected to be drouth that concentrated the birds at water holes (Scott, 1940).

The four species of ectoparasites that have been found on sage grouse are of two types. Two kinds of lice were identified as *Gonoides centrocerci* and *Lagopecus perplexus;* the others were ticks, *Haemaphysalis leporis-palustris* and *H. cinnabarina*. The latter is a probable vector of tularaemia and therefore of potential danger, though that disease is not known to occur in sage grouse. The infestations of the lice and ticks are sometimes an annoyance but are not known to have caused any mortality.

ACCIDENTS TO SAGE GROUSE

PHYSICAL injury from any kind of accident was rare with sage grouse until civilization encroached on their range. With the advent of highways, high-speed vehicles, fences, electric poles and wires, and farm machinery, losses from this source have greatly increased.

There is little loss of nests from mechanical damage. A few may be trampled by livestock, but farm machinery is of little importance in this connection because of the few nests made in crop fields, and the late time for crop harvest in relation to the time of egg-hatching.

Young sage hens are commonly found in alfalfa and other kinds of hayfields in summer. The losses among these chicks during mowing operations is considerable, and may be an important mortality factor in areas where there is much hay in good grouse range.

Both adult and young sage hens are frequently killed on highways, especially in summer. This type of accident appears to be more than mere random happenstance. The highways induce a better growth of vegetation along their margins than prevails generally; this cover attracts sage hens, along with other wildlife, and helps cause an exceptionally high accident rate. On two different occasions, near Rawlins, Wyoming, M. S. McMurtrey observed broods of sage hens settled down on the warm pavement for the night (letter to the author). A check on 15 miles of Wyoming state highway, made by Patterson (1952) in 1949, showed that at least 18 sage grouse were killed there between April and September; and others were no doubt removed by scavengers or obliterated.

Losses of grouse from taking poison in their food have long been suspected. Programs of insect and rodent control on the grouse range have been increasingly intensive in recent years; and many of the new chemicals used in such work are known to be potentially dangerous to birds. Many studies have been made to check wildlife, including sage grouse, losses from these sources. Strychnine used in oats bait for ground squirrels, and aldrin used for grasshopper control, evidently have not caused mortality of sage grouse; on the contrary, toxaphene and chlordane used in bran bait did cause considerable mortality of sage hens and other animals that fed on the poisoned grasshoppers (Girard, 1937; and Post, 1951). Both toxaphene and chlordane proved unsatisfactory for grasshopper control, a fortunate matter for the welfare of range wildlife; aldrin appears to be more satisfactory for this purpose. It is to be hoped that aldrin continues to prove innocuous to game birds. While the widespread use of modern agricultural chemicals does pose a threat to wildlife, it appears that some of the fears that have been expressed may not have been fully warranted.

MAN'S RELATIONS TO SAGE GROUSE

PRESENT-DAY man's impact on the sage grouse is tremendous. As a hunter and rancher he has exterminated the species from many parts of its original range. For a time it looked as though the bird would be completely exterminated, as was its relative the heath hen in the East. The recent decades of protection from excessive hunting and improved land-use practices have given it a reprieve, and probably have made it possible for the bird to have a permanent place in the ecology of the Western range. Perpetual vigilance must be exercised, though, for the welfare of the sage hen will forever be subject to the influence of man as hunter, rancher, farmer, miner, and engineer. The extent to which man's conservation interests influence and shape his other activities will determine the fate of this exceptional game bird.

AS A HUNTER

UNRESTRICTED hunting once decimated great numbers of sage grouse over much of its range. Whether this hunting alone could have exterminated the species cannot be reasoned now, since the decline of sage grouse was also caused by severe overgrazing of its range by domestic livestock. Probably either factor *could* have reduced them to remnant numbers, but almost surely the overgrazing was the more important of the two. At any rate, complete protection from hunting came in time to aid in their recovery. Modern conditions justify only very limited hunting of sage hens. Short open seasons in limited areas under close control are needed to assure the preservation of adequate breeding stock; in late years these rules have been in effect. Under these circumstances it is rather surprising that hunters fare as well as they do in the pursuit of sage chickens.

The number of sportsmen hunting sage grouse is small, because of the sparsely settled country of many of the best sage grouse areas. Even within the open hunting areas the intensity of gunning varies, from heavy near the highways to practically none in the near-wilderness sagebrush prairies far from roads. Thus in some places the kill is high—up to 25% or more of the population—while in others the harvestable surplus of birds is hardly touched. Patterson (1952) presents figures on the 1950 and 1951 hunting seasons in Eden Valley, Wyoming, an example of some of the finest sage grouse range, which is rather heavily hunted. The 1950 season was six days long, and the daily bag was three birds. Over 2,500 hunters gunned the 90,000 acres studied, and killed 6,179 birds. The hunting pressure was 35 acres per hunter, and the hunters averaged 2.4 birds each. Most of the hunters were local people, and less than 1% of the hunting pressure was by out-of-staters. The total harvest was 25% of the preseason population.

An interesting aspect of the Eden Valley sage grouse harvest was the age and sex distribution; males made up only 40% of the kill, and adult males only 14%. In 1951 the cocks composed only 37% of the total. Thus the excessive kill of females may well affect the next year's production unfavorably. Patterson points out that this discrepancy is largely caused by the early (August) hunting season, which tends to concentrate on the more easily accessible summer range, which is populated mostly by hens and juveniles. Biologists agree that late September or October seasons for sage grouse hunting are better management, even though less convenient for the hunter.

Hens and young sage grouse that are bagged are generally used for food, but adult cocks are often discarded as unpalatable. The legs and breast meat of these old cocks is perfectly good if removed from the body at once after the bird is killed; then the meat will not taste objectionably of sagebrush (Girard, 1937).

AS A RANCHER AND FARMER

FARMING and ranching in the arid West have both damaged and improved sage grouse habitat. The period of unrestricted grazing on lands largely owned by the Federal Government brought abuses that destroyed both the livestock forage and the sage grouse cover. This exploitive system has now been fairly well corrected by limitations on livestock numbers on the public range commensurate with the carrying capacity of the land.

Intensive farming invaded the home of the sage grouse with the construction of irrigation facilities. As long as these developments were small and scattered they improved grouse habitat; the lush hayfields provided fine summer cover to supplement the sagebrush prairies. Where farming took over extensive areas the sage grouse was excluded from all but the fringes, where its beloved sagebrush still remained nearby and in adequate amount.

Though the sage hen can get along well enough with some of its range devoted to farming, and with people living and traveling nearby, it is also true that there is a rather close limit to its tolerance of these conditions; basically it is still a wilderness species. Patterson (1952) has shown this relationship clearly in a table that demonstrates the inverse relationship between the quantity of habitat usable by the birds and the human population. Among the nine states that have almost all the occupied sage grouse range today, Nevada and Wyoming have the most grouse habitat and the fewest people, while Washington and California have the least range and the most people. As human populations increase in the West we may expect further encroachments on sage grouse habitat. The bird's range is now reduced to about 250,000 square miles, or about half its original extent.

The diversion of water has affected grouse habitat both favorably and unfavorably. As streams are tapped for irrigation water they dry up sooner each season, and more completely than naturally; as a result more range is seasonally or permanently unsuitable for the sage hen. On the other hand, the same water irrigates crops that in some cases improve the bird's summer range. The net result is a much greater loss than gain, since only a small part of the farmland created is used by the grouse.

A recent trend in range-land management in the sagebrush country threatens further great damage to the sage grouse habitat; this is the eradication of sagebrush to establish a forage-grass cover for cattle grazing. This program is fostered by most of the agricultural agencies, and by the farm equipment companies; it is generally opposed by the sheep interests and the sportsmen. The question involved is whether the landowner or user and the community will be better off with a grazing area converted to grass and populated with cattle, or with the present mixed grass-shrub grazing and browsing cover used by cattle, sheep, antelope, and sage grouse. There is considerable doubt concerning the economics of sagebrush eradication on range lands, as well as its wisdom from the standpoint of the public welfare. Regardless of the agricultural balance sheet in the matter, there is no doubt as to its effect on sage grouse; they are completely eliminated from any large areas successfully treated.

A modification of complete brush removal has several advantages, and is gaining favor. The removal is made in contour strips, which alternate with strips left in natural cover; this prevents the new seeding from blowing, and holds snow that provides needed moisture. Sage hens seem to continue to do well on such areas.

PLATE 33. *Sagebrush land cleared in alternate strips and seeded to grass to improve grazing. This is a better arrangement than complete clearing of sagebrush which destroys grouse habitat. Sage hens continue to use the altered cover in strip pattern and seedings are more successful this way.*

COURTESY SOIL CONSERVATION SERVICE, USDA

AS A CONSERVATIONIST

Man's interest in the sage grouse is unlikely to be a very great influence in determining land use and treatment. Even when he is altruistic in his approach to Western land problems, the welfare of the sage hen will be a small consideration. Nevertheless, since the interests of the sage hen can harmonize with those of the antelope and a reasonable cattle and sheep industry, the possibility of a constructive program to benefit the sage hen along with the other land resources is promising. Habitat suitable for the sage chicken can be preserved, in proportion to the degree that man acts as a conservationist in the broad sense. This prospect is a reasonably good one today, much better than it was a few decades ago.

In addition to his role as a land manager, both private citizen and public servant, in preserving and improving the birds' habitat, man must assure good conservation laws for the protection of the grouse. These will provide adequate protection from overshooting by limited hunting seasons, low bag limits and in some instances by control of numbers of hunters. Such laws are now generally in effect. One more change is needed: the time of hunting should be late September and early October, instead of the earlier periods now generally in effect.

PRODUCTIVITY AND POPULATIONS

PRODUCTIVITY AND MORTALITY

The productive potential of the sage grouse is less than that of the majority of gallinaceous birds, but is larger than that of some upland game birds. The bird is promiscuous in its breeding habits. The yearling males are immature and do not ordinarily participate in the spring breeding. The female breeds the year after it is born, and never has more than a single brood a year.

There is a slight tendency for females to outnumber males in the spring, though not often by more than 2% to 4%. Observations indicate that in autumn there is a widely divergent sex ratio, commonly running about 40 males to 60 females. This is probably more apparent than real, since adult cocks are apt to be segregated by themselves at this time, and often in rather inaccessible areas. There probably is some excess of females in summer and fall, due to the heavy mortality of males through the spring. This is offset by a heavier loss of hens in the fall, especially in the hunting season.

Productivity is generally low compared to other grouse; the fall population commonly has 1.3 to 1.5 immature birds for each adult; rarely as many as 2 or 3 to 1.

The hens all nest, and lay an average of about 7.5 eggs in the first clutch. There are occasionally as many as nine eggs in a nest, and as few as six. Renesting seldom occurs, but may if the first nest is lost before incubation. Second clutches have about five eggs each.

Nest mortality is fairly high—frequently as much as 50%; the normal nest loss is 40% or a little more. Predation and desertion are the two main causes of loss, with predation accounting for two-thirds of the nest failures in most areas. In a study of 161 nests in Utah, Rasmussen and Griner (1938) found that 40% of them failed, 26% from destruction and 14% from desertion. The deserted nests were affected in many instances by the men making the study, and hence may not be a true representation of this factor. Most of the destroyed nests were from predation.

Infertility among the eggs runs a little higher than with most game birds; some 5% or slightly more have been found to be infertile. An additional 3% are commonly lost due to death during embryonic development; thus about 8% of the eggs in successful nests fail to hatch.

The typical brood when hatched has seven chicks, with the average slightly less. Early losses of young are low in most years; such deaths as occur may be due to exposure and accident, and occasionally to predation. Mortality from predation is prevalent in late summer as the young birds become more independent. The total juvenile mortality ordinarily adds up to more than half the birds hatched. The juvenile-adult ratio in the fall is typically only 1.3 to 1.5, so that each brood matures only about 2.5 to 3 chicks as an average. In very good production years the ratio of young to adults may reach 2 or even 3 to 1.

The hunting season arrives in late summer or early fall, soon after the juveniles have joined the old birds as full-grown, immature birds. Where hunting is heavy the kill may be as high as 25% of all the birds. Because of the nature of much of the range, hunting pressure is very uneven, and the average kill from hunt-

ing is less than 20% of the preseason population. Predation and accidents continue to take a toll through the fall and winter months; then in late winter and early spring mortality rises considerably. The increase is due partly to a high differential loss of cocks as a consequence of their courtship activities; the rest is the result of natural increases in predation at this season on account of the weather and harder hunting by predators as food becomes more scarce.

LIFE EQUATION

A SUMMARY of a typical year's population changes in a group of 100 sage grouse in a year of stability of numbers is shown in Table 11. In this instance the losses exactly offset the increase, so that there are the same number of

---

TABLE 11

LIFE EQUATION OF 100 SAGE GROUSE FOR A YEAR

TIME	ACTIVITIES	NUMBER OF GROUSE	
		young	adult
SPRING	(1) 48 males mate with 52 females		100
	(2) All females nest, average 7.5 eggs in first clutch, 6.0 in second. Total first clutch eggs—390		
	(3) 50 % of first nests hatch, or		
	$\qquad$ 26 × 7.5 = 195 eggs		
	4% of hens hatch second nest, or		
	$\qquad$ 2 × 6 = 12 eggs		
	5% of eggs are infertile, or 10		
	3% of eggs die in shell, or 6. Thus, 16 eggs fail to hatch and 191 hatch (av. 6.8 per nest)	191	
	(4) 25 adults die from predation and accident (25%)		75
SUMMER	(5) 5 adults die from predation and accident (7%)		70
	(6) 100 chicks die from exposure, predation, accident, etc. (52%)	91	
FALL	Surviving chicks become adults		161
	(7) 32 are killed by hunters (20%)		129
	(8) 8 are killed by predators and accident (5%)		121
WINTER	(9) 21 are killed by predators and accident (17%)		100
SPRING	(10) Breeding season population same as before in year of equal increase and losses		

birds in the second spring as in the first. This rarely happens in life, and as a result there are more or fewer birds in a given year than the year before. If the mortality is exceptionally low there is a marked increase in population; contrarily, if adverse factors cause abnormally heavy losses, the population will decline. These conditions may be thought of as applying to units of range like a valley or a county. Where the same trend prevails over a wide area, the population of a whole state or even a larger area increases or decreases, and results in better or worse hunting than the previous year. Where the trends vary, the general condition may remain about the same, but with changes spottily distributed.

POPULATION DENSITIES

POPULATION density has less significance with a mobile and gregarious bird like the sage hen than with more sedentary species. At a given time and place there may be dozens of sage hens per acre on a small bit of range, possibly even thousands of birds in a single flock, and outside of that area there may not be another grouse for ten miles. Part of the significance of density concerns the bird's tolerance for its own kind, the maximum tolerance being the *saturation point*. There is no such thing as saturation point in a communal species like the sage grouse; with few minor exceptions they tolerate any amount of crowding. On the strutting grounds each adult male controls a small territory of his own, hence there is a limit there to crowding. The strutting ground may have a hundred birds but each performing bird has his own personal share which he defends with vigor.

The spacing of strutting grounds reported by Patterson (1952) for good range in Wyoming was about one for each five to six square miles. The average number of cocks per strutting ground was about 60 to 80. The population density of males only was about 13 per square mile, or 49 acres per cock. Since the hen population is usually somewhat larger than that of

cocks, the population density of all sage grouse in the spring on such areas may be of the order of 30 to 50 birds per square mile, or 13 to 21 acres per grouse.

Communistic nesting is common with sage grouse, and is consistent with their other gregarious characteristics. Patterson (1952) found six nests on 5.4 acres, the greatest nest density he observed in his Wyoming studies. Rasmussen and Griner (1938) reported 23 nests on 160 acres as the most they found in their Utah studies. Two to six nests per 40 acres was common in the Wyoming study area, and at times individual pairs of nests would be as close as 50 to 130 feet apart; the average nest density there was 42 per square mile. Nesting densities are generally somewhat lower than these figures, which are for the superior Eden Valley habitat in Wyoming. Brood density is ordinarily about half that of nests, or a little more, and reflects the large number of broodless hens whose nests have been destroyed.

FLUCTUATIONS IN POPULATIONS

As more and more reliable information has become available on the sage grouse in recent years, it has become clear that its populations go up and down much as with other species of grouse. It seems quite probable, in fact, that sage grouse populations rise and fall with a regularity that suggests that the species may be cyclic. The years 1949 to 1951 were a period of high populations in most of the bird's range; so was the period around 1940. The intervening years included a low population period in the middle of the decade. This also occurred in the mid-1930's. Prior to that time observations were less complete, and not confirmed by scientific studies; nevertheless the evidence is clear that the first years of the 1930's was a period of relative abundance.

For 35 years after the turn of the century the recorded comment is almost wholly concerned with the declining numbers of birds and their threatened extinction; there appears little doubt that the deteriorating range situation of that period, combined with long hunting seasons, did result in a continually worsening status that obscured any periodic increases in population that would have been natural.

The improvement in land-use practices on the range lands of the West, and adequate protection from hunting since the mid-1930's have made possible the natural ups and downs of sage hen numbers that have occurred. There is even some sign that the sage grouse population may have increased in the most recent high period compared with the previous one; if so it is a tribute to conservation.

THE MANAGEMENT OF THE SAGE GROUSE

THE sage grouse is manageable as a bird of the semiarid sagebrush wilderness and as a by-product of a livestock grazing economy. There will be little of its range allowed to remain as true wilderness, and hence the management problem actually relates to land used mainly to grow domestic livestock. On this range we need to consider problems of land use and development, and the protection and harvest of the sage grouse. We should also discuss the place in management of transplanting sage grouse, predator control, establishment of refuges, and census taking.

LAND USE AND DEVELOPMENT

THE sage grouse depends for its existence on sagebrush land kept in good vegetative condition; it can tolerate man and livestock, provided this habitat requirement is met. Thus there are two things man must do in order to preserve good sage-hen range. First, the use of the range by domestic animals must be kept within the carrying capacity of the forage (with antelope and mule deer counted in, where they occur). Second, the destruction of sagebrush habitat in reclamation programs for the development of farming should be confined to areas of the best soil and water. If these two

matters are resolved satisfactorily, the future of the sage chicken is secure. There is good promise even now that this will be true.

The pattern of land ownership in the range of the sage grouse is a mixture of Federal, state, and private holdings. The better quality lands suited to farming make up much of the private property, with the deserts and highlands in public ownership. The ranching business requires range for livestock at all seasons, which almost inevitably means that each owner must use sections of public land as well as his own. This he does by a permit system that is controlled by public policy, notably the Taylor Grazing Act of 1934. Since he can carry no more animals than can be sustained throughout the year, the number of stock he carries is determined by his permits for use of public land. The private land is thus grazed with about the same intensity as the rest. The preservation of a moderate and fair public policy on the use of public lands for grazing is thus the keystone in sage grouse management. Even though the policy is not set to help game, if it is sound from the standpoint of good land use it will be reasonably good for the sage hen.

Reclamation of sagebrush lands for growing farm crops poses a great threat to grouse habitat. Where such developments are extensive the farms are of little use to the sage hen except along the periphery. Modern advances in engineering have accelerated the rate at which this development has been and is being done. Irrigation techniques and land clearing and leveling machinery have contributed to this trend. Despite this history, the amount of arid land that can be properly and profitably converted to farming is set by the amount of water available; and that is very limited. Hence the reclamation boom should slow down, and in all probability soon enough to retain a reasonable amount of sagebrush range.

PROTECTION AND HARVEST

As long as the land produces sage grouse we shall need laws to conserve them. Such laws should protect the species from hunting at all times, except for limited open seasons in certain years and places; state laws now do this adequately. State wildlife agencies should have delegated authority to set open seasons, bag limits, and other conditions of hunting without recourse to legislative action.

In all probability open seasons in some sections of nine states should be allowable in about five to seven years out of each decade. In most instances the hunting will be prescribed for certain counties or other subdivisions of the state rather than be state-wide. The season should be short in areas of heavy hunting pressure—usually from one to six days; in more inaccessible areas it can be longer. In some locations it is advisable to use a controlled hunting system, with special permits in addition to the usual licensing arrangement. The time for hunting should be in late September or early October; this aspect of the hunting arrangements is the only one that is now not generally in vogue. Bag limits will need to be low—rarely more than three or four birds per hunter per day.

The decision of the state wildlife agency on the hunting regulations should be based on scientific censuses conducted annually on permanently established plots. The sage grouse is easily censused, and the trends of the population from year to year can be accurately followed. The males are counted most easily in the spring on their strutting grounds, from automobiles on still, clear mornings for an hour —half before sunrise and half after (Patterson, 1952). Hens and broods can be counted in a similar manner in midsummer on a specified route in a car. The trends will be accurate if the procedures followed are standardized, the sample areas are representative, and the number of observations is adequate to give good averages.

TRANSPLANTING

A CONSIDERABLE amount of live-trapping and transplanting of sage grouse has been done in recent years. The purpose is to restock where populations are considered inadequate, establish new populations on good range from which the species has been exterminated, and reduce crop damage from local overpopulations.

The first purpose, to increase existing populations, is a waste of time, since the bird is mobile enough to restock all areas accessible to it. Records show that stocking is not very successful, even though the birds are easily trapped. The birds do not adapt well to new territory, and frequently return to the area where they were trapped. To establish new units they should be moved at least 100 miles.

Control of crop damage is much better done by liberalizing hunting than by the expensive trapping and moving system; at times this may not be adequate, and permit shooting or trapping and transplanting are the only solutions.

PREDATOR CONTROL; REFUGES

KILLING the natural enemies of the sage grouse for the purpose of sage grouse management is not warranted, though the control of some of the bird's enemies that also need suppression for other reasons may at times be sound. Ground squirrels, coyotes, and possibly weasels may sometimes warrant such control. There is no evidence, however, that the control of these or any other predators will increase sage grouse populations.

The establishment of refuges has often been suggested as a management measure for sage hens; but since protection from reasonable hunting is not the prime factor in determining sage grouse numbers, the use of refuges would be of little value. It is not recommended as a means of improving hunting.

In summary, it is clear that little can be done objectively to improve the habitat of the sage grouse; it is a by-product of land used mainly for another purpose by man. By good fortune, if the land is used well for its major crop, livestock, it will also produce a good crop of sage grouse; then the harvest of the game crop can be handled with appropriate regulations.

CHAPTER 4

The Sharp-tailed Grouse

CLASSIFICATION

The sharp-tailed grouse, or plain "sharptail," is a single species with three subspecies. The type form is the northern sharp-tailed grouse, whose scientific name is *Pedioecetes phasianellus phasianellus* Linnaeus. As its name implies, it is found in the northern part of the species range in Canada and Alaska. The prairie sharp-tailed grouse (*P. p. campestris* Ridgeway) is the bird of our northern prairie states and the southern Canadian provinces. The third subspecies is the Columbian sharp-tailed grouse (*P. p. columbianus* Ord). It is found in the western intermountain region known as the Great Basin.[1]

The sharptail is a member of the family Tetraonidae, the grouses. Its nearest relative is the prairie chicken, with which it sometimes hybridizes.

DESCRIPTION

It is conventional to describe the prairie sharptail, even though it is not the type form; it is the prevalent subspecies in the United States. Then we shall compare the northern and Columbian subspecies with it.

The sharptail is larger than the ruffed grouse, but slightly smaller than the prairie chicken. Its average weight ranges from 1¾ to two pounds,

the males being slightly heavier than the females. The Columbian subspecies is slightly smaller than the other two. The length is from 15 to 20 inches.

The coloration of the two sexes is almost identical. The general color is brown, with markings of blackish, buff, and whitish. The pattern of the dark markings of the breast is "V" shaped, in contrast to the barring of the prairie chicken. The upper parts are mostly brown and blackish, with buff, creamy, and whitish markings. The wing flight feathers are brown, with white spots on the outer vanes. The brown "V" breast markings are set off with more of the lighter colors than on the back, and the mottled area grades front and back into a creamy throat and white belly and under-tail coverts.

The feathers on top of the head are brown to blackish, and are erectile. There is an erectile yellowish-orange bare space ("comb") above each eye. The neck coloring is similar to that on the back, and these feathers are also erectile. The rump and upper tail coverts are much like the back in color pattern, but paler toward the tail. The central tail feathers are dark, soft, and with some light markings; the outer tail feathers are shorter, stiff, and much lighter in color—almost white on the outer portions. The under-tail coverts are white, or white with dark brown streaks or mottling. The tail when spread has the pointed shape that gives the bird its name. The tail as a whole is short, rarely exceeding six inches, which is in contrast to the very long pointed tail of the somewhat similar female pheasant.

The neck sacs of the male are purplish or reddish-violet areas of bare skin, distensible but

---

[1] Recent revisions have added three additional subspecies to those used here. The northern sharptail (*P. p. phasianellus*) is divided into three, the two added forms being *P. p. caurus* and *P. p. kennicottii*. The prairie sharptail (*P. p. campestris*) is split into two forms, the new one being *P. p. jamesi*. Those wishing to obtain more information on this recent taxonomic arrangement may see H. Friedmann, *Journ. Wash. Acad. Sci.,* XXXIII, 1943.

PLATE 34. *Sharp-tailed grouse.*

not as well-developed as in the prairie chicken; they are well hidden by whitish feathers when not inflated. The legs are dusky brown, somewhat bare on the back, and brown feathered to between the bases of the toes with long, hairlike plumage. The bill is dark horn color, with the under mandible partly flesh-colored. The iris of the eye is brown.

The sexes are very difficult to differentiate, even with a bird in hand. The female, in addition to being somewhat lighter in weight, has a pattern of light and dark markings on the two middle tail feathers that differs fairly consistently from that of the male; the hen's central rectrices have the pattern mostly transverse, whereas in the male it is lengthwise. The eyebrow pigmentation is duller in the female. But all three characters overlap and intergrade to some extent, so that it is necessary to use the combination.

The northern sharptail differs from the prairie sharptail mainly in its predominantly darker coloration; the back is black rather than brown, and the rest of the dark colors are correspondingly darker. On the under parts the area of dark color is larger than in the other subspecies. The tarsal feathers are much longer than in the more southern birds.

The Columbian subspecies is somewhat smaller than the others, and is grayer in dorsal coloration than the prairie sharptail.

The northern and prairie subspecies probably intergrade in character where their ranges overlap; this probably occurs in northern Alberta.

The downy young are grayish yellow, with black and buff markings above and a rather pale greenish yellow below. The black and buff markings on the top of the head are prominent, and there is some black on the back and on the sides of the rump. Throat and breast are somewhat paler than the rest of the underparts.

Because the prairie sharp-tailed grouse and the greater prairie chicken are often found together, hunters are sometimes confused as to the distinguishing marks. These are as follows: the sharptail is paler in color, the breast has V-shaped marks, and the belly is white; the chicken has cross-barring, and these cover the belly too; the legs are dusky brown in the sharptail and tend to be yellowish in the chicken; sharptail cocks lack the pinnae that the chickens have on the neck, and the neck sac is purplish on the sharptail instead of orange-yellow as on the chicken (discernible only in spring); the spread tail is rounded and even in length on the chicken, but longer in the center, wedge-shaped and with white outer feathers on the sharptail.

GEOGRAPHICAL RANGE AND DISTRIBUTION

THE original range of the sharptail extended from west-central Alaska on the northwest extreme, south through the interior valleys of western Canada and the United States intermountain area to northern California and northern New Mexico; southeast from Alaska through central Yukon, the southwestern Mackenzie District of the Northwest Territories, across the northern sections of the prairie provinces into Ontario and western Quebec; from Hudson Bay southwest into Wisconsin, northeastern Illinois, eastern Iowa and northern Kansas.

The present range is both contracted and expanded from the original. The Columbian sharptail, which once occupied the whole intermountain area, is now confined to scattered areas in

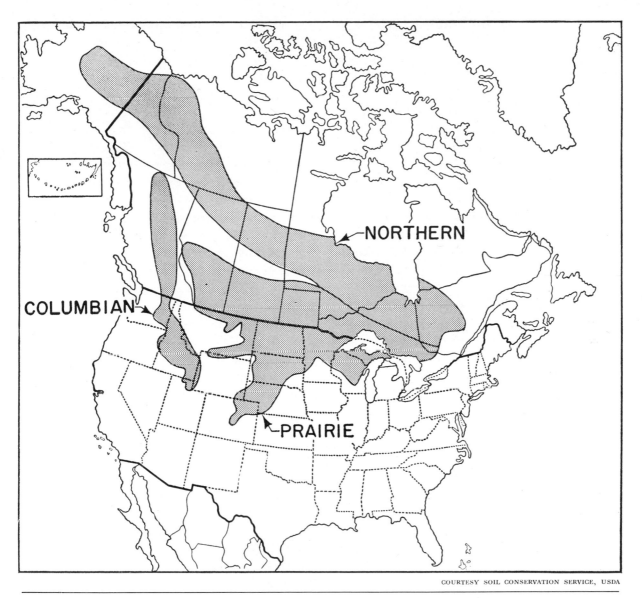

COURTESY SOIL CONSERVATION SERVICE, USDA

FIGURE 12. *Geographic range of the sharp-tailed grouse. Areas inhabited by three sub species are shown. (Adapted from Snyder, 1935; Hart, Lee and Low, 1950; Grange, 1948; Yocom, 1952; and others).*

a rather narrow belt from northern British Columbia southward through eastern British Columbia into Idaho, eastern Washington, western Montana, northeastern Oregon, western Wyoming, northern Utah, and northeastern New Mexico. The northern sharptail is still found in substantially the original range from Alaska to Quebec, and has extended its range somewhat into central Quebec and central Ontario. It is a bird of the forest openings, and its range grades into that of the prairie sharptail in Ontario. The prairie sharptail is still found from central Alberta to east-central Ontario, and south to southern Montana and northern Wyoming, northeastern Colorado, and central Wisconsin. It has extended its range eastward into northern Michigan and southern Ontario, and has disappeared from Iowa and Illinois. See Figure 12.

HISTORY OF THE SHARPTAIL

THE sharptail was first encountered by trappers and others who reached central Canada and the western Great Lakes states in the middle of the 18th century. The type form was described from a bird collected in northeastern Manitoba near Hudson Bay by a representative of the Hudson's Bay Company (Snyder, 1935). In the southern portion of its range it was found in close association with the prairie chicken, and to a considerable degree the two species were thought of as one. Discerning observers soon realized, however, that the sharptail was a bird of the brushlands and brushy prairie, and the prairie chicken an inhabitant of the more open prairies; the fringe of their overlapping ranges was not extensive.

The fact that the sharp-tailed grouse was found over a vast area of North America from our north-central states to Alaska is proof that the forests over this great span were not the continuous mature tree stands that people often envisage. For the sharptail lives only on open and brushy lands, not in the forest proper, and there must always have been a patchwork of brushy openings through the forest. These openings resulted mostly from fires, set either by lightning or by native people. Other openings in the primeval forest were areas of bog and marsh or frost pockets, where the natural plant succession resulted in a climax of low cover.

In the areas where the white man settled, great changes in the habitat occurred; this primarily affected the north-central states at first. Farming cleared some of the brushy land, and sharpened up the edges between prairie and forest; this pushed the sharptails back, with the prairie chickens following. Lumbering opened up great areas of forest, and the terrible fires that followed completed the conversion of these large clearings into excellent sharptail range. The birds moved in quickly, being a very mobile species, and an era of high populations began on this new range. As the Hamerstroms (1951b) say, "The sharp-tailed grouse could almost be called the 'fire grouse,' for it thrives after a burn." These great flocks furnished considerable food for lumbering camps, and to a small extent were marketed in the eastern cities. The number of sharptails shot or trapped for the market was small, mainly because of the lack of transportation facilities over much of the bird's range.

The lush period for sharptails in the cut-over forests was not very long, for many of the burns soon grew back into cover or were reforested by man, and became too thick for their liking. But while this transition was going on, settlements grew and farms were started throughout the range of the prairie sharptail. This change resulted in many brushy transition zones between farms and forests, and here the sharptail found adequate habitat. In recent decades some of these farms have been abandoned, and for a time they increased the sharptail habitat. But abandoned farms eventually return to forest— sometimes aided by man's reforestation—and the ever-changing pattern of the habitat continues to alter the affairs of the sharptail. The farms that remained in agricultural use had their brushy edges sharpened so that clean fields abut the woods, and thus eliminate the basic need of sharptails.

These changes have now reached a rather critical stage for the sharptail. The cut-over forest has grown back to trees, fires are now relatively small and infrequent, abandoned farms have grown up to trees, and farmers have eliminated much of the brushland on their properties. Only new lumbering and occasional fires add to the habitable cover to offset the losses. The habitat losses have now exceeded the gains to such an extent that the future of the prairie sharptail is in doubt. Schorger (1944) expressed optimism, saying, "The anticipated extinction of the sharp-tailed grouse has not been realized, nor is it within the realm of probability. There is every reason to believe that under present land policies the species will continue to be plentiful." Grange (1948), after quoting this opinion of Schorger's, expressed his own disagreement with it.

The future of the Columbian sharptail is even

blacker in its southern range. The once great numbers that inhabited the grassy plains and foothills of the Great Basin are survived by scattered remnants left on those places not consumed by farming (Hart, Lee, and Low, 1950). These authors estimate that only about 1,500 remained in Utah in 1948, whereas as late as the 1890's " . . . it was not uncommon to see flocks of several hundred sharptails in northern Cache Valley." So discouraging is the prospect for the sharptail in Utah that they recommend " . . . that at least one 'perpetuation' refuge be established . . . " In Washington the birds were plentiful and hunting was good until about 1912 to 1914 (Yocom, 1952); but from that time their decline was rapid, as intensive agriculture changed the habitat.

The northern sharptail does not face the same degree of danger as its two relatives; its range is still to a large degree wilderness. What man may eventually do to this far northern range remains to be seen; at least there is the possibility that his influence on much of this habitat may benefit the sharptail as much as hurt it. Only in portions of the southern range of this subspecies is agriculture likely to become so intensive as seriously to deplete the habitat.

IMPORTANCE AS A GAME BIRD

THE northern sharptail is still an important game bird through most of its range. Since it is subject to wide fluctuations in population, there will be years of poor as well as good hunting. Because of the sparsity of the human population over much of its range, the kill is not generally large. It is most significant as a game bird in the eastern portions of the range in Ontario.

The prairie sharptail is important in hunting wherever it reaches good population densities. This includes the southern part of Canada from Ontario to Alberta and six of our northern states: Michigan, Wisconsin, Minnesota, North Dakota, South Dakota, and Nebraska. Over some of this area it is hunted along with prairie chickens, and

the state kill records are usually listed as "prairie grouse," which is the total of the two species. The prospects for the prairie sharptail continuing to be important as a source of sport hunting is not very bright, but it is definitely better than for the prairie chicken.

The Columbian sharptail is no longer present in adequate numbers for hunting in the United States. Some are hunted in British Columbia.

The sharptail is naturally wary in behavior, has good flight speed, and presents a fairly difficult target to the hunter. Its pursuit requires good woodsmanship and hunting ability (as distinguished from shooting skill). Its flight is straight, and has been measured by Deming (in Hart, Lee, and Low, 1950) as between 30 and 46 miles per hour, depending on wind effect. While slightly slower than the pheasant, its wariness and habitat make it more difficult to shoot than the ringneck. Compared to the ruffed grouse, the sharptail is slower and less difficult to hit. It lies well to pointing dogs, and rises with a whir of its wings, accompanied by clucking sounds. Its flesh is considered just fair for eating.

HABITS OF THE SHARP-TAILED GROUSE

COURTSHIP

THE courtship activity of the sharptail is an impressive performance. It is similar to that of the prairie chicken in many ways, and yet is uniquely different. It is done on an area of bare or grassy land, or in a place where there are sparse herbs among scattered shrubs; it is often on a hill or rise in the ground. The area used by a group of birds is usually about 100 feet across; but may be an acre or more. Occasionally the cocks will "dance" on the top of a low stump, or even go through some of the motions and calls from the top of a small tree or bush. The area is usually described as a "dancing ground," since the performance is notable for its emphasis on dancing, rather than on the throat noises as with the prairie chicken.

Young sharptail cocks begin to visit a dancing

PLATE 35. *Sharp-tailed grouse habitat is open brushland. The cocks (right) are performing on a* dancing ground *while the hens (left) look on.*

ground with their elders in early fall; there is some activity throughout the fall and winter. The serious performances and the general participation in dancing-ground activity begins as spring arrives, usually in late March.

Most dancing grounds are used only a few seasons. Some may be used year after year if not destroyed by plowing, the invasion of dense brush, or some other physical change. The birds from a considerable area come to this habitual gathering place. The number of birds using it depends on the population of sharptails, and on the availability of suitable places for dancing. There may be only a few participants or there may be many. Hart, Lee, and Low (1950) found that from 30 to 50 different birds (probably including hens) visited some of 29 dancing grounds they observed, but that the average was only 12.

It is believed that the fall and winter dancing-ground visitors are all males, and that the hens come only during the breeding season; this point is difficult to check, because of the close similarity of the sexes. It is reasonable to presume that performers are cocks intent on attracting hens or intimidating competing cocks.

The birds arrive at the dancing ground about 45 minutes, more or less, before sunrise when the weather is clear and quite calm; rain and high winds slow the activity. Each bird chooses a position on the area, with some slight preference for spots near the center. Much of the activity in the early spring consists of the sparring and bluffing, apparently to resolve the individual territories. As each new bird arrives, those already present perform vigorously and vociferously in greeting.

The sharptail has a dancing ground activity that corresponds somewhat to the booming of the prairie chicken. The sound is best described as hooting or cooing, and it is uttered while the bird is standing in the open or on a bush or other object. The neck sacs are inflated and the neck stretched forward as the hooting sound is made. It sounds much like the notes of a horned owl, and can be heard up to about a half-mile on calm days. It is not nearly as prominent a sound as is the booming of the prairie chicken.

In another more spectacular performance, the head and neck are similarly thrust forward, and the wings are extended horizontally with tips curved downward. The erectile feathers on the neck are raised, and the fleshy eyebrow expands nearly to the top of the crown. The tail is held in an erect fan, and is vibrated sideways with a whirring noise. Viewed from the rear, the white under-tail coverts and outer rectrices show very prominently.

From this stance the cock often rushes forward or goes into a circular movement with short, rapid, stamping steps, meanwhile vibrating the tail continually. The vocal accompaniment to this display is a peculiar froglike sound. After the single performance is over, the bird stands tense or squats for a time. At the height of the mating season the "rest" periods may be only a few seconds to possibly a minute, or about the same time as is devoted to the dance itself. When at rest, the cock remains motionless. Early and late in the season the quiet periods are longer.

There is considerable co-ordination among the birds in this display. When one begins to perform his neighbors join in, so that a section of the group or even all present may be in action at once; in fact, it seems at times as if the entire group begins and ends its dancing simultaneously on some unseen signal. This is indeed a spectacle, with all the birds passing back and forth and around one another. Many observers have remarked on the similarity of the dances of certain Indian tribes to that of the sharptail, and have conjectured that the birds' performances may have inspired the human dances.

Sometimes two birds pair off and oppose each other in "combat." With wings and tail spread they rush at each other, as though to collide at full speed. At the last possible instant they stop short, practically beak to beak, and try to stare each other down. After a few moments of this one will leave, often making a quick pass at his opponent as he does so. As is common with prairie chickens, sharptail cocks occasionally fly up into the air a few feet and then as they land make a short run at an oblique angle. These

PLATE 36. *Two cocks square off for an argument on their dancing ground. Note the lack of pinnae on these sharptails in comparison with the prairie chickens in Plate 40.*

antics are accompanied by a variety of gobbling and cackling calls.

Any disturbance by man or predator causes the birds to freeze or flush; if the trouble is momentary, they return to activity in a few minutes. The morning activity periods last for some three or four hours, beginning before sunrise; the afternoon activity has less participation and lasts one or two hours, until about dusk. The spring activity period wanes by mid-May and ceases a week or two later.

When hen birds come to the dancing ground, the gathering of males sets up a terrific clatter of greeting; the cocks outdo themselves in the dash of their performances. For a while the hens tend to hang around the edge of the area, and act nonchalant about the whole thing. Eventually each one reaches the stage of mating desire, walks among the performing birds, and squats before the cock of her choice, ready for coition.

NESTING

LATE in April or in May each hen seeks out a nesting place; usually the spot chosen is within a half mile of a dancing ground. Soon the dancing grounds are left to the males alone, and each hen begins her task of incubation.

The nest is a rough hollow in the ground vegetation, lined with grass, leaves, and some feathers; close to or among clumps of grass, or next to a bush or stump or some other protecting shelter. The cover type is generally brushland with herbaceous open spots, or an open grassy field with scattered brush. Hart, Lee, and Low (1950) report that the Columbian sharptail in Utah nests " . . . in unplowed and unburned vegetation along fencerows . . . in the hills, benchlands, or adjacent slopes which are frequented by the sharptails most of the year." The nest is usually well hidden from view. The typical clutch size is 12 eggs, and the incubation period is 21 days. Some nests have as few as five eggs, or as many as 17.

The eggs are olive, dark buff, or brown, and have a purplish bloom; there are usually some small dark brown specklings. The bloom soon wears off and the color fades to a lighter shade. The eggs measure about 1.7 by 1.3 inches in length and width.

The hen's behavior during incubation is typical of most grouse. She leaves the nest for feeding in early morning, and again before evening. Early in the incubation period she is easily flushed by any disturbance, but as hatching time approaches she holds closely even with the threat of danger. During much of this time the cocks are continuing their dancing-ground activities, but with gradually diminishing frequency and vigor. As warm weather comes and the hens no longer visit them, the males finally disperse and abandon their life of dancing; this is usually late May or early June. The males become quite inactive for a while, as though worn out by their strenuous life; they spend their time loafing in shady spots in brush or swamp thickets near the edges of fields, slashings, or swamps.

The time of nesting and of hatching varies some with latitude and with the weather. The more southern birds hatch late in May in ordinary seasons, or as much as a week or ten days later in cold, wet years. Birds in the latitude of Wisconsin and Michigan commonly hatch in mid-June or a little later. The northern sharptail, in different sections of Canada and Alaska, has its hatching peak in late June or early July.

There is little information available on the amount of renesting after destruction of the clutch. The fact that in most summer studies some late broods have been observed indicates the probability that hens that lose their nests early in incubation may sometimes nest again; but when the nest is destroyed late in incubation, renesting is unlikely to occur.

THE BROOD PERIOD

THE hatching period is a time of danger for sharptails, as it is for most ground-nesting species; predators find the nests most commonly just before and during hatching. The luck of the weather is the biggest gamble of all, and it continues to be a threat to the young chicks for some time after they hatch.

The brood is led away from the nest soon after hatching is completed. Only the mother provides parental care, as the males and broodless females spend the summer singly or in small groups by themselves. Summer cover is much the same as that used for nesting, and thus the brood may not travel far from the nest area. If danger is encountered they travel more than otherwise. Rarely is the summer brood territory more than a half mile across, but they have been known to move as much as a quarter of a mile in a single day before flight age. When the chicks are young they use rather low cover of grasses, mosses, and low shrubs; as they develop they tend to seek out somewhat more brushy cover.

The chicks grow very rapidly; they are able to fly a little when they are but 10 days old. At four weeks they are well-feathered and fly well, though in their early life they prefer to escape danger by "freezing" rather than by flying. Their early food is mostly insects, and they spend much of their time foraging for food when not being brooded. When the chicks reach eight to ten weeks of age they resemble small adults, and begin to show some independence of the mother. Their behavior is more and more like grown-ups, as they dust, loaf in the shade of low woody plants, and feed on summer fruits and greens; by mid-September to early October they are physically like adults. They still prefer to walk rather than fly short distances, but readily flush when disturbed. They are strong fliers, and will occasionally traverse two or three miles in a single flight.

FALL AND WINTER ACTIVITIES

THE birds always roost on the ground. In warm weather they prefer open grassy spots, but in cold or inclement weather and during the moult period they rest singly or in small groups under the protection of shrubby thickets. As fall approaches, the family units break up and flocking begins. The flock size increases as the fall season passes, but it is always a rather loose social organization. Flocks are largest in late fall and early winter, and generally have from 10 to 35 birds; but may have as many as 50, 100, or more, or as few as three or four. To what degree there may be flock segregation by sex or age is not accurately known, because of the difficulty of differentiating these matters in field observations. Trapping records in Michigan revealed no clear-cut segregation by sex or age on a study area in the Upper Peninsula; but in the Lower Peninsula the adult males showed a distinct tendency to segregate from the hens and young males and to remain near their dancing grounds (Ammann, letter).

There is some activity on the dancing grounds in autumn, probably by males only, but it does not generally show the intensity of the spring breeding season, nor does the active period in the morning or evening last as long.

Feeding is easy in autumn. Where the birds live on agricultural lands they may take to grainfield foraging for wheat and other small grains and the associated weed seeds; on wild lands they use the fruits and greens found in their brushland habitat. During the fall their travels are limited, since there is no urgency to seek their requirements far afield. Winter snows change this sedentary life to a considerable degree; the foods they had been using are harder to find, and roosting places that had been adequate are no longer satisfactory. They turn to budding for much of their food, and to swales, bogs, and thickets for roosting sites. This life may require daily travels of as much as two or three miles; their annual cruising radius under normal conditions is not much more than this.

Roosting in deep snow is common, much in the manner of the ruffed grouse. They burst out from beneath the snow when disturbed, as does the "partridge." Flock size diminishes through the winter, unlike the habit of the prairie chicken, and then increases again in the spring; five to ten birds in a group is normal for midwinter. They visit their dancing grounds occasionally all winter; the dancing ground is rarely more than a mile from the winter roosting cover, and frequently is within the everyday winter territory. As spring approaches the use of the dancing ground increases; the dancing-ground gatherings of spring are larger than the winter groups, but not as big as the fall flocks.

The sharptail's feeding behavior is a random picking while wandering about, rather than concentration on cleaning up the available food in a given spot. They will often feed casually in a wheat field or a brush lot, and then walk 100 or 200 yards across a grass area to another source of food and continue foraging there, even though plenty of food remained in the first area.

EMIGRATION HABIT

THE northern sharp-tailed grouse—and to a less extent the prairie sharptail—is at times somewhat migratory in habit; this occasional phenomenon has been observed particularly in Ontario and Michigan. Two large-scale emigrations of recent times occurred in 1896 and in 1932 (Snyder, 1935). These movements always happen in the fall apparently, and in years of exceptionally high populations. Snyder suggests " . . . that there may be a major cycle approximating something more than thirty years" in addition to the well-recognized 10-year cycle of numbers, and says that he " . . . is convinced . . . that these flights mark at least the greater peak periods of numbers of the northern sharptailed grouse populations which occupy the Hudson Bay region."

Baumgartner (1939) and others have recorded the eastward emigration by sharptails into Michigan's upper peninsula, which began about 1920 and culminated in 1932. The pronounced mass emigration in Ontario in 1932 was predominantly southward from the area around lower Hudson's Bay, but with some birds going southeastward (Snyder, 1935). Flocks numbering hundreds and even thousands were observed, and their travels covered some 200 to 300 miles. They reached places south and east of the normal range of the species. Here the arriving flocks were much smaller than they had been farther north. The birds' behavior on such travels is somewhat abnormal, as evidenced by their having been observed alighting in towns

and showing little fear of man. This may result, however, from their having come from wilderness areas where they had not developed wariness toward man.

The northern sharptail, apparently has a greater tendency to travel in the fall than the other subspecies; this may be due to the scattered nature of its wilderness habitat. With this inclination as a starting point, Snyder (1935) reasons a possible explanation of the mass emigration. The trigger mechanism may be a food shortage resulting from the large numbers of birds competing for food on limited areas of suitable cover. This may be accented by a failure of birch buds (a primary food) to develop, caused by the outbreak of a birch defoliating insect. Once the movement to seek food begins, it is accelerated psychologically as the flocks increase in size from the continual joining of new birds; a momentum may thus be developed that may carry them far beyond their normal haunts.

The large numbers of sharptails that were so prominent in the fall of 1932 were soon dispersed and reduced. Mortality evidently was very high, and caused by all the normal decimating agents; by winter and the following spring there were few left. The birds that reached areas of extended range generally failed to sustain permanently their numbers in the new territory.

ADAPTABILITY TO CHANGING ENVIRONMENT

THE sharptail is very responsive to changes in its environment, but is not adaptable to most kinds of habitat that differ materially from the ones in which it has always thrived. Much of the sharptail's habitat is in a rapid state of change; it depends on new areas changing from noninhabitable to habitable condition, concurrently with transition of habitable cover to a nonhabitable condition. This is especially true in the lake states.

The sharptail is a bird of the plant succession stages between open land and forest. Left alone, much of this land becomes fully forested, and no longer suitable for sharptails. If it is fully converted to farm land it becomes equally unusable for these grouse.

Man has had two great effects on sharptail habitat, through farming and lumbering. Along the fringes of its original southern range the conversion of the land to farming use has eliminated the bird. Where farming has made a patchwork pattern with forest, the species habitat has been improved. Often this improvement is very temporary, and the ultimate effect of intensive farming has been detrimental. The abandonment of farmland that proved to be submarginal to agriculture has resulted in better sharptail habitat on and around these properties for a period of several decades. Lumbering, and the forest fires that followed, speeded up the natural process of creating new habitat for sharptails. These too were temporary, and were usable only as long as they remained in brush that was not too dense. The birds quickly moved into these new habitats, and equally quickly disappeared when the cover changes became adverse. We may thus conclude that the sharp-tailed grouse is quick to take advantage of favorable habitat changes, but is not able to adapt itself to living in new kinds of environment.

TOLERANCE OF OTHER GAME BIRDS

THERE is no serious conflict between the sharptail and other game birds; they live in harmony with prairie chickens and ruffed grouse on the fringes of their habitat. In a few places they are found with ring-necked pheasants, and there are notes to the effect that the sharptails sometimes chase the pheasants. There is no evidence of any significant competition for food or living space between the sharptail and other game birds.

*ADAPTABILITY TO ARTIFICIAL
PROPAGATION AND TRANSPLANTING*

GAME farming and live-trapping and transplanting of sharptails have been tried. Baumgartner (1939) comments on Michigan attempts at game farm propagation. Wild-gathered eggs

were hatched without difficulty, but they were unable to raise the chicks. This is typical of the poor adaptability of all American species of grouse to being reared in captivity.

Sharptails can be live-trapped at winter feeding stations when there is snow on the ground; Michigan has had some success in establishing them in new areas by moving wild-trapped birds. This technique may be a practical one under some conditions.

HABITAT OF THE SHARP-TAILED GROUSE

THE core of sharptail habitat is brushland; brushy cover is to the sharptail what the grass prairie is to the prairie chicken, second-growth woodland to the ruffed grouse, and mature coniferous forest to the spruce grouse. The sharptail uses to a limited degree each of the plant successional stages that precede and follow brushland; these are mainly grass or other herbaceous cover in the preceding stage, and second-growth woodland in the following stage. But the one indispensable cover type is brush of some suitable kind. For most uses its density should be less than 50% of the ground covered with shrubs and small trees; when the land is 75% or more covered with woody plants, few sharptails can live in it (Grange, 1948). The minimum proportions of brush cover to land surface tolerable is about 5% in North Dakota, but somewhat more generally. The plant composition should be varied, both as to type of plant and species; important food-producing plants should be abundant. See Figure 13 for illustration of the habitat relationships among four species of grouse.

The brushland used by the northern sharptail consists of the following: bogs and marshes in low areas of the forest or around lake shores and along rivers, barren sand plains, frost pockets, burned-over forest areas, and man-made cuttings around settlements or where lumbering or pulp operations have been made. The natural areas

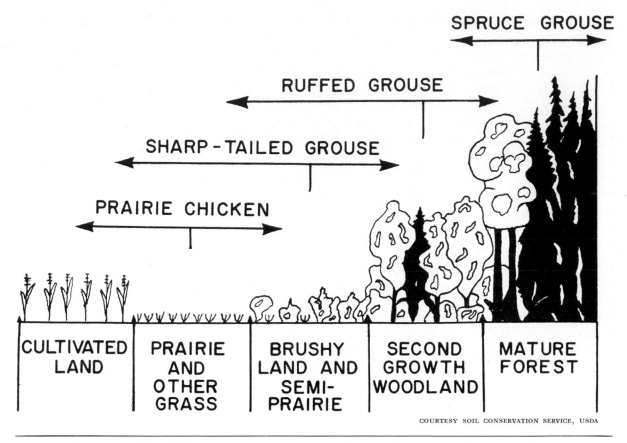

SPRUCE GROUSE

RUFFED GROUSE

SHARP-TAILED GROUSE

PRAIRIE CHICKEN

| CULTIVATED LAND | PRAIRIE AND OTHER GRASS | BRUSHY LAND AND SEMI-PRAIRIE | SECOND GROWTH WOODLAND | MATURE FOREST |

COURTESY SOIL CONSERVATION SERVICE, USDA

FIGURE 13. *Key habitat relations of four species of grouse. Each species has a key habitat type but also uses the next earlier and next later successional stages to varying degrees. (Adapted from Grange, 1948).*

are apt to be relatively small, and widely scattered through the northern coniferous forest and along its margins. White birch, blueberry, and aspen are key plants in the burns and cut-over areas. Many of the wet areas are leatherleaf bogs, cranberry marshes, and muskegs (Snyder, 1935). The burns and cut-over brushlands remain brushy longest on the infertile sandy soils.

The Columbian sharptail in its northern range uses essentially the same kind of brush habitat as the northern sharptail. In its southern range the climate is semiarid, and the vegetation differs from that farther north and east. The shrub cover is a semiclimax to climax plant association and does not develop into forest; it usually has a mixture of grasses and herbs, except along water courses. Common woody plants that compose this brush include sagebrush, Western chokecherry, western serviceberry, river hawthorn, mountain mahogany, bigtooth maple, and rose (Hart, Lee, and Low, 1950; Marshall and Jensen, 1937).

Brushland cover in the range of the prairie sharptail includes more dry soil and cut and burned woodland, and less bog and marsh than in the range of the northern subspecies. The habitat in Wisconsin is of two types, according to Hamerstrom, Hamerstrom, and Mattson (1952): "Wild lands removed from farming operations," as in the northern range; and "the transition zone between farmland and forest." In Nebraska the sharptails use the rough sandhills, where there is brush mixed with the herbaceous cover. Important elements in overgrown land abandoned from farming and on cut-over land in North Dakota, Minnesota, and Wisconsin are jack pine, white birch, quaking aspen, pin cherry, black cherry, serviceberry, wolfberry, hackberry, red hawthorn, chokecherry, chokeberry, hazelnut, wild rose, sweet fern, and shrubby willows (Grange, 1948; Aldous, 1943). The bogs have leatherleaf, Labrador tea, cranberry, and bog birch as the more prominent shrubs. Baumgartner (1939) describes the year-round Michigan habitat as " . . . characterized by the interspersion of large upland grass openings dotted with small patches of upland hardwoods, populars and birches, and small bodies of running or standing water bordered by willows and aspens."

Other cover types used by sharptails include native grass prairie, hay and pasture fields, wheat and occasionally other grain fields, hardwood and coniferous forest edges; all these types are primarily useful where closely associated with brushland. The grass and crop field types are used more on the southern parts of the range of the Columbian and prairie sharptails. The forest edges prevail more in the range of the northern subspecies and in the northern portions of the range of the prairie sharptail, and are therefore more used than the herbaceous cover, which is scarce.

Important components of the grassland habitat used by the Columbian sharptail, according to Hart, Lee, and Low (1950), include the following: blue bunch wheat grass, beardless wheat grass, cheat grass, sandberg bluegrass, June grass, onion grass, giant wild rye, mule-ears dock, cut-leaf balsam, little sunflower, lupine, balsamroot, cudweed sagewort, yarrow (*A. lanulosum*), wild buckwheat, knotweed (*P. douglasii*), and common sunflower. In the range of the prairie sharptail the prominent herbs in the open field cover may include these: bluegrass, bluejoint grass, porcupine grass, blue grama, big bluestem, little bluestem, cord grass, slender wheat grass, wild oat, sedge (*Carex*), smartweeds, lamb's-quarters, hawkweed, aster, goldenrod, pussy toes, and common sunflower. Cul-

tivated hay and pasture fields are used to a considerable extent by both the Columbian and prairie sharptails; alfalfa and clovers mixed with bluegrass, brome grasses, timothy, and other perennial grasses are the common mixtures. Farther north in the range of the northern sharptail there is little "grassland" as such; some herbaceous plants occur in the burns and along the edges of marshes and bogs; sedges (*Carex*), grasses, and mosses are found intermixed with the brushy cover.

Crop fields used most commonly are wheat, buckwheat, oats, rye, soybeans, and corn. These are used most in the fall, when they serve as feeding grounds; they also receive some use in the spring and summer for nesting, dancing, and brood feeding. They are a significant part of the habitat over much of the southern range.

Though the sharptail is not a bird of the forest it does make considerable use of forest cover; this is especially true in the northern range. The edges of tree stands of any type are used where they abut brushland, open herbaceous cover, or bare land that is itself usable cover. Hardwood stands with an abundance of white birch and quaking aspen are specially desirable, since these species furnish staple winter food. Rarely is forest cover, either hardwood or coniferous, used farther than about 200 feet from the edge, and usually not that much; mostly it is the edges that are occupied. The presence of special food supplies, such as acorns, will sometimes cause the grouse to penetrate hardwood stands farther than usual. The greatest use of woodland cover types comes in the winter, when the need for protective shelter is greatest and when more food is sought from trees.

There is an interesting relationship of cover density to seasonal use by sharptails that runs contrary to usual game-bird habits. As the protective cover of vegetation shrinks with autumnal defoliation, the usable habitat of most animals shrinks too; not so with the sharptail. Summer is the season of most restricted habitat, and winter the time of greatest freedom of cover choice. The dense foliage of summer limits the

PLATE 37. *Good range for sharp-tailed grouse, Burnett County, Wisconsin. A mixture of scattered brush, open herbaceous cover, and clumps of thick brush is ideal for these birds.*

sharptail to the more open portions of the more open brushy cover types. When winter removes the foliage from the hardwoods, much of the denser brush and the woodland edge zones become open enough to satisfy this unique bird. Sharptails are evidently inherently afflicted with claustrophobia!

The functional use of sharptail cover types is simple; moderately open brushland serves all functions through all seasons. With this beginning we may see how the variations of brushland and other cover types are utilized.

Nests are located most commonly in *open* brushland, or, we might say, in somewhat brushy herbaceous cover. In the Great Basin area the Columbian sharptail frequently nests in hayfields and grain stubble, and along fence rows on hills and benchlands, and on the nearby slopes (Hart, Lee, and Low, 1950); the prairie sharp-

tail sometimes uses purely herbaceous cover for nesting also. The nest itself is usually in a clump of grasses or herbs, or beneath or beside a bush or tree; it is rarely more than a few feet from woody brush of some sort.

Dancing grounds are in cover similar to that used for nesting, but they are often on rises in the topography that make them a slight prominence in the landscape. Most often they are in completely open cover, away from shrubs and trees. Where the ranges of the prairie sharptail and the greater prairie chicken overlap, they frequently use the same courtship performance grounds.

The summer brood habitat is essentially the same as that used in spring for nesting and dancing. It is varied with visits to somewhat thicker brush, to bogs, marshes, and creek bottoms, and occasionally to woodland edges—particularly during the high heat of the middle of the day.

Fall is a season of change in habitat use. In late summer and early autumn the birds use mostly open cover—grassy areas and scattered brush; about the time the first snow comes they shift to heavier cover. Even the birds that have been feeding on grain travel more to reach brushy roosting cover each night; some abandon the grain stubble entirely. Those living in non-farming areas move from open to heavier cover; they more and more seek out the thick brush-lands and forest edges where palatable buds are plentiful. In late autumn they gather into "packs" (Hamerstrom and Hamerstrom, 1951a) that stay together until spring. Birds in the southern range and in the Great Basin shift in the winter to the brushiest cover available. There is also a tendency on the part of adult males to center the winter habitat at or near the spring dancing ground.

Since there are isolated flocks of sharptails in many sections of the range, the question of the minimum size of a suitable habitat area to sustain them is important. Grange (1948) says that about 2,000 acres is the least needed for a habitat unit in Wisconsin that will sustain a group of sharptails through low population periods. Ammann (1952) believes that a square mile of optimum habitat is adequate in Michigan. It is probable that "holes" in the northern forest considerably smaller than 2,000 acres can carry flocks of the more mobile northern subspecies.

It is easy to see why the habitat of the sharp-tail is constantly and often rapidly changing on parts of its range; change is the most certain thing about it. A forest of today becomes a smoldering burn or an open slashing in a few days or weeks; and within a year the sharptails move in where they couldn't have existed before. If the soil is thin, sandy, and infertile, such an area may serve the birds for 40 or 50 years; if it has fertile, mellow soil, it may close them out with its regenerated tree growth within 10 to 20 years. Such is their gypsy existence (as a species rather than as individuals)—a few years here, and

then on to seek a new home. This is not as true of the parts of the range where brush and prairie grasses are climax plant associations, and where farming is carried on so as to maintain adequate brushy cover continuously between field and forest.

THE FOOD OF THE SHARP-TAILED GROUSE

THE foods used by the northern sharp-tailed grouse today are substantially the same as they always have been. In the northern range the wilderness remains, and few introduced plants have affected the sharptail there. Farther south, the prairie and Columbian sharptails have altered their diet some, as a result of the advent of farming; they get some of their food from both crop and hayfields. In some areas these cultivated fields are an important food source, though they are not vital in the bird's ecology.

These grouse are mainly vegetarians. The exception is the young sharptail chicks during the first few weeks of life, when they subsist mostly on insects. The adults too eat a good many insects during the summer, but even then most of the food is vegetable matter; for the rest of the year it is almost wholly so. More than 90% of the year's food supply is made up of fruits, seeds, grain, greens, and mast (mostly browse). Grange (1948) lists 57 species of plants and 40 kinds of insects and related animals that were found in his own Wisconsin sharptail collections alone. The total kinds of plant and animal foods eaten by sharptails no doubt is several hundred, but the more significant thing is that a relatively few kinds provide most of the bird's food.

The summer foods include a large amount of leaves and flowers of succulent plants, dry seeds, and fleshy fruits; insects make up between 10% and 20% of the total food; very little mast is used. Among the insects taken grasshoppers are most common; beetles, ants, caterpillars, bugs, and spiders are also eaten frequently. Greens of a great variety are taken; leaves of grasses, white clover, alfalfa, sagebrush (in Utah), wheat, rye, dandelion, sheep sorrel, sweet clover, blackberry, and many other plants are eaten in large amounts. Summer fruits like strawberries, western chokecherries, blackberries, and blueberries are important summer foods. Early grains and seeds of grasses, sedges, smartweeds, dandelion, and others are eaten in large amounts.

In the fall the variety of foods taken increases. The consumption of insects declines as cold weather arrives, and wild fruits are eaten more. Grains are important fall foods where the range includes farmland; wheat, corn, buckwheat, rye, oats, and soybeans are all taken where available. Among the important fall fruits are roses, snowberry, bearberry, poison ivy, blueberry, and mountainash. Dry seeds eaten in autumn include smartweeds and knotweeds, dandelion, grasses, prairie ground cherry, sagebrush, sunflower, sedges, and acorns. Among the important fall greens are the leaves of snowberry, white and sweet clovers, dandelion, grasses, wyethia, prairie ground cherry, sheep sorrel, and trembling aspen. Some bud mast is eaten in late fall, mainly from white birch, trembling aspen, pin cherry, and western serviceberry.

By winter there is a great change in the sharp-tail diet; buds, twigs, and catkins of certain trees and shrubs make up the bulk of the food. The farther north the birds live, the more completely is their winter diet made up of the mast that is always available above the snow. The plants that furnish most of this browse are the white birch, bog birch, trembling aspen, pin cherry, black cherry, willow, leatherleaf, maple, mountainash, hazelnut, western serviceberry, hop hornbeam, western chokeberry, alder, larch, blueberry, and Labrador tea. The buds and twigs of the white birch and trembling aspen alone sometimes compose up to 50% or more of the winter food in some areas. Other winter foods of significance include: the fruits of rose (prairie rose and others), bunchberry, juniper, mountainash, cedar, and blueberry; grain of buckwheat, corn, wheat, and soybeans; acorns and seeds of false climbing buckwheat, smartweeds, grasses, sunflower, sagebrush, and sedges (*Carex*); leaves of white clover, sheep sorrel, leatherleaf, wyethia, yarrow, grasses, Labrador tea, and balsam.

In early spring the food habits begin to shift away from the mast diet again. For a time the birds still consume a lot of the buds of aspen, birch, and others, but an increasing amount of greens are eaten as they become available. These include clover, alfalfa, winter wheat, winter rye, blackberry leaves, leaves and flowers of pussy toes, and wyethia. More and more insects are caught as the season progresses, and some seeds and fruits that are still left from the year before are eaten as available. Wintergreen and bearberry have been noted as specially used in spring, after the disappearance of the snow that covered them all winter. A surprising amount of wheat kernels are eaten in spring too.

The seasonal use of these several types of foods is shown graphically in Figure 14. There is some variation in this pattern of food habits in different sections of the range of the bird's subspecies, but the major differences are in the species of the several kinds of foods used. For example, winter browse used by the Columbian sharptail in Utah is mostly from western chokeberry, Western serviceberry, and bigtooth maple (Hart, Lee, and Low, 1950; Marshall and Jensen, 1937). In North Dakota the winter mast comes from willows, chokecherry, and poplar (Aldous, 1943). In Wisconsin the most prominent species of winter browse are white birch and aspen (Grange, 1948; Schmidt, 1936). Farther north the northern sharptail also utilizes the buds, catkins, and twigs of the white birch as the key winter food, with browse of blueberry, mountainash, willow, and aspen also eaten in quantity (Snyder, 1935). Thus the species used varies with the locality and the associated distribution of plants that have palatable browse. But the type of food the birds eat is substantially the same everywhere; the same parallel can be drawn for other kinds of food, and the seasons in which they

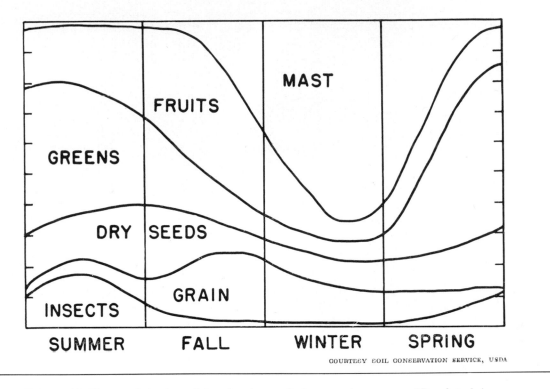

FIGURE 14. *Types of food used by the sharp-tailed grouse by seasons. (Developed from Grange, 1948; Schmidt, 1936; Snyder, 1935; Hart et al., 1950; Swenk and Selko, 1938; Marshall and Jensen, 1937; Aldous, 1943; Judd, 1905).*

are used. The major exception is that the cultivated grains and greens are not found in most of the range of the northern sharptail, and thus are not used there at all.

Sharptails are frequently found close to water, or in wet bogs and marshes. Their choice of this kind of habitat stems from their needs for open cover and some kind of brush or rank vegetation, rather than any need for drinking water. Some water and snow are ingested, but this need for water is adequately met by dew and succulent foods.

In most of its range the food habits of the sharptail have no beneficial or detrimental effects of interest to man; their eating habits are essentially neutral economically. In a few areas of the southern range of the Columbian and prairie sharptails their consumption of grain might cause some local damage. In Utah it was

noted that "The only known action by the sharptails which may be considered harmful to agriculture is the spring dancing of the birds in young grain. This is rather rare, and occurs only where the birds persist in using traditional dancing grounds that have been placed under cultivation" (Hart, Lee, and Low, 1950).

EFFECTS OF WEATHER AND CLIMATE

THE sharp-tailed grouse is eminently well fitted to cope with a rigorous climate; it thrives over a range that includes such varied climate as on the frigid tundra margins of central Alaska and Yukon Territory as far north as the Arctic Circle, and the semiarid, semiprairie country of the Great Basin, with its very hot, dry summers. The bird regularly endures extremely low winter temperatures, deep snows, and high winds. Few other game birds are as hardy as the sharptail when it comes to facing rough weather.

Climate exerts a general influence in determining the habitable range of the sharptail. In so far as it affects the character of the soils and vegetation that compose the habitat, it is significant. Climate excludes the sharptail from the drier prairies because of inadequate rainfall, from the arctic tundra by lack of adequate growing seasons, and possibly from many forested areas by humidity, with or without mountainous topography.

The behavior of the bird is influenced in many ways by weather conditions. A terrestrial bird by choice, it resorts to tree budding when snow covers its preferred foods. The same snow induces the grouse to roost beneath its warming surface to avoid wintry winds and low temperature. The habitat chosen in winter includes more woodland types than usual, a concession to the weather and the snow. But even at these times they rarely use this heavy cover more than a few hundred feet from the edges of their beloved brushland. Marshall and Jensen (1937) showed a correlation between cover types chosen and snow depth with Columbian sharptails in Utah. They also found that when the snow crusted heavily, the birds preferred to roost in bushes above the snow. Baumgartner (1939) describes the influence of stormy winter weather on the grouse's daily activities in Michigan: "On bright warm days, sharptails were observed to leave their snow roosts shortly after sunrise, spend a few minutes in a sketchy courtship display, and then fly to feeding grounds. By the middle of the morning, after their crops are stuffed, they either bury themselves beneath the snow or sit out in some open spot, apparently to enjoy the rays of the sun. Active feeding is resumed again in mid-afternoon and lasts until dusk. The contrast between this period of 8 to 10 hours and the very limited activity on extremely cold or stormy days is quite marked. On such days the sharptails do not leave their roosts until 8 to 9 a.m. Immediately they fly to a nearby feeding station or grain field or commence to fill their crops with birch or aspen buds. By 9:30 or 10 a.m. they are back into their snow forms for a 22-hour period of inactivity—not emerging again until the following morning."

The dancing-ground activity varies with the weather as well as with the season. Cold, crisp, clear, quiet days are most conducive to energetic displays, but warm, windy, rainy, or stormy weather noticeably suppresses the birds' courtship activity.

The heat of midday in summer frequently makes them seek shady spots, where they take life easy until evening; but stormy, cold weather often stimulates them to activity. Hamerstrom (letter) relates an occasion when he was hunting sharptails in western North Dakota. He "had trouble finding birds in new and unfamiliar country. Came a miserable snowstorm—howling wind, raw, cold, driving snow. Thought we'd surely find them then, for with so little brush and so much open grassy cover, they'd just naturally draw into the lee of what little brush there was. Darned if we didn't find them, finally, in the very tops of some leafless trees along a narrow draw—the most exposed position imaginable; sitting up there in the middle of the storm, happy as clowns. What a bird!"

Weather has been suspected as possibly being associated with the occasional mass migrations of sharptails in Canada, but Snyder, (1935) in his study of the 1932 emigration in Ontario, concluded, "The effect of weather conditions immediately prior to or during the flight, therefore, cannot be supposed to have been a contributing cause of the emigration of sharptails in 1932."

Relatively little is definitely known about the significance of weather as a mortality agent for the sharptail. Some observers have reported that northern sharptails have been known to die in numbers, presumably from freezing, when winter temperatures sank low, winds were strong, and no snow was available for protective roosting. Snyder (1935) indicates some plausibility to this theory, but it is difficult to say how important it is.

It is possible, in fact probable, that there is considerable loss of young chicks from bad weather at hatching time and shortly after. Hart, Lee, and Low (1950) note that "Some young chicks may succumb to chilling or wetting by heavy, early summer rainstorms, but there is no evidence to show that this constitutes a serious loss" in Utah. It is my guess that this early summer loss of young sharptails from inclement weather is probably more serious in the range of the prairie and northern subspecies than in the southern range of the Columbian sharptail. But this is mainly conjecture, based on the parallel conditions with the prairie chicken and ruffed grouse.

When weather conditions during the hatching and early brood period are exceedingly bad, this factor may cause failures of nest and brood survival so serious as to result in a sharp drop in population; two successive years of this sort and the result may well be a "cyclic" low in numbers of sharptails. Such a situation was reported to have happened in portions of the Canadian prairie provinces in 1942 and 1943 (Cartwright, 1944). Low temperatures and high precipitation at hatching time were followed by general declines in the numbers of both sharptails and Hungarian partridges in the area affected. Fall populations had few young birds, as revealed by checking hunters' bags. In contrast, the birds increased in numbers in an area unaffected by the bad weather.

Floods are not ordinarily a problem with the sharptail, because of the nature of its habitat and particularly its nest locations. Neither is drouth especially significant to the birds in itself, but it may be a very important influence, partly harmful and partly beneficial, in so far as it is related to the prevalence of forest fires.

To sum up: while weather and climate are very significant in affecting the distribution and activities of the sharptail, it is not possible adequately to appraise its part in influencing populations of the bird. There is little doubt that it is a major factor in periods of large declines in population.

PREDATION; DISEASES AND PARASITES; ACCIDENTS

PREDATION

MOST authorities agree that predation is not important in the determining of population levels of sharp-tailed grouse. The sharptails do suffer losses from predation of the eggs, young, and adults, but it is a normal attrition that rarely becomes a limiting factor. It appears that predation with this grouse is even less of a mortality agent than with some of the other grouse, but this may be due to lack of adequate study and information. Snyder (1935) notes that "There are no actual observations of northern sharp-tailed grouse being caught and devoured by natural enemies." Then he adds that " . . . it seems reasonable to suppose that a few of the birds from this [1932 emigration] flight served as food for the various carnivorous mammals and raptorial birds." This indicates the paucity of information on the subject, but also illustrates the fact that predation is not prominent in the hunter's observations on the northern sharptail.

Evidence of predation with the prairie sharptail and the Columbian sharptail is not wholly lacking; but even in areas like Utah, North Dakota, Wisconsin, and Michigan, where the bird has been carefully studied, the specific data on the importance of predation is slight.

Among the known nest predators the skunk, crow, and red fox are probably the most destructive. The magpie, coyote, weasel, gray fox, pine snake, bull snake, great horned owl, and others are occasionally responsible for the loss of a sharptail nest; but their depredations either singly or as a whole are generally incidental to their random food gathering, and not a critical matter in sharptail ecology.

The same accipitrine hawks that are the commonest predators of the young of other species of game birds also rate highest as destroyers of young sharptails; they are the Cooper's and sharp-shinned hawks. Other hawks and owls and some of the mammalian flesh-eaters also catch a juvenile sharptail occasionally, but not in large enough numbers to be a significant influence on fall populations.

Adult sharptails are regularly taken as food by a number of natural enemies. Possibly of greatest significance over the greatest area is the goshawk, but this is based on opinion more than on gathered evidence. Other predators that may be locally significant as destroyers of adult sharptails are the great horned owl, red and gray foxes, coyote, and Cooper's hawk. Others known to kill a sharptail occasionally are the red-tailed hawk, golden eagle, mink, weasel, dog, and house cat.

The sharptail is specially vulnerable to predation under one condition: it habitually snow-roosts in the winter, and then is easily caught by such astute hunters as foxes and coyotes. One would also expect them to be vulnerable when on the dancing ground. They are stalked there by these same mammals, and are commonly attacked by those skilful hunters the goshawk, Cooper's hawk, and horned owl; but few are captured. Hamerstrom (letter) says, "In hundreds of hours of blind-watching . . . we've seen hawks, owls, fox, coyote, dog, and just about all conceivable predators (except goshawk but including duck hawk) try for them, with a score of almost zero."

An interesting angle on the effect of nest predation on the production of young sharptails in certain years is presented by Cartwright (1944). In reporting on a "crash decline" of sharptails and Hungarian partridges in Alberta and Saskatchewan in 1942 and 1943, the relation of bad weather at hatching time to the survival of young was vital. Had *all* nests hatched in a short period, say a week, when very cold, wet weather struck, the production of young birds for the year would have been virtually wiped out; but according to Cartwright, "Predation on eggs, by staggering the nesting attempts (by renesting following nest destruction), guarantees the survival of a . . . proportion . . . against a general disaster to the juvenile component at any one critical period of the nesting season." Thus predation may well be one of nature's aids to the survival of prey species rather than the purely destructive phenomenon usually envisaged.

DISEASES AND PARASITES

THE parasitic fauna of the sharp-tailed grouse is very imperfectly known. Infectious disease has not been known to occur at all in this grouse. Such parasites as have been found in sharptails are not known to have been lethal in any instance. Thus about all we can say in our present state of knowledge is that disease and parasitism are not known to be important factors in the determining of the population levels of this species; that some of the species of parasites that do occur in the sharptail *could* be troublesome under circumstances of heavy infestation; and that these decimating agents are probably more effective in the young birds than in the adults.

Between 300 and 400 sharptail autopsies have been made in connection with studies of the bird and the results published. These birds were mostly from Minnesota, Wisconsin, and Michigan (Boughton, 1937; Baumgartner, 1939; Gross, 1930; Morgan and Hamerstrom, 1941; *P-R Quarterly*, July 1943). These birds were all of the prairie subspecies. Notes on four specimens of the Columbian sharptail are given by Hart, Lee, and Low (1950), and on 11 of the northern sharptail by Snyder (1935).

From these records we can say that most sharptails harbor some parasites, though, as Snyder commented, "The absence of parasitic worms in these northern birds was remarkable . . ." Morgan and Hamerstrom (1941) found that 77% of 126 Wisconsin specimens harbored one or more kinds of parasites. Altogether 19 species of parasites have been reported from sharptails, 16 of them internal and three external; they include nine kinds of roundworms, three species of tapeworms, one fluke, three protozoans, two kinds of bird lice, and one tick. Almost surely there are others that will be revealed by further studies.

The parasites known to occur in the sharp-tailed grouse are as follows:

NEMATODES

Intestinal roundworm	*Ascaridia lineata*	Common.
Caecal worm	*Heterakis gallinae*	Common.
Gizzard worm	*Cheilospirura spinosa*	Fairly common.
Caecal worm	*Subulura strongylina*	Fairly common.
Gizzard worm	*Seurocyrnea colini*	Fairly common.
Crop worm	*Capillaria contorta*	Fairly common in Wisconsin.
Caecal hook worm	*Trichostrongylus pergracilis*	Found in 19 of 27 Minnesota birds (*P-R Quart.*, July 1943).
Muscle worm larvae	*Physaloptera* sp.	Rare, one from Minnesota (Boughton, 1937).
Eye worm	*Oxyspirura* sp.	Reported only from Michigan (Saunders, 1935).

CESTODES

Small intestine tapeworm	*Choanotaenia infundibulum*	Common.
Small intestine tapeworm	*Rhabdometra nullicollis*	Fairly common.
Tapeworm	*Raillietina* sp.	In one juvenile from Wisconsin (Gross, 1930).

TREMATODES

Breast muscle fluke	*Agamodistomum* sp. larvae	In one Minnesota bird (Boughton, 1937).

PROTOZOANS

Coccidia	*Eimeria dispersa*	Fairly common.
Coccidia	*Eimeria angusta*	Uncommon.
Blood parasite	*Leucocytozoon* sp.	Reported only from Michigan (Saunders, 1935).

MALLOPHAGA

Bird louse	*Lipeurus protervus*	Reported only from Ontario (Snyder, 1935).
Bird louse	*Goniodes mammilatus*	Common.

ACARINA

Tick	*Haemaphysalis leporis palustris*	Fairly common.

None of these parasites has been demonstrated to be a significant mortality agent with sharptails, but a few of them are believed to be potentially dangerous. Both the eye worm (*Oxyspirura* sp.) and the *Leucocytozoon* blood parasite found in Michigan grouse were believed by Saunders (1935) to be potential threats; but subsequent autopsies have not confirmed these fears. The tapeworm *Raillietina* can be very destructive of young birds, and the coccidia *Eimeria* are capable of building up serious infestations (Boughton, 1937).

ACCIDENTS

Sharptails suffer less mortality from physical accidents than most species of grouse. A few die from flying into tree trunks and the like, but this is an insignificant number. In the southern range, where the birds live partly on farm land and near highways, there are some losses from flying into electric wires, fences and autos; telephone wires are the most common hazard on the plains. Some hayfield nests are destroyed by mowing machinery, and an occasional nest made in pasture may be trampled by livestock. These losses may be locally high in some years, but are not a large mortality factor with the species compared to similar losses suffered by pheasants, prairie chickens, and some other farm game birds.

MAN'S RELATIONS WITH THE SHARP-TAILED GROUSE

Man's impact on the sharp-tailed grouse presents two contrasting pictures—according to geography. In its vast northern wilderness range man has had but a negligible influence on the bird's welfare. In its southern range, from the Great Basin to the lakes states, man's influence has been and continues to be vital; it is almost as complete a limiting factor there as it is with the prairie chicken. We may therefore limit our discussion of man and the sharptail to the prairie and Columbian subspecies in the southern range. The northern sharptail's relations with man can be dispensed with by saying that the few that are shot in hunting are a minor loss. The habitat has been but little changed by man; lumbering and occasional man-set fires do provide some improvement to the habitat.

AS A HUNTER

THE sharptail did not contribute as many pieces of game to the early game harvests of the north-central states as did the prairie chicken. Some were shot and trapped for home use, sport, and commercial marketing, but were scarcely considered apart from the abundant prairie chicken. Part of the reason for this discrepancy was that the early settlers completely invaded the range of the prairie chicken, but mostly skirted the fringes of the sharptail country. It seems probable that the sharptail was not generally as abundant as was the prairie chicken, but there is no doubt that it was locally abundant where the habitat was suitable.

In time the sharptail outnumbered the prairie chicken in its overlapping range; Schorger (1944) reports that by 1840 the sharptail was the more prevalent species in Wisconsin. This trend has remained until today. In the states where the sharptail is hunted today it is frequently hunted along with the prairie chicken and the ruffed grouse. The ratio of sharptails to prairie chickens in mixed bags of these prairie grouse runs from 6.5 to 1 in Nebraska in 1951 (*P-R Quarterly,* April 1952), to 16 to 1 in Wisconsin (Grange, 1948), and 32 to 1 in South Dakota in 1950 (*P-R Quarterly,* April 1951).

The rate of success of hunters in taking sharptails varies greatly in different areas and different years. Grange (1948) reported on a 1941 study of a "kill-check" area in Wisconsin, where the hunters got a total game bird bag of .66 birds per hunter-day, of which prairie grouse (almost all sharptails) made up but .06 per hunter-day, or an average of one bird for 17 hunters in a day. In contrast, 1950 hunters in South Dakota bagged 1.1 sharptails per day, or at the rate of one bird for every 4 man-hours. This was not as good as in 1949, when the daily bag was 2.1 birds (*P-R Quarterly,* April 1951). From 1949 through 1952 Michigan sharptail hunters averaged one bird for every four hours of hunting (*Mich. Game Div. Rep.* #1177, May 27, 1953). Minnesota hunters in 1951 bagged 1.4 sharptails per hunter-day, or .36 birds per gun-hour; this was a little better hunting than in 1950 (*P-R Quarterly,* July 1952). Since these records apply exclusively to men hunting in sharptail range, the figures are higher than would apply to hunters in general.

There is very little information available on the proportion of the fall population taken by hunters. Grange (1948) estimated it to be 24% on a Wisconsin study area. Ammann (letter) calculated an average hunter take of 28% on Drummond Island, Michigan, for three years, 1945–1947. In most of the bird's range it is probably less than these figures. Even with the little information available on the question, it seems clear that hunting is not ordinarily a limiting factor in the determining of population levels of sharptails.

The total harvest of sharptails in the six states that currently allow hunting of them approximates 200,000 in good years. About half of the years in a decade will have relatively poor hunting and the figure will be lower. Occasional years will have irruptive populations, as in 1932, and then the harvest may jump way above the normal figure. In that year of peak populations the Wisconsin bag alone was 140,000, but included some prairie chickens (Scott, 1947), and Snyder (1935) quotes Ontario observers as saying that " . . . one would have no trouble in bagging 100 in a single day."

The general outlook for sharptail hunting in its southern range may be somewhat poorer than indicated above. Hunting has already ceased in Utah, Idaho, Washington, Montana, Wyoming, and Colorado, due to the greatly reduced numbers of birds. Grange (1948) predicts that "The sharptail in Wisconsin is . . . doomed as a hunted species . . . It may conceivably survive another five decades but . . . it inevitably will go on the rare and nonhunted bird list." This gloomy outlook is not shared by all observers; the outcome depends on what man does as farmer, lumberman, and conservationist, and on what nature does with drouths, forest fires, and the like.

AS FARMER AND LUMBERMAN

MAN'S activities as lumberman and farmer have had a most interesting chain of effects on the welfare of the sharp-tailed grouse. The initial effect after the settlement of the land in the lakes states was greatly to improve the bird's habitat. Farms were cut out of the forest, which made more holes in the wilderness, with their accompanying brushy edges. Cut-over forests themselves became great new areas of brush suitable for sharptail use. Then followed man-caused fires, that further reduced much of this forest cover to a growth of aspen, pin cherry, serviceberry, and blueberry, a favorite cover association for these grouse. The character of the farming itself included extensive "pastures" of stump land where the limited grazing maintained an association of grasses, weeds, and brush that afforded good sharptail habitat. Sharptails thrived on this kind of land use.

These ideal conditions for the sharptail could not last. Not only does sharptail habitat in the lakes states continually change under any circumstances, but the changes were accelerated with man's occupation of the land. The forests that were cut over were bound to grow up again; and the frequency of forest fires that followed the early lumbermen was also due to change. The primitive farming system was destined to give way to modernization. Brushy fields became unacceptable to the modern farmer; either he cleaned the field to the forest edge and improved the cropping system, or he abandoned the brushy fields to the forest. Both happened, and either way it spelled bad news for the sharptail. Thus the semifarming habitat, which became the best sharptail cover in many areas from Michigan to North Dakota a few years ago, has gradually disappeared. As though the natural process of this conversion were not bad enough, man has speeded the destruction of much of the abandoned farmland habitat by reforesting the open areas with coniferous trees. It is ironic indeed that man, in an effort to be a conservationist, should destroy one valuable resource while he builds another.

Man's influence on sharptail habitat continues today much as in the past—in type of effect if not in as spectacular a way. The first lumbering of the virgin forest is done, but wood-cutting continues. The big forest fires are nightmares of the past, but forest fires still occur. These changes still benefit the sharptail. Likewise the intensity of farming grows; brushy margins are still being "cleaned up," marshes are still being drained. As an example, M. S. McMurtrey (letter) says that the sharptail population has decreased 80% in the last few years in an area of McHenry County, North Dakota, due to the increased intensity of tillage farming and the overgrazing of pastures. Thus the brushy transition from farm fields to forest (neither by itself good sharptail habitat) is eliminated, and with it the sharptail.

What, then, is the prospect for the sharptail in this part of the range that is so influenced by farming? It is probably rather poor, for the brushy land between field and forest that still remains is almost surely destined to be plowed or reclaimed as forest. The trend to more intensive farming continues; the era of exploitive lumbering is past. Extensive clear-cutting and subsequent burning are not likely to be repeated. It seems rather clear, then, that the farmer is not going to improve sharptail habitat as a general thing, and more often than not will destroy it. The lumberman may continue to help some, but not on the scale that happened in the 19th century and early in this century. One last question remains, then: can man *as a conservationist* do any more for the sharptail in the future than man as a farmer and lumberman has done in the past?

AS A CONSERVATIONIST

MAN has for several decades been concerned about conserving sharptails. In that time his main tangible effort to help the cause has been to provide the bird with more and more legal protection from hunting. This process has reached its limit in many states, where the species is no longer legally hunted at all. But since the sharptail is not limited by man's hunting, this legal protection has not helped much.

In some places winter feeding stations have been maintained to feed the birds during bad weather. But food is not the limiting factor either, and so this well-meant practice is also futile as a means of maintaining or increasing the numbers of sharptails.

The one thing the sharptail needs is brushland habitat, extensive enough and well enough distributed to give it adequate living space. Man does have the tools with which to provide this need. He has demonstrated their use in research (Grange, 1948), but not to any appreciable degree in practice. These tools include: planned forest cuttings; controlled burning of some kinds of woody cover; the inclusion of brushy cover in acceptable farm land-use patterns; establishing land-use zoning for wildlife in forest and marginal farm-forest areas. We shall discuss these matters further under "Management of the Sharp-tailed Grouse," but for now we may merely say that it is *possible* for man as a conservationist to save the sharptail as a hunted species, but only time will tell how well he will do it.

PRODUCTIVITY AND POPULATIONS

PRODUCTIVITY

THE potential productivity of the sharp-tailed grouse is similar to that of the ruffed grouse, but is not quite as high. The birds are polygamous and probably promiscuous in their breeding habits; they breed the year after they are born, and the hens have but one brood a year.

Sex ratio is approximately even, but there is a slight tendency for an excess of males more often than otherwise. Information on sex ratio and other phrases of sharptail productivity were very inadequately known until recently. During the past decade all six states that are important in sharptail hunting have conducted studies of the bird under P-R (Pittman-Robertson Act) projects. In issues of the P-R Quarterly progress reports on this work have shown, for example, that in three years out of four, 1949–52, North Dakota birds included 50% to 54% males; in another year there were only 36% males. In Michigan, Wisconsin, Nebraska, and South Dakota other studies revealed a sex ratio varying from 42% to 55% males. There seems to be a greater number of cases where the males slightly exceeded the females than the reverse, but these data are not yet conclusive.

Summer productivity in good years is reflected by age ratios in the fall of from two to three young birds for each adult, but in poor production years there may be only one new bird or less for each old one. For example, in the January 1953 issue of *North Dakota Outdoors* biologist Wallace Blomquist reported a young-old ratio of North Dakota sharptails for 1952 of only 1.05:1, and then commented, " . . . poor reproduction occurred . . . we will go into the spring with a potentially lower breeding population. . . . " By contrast the age ratio in 1947 had been 3.7:1, reflecting as exceptionally high a rate of reproduction that year as a low rate in 1952 (*P-R Quarterly,* July 1948).

Though conclusive evidence is lacking, there is no reason to believe other than that all sharptail hens attempt nesting each year. The average clutch is about 12 eggs, though some nests have as few as five and others as many as 17. Renesting evidently occurs to a limited degree, probably by hens whose nests were destroyed early.

Sharptail nest losses are on about the same

scale as with the prairie chicken and ruffed grouse. Observations on the fate of about 200 sharptail nests have been reported in studies made in Wisconsin, Utah, North Dakota, and South Dakota. The lowest loss was 30% of 54 nests in Wisconsin, added from the work of various observers by Hamerstrom (1941). The highest loss was 75% (six of eight nests) given in a progress report from South Dakota (*P-R Quarterly*, July 1948). The largest number of nests checked in a single study was 110 in Utah, of which 63% failed (Hart, Lee, and Low, 1950). A progress report from North Dakota (*P-R Quarterly*, July 1943) reported a 32% nest loss, but did not state the number of nests observed. Grange (1948) observed eight sharptail nests, of which three were destroyed. Adding up the evidence, about 50% or more of sharptail nests are broken up for one reason or another in most years. Predation is the commonest cause of nest destruction in the range of the prairie sharptail (and probably in the range of the northern sharptail also). Desertion is a common cause of nest loss too. Farm machinery is the biggest cause of nest destruction of Columbian sharptails in Utah; nesting there is mostly in hay and stubble fields, and the result is a high loss from mowing and plowing operations (Hart, Lee, and Low, 1950). The contrast between nest losses in different kinds of cover in Utah is well illustrated by these studies; over 82% of the nests in stubble fields were destroyed, as compared with only 30% loss in "native vegetation." During periods of severe drought, as in the early 1930's, many nests are destroyed by drifting dust.

Of the small number of hens that renest, probably about half succeed in hatching their second clutch. These, added to the number of hens that hatch their first nests, make a total of a little more than 50% of all hens that have broods in most years.

The proportion of eggs that are infertile or that die during embryonic development is probably about the same 5% to 10% as for other species of grouse, but there is very little data on this matter for the sharptail. The usual number of chicks hatched is 11 for a 12-egg nest, which indicates the scope of loss from undeveloped eggs.

Broods that begin with an average of 11 chicks have the same high early losses that all kinds of grouse suffer. By the end of one month, in most years, the brood size drops to between six and nine. In years of very bad weather during and after hatching the early mortality of youngsters may be almost complete (Cartwright, 1944). At the end of two months the brood size is down to about four or five chicks; there is a further period of slight loss before the chicks become adults. But brood size then is difficult to ascertain because of the breakup of family units and the recombining of the birds into small flocks. Fall age ratios indicate the season's production and reflect brood losses. When the juvenile-adult ratio is two or three to one it reflects brood mortality of 45% to 65%. When the ratio drops close to even, or one to one, as it does some years in each decade, it indicates brood losses of 75% to 80%. Only in rare years of "crash decline" does the juvenile loss exceed 80%.

The mortality of adult sharptails from fall to spring is mostly from predation and hunting, though in some areas mechanical accidents take a significant toll. Hunting may remove as many as 25% of the birds in a few weeks in the more heavily hunted areas. Elsewhere hunting is either illegal, as in the present southern fringe of the range, or is a smaller mortality factor, as in the northern wilderness range. Total fall and winter losses from all causes are likely to be about 50% of the early fall population but accurate data on this subject are lacking. In early spring the mortality rate from predation increases as nesting activities get under way. The summer mortality of adults is very low.

LIFE EQUATION

THE yearly balance sheet of gains and losses of sharptails and the accompanying causes varies greatly in three sections of the range: the northern wilderness; the core of the range of the

TABLE 12

LIFE EQUATION OF 100 SHARP-TAILED GROUSE FOR A YEAR*

TIME	ACTIVITIES	NUMBER OF BIRDS	
		young	adult
SPRING	(1) 48 females mate with 52 males		100
	(2) All hens nest, av. 12 eggs in first clutch, 8 in second. Total 1st eggs 576		
	(3) 50% 1st nests hatch, or 24 × 12 = 288		
	⅙ hens broken up renest, 4 × 8 = 32		
	Half of renests hatch, or 16 eggs		
	5% of 1st clutch fail to hatch, or 15		
	10% " 2nd " " " " or 2		
	Thus, 17 of 304 eggs in hatched nests are lost and 287 hatch (av. 11 per nest)	287	
	(4) 30 adults die from predation, accident (30%)		70
SUMMER	(5) 5 " " " " " (7%)		65
	(6) 230 chicks die, mostly from exposure, some from predation and accidents, or 80%		
FALL	Surviving chicks become adults		122
	(7) 30 are killed by hunters, or 25%		92
FALL & WINTER	(8) 24 " " " predation, accident (20%)		68
SPRING	(9) Breeding season returns with far fewer birds than the year before.		

* The year chosen is one of marked decline in population, a common occurrence.

prairie sharptail in the north-central states and southern Canadian provinces; the southern fringe zone, where the species is reduced to more or less isolated remnants. For our purpose in illustrating a typical year's life equation, we will assume a population of 100 prairie sharptails living on good range. The figures used are illustrative, and should not be considered as scientific data; much more research is needed on the mortality factors of this species. This series of events is given in Table 12. It illustrates a year in which the losses exceed the gains and the "equation" is far from true. This is a common occurrence with these cyclic birds. The details of these events will change according to time and place. Where hunting is illegal or not intensive, this factor will be smaller than shown, and other factors will be larger to take up the slack. When the nesting and juvenile losses increase above the rates shown,

later predation is likely to take a smaller number of birds, but the net result of the year's changes may be a reduction in population. In years when the nesting and brood losses are lower than shown, there will probably follow an increase in numbers.

POPULATION DENSITIES

THE number and distribution of spring dancing grounds depends both on the number of birds and the availability of suitable locations. On a 130,560-acre study tract in Wisconsin Grange (1948) found 69 sharptail dancing grounds in 1941 (some of them were used jointly with prairie chickens), or one for every 1,900 acres. The sharptail population, calculated from counts of cocks on the dancing grounds, was 555 birds, or one per 235 acres. The following year the population increased 26% to a bird per 187 acres (or one per 131 acres of actually occupied habitat), but the number of dancing grounds used dropped two. Hamerstrom (1939) found seven dancing grounds on a 100,000-acre Wisconsin area, but he felt that there were others not located. The sharptail population wintering on this tract was estimated at about one per 85–100 acres. A later survey on three Wisconsin areas showed that there were from 10 to 14 square miles of land for each dancing ground in 1949 (*Wisconsin Wildlife Research,* July 1949). On Drummond Island, one of the best areas of sharptail habitat in Michigan, Ammann (letter) found "slightly less than one dancing ground per square mile of occupied range over the past nine years (prior to 1947). Spring populations for three years (1945–47) averaged about 213 birds (cocks and hens) on the 15 square miles of occupied range, or a bird per 45 acres."

There is little data on nest densities, but one may presume that they would average slightly less than half the concentration of the total spring population. For Wisconsin conditions, as noted above, nests might be distributed about one for every 200 to 500 acres. A South Dakota survey in 1947 revealed one nest per 110 acres for a small area (*P-R Quarterly,* July 1948).

Fall populations have been estimated in several localities. Grange (1948) quotes Leopold's survey that showed a bird per square mile for the whole state of Wisconsin in 1930, or one per 50 acres of occupied range; and Schmidt's estimate of one per 60 acres for the occupied range in a single Wisconsin county. Aldous (1943) refers to a 1936 November census of 4,000 birds (including a few prairie chickens) on 483,000 acres of North Dakota dune country, or one per 125 acres. Michigan study area censuses have shown densities of 40 and 75 acres per bird in the summer of 1941 (*P-R Quarterly,* January 1942), and 27 acres per bird in 1949 when the population neared its maximum (*P-R Quarterly,* January 1950). Amman (letter) calculated that the fall population on Drummond Island was a bird per 18 acres of occupied range. It changed little in the seven years after 1945.

These "average" figures even though accurate, tend to be somewhat misleading. Because of the special nature of sharptail habitat much of the cover in an area may not actually be used, especially farm fields and forest; even on a very local basis, when we say that there are 50 acres per bird, or some such figure, most of these acres may not be actually used by the birds. If the acres of actually occupied habitat could be determined easily, the population density figures would be much more impressive. But the vital fact remains that the land as a whole in sharptail range supports rather limited numbers of these birds today.

FLUCTUATIONS IN POPULATION

THE trends in population levels of sharptails have shown pronounced changes periodically; this fact is in accord with similar changes in the numbers of many species of animals throughout the northern states and Canada. Grange (1948) reviewed evidence of high and low periods of abundance, especially in the works of Schorger and Criddle, and concluded that for prairie grouse there is a record of " . . . 10 consecutive lows in 90 years (from 1857 to 1947) . . . with no time lag of more than one year from a regular periodicity of ten years. This series is so truly remarkable that it is startling." He agrees with Schorger's conclusion that prairie chickens and sharptails " . . . exhibit cyclic behavior simultaneously or identical in time."

There is no doubt about the ups and downs of sharptail numbers; and it seems clear that when large declines occur they are likely to be precipitous. The regularity of the decline in time and geography is imperfect, as with other cyclic species. For example, the crash decline of sharptails in the Canadian prairie provinces in 1942 and 1943 (Cartwright, 1944) may have happened a little ahead of the Wisconsin decline, which reached its last low period in 1946 or 1947. The period of 1946 to 1950 was one of continuous increase in the sharptail populations in Michigan; it was a year or two later, 1948, before the Wisconsin population began to rise again. No evidence of cyclic population changes in Utah sharptails has been recognized (Hart, Lee, and Low, 1950). Thus there are some discrepancies in the clarity of the cycle for sharptails, as for other grouse; but this is merely to say that we do not yet understand the phenomenon well enough.

In addition to the cyclic ups and downs of the sharptail populations in most of its range, there are sometimes other population trends. In the southern fringe range the influence of farming has caused a progressively downward trend for several decades, and may eliminate the sharptail from even more of its former range. The opening up of the forest area of the north-central states and southern Canada caused an upward trend in sharptail numbers for several decades, which we presume was superimposed on the cyclic changes. This trend is now reversed as the forest closes again, and there probably will be fewer and fewer sharptails for some time in the area from Michigan to Minnesota. Cyclic changes will modify the steadiness of this trend, but will not alter its general direction.

MANAGEMENT OF THE SHARP-TAILED GROUSE

MANAGING the sharp-tailed grouse involves three kinds of situations or areas, each very different from the other two. They almost but not quite correspond to the distribution of the subspecies.

The simplest management situation is the northern wilderness country, populated by the northern sharptail, which extends from northern Ontario to central Alaska. There is little hunting for sharptails in this range, and little urgency for objectively managing the species. Most of what will be said about land use and development for sharptail habitat will apply here only in principle, and will find little practical application.

The second management area has two parts: the southern range of the Columbian sharptail from northern Utah northward into British Co-

lumbia; and the southwestern portion of the range of the prairie sharptail. In portions of this area agricultural demands on the land have reduced the sharptail to remnant populations, and management must be aimed at preventing extermination. There is little likelihood of developing huntable populations. Other parts of this zone, especially in sections of the Dakotas and Nebraska, are semiprairie country, with predominantly sandy soils; here the land is partly farmed, but has a considerable mixture of poor land. The opportunity for sharptail management is rather good, and revolves around the proper use and treatment of the nonfarm areas. Sharptail management in this entire zone relates to agriculture, and to semiarid country with little forest as such.

The third management situation is the core of the prairie sharptail range, from Michigan and southern Ontario to the eastern Dakotas and the Canadian prairie provinces. Some northern sharptails may be found in the Ontario portion of this zone. The management problems here are primarily concerned with forest land and the farming area intermixed, or along the edges of the forest; it is here that the primary hunting opportunity exists. Much of what follows will apply mainly to this area.

LAND USE AND DEVELOPMENT

THE key to sharptail habitat is brushland; it makes less difference how and of what that brushy cover is composed than that there be plenty of it. This is most unfortunate for this fine game bird, since brush cover, however it may be developed, is always in conflict with man's most urgent land-use interests. This is partly due to his lack of appreciation of the values of brushland; but it derives more importantly from his determination to make land grow either farm crops or tree crops. If land is suitable for agriculture, the farmer wants to remove any brush that may be on it so that farm crops can be grown. If the land has been lumbered or is suitable for growing trees but not for farm field crops, then the owner wants to regenerate trees as fast as possible. He even re-forests soils that have little chance of growing merchantable timber, in the belief that tree-planting is always good "conservation." The great problem in sharptail management is to fit brushland into an acceptable land-use economy.

If adequate brushland is available, the sharptail can make good use of nearby cover of woods, grass, or even crop fields. We shall therefore discuss the development of brushland and the associated cover types in the forest climax plant association and in the semiprairie country.

FOREST HABITAT IMPROVEMENT

BRUSHLAND can occur in a generally forested area in several ways. There may be natural glades that develop on thin, light soils or in frost pockets; wet areas that have a climax cover of marsh or bog vegetation; farm and prairie edges where land is abandoned or partly grazed; cut-over land, after lumbering; regeneration after forest fires. Sharptail management should take advantage of all natural openings and edges that occur in the forest, even if they are too small for use by themselves. The unit can be developed most economically by making clear-cuttings or controlled burns adjacent to marshes, bogs, and glades. About 2,000 acres is the minimum size unit to be adequately useful for sharptails; of this at least one-quarter must be open or brushy —preferably more. Where natural openings are not available to serve as nuclei for habitat units, they can be developed only by cutting or burning.

Tree harvests that are to be useful in the creation of sharptail habitat must be clear-cuttings. This system is not considered good forestry practice for most types of woodland, but is suitable for pure stands of jack pine and aspen. These types provide considerable opportunity for such cuttings in sharptail range, and the only adjustment needed from regular forest harvest objectives would be the areal pattern and the timing of the cuttings. It is desirable to have the harvest made in blocks of from 40 to 500 acres,

and with each newly cut block adjacent to the previous one; a succession of age classes of brush and second-growth woods will result over a considerable area. When the first unit of a cutting rotation becomes closed in by regeneration after a decade or two, another unit close to it can be cut. Such a rotation, if on a 50-year cycle, for example, with annual cutting units, would have 10% of the area under five years old at all times. If the blocks of each age are well dispersed, the sharptail carrying capacity should be well sustained.

Controlled burning offers a low-cost method of maintaining limited areas in sharptail habitat where the forestry system will not do the job as a by-product of its operations. There has been enough trial and demonstration of this type of work in Wisconsin and Michigan now to establish its feasibility (Grange, 1948; Jenkins, 1948). Burning should be limited to sites unsuitable for growing commercial timber; these will be areas of sandy or wet soils. Frequently they are clothed with poor stands of aspen, birch, scrub oak, serviceberry, cherry, willow, and jack pine. Units burned may be from 40 to 200 acres or more, unless a smaller unit can be combined with a natural opening to make the desired size. Such areas may need to be reburned every five to ten years, depending on the rapidity of regrowth. The job should be supervised by experienced men. The time for burning is early spring before plants start growing, when the weather is quiet and the ground moderately dry, and before sharptails are nesting. The treated area should be delimited by roads, water margins, or plowed fire breaks. Grange (1948) found the cost to be 30 cents per acre, but he felt that it could be cut to 10 cents; Jenkins (1948) did his work for 27 cents an acre. Jenkins points out that in some areas the blueberry harvest that is aided by the burning treatment can help offset the costs.

The concept of burning for habitat improvement will no doubt surprise and shock many conservationists who have felt that land—especially woodland—should be completely pro-

COURTESY MICHIGAN GAME DIVISION

PLATE 38. *Controlled burning is a technique for managing sharp-tailed grouse habitat. A burn is set along a firebreak, a road in this instance.*

tected from fire. Unquestionably there will be objections to it raised; but before the reader reaches an opinion on the subject he should consider several points. The Indians burned the prairies and some wooded areas for untold numbers of generations; they did it mainly to improve game conditions. After all that history of fire use, the soil and the land cover were in wonderfully fertile condition when the white man took it over. Blueberry farmers in Maine and Michigan have long used controlled fire to "cultivate" their berry crop on land similar to that suggested for sharptail management. Good forestry practice now includes "controlled" or "prescribed" burning in stands of longleaf pine in the Southeast and of pitch pine-oak stands in New Jersey, as a means of preventing wild fire and controlling reproduction. Controlled burning in the same longleaf pine stands of the Southeast has proved its value in bobwhite quail man-

agement. It should be clearly understood that controlled burning such as is suggested here has no relation to wild forest fires.

The use of fire in land management for growing crops of fruit, trees, and game is finding its proper place as we gain experience and overcome prejudice. As far as managing sharptails in forested areas is concerned, it appears that controlled fire is the only tool that is inexpensive enough to use on a large enough scale to be significant. The alternative is to rely wholly on the accidental bounty of the lumbering business and nature's own forest fires; but where sharptail hunting is important that alternative is not enough.

FARM HABITAT IMPROVEMENT

ALONG the farming fringes of the lake states forests, in the sand dune country of the Dakotas, on the semiprairie grazing lands of Nebraska,

PLATE 39. *A burned area after treatment, with unburned cover in the foreground separated by a plowed firebreak.*

and in the Great Basin the management of the sharptail involves mainly land used for agriculture; it is frequently a mixture of cropland and grassland or range, often with some nonfarmed land also.

Where the extent of brushland and brushy grassland has not been too severely reduced by cultivation and overgrazing, fairly good sharptail populations are still produced; where cultivation and grazing have destroyed the brushy habitat, sharptails are likely to remain in scattered remnants, if at all. Only if some of such land can be retired from farming, or—in the lakes states—if some of the bordering forest can be converted to brush, is there much chance of improving the sharptail habitat.

Grazing control is often the key to the problem of improving sharptail cover. Land subject to serious deterioration under livestock grazing, like the dune areas in North Dakota, should be fenced to exclude all livestock (Aldous, 1943); other grassland should be grazed within its carrying capacity for sustained use without damage. When this cannot be accomplished, recourse to public ownership of the land may be warranted to preserve some suitable habitat. Light grazing on cut-over lakes states forest is helpful in maintaining habitat. Fires should be discouraged on most of this rangeland, except where needed to open dense stands of sagebrush or other brush that is too thick for livestock and sharptails.

Delaying hay harvest until after nesting is completed is advantageous, where it can be done without loss of crop quality. Plowing of grain stubble or hayfields is best completed early in spring before nesting begins, wherever the weather permits.

Plantings of shrubs on sand dunes, hedgerows, and windbreaks, and on other areas where brush cover is desired, are feasible where the species planted are preferred to the ones that would come in naturally under the exclusion of grazing.

The cultivation by plowing of glades, semidry marshes, and similar openings is suggested by Grange (1948) as a means of maintaining such areas, where heavy sod- or brush-breaking machinery can be used. This practice may be feasible on some public game lands, but it is costly.

LAND-USE POLICY AND ZONING

ONE of the problems that has aggravated the loss of sharptail habitat in Wisconsin and Michigan has been the foresting of abandoned farm lands with conifers under the encouragement of state and Federal forestry programs. It is regrettable that this work, which is done as "conservation," should destroy one valuable resource while developing another. One may debate the question of which resource is the more valuable, conifers or sharptails; possibly there is a compromise policy that would favor each to a degree, and be best for the public interest. Wisconsin authors in particular have warned that unless this tree-planting program is adjusted the sharptail may be driven out of much of its present habitat in that state (Scott, 1947; Grange, 1948; Hamerstrom et al., 1952). They suggest that there is a need for a public policy that would reserve certain kinds of open areas to be left unplanted. A policy could well be established for public lands, and a start already has been made in Michigan; there all plantings on state lands are reviewed by a district game supervisor before approval (Ammann, letter). Whether such a policy could be implemented by land-use zoning is at least doubtful, but it certainly could be carried out to some degree with an attitude that encouraged it. To be as consistent as possible with forestry practice, the areas to be left unplanted—and presumably to be maintained in brushy cover—should be those on the poorest soils—the shallowest, sandiest, most infertile situations. These would be the easiest to keep open, as well as the least useful for growing trees; regrettably they are also least productive of sharptails.

Whether such a public policy is achievable de-pends on public understanding of the problem, and public demand that sharptail habitat be managed where it can be done economically. The present public policy is more likely to discourage the development of sharptail habitat. Hamerstrom, et al. (1952), describe the case of the Namekagon Barrens in Wisconsin. These are sandy barrens of mixed grass, blueberry, sweet fern, and scrub oak cover, ideal for sharptails; they were recently planted to pines. These authors ask, "Why was it not saved for sharptails?" They answer their own question, "Because there is a forest crop law which offers a strong inducement to plant trees, but there is no comparable inducement to leave openings unplanted for wildlife." We talk glibly of "multiple use" management, but we have not practiced it very well. Here is a case where the care of one resource requires that the full development of another resource be modified; it is a chance to practice what we preach about multiple use. The sharptail requires some special consideration if it is to be retained as a game species. As Grange (1948) says, "The management of . . . sharptails begins and ends with *land management*, for which the control of hunting and other factors is not even a poor substitute."

MISCELLANEOUS MANAGEMENT PRACTICES

DESPITE Grange's comment above, on the limits of sharptail management, there may occasionally be other practices than habitat management that are worthy of consideration.

It has already been mentioned that *refuges* may have a place in preserving remnants of sharptail populations against the onslaught of intensive farming. This is an exception to the general rule that refuges are of no value in sharptail management. Ordinarily refuges are used to protect the species from hunting. The refuges that may be properly established for sharptails have no relation to hunting; they are to provide an island of suitable habitat for a group of birds that would otherwise be completely lost.

Winter feeding and food patches have been

used some for sharptails, but on good range are not needed, and are not believed to be worth while; they have some possible value in poor quality habitat. The control of predators in order to benefit sharptails is equally unnecessary and futile; without good habitat, predator reduction is useless; and where the habitat is adequate, predator control is not needed.

The restocking of wild-trapped sharptails in areas where the species is present is wasted effort. There are possibilities for establishing new colonies of sharptails in areas of suitable range not naturally occupied; this has been done with success in the eastern part of Michigan's upper peninsula and in the northern part of the lower peninsula (Baumgartner, 1939; *P-R Quarterly,* January 1951). It is being attempted in parts of northern Pennsylvania this year (1953).

PROTECTION AND HARVEST

OPEN seasons for hunting sharptails may be justified in most years in states having good enough range to warrant hunting them. The years at the bottom of a population cycle will not offer good hunting, and possibly the season should be closed then—at least in the fringe portions of the range, where the sharptail populations are least secure. The birds should be completely protected, as they now are, in the southern portions of the range, where the populations are already reduced to remnants.

In years of shootable numbers, a season of from two to four weeks is warranted, and daily bags of from three to five birds are safe. In the northern portions of Canada the restrictions may well be more liberal. These arrangements are now generally followed in the sharptail-shooting states.

The primary problem in setting seasons and bag limits is to determine the population level. This requires a system of annual censuses by the state wildlife agency. Such counts can give an accurate appraisal of *trends* in the sharptail populations.

The most effective census technique involves a spring count on dancing grounds, and a summer check of brood sizes. Sample areas should be selected, and the same ones used each year. All dancing grounds in a census unit, such as a township, should be located by listening for hooting at points along roads; this is a difficult task to do thoroughly. Counts of males should be made during the height of the courtship season. Cool, clear, quiet mornings should be chosen, and the time limited to from three-quarters of an hour before to about two hours after sunrise. The sex ratio would be very desirable to have, but it is difficult to obtain in extensive management census work; it requires careful observations with binoculars or 'scope, and frequent stalking to get adequate views.

The summer brood count can be made by covering the census area on foot with the aid of trained dogs; it should be done early in the day, when it is cool and dewy. In open cover the habitual shady summer loafing places can be found and checked; in habitat with lots of loafing cover, it is necessary to traverse the area systematically. These counts are laborious, and often less than satisfactory.

The data from these censuses becomes most valuable after several years, because of the importance of comparing the current data with those of past years to determine trends and population levels.

Another means of keeping check on productivity (though it is not useful in setting hunting seasons) is the fall age ratio. Specimens are obtained from hunters for examination. The procedure for getting the age ratio for sharptails is exactly the same as that described for the prairie chicken (see page 194).

CHAPTER 5

The Prairie Chicken

CLASSIFICATION

THERE are two species of prairie chickens native to our Western plains states. The greater prairie chicken, or plain "prairie chicken," is the common one over the greatest area; its scientific name is *Tympanuchus cupido americanus* Reichenbach. There are three subspecies, of which the greater prairie chicken is one. The Attwater's prairie chicken (*T. c. attwateri* Bendire) is a somewhat darker variety, that still exists in small numbers in southeastern Texas. The third subspecies is the type form, the extinct heath hen (*T. cupido cupido* Linnaeus), which was once found in the Atlantic coastal area from Virginia to Massachusetts. The second species is the lesser prairie chicken (*Tympanuchus pallidicinctus* Ridgeway); it has only one form.

These birds belong to the family Tetraonidae, the grouses; they are also called pinnated grouse. Along with their close relative, the sharp-tailed grouse, they are also commonly called prairie grouse. The sharptail and the greater prairie chicken sometimes cross and produce hybrids.

All the varieties of the prairie chickens will be treated together; such comment as is necessary to distinguish species or subspecies will be given where appropriate.

DESCRIPTION

THE prairie chicken, as its name indicates, is a chickenlike bird. It is more than a third larger than the ruffed grouse, slightly larger than the sharptail, and much smaller than the sage grouse. The average weight of males is a little over two pounds, with the largest about two and one-half pounds. The females average about one pound ten ounces, and occasionally weigh almost two pounds; the lesser prairie chicken is somewhat lighter. The length is from 15 to 18 inches.

The color of the male is predominantly rufous brown, broken up by cross-barring over most of the body. On the back and wing coverts the pattern is variegated with irregular blackish bars. The primaries and secondaries are brown, with whitish spots on the outer webs; the under wing coverts are brown and white. The breast and belly are barred about evenly with brown and white.

The brownish head has a slight crest. Chin, cheeks, and throat are buff, with some darker spots; and a dark brown line runs from the base of the bill under and back of the eye. They have a fleshy, orange-colored eyebrow. The sides of the neck have tufts of erectile, elongated, stiff, blackish feathers marked with buff and brown, and rounded at the ends. These feathers are very distinctive (on the heath hen they were similar, but *pointed* at the ends); beneath each of these "pinnae" is a loose sac of bare, yellow-orange skin, and capable of great distention. These are called air sacs or tympani.

The tail is short and rounded; it is made up of 18 rather wide rectrices. Its color is brown, like the wing flight feathers, and it has a whitish tip. The upper tail coverts are colored like the back feathers, and extend at the center almost to the tip of the tail. The under tail

PLATE 40. *Prairie chicken.*

GEOGRAPHICAL RANGE AND DISTRIBUTION

THE prairie chicken once lived on all the prairie lands of the United States east of the Rockies, and well into the Canadian prairie provinces. One of its subspecies, the extinct heath hen, occupied the Atlantic coastal prairies from Virginia to Massachusetts, and possibly into New Hampshire and southern Maine. This shows that at some time in recent geologic history—but probably some thousands of years ago—the species had a continuous range from the central prairies to the Eastern coast.

The range occupied today is a small remnant of the original; it consists of one large area and several smaller ones. The large northern range extends from the eastern part of Michigan's upper peninsula west to the northeast corner of Montana, north into three Canadian provinces, and south in two sections to northern Illinois, central Nebraska, and northeastern Colorado. In most of this range the birds occur in scattered small areas. The second largest area of the greater prairie chicken's range extends across the central plains states from south-central Iowa south, through northeast, central, and southwestern Missouri into southeastern Kansas and northeastern Oklahoma. The birds actually use only small portions of all this area. There are a few other small areas where small remnants remain in southeastern Illinois, northwestern Indiana, and northeastern Illinois. The Indiana range includes parts of nine counties, but most of the birds occur in one county. All this range so far described is that of the greater prairie chicken. Accurate maps that show the range actually occupied are given in Schwartz (1945) for Missouri, in Baker (1953) for Kansas, in Janson (1952) for South Dakota, and in Scott (1947) for Wisconsin.

Attwater's prairie chicken now occurs only in a small area of Gulf coast prairies in southeastern Texas, from about Galveston south for 200 miles; Lehmann (1941) gives an accurate

coverts are white, with some spots of various shades of brown. The tarsi are feathered to the toes, and are bare and yellow behind. The feet are yellow, and slightly webbed at the base of the toes. The bill is horn brown; and the iris of the eye is hazel.

The female is similar to the male, but somewhat smaller, and the pinnae are shorter. The neck sacs are very small, and the orange flesh colors are lacking on neck and eyebrows. Her tail is more barred.

Attwater's prairie chicken is slightly smaller and generally darker than the greater prairie chicken. It is somewhat tawnier on the upper parts. The total difference in the two subspecies is slight.

The lesser prairie chicken is several ounces lighter than its relative. Its general color is paler, and the pattern of barring on the back is different; the smaller species has the barring in groups of three instead of two, the brown stripes being flanked by narrow black lines on both sides instead of one.

The juveniles are similar to the female, but lack the pinnae. The downy young are mottled brown and yellowish with black spots above and greenish-yellow below.

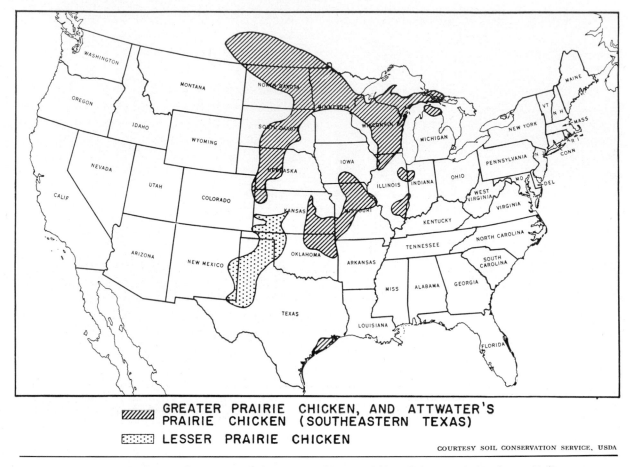

GREATER PRAIRIE CHICKEN, AND ATTWATER'S
PRAIRIE CHICKEN (SOUTHEASTERN TEXAS)

LESSER PRAIRIE CHICKEN

COURTESY SOIL CONSERVATION SERVICE, USDA

FIGURE 15. *Geographic range of the prairie chickens. (After Schwartz, 1945; Scott, 1947;*
Baker, 1953; Janson, 1952; Lehmann, 1941; and others).

map of the several locations in this area where this vanishing bird is still found.

The lesser prairie chicken is also restricted to small parts of its original range. The area in which it is still found runs from southwestern Kansas south through western Oklahoma to western Texas and eastern New Mexico.

All these parts of the prairie chicken range are shown in Figure 15.

HISTORY OF THE PRAIRIE CHICKEN

THE early colonists became acquainted with the eastern subspecies of the prairie chicken, the heath hen, as soon as they arrived in Mas-

sachusetts and Virginia; it was very common in the restricted areas of scrub oak plains that mostly composed its habitat. It was used on the table of the local residents, along with the ruffed grouse and wild turkey. For a time it was sold in the Boston markets, but its numbers soon decreased as the new civilization engulfed its narrow homeland; by 1870 it had been completely extirpated from the mainland, and only a single remnant remained, on Martha's Vineyard island. The story of the effort to save the heath hen on Martha's Vineyard from extinction is one of the early epics of game-bird conservation in this country (Gross, 1928).

By 1890 the Martha's Vineyard heath hen

population had dropped to about 100 birds, and in 1908 it had dwindled to 50 (Gross, in Bent, 1932). Then the state of Massachusetts and private citizens co-operated in purchasing about 1,600 acres as a reservation for the heath hen, provided vigilant protection, and planted corn and clover to improve the food supply of the habitat. As a result the population had increased to about 2,000 birds by 1916, when a succession of catastrophies ended the good work. A fire swept most of the island on May 12th, destroyed cover and nests, and some of the birds. The following winter, one of the worst on record, caused some mortality. At the same time a southward migration of goshawks contributed to the reduction of the hens, so that fewer than 150 remained in the spring; and these were mostly males. A few more birds were produced in the next few years, but disease—probably blackhead—which attacked the flock proved to be the "last straw"; the birds dwindled, until in 1928 a single male remained. He died sometime in 1931, the last of his race, but fortunately not the last of his species.

When the early pioneers came over the Alleghany Mountains and out upon the plains of the Midwest, they found the prairie chicken abundant. Here was its optimum habitat—prairies of big and little bluestem and associated grasses, stretching as far as the eye could see, and broken only by the bands of woody cover along the stream courses. The stories of the early abundance of chickens parallel those of the buffalo. It was unthinkable that men could seriously reduce the numbers of a bird that was abundant over thousands of square miles of the middle of the continent. What was not anticipated was that the prairie chicken range would become the "bread basket" of a great nation.

The chicken did in fact prove very adaptable to the early changes that came with the development of prairie agriculture. The grass sod was broken to grow corn and wheat, and the birds found this cultivated land quite acceptable as a component of their range. They soon took to eating these grains, and their habitat was actually improved in many areas—just as long as the conversion to cultivation was not too complete. The birds' great mobility enabled them to take advantage of man's expanding agriculture; and they actually extended their range north and west far beyond its natural extent, as the plow broke the way. For example, they first appeared in North Dakota in 1870. They came east from Wisconsin into Michigan, until the great decline of the 1930's halted the trend. Transplants helped to establish them in the northern portion of Michigan's southern peninsula—though this remains a precarious holding.

A good share of the present range that the bird occupies in the northern states and Canada is in the extended area. It has enough agriculture to help the chickens, and yet not so extensive as to ruin it for them. Most of the best of the original range was so completely turned into plowland that the prairie chickens had to give way; they still required a considerable amount of their beloved prairie grass.

The tales of the numbers of chickens shot and trapped by hunters and homesteaders in the late decades of the 19th century sicken the conservationist of today; Lehmann (1941) tells of birds being piled by the hundreds after a hunt and left to rot. Coveys would be flushed in such rapid order that the singles of one were still being shot when another group would rise. He estimates that at that time there were probably a million Attwater's chickens on 6 million acres of south Texas coastal plains alone; now there are fewer than 10,000 on the 450,000 acres still in the occupied zone.

In addition to the large numbers taken by gunning, there were many trapped by the prairie homesteaders for home use on their tables. These were rarely wasted, and probably did not deplete the population appreciably.

The conversion of the prairies to grain farming drove the chicken from much of its range, though that change was aided by other factors as well. The bird managed to hold on where the agricultural pattern retained a large amount of grassland. Since the modern trend in agricultural land use is toward increased amounts of grassland and a less amount of tilled land, the worst period for the prairie chicken may have passed; it should be able to remain in most of the range it now occupies, and may even be able to extend its range back into some of the country from which it was eliminated. This optimistic note is not an assured fact, but is at least a reasonable hope.

As the chicken populations declined rapidly after the turn of the century, the species was given increased protection from hunting. Since hunting was not the main cause of its trouble, the chicken continued to disappear. Most states discontinued hunting seasons for prairie chickens entirely; Missouri closed the season in 1907, and it has been closed ever since. Only four to seven states have had open seasons in recent years—North Dakota, South Dakota, Nebraska, Kansas, Wisconsin, Oklahoma, and Michigan. The total kill is small in comparison with many other game species. Its importance as a game bird thus lies primarily in the hope that sometime in the future it may once again provide much more hunting over a great area of our plains country.

HABITS OF THE PRAIRIE CHICKEN

COURTSHIP

THE courtship of the prairie chicken cocks is a marvelous and unique performance. It is done on a *booming ground,* which is an open area of sparse cover, often on a rise of land; the area used may be from 150 to 500 feet in diameter. The cocks from a wide area begin to gather on the booming ground on balmy days in midwinter, but the activity begins in earnest in March. The height of the activity is early April, but it continues with lessening vigor and participation until June.

The number of cocks that gather on a particular area varies with the density of the population and the prevalence of suitable sites; generally there are about a dozen. There may be from two up to 40 or more, but any booming ground with more than 15 cocks is a large one. The birds arrive by flight or walking, usually a little before sunrise, for the morning performance; its duration is about an hour and a half. In the afternoon they arrive an hour or more before sunset, and leave soon after sunset; they almost always leave by flight. On cloudy days they may remain all day. These grounds are used year after year; some have been used continuously for at least 40 years, despite changes in the use of the land from native prairie grass through cultivation, hay, and pasture (Schwartz, 1945).

Each cock goes to a specific part of the booming ground which is his special territory; the amount of the ground each bird defends is 10 to 15 square yards—occasionally more or less. In the early season much of the activity is the real or shadow fighting that goes on between the cocks in connection with the establishment of their individual performance areas. Competition seems greatest for interior positions, for it is here that the hens come later on. By the time the breeding period comes there is little fighting among the males for territory; they then concentrate on courtship.

The performance is an individual one, even though there are many birds performing at once. There is little or no co-ordination of the acts, except as one bird may involve another as a protagonist. The act begins with a short run, ending with a quick stop. The cock then stamps his feet on the ground rapidly in one spot, sometimes pivoting as he does so; while so doing he erects his pinnae, and inflates the neck air sacs like small oranges. His tail is spread in an upright fan, and his wings droop. Then he makes the booming sound for which he is famed. It originates in the voice box, and is amplified by the resonant effect of the air sacs. It is a three-note call, each note being a bit higher in pitch than the one before; the total interval for this performance is two or three seconds. The char-

PLATE 41. *Wisconsin prairie chickens booming on abandoned farm land.*

acter of the sound has been well described by Schwartz (1945) as like ". . . the lower notes of an ocarina or the sound made by blowing across the open neck of a bottle."

When a number of cocks are booming at once the total effect is that of a continuous hollow roar. The sound is penetrating, and can be heard for a mile or more on still days. The direction from which the sound comes is often difficult to tell because of the ventriloquistic quality of the notes.

When the cock finishes booming, the air sacs are quickly deflated. The bird then jumps a foot or more into the air, all the while uttering a wild mixture of cacklings. The body twists in the air, so that he often lands facing in the opposite direction from which he started. He may then lower his head and run toward a nearby cock; this may be merely a bluff, or they may actually exchange a few blows. A few feathers

may fly, but they are seldom hurt in these skirmishes.

The reason for all this mad act is the same as with the analogous performances of the other kinds of grouse—namely, to attract and impress the females, or to challenge or intimidate other males.

The hens begin coming to the booming grounds in March. At first their visits are short, and their arrival is greeted by great activity by all the cocks. The cocks leave their own territories and fight for the attention of the hens, but the hens give little heed; there is almost no mating at this time. By early April the hens visit the booming grounds regularly, and stay long. The hens tend to gather at the center of the area, and generally display little emotion over the bizarre activities all around them. The cocks now keep to their own territories, and wait for a hen's acceptance. When this is given, the cock displays continuously for a while, and before mating goes through a rather elaborate bowing act in front of his lady. When breeding time comes, most of the hens accept the males near the middle of the booming ground, so that most of the mating is done by just a portion of the cock birds.

The booming-ground activity is greater in the morning than in the evening of any day. At the time of greatest activity, in early April, most of the birds that use the area at all attend regularly. There is also some activity on some of the booming grounds in the fall; this begins when the moult is finished. Most of the early fall arrivals are birds of the year, since they moult first. Participation in fall displays is not nearly as great as in the spring, and the vigor of the booming is indifferent. Most fall booming is in October.

The booming activity is affected by the weather; stormy days see little or no activity. Protracted periods of cold, wet weather in the spring delay booming activities until the adverse conditions abate.

NESTING

NESTING begins in late March or early April in the south, and in April or early May in the northern range. The areas selected for nesting are usually grass cover; pastures, hayfields, native grass areas, and marsh edges are all satisfactory. In the northern range, woods clearings and other open, brushy areas are sometimes selected for nesting sites. A preference of the Attwater's chicken for sites "within five yards of a trail" was noted by Lehmann (1939); he also noted that they seem to prefer dry vegetation of the previous year's growth instead of green plants. The general cover for nesting is quite open, though the exact site is usually a dense clump of grass, briars, or other plants, on a well-drained spot that affords protection from view and from the weather. The nest itself is hollowed out from the vegetation, and is sometimes partly covered with a canopy of plants.

If there is any connection between the choice of the nesting site and the location of the booming ground that the hen visits, it is a negative one; few nests are within a quarter of a mile of the booming ground, and many are a mile or more away. The prairie chicken is not considered gregarious in its nesting habits, but occasionally two or more hens will nest close together.

Eggs are laid at a rate of almost one a day, until the clutch of 11 or 12 is completed; some nests have fewer eggs, and others may have as many as 15 to 20. Incubation takes 23 or 24 days. The eggs are olive or tan color, with various-sized spots of brown or reddish-brown; these colors vary in shade considerably. The average egg size is about 1¾ by 1¼ inches.

During the incubation period the hen leaves the nest for feeding for a short time in the morning, and again in late afternoon; she usually covers the eggs with vegetation to obscure them from view while she is gone. She is very wary when disturbed early in the incubation period; but later she is very determined to stay on the nest, even in the face of danger. The height of the hatching period is from middle to late May in the southern range, and from late May to mid-June farther north. Some nests hatch in late June or even in July, but these are usually renests after the destruction of the first nest.

Hatching time is one of crisis for prairie chickens, as it is with most ground-nesting birds. The inevitable motion associated with the hatching process, and the impatience of the chicks, increase the chance of discovery by a predator. Lehmann (1941) also found that the nests emit strong odors at hatching time, which would increase this danger. The hens recognize their precarious situation, and are exceedingly nervous until they get their brood away.

Renesting is fairly common with the prairie chicken when the first nest is broken up before incubation starts, or early in the incubation period. They seldom make a second nest after the loss of the first nest late in incubation.

THE BROOD PERIOD

As with other precocial birds, the young prairie chickens leave their nest a few hours after hatching; as soon as they are dried off, and the daylight and weather are suitable, the mother leads them away. The adult cocks have no more part in bringing up the youngsters than they had with the incubation of the eggs.

Short periods of foraging for insects are interspersed with the brooding times, so that the family remains close to the nest area for a day or two. If there is no dense cover near, they move on to some nearby marsh or swale; here they stay for two or three weeks, while their food is mostly insects. As they learn to fly, they also vary their food with seeds and the small fleshy summer fruits such as grow on the brambles.

The chicks are closely controlled by the hen, and they respond well to her instructions. Yet, according to Lehmann (1939), the Attwater's chicken does not use a very effective call to hold the chicks in close, and as a result some are lost by straying away. It may well be that this loss is due more to the difficulty of handling a large group of active chicks than to a weak call, since the same kind of loss occurs commonly among most grouse.

When the chicks have developed some aptitude for flying, and are able to feed regularly by themselves, the broods tend to move to higher ground, and particularly to grain fields. Soon their diet includes a lot of grain kernels, and the seeds of plants associated with grain fields. As the grain is harvested they move to adjacent or nearby fields of better cover, and venture into the barren grain fields for feeding only in the early morning and evening.

The chicks are relatively independent of water areas in most of the range; dew, berries, and succulent greens meet their needs for moisture. Their use of swales and marshes in the early brood period is due more to the cover and insect supply than to their need for water. In the driest sections of the range they may choose their midsummer cover close to water sources, both for the water itself and for the rank vegetation associated with it, that offers shade from the hot sun.

At about eight to twelve weeks of age the broods begin to break up. By this time there usually has been some mortality from exposure, accidents, and predation. As the chicks live on their own resources more, the number taken by predators increases for a time. Those that survive these attacks soon learn to escape their enemies quite effectively. By early fall the birds start flocking; those from a single brood may be in one or more flocks. In September the flocks tend to be separated according to sex, with the adult and young males in groups segregated from old and young hens.

During the summer the adult cocks stay by themselves, either singly or in small groups. They do not travel much, but take life rather easily; food is plentiful, shelter adequate, and they are little disturbed by enemies or weather. The moult adds to their incentive to lead a sedentary life.

FALL AND WINTER ACTIVITY

FALL flocks of prairie chickens are commonly about 20 to 30 birds in size, rarely 50 to 100. The flocks are then made up of birds of both sexes, and of both adults and young of the year. They frequent grain fields for feeding; and the grasslands, swales, and marshes for roosting. When going to roost they fly in to the roosting cover, and then walk around a few minutes after alighting. Then they settle down, each bird singly, and usually spaced several feet apart. Each bird works a form in the vegetation in which to sleep. They use the same roosting area regularly, but seldom the same form. They all leave the roost together soon after dawn. Roosting is always on the ground, even when the snow is deep; marshes, lush swale grasses, and uncut grass fields make the best roosting places when snow is deep.

Some booming grounds have limited activity in the fall—mostly in October and November.

Not all cock birds participate, and those that do show little vigor in their displays; there is little booming, and what is done is without the intense enthusiasm of spring activity.

Since the chickens are not hunted over most of their range, many of the birds never become acquainted with man as a hunter. Those that are hunted are moderately difficult targets for the sportsman. Where the chicken populations are adequate to warrant legal hunting, the numbers taken in sport are not a major factor in determining their next year's numbers.

As the fall cover shrinks with the corn harvest and the snow that covers the closely cut and grazed fields, the birds enlarge their flocks; groups of 50 or more are average, and 100 to 150 may occasionally be seen in single flocks. Larger flocks of 300 or more, which once were common, are rarely seen today. The winter flocks concentrate on the remaining sources of food, and hence are found on limited areas. The largest flocks are seen in the worst winter weather—a further result of limited feeding places. Their daily movements at such times are very restricted, usually amounting to two trips each day between roosting and feeding areas; a quarter to three-quarters of a mile is the usual daily cruising range, but under adverse feeding conditions the flocks may range over several square miles. On balmy winter days the birds like to loaf in the open grasslands. These may be the same areas used for roosting, but often are places with less dense cover than is most suitable for that purpose.

In early times the chicken was considered to be migratory; probably they did make greater seasonal movements under original cover conditions, since feeding areas were likely to be widely separated. The varied land-use pattern brought about by farming has distributed food supplies more generally, and the need no longer exists for extensive travels to find suitable winter feeding conditions. Today the prairie chicken is not considered to be migratory even in a limited way.

As spring approaches the cocks begin to visit the booming grounds again. The trek from winter range to booming ground may be no more than they have been accustomed to travel through the winter, but more commonly it is from one to three miles. There is some evidence that the males winter closer to their own booming ground than the females do to the booming ground that they visit; thus the seasonal change of territory involves greater travels for the hens than for the cocks. Sometimes it may be a move of five to ten miles for some females.

With the advent of the spring booming-ground activity, the flocks become separated again, according to sex. Males congregate at and near the booming grounds in groups of a dozen, more or less; the hens remain longer on the winter range, with their own flocks reduced to from five to twenty birds each. Toward the end of March they move in to the area around the booming grounds, for by then the cocks have completed their masculine feuds and are ready for the ladies.

ADAPTABILITY TO CHANGING ENVIRONMENT

The fact that the prairie chicken is still with us at all is evidence of its ability to adapt to changing conditions. The equally significant fact that its numbers are vastly reduced where it does remain, and that it no longer exists over much of its original range, is clear evidence of the specie's *limited* ability to adapt itself to changed environment.

The habitat throughout the range of the prairie chicken has been greatly altered in the past century. The vast grass prairies have been replaced by a varied mixture of cornfields, wheat fields, hayfields, and pastures. In the northern range many of the marshes and swales have been drained, and converted to growing farm crops instead of rank grasses. The pastures that most nearly resemble the original prairie cover have been overgrazed and burned so much that their value to prairie chickens has been mostly lost.

Where the conversion from grass to cropland exceeded 60%, the chicken was almost entirely eliminated; this happened on all the best agricultural soils, so that the bird has come to be restricted to the parts of its former range that proved to be less productive agriculturally. In contrast, there were large areas of the northern prairie country that were unsuited to the chicken in their primitive condition, but that were improved with the advent of agriculture. The birds quickly took advantage of this opportunity, and widely expanded their northern range.

The newly introduced crops of corn, wheat, sorghum, lespedeza, and clover were in themselves much to the prairie chicken's liking. They vastly improved its food supply, and as a result the chicken has become strongly dependent on farm crops. Still, with all its liking for the grain and legume crops, it required good grasslands in which to roost and nest; without these, all the food in the world could not meet their full needs. Thus the limit of adaptability of the prairie chicken rests in its minimum requirement for grassland of reasonably good quality. This minimum requirement appears to be about 40% of the total land cover. It must be in sizable units, but not arranged in a pattern of multi-thousands of acres of cropland and grassland, each in solid blocks.

TOLERANCE OF OTHER GAME BIRDS

THE prairie chicken comes in close association with several other game birds. Most significant is its close relative, the sharp-tailed grouse, in its northern range; not only does their range and habitat overlap, but the birds even flock together to some extent. Hybridization is not uncommon. There seems to be no conflict of interest among them, except to the minor extent of food competition.

The ring-necked pheasant occurs in the same areas with the prairie chicken on many of the fringes of its northern range. The overlapping is not complete, since the ringneck prefers the intensively cultivated farming areas, whereas the chicken holds more to the grassland. They do eat substantially the same foods where they occur together. Food is not ordinarily the limiting factor for the prairie chicken in such range, and it is probable that this competition is not very serious for either species; it might well be, though, if the range overlapped to a great extent. Some reports of cock pheasants killing young prairie chickens have been made (Mohler, 1952), but this is probably not prevalent.

Some waterfowl nest and feed in and around marshes used by prairie chickens, but there is no conflict between them. Bobwhite quail also live in some of the central, eastern, and southern sections of chicken range, but with no difficulty between the species. The mourning doves that are found in parts of the chicken range do not use the same habitat to a very great extent.

ADAPTABILITY TO ARTIFICIAL PROPAGATION AND TRANSPLANTING

THERE have been a number of attempts to raise prairie chickens on game farms. Scott (1947) mentions the efforts to raise them on a Wisconsin state game farm in 1931 and 1932; only two birds were raised to nine weeks old, and then they died; all other attempts have failed also. Apparently the prairie chicken is like all other American grouse in being unadaptable to artificial propagation.

The value of restocking with game-farm birds is very doubtful, even if such were available. The prairie chicken does not establish easily when transplanted from its chosen environment, many efforts to establish it in the Eastern states have failed completely. Attempts to transplant lesser prairie chickens in Oklahoma and Texas have been equally unfruitful (Lehmann, 1941). The single instance of successful transplanting of wild-trapped prairie chickens is the establishment of a colony in the northern part of Michigan's southern peninsula, some years ago; even here there remains doubt as to whether this transplant is a permanently successful one.

HABITAT OF THE PRAIRIE CHICKEN

In describing the habitat of the prairie chicken we must describe second-rate habitat rather than the optimum. Much of the best habitat is irretrievably lost to intensive agriculture—or at least the area that *was* the best habitat and still is, potentially. Some of this may revert to grassland, but it is unlikely to be a large proportion. This being the case, the first characteristic of most modern prairie chicken habitat is that it is underlaid by soils of low to moderate agricultural productivity.

The one fundamental cover type required by the prairie chicken is *grass*, or more properly, grassland. The extent, quality, condition and variety in the grass cover determines how good it is for the chicken. Other kinds of cover or land use may be useful too, but none is essential. Cropland, marshes, swales, brushland, and woodland may each be of use to the birds, if present in conjunction with adequate grass; without the grass they are useless. This emphasis on grass does not mean that optimum range should be all grassland; it does mean that the grassland requirement must be met before any other aspect of the habitat is worth considering. Ideal habitat would in fact include some each of cultivated land, marsh, and brush.

Since the prairie chicken is a gregarious bird, a unit of range must support not a pair or a covey, but at least a flock; in fact an isolated unit of range would have to support several flocks, in order to be able to sustain the birds through periods of low numbers. It is estimated that some 5,000 to 10,000 acres of habitable range in a contiguous unit is the minimum that can carry a population of prairie chickens continuously.

The *minimum extent* of grassland for suitable habitat is 33% to 40% of the land. This must include grassland units of several hundred acres, since small units are inadequate for all needs. It is better if some 60% to 80% of the land area is in grass cover of one sort or another. The balance should be mostly grain, with a scattering of dense cover in the form of marshes, swales, or brush patches.

Grassland of one type or another furnishes every need of the prairie chicken. Sparse, short grass cover makes the best booming grounds, and is used for feeding and for wet-weather loafing. Medium dense grass of moderate height is used for roosting in good weather, for feeding, and as early brood cover. Grass that is of moderate density and rather high serves as nesting cover, for general feeding, and for loafing except in summer. Dense, rank marsh and swale growth is valuable for escape cover, bad weather roosting, and fall feeding.

The condition of the grass is determined by the soil and topography and by man's use of it. Burning, grazing, plowing, and mowing all have great influence on its character and suitability for use by prairie chickens. A rolling topography, even if only slightly off level, is better for chicken habitat than flat land. The variations in topography are related to soil differences, and these in turn cause different use and treatment by man. Thus the knolls, ridges, and depressions have different densities and types of grass, which give variety for the different uses made of them by the birds.

The native grass prairie which sustained the large numbers of prairie chickens in the past is now mostly gone; its components remain, however, in many wild hay and pasture areas. The big and little bluestem grasses, Indian grass, wild rye, switch grass, and sand dropseed are just a few of those that are still found in some abundance. "Tame" pastures and hayfields make up much of the grasslands of today, and they include introduced species mainly, such as white clover, sweet clover, lespedeza, bluegrass, timothy, and redtop. These grasslands are very acceptable to the prairie chicken, except that their management is likely to be so intensive that their usefulness to the birds is reduced a good share of the time, if not eliminated. With moderate grazing and a conservative hay harvest they can make important chicken cover.

COURTESY SOIL CONSERVATION SERVICE, USDA

PLATE 42. *Grass, sage and shinnery oak habitat of the lesser prairie chicken in the Texas Panhandle.*

In the southwestern portion of the prairie chicken range, the grass prairies merge into the sagebrush lands to the West; along the transition zone will be found all degrees of mixture of grass and sagebrush. The chickens occupy some of this zone; but the more sagebrush present, the poorer the habitat is for them. They definitely prefer the pure grass cover, and make only temporary use of sagebrush.

In the northern glaciated country, where the prairie chicken extended its range with the advent of agriculture, the grassland requirement today is met to some extent by abandoned farms. In these sections the chickens are almost surely doomed, since most of these lands will grow into forest in accordance with the natural plant succession. This trend has already begun, and some areas of Wisconsin and upper Michigan that have supported chickens in recent years have in 10 to 20 years reverted from grass to scrub forest; the chickens are now gone. In other parts of the northern range where agriculture remains, the chicken depends on a combination of pasture, hay,

grain, marsh, and brush for its cover needs; here the winters are severe, and winter food is a more vital factor than farther south. The rank growth of the marsh cover also is more important here than in the southern range; it makes excellent winter shelter and furnishes some food. Some authorities believe it to be an essential habitat type in this northern range (Gross, 1930).

Grainfields are an important element in most of today's prairie chicken habitat. As with grassland, the kind of grain and the way it is managed determines its usefulness to prairie chickens; corn is the best grain, *provided* the stalks are left in the field over winter, either uncut or shocked. Corn cut for ensilage is valueless, and grain corn that is entirely removed from the field in the fall loses most of its value for furnishing winter food. Sorghum is probably next in value to corn, for like corn it stands above the snow in winter. Wheat, rye, and other small grains are most useful in summer and fall; but are also foraged in the winter when the snow is not too deep. The weeds associated with all the grains are of some importance too, in making these fields useful for feeding.

Wet areas are important in two ways. In the northern range marshes are valuable winter shelter; throughout the range, wet areas associated with rank vegetation are used for early brood cover and for escape shelter. More significant in some ways is the place well-watered areas play in helping the birds through drouth periods; in very dry summers most of the prairie chicken broods will be found along ungrazed creek bottoms, in marshes and swales, and around protected ponds. Adult chickens resort to such cover more than usual when dew is lacking and succulent greens are dried up.

To summarize the critical aspects of the habitat, it seems clear that roosting and nesting cover are the limiting conditions in most areas; in the northern range winter food supplies are also a limiting condition.

FOOD HABITS

BEFORE agriculture invaded its range the prairie chicken fed predominantly on wild seeds; this diet was varied with some greens and fruits, and in the summer with insects. Today it is to a considerable extent a graniverous bird; the change from wild seeds to grains, legumes, *and* wild seeds is the biggest adjustment in its food habits. One other change is also notable: in the present northern range the winter diet includes considerable tree mast, much like that of the sharptail.

The prairie chicken is known to eat various parts of well over a hundred different plants. Gross (1928) lists 93 as a result of his Wisconsin studies alone; Lehman (1941) lists 56 plants eaten by Attwater's prairie chicken in Texas. They also eat a wide variety of insects and spiders. Gross lists 99 kinds and Lehmann 68. It is thus clear that these birds pick at a great number of animal and vegetable foods. Most of these are random pickings and do not bulk large in the total diet; a dozen plants and

a few kinds of insects furnish most of the bird's food in any particular part of the range.

In summer the diet is unique, in that much of the food is insects and much of the insect food is grasshoppers; they seem to have a particular fondness for them. The early food of the youngsters is for a few weeks almost all insects, and much of it is made up of slow-moving kinds found on or close to the ground. Later they join the old birds in taking grasshoppers, beetles, and just about any kind they can capture. In midsummer insects often make up a third or more of the total food; this tapers off through late summer and fall and into the winter. Few animal foods are used in the northern range in winter, but some are taken in the southern areas. Spring brings an increase in their use of animal food again, when the insects stir once more; the rate of use increases to midsummer. The rest of the summer diet is composed of a balanced mixture of greens, early grains, early seeds, and summer fruits. Some of these are kernels of wheat, corn, and oats; buttonweed, polygonum (including smartweeds, knotweeds, false climbing buckwheats, black bindweed, lady's thumb), and foxtail seeds; blackberry and other bramble fruits; clover, ruellia, flowering spurge, and other leaves.

Autumn brings about a great change in the diet. Animal foods become secondary, and grain kernels and other seeds make up the bulk of the food. Corn is the staple grain in all but the most southern range. Wheat, oats, sorghum, other grains, lespedeza seed (the annual species), and soybeans also furnish important fall foods. Among the wild seeds eaten in quantity at this season are those of the polygonums, ragweed, buttonweed, ruellia, and acorns. Some greens are eaten but less and less as winter comes. Rose hips and a variety of other fruits, such as those of dogwoods, plums and hawthorns, are eaten. The main food items found in 29 crops and 20 gizzards of chickens taken in Kansas in October were these seeds: sorghum, 22.2% of total food;

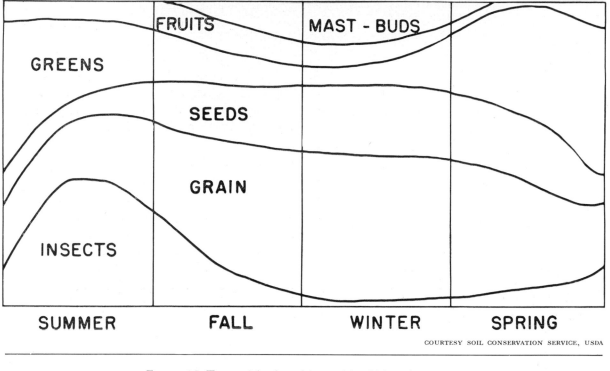

FRUITS   MAST - BUDS

GREENS

SEEDS

GRAIN

INSECTS

SUMMER   FALL   WINTER   SPRING

FIGURE 16. *Types of food used by prairie chickens by seasons.*

wheat, 15.3%; corn, 14.9%; Korean lespedeza, 9.0%; and soybeans, 7.6% (Baker, 1953).

The winter diet is even more predominantly from grains than the fall diet. Half the total food may be grain kernels at this season, and corn is the primary one—except in the noncorn-growing parts of the southern range; in this southern zone sorghum seeds are used a good deal, and to some degree replace corn. Acorns and seeds of the polygonums, ruellia, and ragweed make a large share of the balance. In the northern range the buds of the birches, aspens, elm, hazelnut, and some other plants are browsed through the winter; some winter fruits are eaten. Greens and insects make up a small part of the winter diet, except in the southern range.

The grains and weed seeds are still the major foods through the spring months, despite their having been fed on for half a year; especially in the north, the melting snows expose grain kernels and weed seeds that had been unavailable through the winter; in the south seeds of the blue-eyed grass are eaten. The winter grains provide spring greens, along with the clovers and a variety of other kinds of leaves. Insects become plentiful again. The tree mast is abandoned as the more acceptable foods become available.

The seasonal uses of the various types of foods eaten by the prairie chicken are shown in Figure 16.

The water needs of the prairie chicken were discussed briefly in the habitat section, but it should be repeated here that the bird rarely has to seek open water to drink; only under conditions of extreme summer drouth are dew and succulent foods inadequate as a source of water. When such a severe drouth does occur for a prolonged time, the chickens, along with all other animals, need ponds and streams and need them badly.

Under most circumstances the economics of the food habits of the prairie chicken are substantially neutral. Most of the grain the birds eat is waste, and the greens taken from farm crops are not enough to cause farmers concern. There are some occasions, however, when the bird's consumption of corn, wheat, rice, peanuts, sorghum, clover, and other crops may be bad enough locally to cause some damage; this is most likely to happen in the fall, when the birds feed in flocks, and crops are not yet harvested. Some game departments have undertaken the live-trapping and transplanting of chickens doing crop damage, but this is not generally very practical. The benefit that accrues from their summer consumption of grasshoppers and other insects is generally beneficial, but is of little importance in reducing insect damage to farm crops.

THE EFFECTS OF WEATHER AND CLIMATE

CLIMATE has a fundamental influence on the range that prairie chickens can inhabit, through its determination of the character of the vegetation; this limitation is clearest on the western edge of their range, where aridity and soil changes sharply limit the prairie cover. On the northern side the extremes of cold and snow in winter set limits on the suitability of the country for prairie chickens, though over much of this area the character of the land use may set an even more restrictive limit. The eastern edge of the range once extended to the Atlantic Ocean, but in recent geologic times the humidity and its related forest cover established the habitable limits. This condition left a remnant population along the coast, the heath hen; which indicates that the forest cover caused by the climatic condition was the actual limiting factor rather than the humidity itself. This eastern limit of the prairies has now been further restricted by land-use changes. The southern edge of the range is determined largely by the lack of rainfall and soil changes that end the prairie cover, and by the Gulf of Mexico.

The movements and behavior of prairie chickens are influenced considerably by weather conditions. Severe winter snow in the northern range forces them to feed partly on tree buds, to roost and feed in marshes, and to spend more time huddled in roosts than they otherwise would. The onslaught of winter at one time stimulated significant southward migrations of the northern birds, but the advent of grain fields has reduced this habit greatly. Deep snows cause the birds to roost beneath the snow. Bright, sunny, and calm days in late winter stimulate activity on the booming grounds. Delayed springs cause delays in nesting. Dry weather in summer results in the greater use of stream bottoms, marshes, swales, and pond surroundings, by both adults and broods. In many ways throughout the year the chickens modify their activities according to the weather.

The effects on mortality of ordinary adjustments of behavior with the weather are slight. Predation is conditioned somewhat by snow roosting and in other ways. Young chicks living in a swale because of the cover and moisture may be drowned by a quick summer thunderstorm. Some nests are drowned out by heavy rains; and a few birds may be killed by hail storms. Those losses are part of the expected reduction of each year's production.

Extremes of weather are a different matter; some of the greatest limitations on both production and survival are weather abnormalities. The most important is excessive rain at hatching time and for a couple of weeks after. This occurs throughout the bird's range; in Texas it comes in May. Lehmann (1941) recounts how seasons of excessive May rains reduced the yield of Attwater's chickens to less than 10%. In such seasons even birds hatched in late April were still vulnerable. Lehmann figured that on an average only about two years in five would have seasons of good nesting success in any given area, while two would be fair and one bad.

The floods that come from very heavy rains may flood out nests or broods almost completely in localities where conditions cause the birds to nest and raise broods in the stream bottoms. Lehmann (1941) says that the birds in a part of Colorado County, Texas, were "extirpated" by a flood in June 1936; he also records that a Gulf hurricane in 1917 flooded the coastal plains with salt water, and so reduced the prairie chickens that they were scarce for 15 years. Schwartz (1945) tells of an instance in a Missouri locality where a flood destroyed "75% to 85% of the nests and young" in June 1939.

Great extremes of drouth can be equally disastrous; vegetation dries up, food supplies wane, and the birds compete with all other creatures, domestic and wild, for the remaining food and shelter. When such conditions continue for long—as they do every few decades—the prairie chicken may be nearly exterminated in the affected areas.

Extremes of winter cold and snow are important mainly in the northern range; in the central and southern range deep snow does not often occur, and doesn't last long when it does happen. Neither lack of food nor winter exposure is a critical factor there, unless preceded by extreme drouth. In the northern states and southern Canada the wintering birds may be hard pressed at times. Their partly lost habit of winter migration for a hundred miles or more southward adds to the trouble when such winters strike. The grain fields that have held them are so covered with snow that they are of no use; only their resort to tree buds helps then, and there is some doubt as to how well that diet serves them over long periods of time.

In summary, weather is a constant influence on the bird's habits, a minor cause of mortality most of the time, and occasionally a direct cause of great losses that are a major influence on chicken populations over large areas.

PREDATION; DISEASES AND PARASITES; ACCIDENTS

PREDATION

Loss of prairie chickens by predation is singularly unimportant in its population changes; even where predation may be high locally, it is usually conditioned by the weather, or by habitat changes such as mowing around hayfield nests.

There are many predators that partake of prairie chicken meals. They are probably most destructive to nests; skunks, opossums, coyotes, house cats, red foxes, ravens, and crows are the commonest culprits that eat eggs from chicken nests.

During the juvenile period chicks are occasionally taken by Cooper's hawks, sharp-shins, marsh hawks, Krider's hawks, house cats, red foxes, and coyotes; but it is so small a source of loss that it is of no significance in management.

The most significant predators of adult prairie chickens are the great horned owl, red fox, and coyote; though Cooper's hawks, ferruginous roughlegs, golden eagles, duck hawks, and occasionally others catch them. Rarely is the predation of adult chickens a large mortality factor, except in the northern range; here the winter losses to natural enemies may occasionally be high, especially when the birds are snow-roosting or are hard pressed to find food.

There are many accounts of various predators harassing prairie chickens, which have led some observers to conclude that these predators actually caught many of them. The marsh hawk is an example; Lehmann (1941) tells of observing marsh hawks repeatedly darting at chickens on booming grounds; the intended prey cowered, or merely ran away a little, as though parrying the thrust. Schwartz (1945) made similar observations, and even saw some cock chickens attack the swooping hawk. Neither observer ever saw a marsh hawk succeed in such forays, though it is quite certain that booming-ground activities do somewhat increase predation.

DISEASES AND PARASITES

THOUGH sometimes suspected of being a serious mortality factor, disease is not known to be so with the prairie chicken. Referring to the prairie chicken along with other grouse, Gross (1930) said: "It is highly probable that the cycles in grouse are primarily dependent on some disease either in itself or in combination with other factors." Subsequent research has failed to confirm this opinion; it has been shown that the incidence of parasitic organisms generally increases with the increasing abundance of ruffed grouse (Edminster, 1947), and this is probable with other species of grouse. It has also been found that some grouse—including prairie chickens—do die of disease. Though the possibility remains that sudden prairie chicken declines may be influenced by some disease, we cannot now state this even as a probability.

The one disease that is known to be lethal to the prairie chicken is blackhead (enterohepatitis); it is a disease common in the domestic turkey, and is caused by a flagellate protozoan (*Histomonas meleagridis*). It was found in two Wisconsin prairie chickens (Gross, 1930), in two others in Missouri (Schwartz, 1945), and in one Illinois specimen (Yeatter, 1943). Because of its great virulence, and the possibility of prairie chickens getting it from ground infected by turkeys, this disease must be regarded as a potentially serious threat.

Prairie chickens have a normal fauna of endoparasites and ectoparasites; these do not ordinarily cause any more trouble than some annoyance. Analyses of 52 Wisconsin chickens by Morgan and Hamerstrom (1941) showed that 44% of the birds were parasitized. The parasites known to occur in and on the prairie chicken include seven helminths (four nematodes and three cestodes), two other protozans in addition to the organism of blackhead (Morgan and Hamerstrom, 1941), one spiny-

headed worm (Yeatter, 1943), three kinds of bird lice, and one species of tick. Since autopsies and disease studies of this bird have been very limited, it is probable that other parasites attack the bird that have not yet been found; it is also probable that any such parasites will prove to be of little significance in mortality. The parasites that are known to attack the prairie chicken are as follows:

Gizzard worm	*Seurocyrnea colini*
Intestinal round worm	*Ascaridia lineata*
Caecal worm	*Heterakis gallinae*
Crop worm	*Capillaria contorta*
Tapeworm	*Raillietina* sp.
Small intestinal tapeworm	*Rhabdometra nullicollis*
" " "	*Choanotaenia infundibulum*
Spiny-headed worm	*Acanthocephala* sp.
Protozoan coccidia	*Eimeria dispersa*
" "	*Eimeria* sp.
Bird louse	*Chapinia* sp.
" "	*Menopon* sp.
" "	*Lipeurus perplexus*
Tick	*Haemaphysalis leporis-palustris*

Only one of these parasites has been suggested as being of possible mortality significance to young prairie chickens; Leigh (1940) found the three tapeworm species entirely in young chickens. They were present in 10 of 14 birds four to eight weeks old, and in none of 14 adults examined. The four worst cases of cestode infestation occluded the lumen of the small intestines; they were of a new species of *Raillietina*.

ACCIDENTS

LOSSES of prairie chickens that occur as a result of various kinds of accidents is a secondary mortality factor of some importance. During the spring a few nests are destroyed by the trampling of domestic livestock; an occasional nest is lost by man's disturbing the hen by plowing, mowing hay, fence-building, or other farming activity. Sometimes these farming disturbances are locally very destructive; Schwartz (1945) tells of a single farmer plowing over seven nests in a 15-acre clover field in one day. Prairie fires have at times caused great nest losses, but this is less common now than some years ago.

Young juveniles are sometimes lost by straying too far from the brood and succumbing to exposure; a few others are killed by automobiles as they cross roads, and some fall into holes in swale cover, and are trapped in rice fields at flooding time or other places from which they cannot escape. All this may add up to a considerable share of the chick mortality.

Adult chickens are occasionally automobile victims, and sometimes die from flying into wires, fences, and other obstacles; the total number lost from these causes is rarely large.

MAN'S RELATIONS WITH THE PRAIRIE CHICKEN

THERE are several game birds and mammals whose welfare and species survival have depended and do depend more on man's activities than on any other consideration. Some have been exterminated or reduced to sanctuary remnants; the heath hen and bison are examples of these. Among those that have survived in the truly wild state is the prairie chicken. Its ultimate place in the modern scheme of things is still in doubt. It may be exterminated throughout its range, as its eastern subspecies was in the early part of this century; it may adapt itself enough to remain in parts of its range where it now persists. It is doubtful if it will ever become generally abundant. In only a few states is it now a game bird subject to legal shooting.

Man's activities are the prime factor in prairie chicken ecology. At one time his hunting was a considerable item in this picture; now man's hunting is a secondary mortality factor, even where it is still legal. The business of farming and ranching has played the dominant role in the great decline of the chicken, and it continues to be the major limiting factor today.

AS A HUNTER

THE stories of the vast numbers of prairie chickens living on the Western grass plains in the mid-19th century when that land was being settled are part of the epic of those times. It became the primary game bird of the area from Texas to Wisconsin and the Dakotas; great numbers were killed, both for sport and for the food markets. For a while the supply went only to local markets, but as the railroads developed large numbers were shipped to the big cities. Schorger (1943), in reviewing the history of the prairie chicken in Wisconsin, said, "The sole tenable cause for the decline [of prairie chickens] is the construction of railways that permitted the rapid transportation of game to Chicago and thence to the Eastern markets."

By the early 1900's the land-use changes on the prairies had nearly finished what market shooting had begun; the population of prairie chickens had dropped so low that complete protection was afforded the bird in the eastern parts of its range. Missouri removed it from the shooting lists in 1907, and most other states did so a little later; now only four to seven states (depending on the year) and one or two provinces of Canada—all but two in the northern range—allow any shooting of prairie chickens. It is doubtful if even this legal shooting will continue many more years, unless current trends change. Despite the protection afforded the chicken over much of its range, illegal hunting continues to be a factor of significance in some places (Bennitt, 1939).

The hunting of prairie chickens today is mostly done in conjunction with the hunting of other game birds, such as the pheasant, sharptail, and ruffed grouse. Grange (1948) reported on a hunter check in Wood County, Wisconsin, in 1941, in which all three grouse species were present and hunted; the kill of prairie chickens was surprisingly low; only ten were taken, which was but 2% of the fall population. By contrast, the sharptail kill was 24%, and the ruffed grouse kill was 22%.

Even more surprising, the population of chickens and sharptails on the area was believed to be almost equal.

Hunter success is usually better than indicated in Grange's study; daily bags averaging one to two birds are still not exceptional in the better hunting areas, but the general average is well below one bird per hunter-day. The total kill in the entire shooting area open to hunters at the present time probably does not exceed 70 to 80 thousand birds. A recent estimate of the harvest in North Dakota was 20 thousand chickens, according to a P-R progress report; the harvest in Michigan declined rapidly in the late 1940's and early 1950's. Wisconsin, South Dakota, Oklahoma, Nebraska and Kansas have also permitted some chicken hunting in this period, and all have shown a discouraging downward harvest trend. One thing is sure—the hunting itself is not the reason for these declines. They may be temporary because of cyclic changes, though the anticipated time for recovery from the low period of the mid-1940's is passing without very good evidence of improvement; the current outlook for prairie-chicken hunting is very, very dark.

AS A FARMER

THE original range of the prairie chicken covered the most fertile grasslands of the mid-continent—the lands that are now the "bread basket" of our nation. In the last century they were converted to an intensive agriculture; little of the original prairie is left, and that little is on poor soils. Such grass as is grown on the fertile soils today is "tame" hay and pasture, and usually is found in rather small patches. This vast change has been disastrous to the prairie chicken.

It is rather ironic that the chickens found some of man's new crops very much to their liking; corn, wheat, and other grains have become sources of their most important foods, and though prairie chickens probably ate some Indian maize before the white man came, their present granivorous diet is a great adapta-

tion to the changed conditions. Had the land use changes gone only *half*way—had just half of the old grass prairie been plowed and half kept as climax grassland, the chicken might have thrived as never before; with vast new food supplies *and* enough grass for their booming, nesting, and roosting needs, the story would surely have been a different one. But such was not to be, and the chickens just could not do without their prairie sod.

That is the fundamental background against which all other of man's relations with the prairie chicken must be measured; man's activities affect the prairie chicken in many other ways, but none is of comparable significance with his destruction of the grasslands. Even the malpractices of overgrazing grasslands, and of the burning of the prairies annually, are not as permanently destructive as is the conversion of the range to cropland. Overgrazing and burning have, however, caused less damage to chicken habitat in recent years than in the past.

Man's farming activities cause chicken mortality in a number of ways, such as loss of nests from plowing and mowing and livestock trampling (see also under "Accidents"). Man's fences and electric wires and highways are all death traps to a small but significant number of prairie chickens each year. Man's poultry—especially his turkeys—cause some disease in the prairie chicken, and pose a never-ending threat of epidemic.

The drainage of marshes to develop agricultural land has deprived the chickens of some valuable habitat; but drainage channels have in some instances also resulted in improved cover along their margins. The development of rice fields along the Gulf coast of Texas has ruined much habitat of the Attwater's prairie chicken in the very limited remaining range of this subspecies (Lehmann, 1941).

OTHER WAYS MAN INFLUENCES PRAIRIE CHICKENS

FARMING and hunting have been the two most significant of man's activities in affecting the prairie chicken, but other works of man may be locally important. The mortality caused by highways and electric wires has already been noted. Grass fires have been described as an important destructive agent of nests and young; fires in brush and forest cover sometimes affect chicken habitat too—and often beneficially. Grange (1948) states that some northern woody cover areas have been made habitable for prairie chickens by fires; in such areas if fires (or other plant succession controls) recur at intervals, the habitat may continue to support chickens, without this control of woody cover the chickens would soon be eliminated by the developing forest. This is now occurring in some of the northern range.

The development of industrial enterprises has eliminated some prairie chicken range; the oil fields of Texas and Oklahoma are examples.

It is clear that man is the biggest factor in prairie chicken ecology; his taking over of the bird's ancestral home for agriculture and other purposes has nearly "done them in"; it may yet do so. Yet it is also true that with some reasonable adjustments in land use and farming practices—changes that would be sound and desirable for man's welfare—the bird's range could be much improved. It might still be possible for the prairie chicken to regain a semblance of good populations—but it can do it only if man makes it possible. That possibility lies in his becoming a conservationist; not especially a prairie chicken conservationist as such, but more—a land and soil conservationist. A conservative and permanently productive system of land use and farm practices in the range of the prairie chicken would be the basis of such an accomplishment.

PRODUCTIVITY AND POPULATIONS

PRODUCTIVITY

THE potential productivity of the prairie chicken is high, but not quite as high as that of the ruffed grouse. The birds are polygamous and probably promiscuous in their breeding habits. Both sexes mate the year after hatching. The female has only one brood a year.

The sex ratio is difficult to obtain accurately, but appears to be somewhat unbalanced, with an excess of males. This is not only true of the breeding season population, but of the young birds as well. Davison (1940) found that Oklahoma populations of the lesser prairie chicken had from 140 to 163 males to 100 females among the young. Schwartz (1945) records the breeding season ratio in Missouri, in the different years he made observations, as ranging from 1.4 to 1.7 males per female. The explanation for this differential is a matter of conjecture, but it may well relate to the precariously low population densities that now prevail. There is some evidence that when a species sinks to a certain population level the sex ratio becomes unbalanced, with an excess of males. Though this is illogical from a survival viewpoint, it clearly happened with the heath hen, and may now be happening with the rest of the prairie chickens.

The nesting of females is complete, and the average first clutch is 11 or 12 eggs. Renesting may occur when the nest is destroyed before or early in incubation; this may amount to some 25% of the number of first nests destroyed. From 50% to 85% of the hens finally manage to hatch a nest of eggs.

Nest mortality is usually about 50% (Gross, 1930; Hamerstrom, 1939; Yeatter, 1943), but may be higher in some years and lower in others Lehmann (1941) found a 68% loss of nests of the Attwater's chicken. Baker (1953) gives the fates of 16 Kansas nests observed in 1951; of these, seven hatched, three were destroyed by predators, three more by farm machinery, and the other three failed from unknown causes. There is considerable evidence that the nest loss is reflected in the population trend; that is, the population declines with high nest mortality, and increases when the nest loss is low. From half to three-quarters of the nest loss in normal years is from predation, the rest being from weather (rain, flooding), man's interference, and desertion. But these are not the years of big population changes—especially of big declines. When the nest loss is very high it is likely to reflect high losses from flooding, farming operations, or other normally secondary influences.

The hatchability of eggs in first clutches is high, with about 5% to 7% loss from infertility and the death of embryos; this loss is higher for second nests.

The brood begins in most cases with 10 to 11 chicks, and ends in the fall with about half of them left in good years—fewer in most years. Early losses arc high, and relate mainly to weather conditions and accidents; late summer losses are low, and are mostly from predation. This chick mortality may be much higher in years of bad weather during the early weeks after hatching. Productivity in good production seasons is shown by a fall age ratio of 1.5 or more young birds to each adult; in poor years the age ratio falls to 1 to 1 or less. Seasons of very bad weather produce so few birds that the ratio drops to 0.2 to 1 or worse. There have been few years with high production in the last half century, for the depressing influence of lost habitat has compounded the problem.

Adult mortality is rarely more than normal losses from predation, hunting (legal in some states, poaching in all), and accidents. The changes in population result more from increases or decreases in the *production* of chickens than in their survival, once grown.

LIFE EQUATION

AN analysis of a typical year's changes in a prairie chicken population during a period of gradual decline is shown in Table 13. A unit of 100 adult birds is used in the example. A year of decline rather than one of stability in numbers is used, since that has been typical of the species in recent times; but, if the production-limiting factors are relaxed, the year's changes may well end with more birds than at the start. When this happens generally, the result is a population increase that may be reflected in more and better hunting. It is to be hoped that the latter condition will prevail more commonly in the future than it has in the recent past; as things now stand this prospect is more of a hope than a probability.

POPULATION DENSITIES

NOT only has the occupied range of the prairie chicken shrunk tremendously from former times, but the numbers of birds in the present range are much less concentrated than they used to be; that is to say, the carrying capacity has gone down as well as the area. Nests at the rate of three or four per acre were once common, but now are rare. Hundreds of birds per square mile was at one time the rule; now they are measured in multiples of ten to the square mile on the better remaining range.

The frequency of booming grounds depends both on the available range unit sizes, and on the population density of the birds; Schwartz (1945) found them half to three-quarters of a mile apart in Missouri. He comments that the best booming-ground distribution is on range units of 25 square miles or more, *and* having five or more chickens to the square mile; with *either* a smaller range unit size or a thinner bird population, the number of booming grounds is greatly reduced. Grange (1948) estimated that there was one booming ground per 876 acres on 131,000 acres of Wisconsin range, but these included sharptails as well as prairie chickens; other Wisconsin data from P-R studies indicate that there are around 1,400 to 2,400 acres of range per booming ground. Davison (1940) took a census of Oklahoma booming grounds of the lesser prairie chicken that averaged from 1.5 to 2.5 per square mile in different years of the 1930's.

Nest concentrations comparable with those of the days of high chicken populations are rare now, even on exceptional small areas; yet the nesting density is often surprisingly high, because it is concentrated on the very limited amount of cover suitable for nesting. For example, Yeatter (1943) found four nests on four acres in

TABLE 13

LIFE EQUATION OF 100 PRAIRIE CHICKENS FOR A YEAR*

TIME	ACTIVITIES	NUMBER OF BIRDS	
		young	adult
SPRING	(1) 40 females mate with 60 males		100
	(2) All females nest, av. 12 eggs in first clutch, 8 in second; total 1st eggs 480		
	(3) 50% 1st nests hatch, or 20 × 12 = 240		
	¼ hens broken-up renest, 5 × 8 = 40 eggs		
	Half of renests hatch, or 20 eggs		
	5% of 1st clutch fail to hatch, or 12		
	10% " 2nd " " " " or 2		
	Thus, 14 eggs of 260 in hatched nests are lost and 246 hatch (av. 10.9 per nest)	246	
	(4) 30 adults die from predation, accident, or 30%		70
SUMMER	(5) 10 " " " " " or 14%		60
	(6) 148 chicks die from accident, exposure, predation, or 60%		
FALL	Surviving chicks become adults		158
	(7) 32 are killed by hunters, or 20%		126
	(8) 16 " " " predation, accident, or 10%		110
WINTER	(9) 22 " " " " " or 20%		88
SPRING	(10) Breeding season arrives with 12 fewer birds than the year before		

* A year of slightly declining population is used as typical of recent times.

southeastern Illinois in 1936; all or most of the females in the locality had nested in this one patch of grass fringed with blackberry bushes. Nests are well scattered if satisfactory nesting cover is itself widely available.

The spring populations of prairie chickens have been counted in a number of parts of the range in the last two decades. Davison's (1940) Oklahoma figures varied from 29 to 46 per square mile. Wisconsin figures by Grange (1948) averaged only 5.8 per square mile; and other Wisconsin counts in later years of the 1940's by P-R studies (*P-R Quarterly* reports) ranged from about five to eight per square mile. The Missouri range averaged 4.8 birds per square mile in 1943 (Schwartz, 1945). Lehmann's (1941) work with Attwater's prairie chicken in southern Texas included spring

censuses of about 10 to the square mile. Baker (1952) found a one-flock population of 104 and 47 birds on a single square mile unit of the best Kansas range in the springs of 1950 and 1951. In summary, present spring populations of from five to ten birds per square mile are widely prevalent, and are not producing good huntable fall populations. In the best range the spring populations in good years may be as high as 100 birds to the square mile over small areas, but are more likely to be less than 50 to the square mile over large areas.

Fall populations are generally at least double those of the spring, but this depends on the year's production. Fall populations that have been reported for different parts of the chicken range in recent observations include these: from two to six per square mile as a state-wide average in Missouri, from 1929 through 1949, and up to 15 per square mile on the best units (Schwartz, 1945; Bennitt, 1939; and P-R Project reports); 12 birds per square mile average in 1937 in Texas, with a maximum of 64 on the best 42,000 acres (Lehmann, 1941); from 42 to 100 per square mile on a single small unit of good range in Kansas (Baker, 1952); from 35 to 66 per square mile in southeastern Illinois in the late 1930's (Yeatter, 1943); 6.8 per square mile in Wisconsin in 1930, but as low as 4.8 in later years (Grange, 1948); about 19 per square mile in North Dakota in the late 1940's (estimated from *P-R Quarterly* reports). These averages for large areas tend to depreciate the actual relation of birds to their range, since the area of range may include portions not actually used. Contrarily, censuses on small units of land may exaggerate the population density by not including all the year-round habitat used by these rather mobile birds. It is quite clear, though, that much of the present chicken range does not carry more than 5 to 20 birds to the square mile in the fall; the best parts of the range may have fall populations of from 50 to 100 birds to the square mile.

FLUCTUATIONS IN POPULATION

Because of the depreciation of the range in the last 75 years, there is a tendency to think of the prairie chicken population as going continuously down; such is not quite the case. There have been well-marked periods of increase, even as late as the end of the 1940's, though the amplitude of these fluctuations in recent decades has become lower and lower; Grange (1948) illustrates this trend by a wavy line crossing a straight line at each wave; the straight line slants downward—the direction of the population trend while the waves rise above and below it with ever-decreasing height; the wavy line is the fluctuating level of chicken numbers.

The existence of such fluctuations raises the question of whether they are cyclic in nature; the evidence indicates that the changes are regular and cyclic in character in the northern range, but are not so farther south. This supports the view that animal cycles are more a function of geography and climate than they are of the species themselves. Grange (1948) summarizes the history of prairie chicken numbers in Wisconsin, and shows that low-population years have occurred once each decade from 1857 to 1947; the bottom of the decline came in the year ending in seven in each decade but two—the exceptions were in 1878 and 1918, each one year late. Many other recent studies confirm the general trend of a period of relatively high abundance in the early 1930's, a low about 1937–38, another increase phase in the early 1940's, a decline in the years 1945 to 1948, and an increase from then until 1951 at least. These trends show most clearly in the areas having the best chicken populations, and particularly in the more northern areas.

The remnant population in northwestern Indiana has been studied since 1942 (*P-R Quarterly* reports); it declined steadily from 1,000 birds in 1942 to 511 in 1948, and had dim prospects for the future. But then it increased to 650 in 1950, and held steady in 1951, which indicated that even such small and isolated units may follow essentially the same population changes as are general.

The population trend of the prairie chicken is thus shown to be fluctuating rather than steadily downward. It can recover periodically in habitable range, and if that range becomes more suitable by changes in land conditions then the general level of chicken populations can increase.

THE MANAGEMENT OF THE PRAIRIE CHICKEN

The management of the prairie chicken is a frustrating, discouraging matter. The basic problem concerns the production of the bird crop. Where this involves agricultural lands, the prairie chicken unfortunately is but a minor consideration; it has little more than the sentimental interest of the landowner, who is the only man in a position to do the managing. Where it involves rangeland, as in much of the Texas and Oklahoma range, prairie chicken and livestock interests can both be served.

Even poor chicken range is not generally feasible for public purchase, except as sanctuary for the preservation of a remnant of a disappearing species. There may be some exceptions, where other wildlife management opportunities are combined with that of the prairie chicken; New Mexico, for example, has purchased several thousand acres of land to improve for prairie chickens and other game.

As habitat improvement goes, we can only describe what is good for the birds; where these things fit soundly into the development of the agriculture of an area, the welfare of the prairie chicken may then be included in the plans. Where the interests of the chicken are in conflict with agriculture, there is no doubt as to which interest will prevail: it will be farming and ranching, and the game species will have to get along or get out.

LAND USE AND DEVELOPMENT

THE essential minimum need for chicken habitat is extensive grassland amounting to at least 40% of the land total; this grassland should be in parcels of from 20 to several hundred acres, and with at least 2,000 acres of grass in a unit of 5,000 acres of land. Unless such units are close together, so that flocks can move from one to another, the minimum for a single flock range would be even higher. The balance of the land may vary greatly, but should include mostly crop fields for feeding areas; corn and small-grain fields are most important. An important element—but one that may not use much of the acreage—is a network of swales, marshes, stream bottoms, ponds, and shrubby thickets; these parts should be excluded from grazing by domestic livestock.

The grasslands may be either pasture or hay, or preferably some of both. The management of the grass is of the utmost importance; overgrazing is most urgently to be avoided; and a complete lack of mowing or grazing on all good quality grass fields would not be desirable either. Some rank grass is good for summer and winter roosting use, but this is best supplied by marshes or swales or other wet-ground areas. Uncontrolled burning should be avoided, and controlled burning limited to places where it is needed to control plant succession. Any burning should be done in winter or very early spring (see Grange, 1948); elsewhere the grass should be managed by grazing or mowing.

The three great uses the birds make of grassland that must be met in order for them to thrive are nesting, booming ground, and roosting cover. Nesting cover should be moderately dense, unmowed until late spring after hatching time if it is hay, and moderately grazed if it is pasture. Booming-ground areas are on high, well-drained ground of sparse grass only a few inches high; it must be unburned, not too lush, and yet not barren; moderately grazed pasture is best. Roosting cover must be at least six inches tall—preferably more—and fairly thick; in winter it should be heavier than that in the northern range, with marshes serving best. Hayfields should not be mowed in the fall, so that the late-season growth will be adequate for winter cover.

Corn, wheat, sorghum, and other grainfields can provide excellent fall to spring feeding areas. The corn crop should be picked and stalks left standing, or the stalks cut and stacked in shocks and left in the field. Fall plowing should be avoided. Crop fields should not be grazed by livestock after the harvest. These recommendations are sound farm management, as well as good wildlife practice.

Where marshes, streams, and swales are scarce, or water is inadequate for dry seasons, farm ponds may be developed wherever needed for watering livestock and other uses; they should be fenced to exclude domestic stock, and some of the pond surroundings included in the fenced area. This can usually be done without sacrificing valuable crop land. Except for parts of the pond margin that are to be used for recreation, the edges should be mowed only as needed to maintain the grass; the unmowed margins provide the rank cover that is needed for summer broods and winter roosting. Windmill pumps, springs, and other small water sources should be fenced from livestock, and allowed to form wet-ground puddles in the summer.

Those interested in the welfare of the prairie chicken may be able to help accomplish some of these needs; the job need not be left entirely to the landowner; there are many ways in which it is fitting and proper to help him. The protection of needed rank cover by the fencing of selected areas is a case in point; where other basic requirements are met, but the landowners are unable or unwilling to fence out the needed wild-grass, marsh, and thicket areas, help in doing so may be provided by sportsman groups, wildlife agencies, and others. In many localities this sort of co-operative development work can best be arranged through the operations of the local soil conservation district.

In the northern range the use of planted food patches for chickens may be warranted in some instances. Where grain is grown, and is completely removed from the field after harvest, arranging with the landowner to leave edges of the field unharvested is the best food patch arrangement; corn, wheat, sorghum, oats, buckwheat, and soybeans can be used for this purpose. If it is located away from woods, so as to avoid competitive use by other wildlife, an acre of grain can overwinter a flock of about 30 chickens. Where unharvested edges of regular crop fields cannot be arranged for, there may be odd areas of good soil on farms or on public lands that can be planted to these grains for feeding areas; this is not an economical practice by ordinary standards, but under some circumstances it may be recommended.

The planting of shelter belts and hedges and thickets on odd areas, may be needed in some sections of the northern range where the land is lacking in other forms of winter cover. It should be recognized, however, in considering this type of development for chickens, that these forms of woody cover may encourage other species, like the pheasant, even more than prairie chickens; that raises the question of whether the pheasant might tend in such areas to displace the chicken.

In the northern, extended chicken range, where the natural plant succession is toward forest, a prime problem in maintaining prairie chicken habitat is how to prevent afforestation; this applies especially in northern Michigan and Wisconsin. Plowing, grazing, and controlled burning are the tools that may be used for this purpose; they are all expensive to apply on nonfarm land, and the justification must be more than just prairie chicken welfare. By combining the interests of the prairie chicken with that of sharptails, ruffed grouse, and deer, and integrating such a program with good forest management, it may be possible to hold some of this chicken range. The poorest forest sites are the areas that should be kept open, by setting back plant succession periodically; the sandy soils and the wet soils are the ones most suited for this purpose. In addition to the fact that such areas will detract least from forest growth, they are also the easiest to keep open, because of the slow natural rate of woody plant succession on them. The best of the well-drained sites that are to be maintained in an early stage of plant succession can be handled most effectively by plowing; the wet sites are best handled by controlled burning. In recommending controlled burning, it should be very clear that this does not countenance forest fires, or the careless use of fire; the use of fire as a tool for controlling the vegetation on selected areas should be done only by trained men, and under proper conditions of control.

Winter feeding at stations supplied with grain have been used considerably in the past, and the chickens will readily use them. They are not generally a practical management measure, and are of value only as an emergency practice in the northern range; even under these circumstances their effectiveness is open to question.

MISCELLANEOUS MANAGEMENT PRACTICES

IN addition to habitat measures—and especially the provision of shelter and food—several other practices are commonly recommended, and therefore need discussion.

Predator control is impractical for prairie chicken management alone; the normal fur harvest, plus sport-shooting of crows, foxes, and other legitimate sport species, is all that is justified. The proper control of domestic cats and dogs is very desirable. The shooting of hawks and owls is not recommended as an aid to prairie chickens.

The establishment of refuges to aid in managing the prairie chicken as a game species is of little use on private land. The use of refuges in conjunction with public shooting areas on public lands that are subject to heavy hunting may be warranted in some cases; Baker (1953) recommends state-owned refuges of one square mile per township in the Blackjack Prairies and Bluestem Hills of Kansas, and one section of nine in refuges (public and private lands) in eastern Kansas where the hunting pressure is very high.

The stocking of game-farm-reared prairie chickens is not a practical matter, since it is not feasible to raise these birds in captivity. The trapping of wild prairie chickens from areas where they are damaging farm crops and transplanting them elsewhere is sometimes justified; there are times when it may be desirable to stock vacant range areas that have been restored to satisfactory condition. When this is done, care should be taken to obtain enough females, as they are more difficult to trap (Baker, 1953).

PROTECTION AND HARVEST

THE harvesting of a crop of prairie chickens by hunting is an academic matter over most of the birds' range today. The problem is simple as far as legal protection is concerned: provide full protection by law, and enough law enforcement facilities to control illegal shooting.

When the populations of prairie chickens reach about 20 per square mile or more over considerable areas of range, a hunting season is warranted; this may occur under present conditions only in about half the years in each decade, even in the best range. Two to three weeks of open season, with a daily bag limit of three to five birds, is the prevailing practice in the chicken-shooting states, and is an adequate arrangement for harvesting the crop. The discretion of providing such open seasons when they are warranted should be provided for as regulations of the state wildlife agency.

The determination of the times when open seasons are justified is a phase of management that requires annual censuses and population status evaluation. This may be done by sample counts made by trained observers in a systematic way; such a system is now in use in most of the important prairie-chicken states, and is described by Dalke (1943).

Sample areas totaling at least 5,000 acres for a state are needed. Observers drive selected roads within a uniform range type (based mainly on soils), and laid out to give a proper representation of the cover types and topography present. The work should be done at the height of the booming and mating season, which is usually in early April; the time for each count is from 15 minutes before sunrise until two hours later. Only quiet days should be used. A stop is made every mile, and booming activity listened for; each booming ground located is then spotted on a map. The sample area thus covered is thus based on audibility distance, which under right conditions is about one mile. The percent of the total range that is covered in the census can be worked out from the map by the use of strips two miles wide along the travelled roads as the sample.

The booming grounds are then visited and

the birds counted, with care to make enough careful observations to distinguish females from males. The data are then compiled for all booming grounds, and applied to the total area of range represented.

This census method gives a fair appraisal of the actual spring population, but it is most useful and most accurate in tracing trends; thus its value grows with years of use. Further, since it is a *spring* census, it is not fully dependable as a gauge of fall populations. A measure of the year's productivity must also be obtained, in order to make sure that there has not been a production failure; this can be gauged by the weather conditions from the peak hatching time for three weeks. When there has been protracted rain at this time, field checks of broods by trained technicians are needed to appraise the situation; Lehmann (1941) describes a rope-dragging technique that can be used for this purpose. Baker (1953) recommends early morning midsummer counts made with the aid of trained dogs.

Another check that is important in following population trends is the fall age ratio. Young birds are difficult to tell from adults at the hunting season, but there are two methods that can be used for this purpose. The second and third primary feathers are compared; in birds of the year the tip of the second primary is frayed from wear (it was not moulted), as compared to the third; in an adult bird the wear on the two is even but slight, since both were moulted. This technique is most accurate in winter, is fairly good in the fall, but is no good in spring or summer.

The other method is to check for the presence of the bursa of Fabricius, its presence being positive assurance of immaturity; this technique requires some skill, and can be depended on only in the fall, since the sac disappears during the bird's first winter (Ammann, 1944).

PROSPECTS FOR FUTURE MANAGEMENT

IN general the future of the prairie chicken is not very promising. Grange (1948) says that "the prairie chicken in Wisconsin is a doomed species. It will pass from the hunting picture within a few decades at most, and may become extinct in the state after 1967." His reference to 1967 is to the likelihood that that will be a time of minimum population, according to cyclic trends. An equally pessimistic view is warranted for the eastern and southern sections of the range, as well as for the rest of the north-eastern range in Michigan, which is like that in Wisconsin. The prospects in the central and north-central portions of the range are at least better; they hold some hope. The possibilities in Missouri, as reported in the *P-R Quarterly* for April 1945, are that the birds might reach a population of 150,000 on 15,000 square miles —an increase tenfold over the present maximum population—on a range expanded six times; this is an optimistic view, but one that could come true. Its happening would, of course, depend on the widespread adoption of proper land-use practices. That's the story—a big *IF*. The fringes of the range are almost surely a lost cause; but the center of the range could resound once again to the booming of reasonably good prairie-chicken populations—*if* . . . .

CHAPTER 6

The Ruffed Grouse

ORIGIN AND CLASSIFICATION

THE ruffed grouse is a native of North America; it has been living in the forested sections of the northern United States and Canada for at least 25,000 years, having been found in remains from the Pleistocene period in both eastern and western parts of the continent. It belongs in the family Tetraonidae and in the genus *Bonasa*, and is called *B. umbellus* (Linnaeus). It is the sole member of its genus on this continent. It is a close relative of the hazel hen (*Bonasa sylvestris*) of Europe.

Its scientific name is derived from Latin and Greek names meaning "a bison," which refers to the bison's bellowing and the grouse's drumming; and "an umbrella," which is somewhat descriptive of the bird's ruffs. It goes by many provincial common names, the most common of which are "partridge," "patridge," or "birch partridge" in New England; "pheasant" or "mountain pheasant" in the Appalachians. These names lead to much confusion, since the ruffed grouse is neither a partridge nor a pheasant.

Many subspecies of *Bonasa umbellus* have been described by various authors; six are described by the A. O. U. Check List (1931), and a seventh later accepted (*Auk*, Vol. 61, No. 3, July 1944). A comprehensive revision of its taxonomy by Aldrich and Friedmann (1943) includes 12 subspecies; but these authors recognize that the characters of the various subspecies grade from one to another along the boundaries of their range; hence the number of subspecies that exist in a species like the ruffed grouse, which has so variable a color pattern, is a some-

what arbitrary matter. For those who wish to delve into taxonomic detail, I suggest the Aldrich and Friedmann revision. Here I shall name only the seven recognized by the American Ornithologist Union. The type form is the eastern ruffed grouse, *B. umbellus umbellus;* the others are: the Canada ruffed grouse, *B. umbellus togata* (Linnaeus); the Nova Scotia ruffed grouse, *B. umbellus thayeri* (Bangs); the gray ruffed grouse, *B. umbellus umbelloides* (Douglas); the Oregon ruffed grouse, *B. umbellus sabini* (Douglas); the Yukon ruffed grouse, *B. umbellus yukonensis* (Grinnell); and the Vancouver ruffed grouse, *B. umbellus brunnescens* (Conover).

THE HISTORY OF THE RUFFED GROUSE

THE grouse was a staple item of food for the Indian tribes that inhabited the northern United States and Canada. As far as we can tell, these people never seriously reduced the numbers of grouse by their hunting, nor did they cut down the range of the species by land clearing. The relationships of man, bird, and beast were balanced, and the grouse was a fairly stable element in that environment. There were years when the grouse, as well as other game species, were scarce, and the Indians suffered winters of famine as a consequence; these periodic declines in the abundance of the game species of the North were not caused by overhunting, but rather were the cyclic times of scarcity that strike these creatures at intervals, regardless of how many are killed by hunting.

After the landing of the Pilgrims in Massachusetts, the Dutch at New Amsterdam, and the

English and Swedish in Delaware and Virginia, white men came to know the grouse, or "wood hen" as it was first called, as one of the finest table delicacies among the game species of the new land; the concensus was that only the wild turkey rivalled it in flavor. It served as one of the main foods of the pioneers until their settlements became stabilized, and farming well started.

As they cleared the forests for conversion to farm fields, the settlers began the great change in the physical habitat of the ruffed grouse that finally resulted in a considerable reduction of its habitat. At first, however, these openings in the almost solid forest were improvements in the habitat; since, being small, they increased the interspersion of cover types, and the amount of edges that are so important to grouse. The continuation of land-clearing soon passed the optimum balance between forest and field, and from that time on the area of habitable range was more and more restricted. Areas of considerable size, such as southeastern Pennsylvania and eastern Maryland, and the lake plain of Ohio, Indiana, and Illinois, were so completely deforested that the grouse were entirely eliminated; in most of its range in the northeastern and north-central states it was pushed back, so to speak, to the hills, while the fertile valleys were taken over by agriculture.

As the country grew during the 18th and 19th centuries, cities developed; and the people no longer were pioneers depending on the natural crops of the land for sustenance; game species like the grouse no longer were staple foods. Hunting became a commercial venture, engaged in by a few, who sold their kill in the city markets. Since transportation was slow, most of this hunting was done fairly close to the cities; consequently grouse became scarce in these areas, unable to survive against all-out hunting by men using snares and traps as well as guns. Prices for grouse were as low as 25 cents a brace in some years early in the 1800's; later, before the traffic was finally ended, the market price went as high as two dollars a bird in New York City.

The declining importance of game in the mar-

kets, the increased difficulty of procuring large bags of grouse, and the increasing interest in hunting as a sport, all combined to cause the legal elimination of commercial hunting at about the turn of the 20th century. The sale of grouse was prohibited in Pennsylvania in 1897, and in New York in 1903.

The emphasis on hunting as a form of recreation increased rapidly in the early 1900's. The favorite upland game bird in the Northern states was the grouse, while in the Southern states it was the bobwhite quail. Hunting dogs were highly trained to point these birds, and breeds skilful in finding and "holding" grouse were most prized of all. Today the native patridge is considered as the "king of game birds" by those who know him best; it is the official state bird of Pennsylvania.

That this bird should become so esteemed as an object of sport is a tribute to its ability to adjust itself to changing conditions. It was not always the wary, fast-flushing, fast-dodging bird we know today; in fact, the early writers made fun of the stupid character of the "wood hen." They recounted how the birds could be flushed up into a tree by a yapping dog, and then shot down one by one, while each bird watched the dog—as long as the lowest bird was shot, the ones above would not fly. Others told of knocking them off low tree limbs with sticks. In my own experience within the past 25 years I have seen wilderness grouse in the central Adirondacks of New York run ahead on the ground rather than flush, and well within gun-shot range all the time; if we needed camp meat we would shoot off their heads with a rifle. Such occurrences are rare today, even in the near-wilderness areas that we have left. The ruffed grouse, unlike its near relative, the spruce grouse (*Canachites canadensis*), has changed with the times, and has survived to live in the white man's world; the spruce grouse was unable to change from its "fool hen" character, and has been exterminated from all but the largest uninhabited wilderness areas.

As more and more sportsmen took to hunting the ruffed grouse, its significance to man far surpassed the part it played during the commercial hunting era. Formerly, when the birds were abundant, people could buy them in quantity and at a low price in the market; when the grouse were scarce, the only result was a modification of some people's eating habits. In contrast today, as hundreds of thousands of hunters look forward to pursuing the wily grouse as a form of recreation, the abundance or scarcity of the birds assumes tremendous importance. It is not surprising, then, that the first period of the scarcity of grouse that occurred after the beginning of the sporting era occasioned great concern. Investigations of the causes of the 1906–07 decline in grouse were made in Massachusetts and in New York (Woodruff, 1907); it was concluded that disease, bad weather, overhunting, and predation were probably responsible. This seemed adequate to cover the subject; but since the birds recovered promptly to satisfactory numbers, little more was heard on the subject for several years.

The next period of decline began in 1914, and continued for about four years; it too was studied by the New York State Conservation Department, and a report on it made by Stoddart (1918). Many more possible causes of grouse losses were listed, and particular emphasis was placed on predation—eighteen factors of this sort were named. By this time the sportsmen and game departments were very sensitive to changes in grouse populations. In 1919 Dr. Arthur A. Allen of Cornell University began studies on the methods of propagating grouse in captivity; it was thought that game-farm grouse might be used to offset the scarcity of wild birds. By 1924, when a minor decline in grouse numbers occurred in the Northeast, Dr. Allen was able to report to the American Game Conference that he had discovered a stomach worm in grouse, *Dispharynx spiralis,* that was of such severity that it could cause epidemics; as a result, the emphasis on grouse research concentrated on diseases for several years, since it seemed possible that the cause of the periodic declines might be

of this nature. Dr. A. O. Gross at the same time conducted a similar grouse-disease study for the Massachusetts Fish and Game Association.

The drop in grouse numbers in 1924 was not of great significance, since the population went up again the next year; but by 1927 the birds had dropped to the lowest level ever known. Hunting seasons were completely closed in 1928, for the first time in history. Allen and Gross studied specimens from all over the Northeast, but found nothing conclusive—though *Dispharynx* still seemed to be the most significant cause of trouble. Grouse numbers did not rise appreciably for the next two seasons, and so by 1929 sportsmen were greatly alarmed. A group in New York persuaded the State Conservation Department to undertake a comprehensive scientific study of the species, to ferret out the cause of the trouble; thus in 1930 began the New York State Ruffed Grouse Investigation, which continued for 13 years, and made the most complete and detailed study of a game species that has ever been done. Unfortunately the World War forced its termination before another major decline of grouse occurred. Two books, however, resulted from that study: *The Ruffed Grouse* (Edminster, 1947), and the official report, *The Ruffed Grouse—Life History, Propagation, Management* (Bump, Darrow, Edminster, Crissey, 1947).

At the same time that the New York studies were progressing, other studies were being made of the bird in other areas; the alarm over the species was country-wide. Dr. Ralph T. King studied the grouse in Minnesota from 1929 to 1934, when a marked drop occurred in the bird's numbers. The decline was attributed to a failure in the bird's reproduction, caused by forces beyond the control of man (King, 1937). C. H. D. Clarke studied the grouse in Ontario from 1932–36 (Clarke, 1936); L. W. Fisher, F. W. Baumgartner, and others in Michigan from 1932 to 1939 (Fisher, 1939); and others conducted smaller investigations during the late 1930's and 1940's in Connecticut, Maine, Massachusetts, New Hampshire, Ohio, Pennsylvania, Virginia,

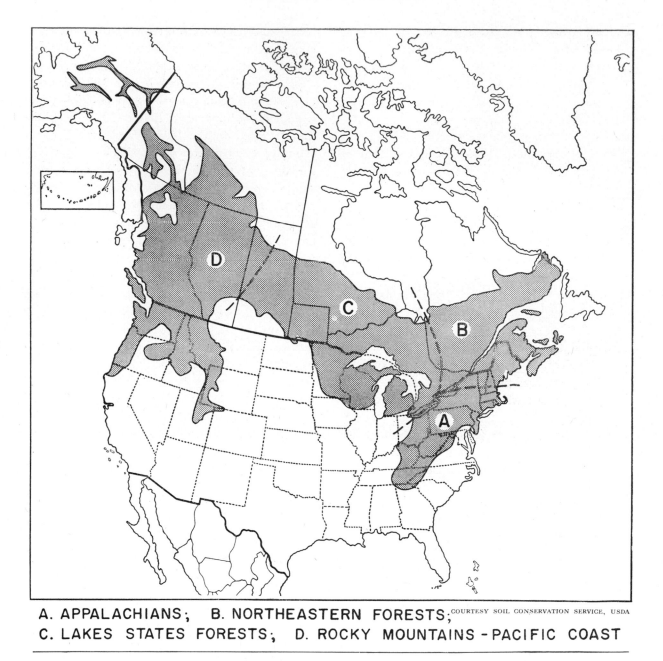

A. APPALACHIANS;   B. NORTHEASTERN FORESTS; ^{COURTESY SOIL CONSERVATION SERVICE, USDA}
C. LAKES STATES FORESTS;   D. ROCKY MOUNTAINS - PACIFIC COAST

FIGURE 17. *Geographic range of the ruffed grouse showing areas of four range types.*

and Wisconsin. With all this attention, the ruffed grouse has become one of the most completely studied game birds in the world.

It now seems certain that the ups and downs of the populations of *Bonasa* are beyond the influence of man. Another major low period oc- curred in the mid-1940's; and then the birds re- turned to high abundance; some of the best grouse-hunting of modern times was found in the Midwest and Northeast in the early 1950's. If man is not so foolish as to ruin the grouse habitat, there appears to be no reason why there should not be good grouse-hunting for a long time to come; in seven or eight years out of each ten the birds should be plentiful enough to provide good hunting.

GEOGRAPHIC RANGE

THE ruffed grouse is the one native, sedentary game bird that is found from the Atlantic to the Pacific; it inhabits a larger area than any other nonmigratory game bird. The extremities of its range are even greater north to south than east to west.

As a generalization, the species occupies almost all the forested area of Canada, the northeastern United States, the lakes states, the Appalachians, the Rockies north of central Utah, the Cascades and other ranges of the Northwest, and the valleys of central Alaska. Except for a few areas on the southern fringe, a large area in the middle Mississippi Valley region, and parts of Colorado, it still lives in the same range it lived in when the white man first came here. The development of agriculture drove the grouse from the area extending from western Ohio to Iowa, and down to Arkansas and western Tennessee (see Figure 17).

Following is the distribution of the seven subspecies. *B. u. umbellus* ranges through the Appalachians from northern Georgia to the southern parts of Ohio, New York, and Massachusetts; here it merges with *B. u. togata,* which ranges through Minnesota, Wisconsin, Michigan, upper New York, and Massachusetts, and thence on north to the limit of the forest and including New Brunswick. *B. u. umbelloides* is found in the Rocky Mountain region and portions of the Prairie Provinces. *B. u. thayeri* is found in Nova Scotia; and merges with *B. u. togata* in eastern New Brunswick. *B. u. sabini* ranges from northern California to British Columbia. *B. u. brunnescens* is found on Vancouver Island. *B. u. yukonensis* is found in portions of the Yukon Territory, and in the major river valleys of central Alaska.

COURTESY SOIL CONSERVATION SERVICE, USDA

PLATE 43. *The ruffed grouse.*

DESCRIPTION

THE grouse is a plump bird about 15 to 19 inches long, with rather short rounded wings that spread from 22 to 25 inches, a prominent tail 4½ to 7½ inches long, and weighing from 16 to 28 ounces. The legs are strongly built, and the beak is typically heavy for a gallinaceous bird.

The color is predominantly brown in the majority of birds, but is more gray or more rufous in some; the Western birds tend toward the gray; the most reddish specimens come from the southern Appalachians. The brown background color of the upper parts is broken by a pattern of black and whitish markings that varies greatly among individuals. The lower parts are grayish white, broken on the flanks by bars of brown or blackish brown.

The feathers on top of the head are erectile, and make a small crest when raised. A buff eye line and chin patch are prominent. The ruff feathers that give the bird its name are in triangular patches on each side of the neck; they are black, with a greenish to purple iridescence; rarely a grouse is found with a chestnut-colored ruff. These ruff feathers are erected into a collar about the neck during courtship performances, during the drumming, and at some other times of excitement. When not erected the ruff is carried obscurely beneath the brown neck feathers.

Grouse grow appendanges on the sides of the toes in the winter called "snowshoes," which serve just that purpose; they are shed each spring.

In addition to great color variability among the several subspecies, grouse have a tendency to dichromatism within each subspecies; a single brood of grouse may develop some "gray phase" birds and some "red phase" birds. This characteristic adds to the confusion of the subspecies concept.

The sexes are similar. With a specimen in the hand it is usually easy to determine the sex from external characteristics; but field identification is difficult in about half the birds. The male is bigger and heavier than the female, but a large female is often heavier than a small male. The tail feathers of the male are longer than those of the female, but here too there is overlapping. The cock bird has a more prominent ruff than the hen, but this is not easily seen. When the bird is in the hand this characteristic is usually quite dependable, since the ruff feathers on the male continue across the breast, while on the female they fade in the middle. The dark, subterminal band on the tail is always broken in the center in a hen bird, whereas in the cock it is often continuous. In a general way the colors of the male are brighter and less subdued than those of the female.

Field identification of sex is best made by the tail length and barring characteristics; it can often be aided by action characteristics, like strutting, broodiness, and drumming. The angle of flight in flushing from the ground is fairly dependable for sex identification; the male usually rises steeply and the female flies low.

The plumage of the juveniles is similar to that of the adults, but with less contrast and more somber browns; the ruffs are not visible, and the sexes are alike. The downy chicks are mottled brownish buff above, and a more yellowish buff below. A black line through the eye is prominent.

The eggs of the ruffed grouse are ovate, creamy white to buff, and average about 38 mm. long and 29 mm. wide; they weigh about 18 gms. when first laid.

IMPORTANCE AS A GAME BIRD

THE "importance" of a game bird is measured by a number of factors that when added up, give it some sort of rank in comparison with other species. The first criterion that comes to mind is the number of the species harvested and the volume of hunting that it furnishes; these are closely related. On this score the ruffed grouse fares rather poorly compared with the leaders, the bobwhite quail and the ring-necked pheasant; but it compares favorably with most other upland game birds. The annual harvest in years of good abundance in the United States is about 3 million birds; the harvest in Canada would probably raise this total close to 4 million. More than 2 million hunters participate in grouse hunting, and they spend about 20 million man-hours a year in doing so.

The second criterion of importance is the quality of the hunting; and here the partridge shines; in fact, it is the thrilling nature of the sport that makes grouse shooting so outstanding. On this point the ruffed grouse ranks as high as any species. The kind of habitat where grouse are hunted is about as pleasant to be in as any, and this in itself adds to the pleasure of the hunter.

Grouse hunting is allowed over a long season in most areas, and thus provides opportunity for recreation for a protracted period. Since the bird occurs in good abundance over a wide range, it provides hunting opportunity to a widely distributed population. The grouse is legal game in 23 states and in all of Canada.

The amount of money spent for grouse hunting is not nearly as large as with the bobwhite and ringneck, but is more than is spent hunting most other upland species. The quantity of ammunition used in grouse hunting is less than in bobwhite quail, pheasant, and mourning dove hunting.

The choice quality of grouse hunting has already been mentioned, but another word on this matter may be in order. Probably no other game bird lies as nicely to well-trained hunting dogs as does the grouse; yet there are few good grouse dogs today. Most bird dogs in the northern states are used on pheasants, and once they have pursued the running ringneck they are somewhat spoiled for use with grouse. The periodic poor years of grouse hunting have discouraged many dog owners from keeping grouse dogs; for those who do keep and train them, the thrill of hunting the partridge is increased many fold.

The grouse is an almost perfect game bird as far as the landowner is concerned. Since it keeps mostly to the woods and brushy areas, it rarely causes any trouble for the farmer. The trespass nuisance is negligible in connection with grouse hunting. Farm crops are not damaged, except in occasional instances of apple-tree budding. Where apple orchards are adjacent to good grouse cover the birds can damage the next year's crop somewhat by overbudding; but these instances are not common in commercial orchards.

HABITS OF THE RUFFED GROUSE

COURTSHIP

GROUSE may winter singly or in small, loosely organized groups. As spring approaches they frequently leave the sheltered conifers, or other winter cover, to visit the open hardwoods; more and more they spend their time alone as spring territories are selected. With the lengthening days of March, the swelling gonads stimulate the birds to start their courtship activities.

Male grouse seek out a drumming territory, and choose one or more logs on which to drum; if no prostrate logs are available, they use mossy rocks, mounds, wooden fence rails, or other similar prominences; the largest and mossiest logs are preferred. The drumming location is almost always in rather open woodland, but with some thick shelter close by; it is rarely in brush or very open cover. A single spot on the log is used for drumming, and often is well worn. Grouse sleep on their favorite log many of the nights during the height of the drumming season; thus the identity of logs used for drumming is easily seen by the piles of droppings as well as by the worn drumming spot.

Male grouse occasionally drum at any time of the year, and at any time of day or night. The frequency of drumming increases in the spring, until there are only a few minutes between drums from before dawn until an hour or two after dawn, and again in late afternoon. Another period of somewhat increased drumming activity takes place in autumn.

The drumming act is one of the most fascinating courtship displays of any of our game birds. It is done instinctively, but proficiency requires some experience; a young cock's first efforts produce only a swishing sound. The bird stands crosswise on the log with its tail serving as a rear brace; the wings are moved forward and upward in quick strokes against the air. At first the strokes are slow and evenly spaced, but gradually they increase in tempo until the final phase is a blur of sound and motion. The word "drumming" aptly describes the quality of the sound; it may also be likened to the noise of a one-cylinder gas engine starting. It is often difficult to tell from just which direction the sound is coming, and how far away the bird is; the sound seems to have a ventriloquistic effect, and a bird a quarter of a mile away sometimes sounds as close as one only a hundred yards off.

The means by which the sound is made was debated for a long time; some believed that the bird's wings hit its breast, others that they struck each other in front or back, or hit the log. Dr. Arthur A. Allen finally showed by slow-motion movies that the wings struck only the air.

The purpose of drumming is twofold: it is a challenge to all grouse that the territory of the drumming bird is established and others should keep out, especially males; it is also an invitation to females for mating. It is not the same call to the female at all times. Whether the cock bird is ready to mate with any hen that responds to his drumming, or whether he will repel her with fighting, depends on the stage of the oestrus (sex cycle) he is in. Both sexes have a mating cycle, with short periods through the spring when they are in condition to mate, interspersed with periods when they are not interested. In order for mating to take place both birds must be in the same ready phase of their cycles (Allen, 1934).

The male grouse engages in another rather spectacular display, usually associated with fighting, though it is also connected with the courtship period. When one grouse approaches another that is drumming but is not in mating condition, the drummer will beat off the intruder even if it is a hen seeking coition. The cock frequently will strut very slowly toward the visiting bird, with his tail held erectly spread in a fan. He watches the visitor intently, and takes slow, measured steps while shaking his head from side to side and emitting hissing sounds, that parallel the drumming in pattern, and are in time with the head-shaking. They begin slowly, then pick up speed, and finally end in a whir of fast head-shaking and hissing sounds that are merged into a long final *shhhhhhh*. A short, quick run toward the visiting bird is made at the end of the performance, and then the cock bird makes his attack and beats off the intruder. The same bird visiting the next day might receive entirely different treatment, if the cock's condition had changed to the mating phase; in that case he would receive the hen bird with tender attention, and favor her with coition.

All grouse strut at times, and display "masculine" behavior. This may not have anything at all to do with courtship and usually doesn't; it seems rather the effort of each bird to demonstrate its superiority over its associates. Young grouse only a week old start this strutting and displays of courtshiplike behavior, even to the extent of going through the motions of coition; but this probably has no connection with sex, but is just an effort to intimidate.

NESTING

ABOUT two weeks after courtship the hen begins nest building; this is usually in early April. She selects a place at the base of some obstacle like a tree, stump, or rock, and near an open cover edge. The cover type in which the nest is built is most commonly young hardwoods, and the spot is usually open; the obstacle serves as protection from the rear, while the open area in front enables her to keep watch for enemies, and to make a quick flight when necessary.

The nest is hollowed in the duff on the ground, and is lined first with dead leaves and later with some down. The first egg is laid about a week after the nest is made, and the rest of the clutch at intervals of about a day and a half; the average clutch is 11 or 12 eggs, and takes a little over two weeks to lay. The hen keeps the eggs well covered with leaves when she is off the nest, which is most of the time until incubation starts.

She does not wander far from the nest during the laying period, except for the occasional visits to a cock grouse; usually there will be two or three matings before and during the laying of one full clutch. When the clutch is complete she loses interest in courtship, and soon the drumming of the cocks stops also. As soon as the hen is broody she begins the long ordeal of incubation.

Except for a short feeding period in early morning and again in late afternoon, the grind of keeping the eggs warm is continuous; the only exception is the happenstance of some man or animal intruding and forcing the bird to flush. Early in the incubation period the hen flushes easily; but as the period goes on she takes greater and greater chances with creatures that approach closely, and by the time two and one-half weeks have gone by she stays on the nest until the very last second before an approaching enemy reaches her. Once in a while a fox will actually catch an incubating bird before she escapes; I have even touched a number of grouse before they flushed from the nest.

If the bird is fortunate enough to escape

PLATE 44. *The ruffed grouse often selects an open spot at the base of a tree to nest.*

COURTESY SOIL CONSERVATION SERVICE, USDA

having her nest destroyed, the eggs hatch in 23 or 24 days. If she loses her eggs to a predator she may or may not renest, the probability of renesting is rather good if the nest is destroyed during the first two weeks of incubation—about half the nests so destroyed will be replaced. The longer the incubation has proceeded before the destruction of the nest, the less the chance of renesting; those pilfered in the last week of incubation are rarely replaced. When renesting does occur the clutch is smaller than the first one, and there is a higher proportion of infertile eggs. The male bird does not participate at all in the duties of incubation, or in the care of the young birds later.

THE BROOD PERIOD

HATCHING time is a most critical one for ruffed grouse; the fate of the little chicks in their first few days of life depends on the luck of the weather. If they are fortunate enough to have warm, fair days at hatching time and afterward, they are lucky; little loss will occur. If, however, the weather is cold and wet, the majority of the chicks may die before they are a week old. That is the reason that the early June weather is so vital a matter to grouse; a spell of bad weather at the time the majority of grouse nests are

hatching spells poor hunting three or four months later.

Most of the eggs hatch in a period of a few hours, and the chicks are dried off soon after. As soon as the day is warm and sunny the mother bird leaves the nest with her new brood, never to return; she pays no attention to the egg or two that often remains unhatched in the nest. Many of these would hatch if incubated for a few hours more, for their delay was caused by inadequate incubation during the regular period; occasionally one of these abandoned eggs is infertile.

The little swarm of chicks does not go far from the nest on the initial trek; they have had no chance to build strength for walking long distances. The hen broods them for a while, and then starts out again. Soon she catches insects for them, and teaches them to catch their own food. The time between broodings increases until the first night. By then the mother may well have guided the little family to a brushy area, either an overgrown field or a slashing in the woods; here are lots of insects and summer fruits, and it is in this kind of cover that most young grouse are raised.

Keeping a group of about ten active little grouselets under surveillance is quite a job; and though the mother grouse is a very attentive parent she frequently cannot avoid tragedy. A youngster may stray too far away and get lost, or fall in a hole, or be picked off by a marauding sharp-shinned hawk. The family may be disturbed while brooding in the night, and some of the chicks may be badly chilled before the hen can get them under her again. All these things happen, and young grouse chicks disappear, until by midsummer there are usually only about half of them left.

The chicks begin to fly when they are two weeks old, and at three weeks can manage a fairly good flight. By six weeks their plumage is well enough developed so that they resemble the parent in coloration. Dust-bathing is engaged in by young and old, for feather growth and care. After they reach eight to ten weeks of age, the mother's control begins to wane as the chicks strive for independence; then the mortality curve rises for a while, as they become accustomed to the danger of the accipitrine hawks. In September they moult into adult plumage. If by that time there are four or more chicks left per brood, the hunting season population will be good; if the losses have been more than 60%, the fall population will be poor by the amount that the mortality exceeds that figure.

The food of the young grouse is almost entirely insects for the first couple of weeks. As the summer fruits ripen they partake of them, and gradually reduce the amount of insects taken; strawberries, raspberries, and blueberries are specially important in their summer diet. Toward late summer the food of the young birds becomes the same as that of the adults.

FALL AND WINTER MONTHS

THE advent of autumn brings many changes in the life of the grouse. The young birds are then grown, and can be identified from the adults only by careful examination. An easy way to tell the birds of the year in autumn is by examining the outer two primary feathers of the wing; it is generally true that these feathers are not moulted by the young grouse, the first year, and remain pointed at the tip, in comparison with the same feathers on older birds. A more precise way to determine age is to check the presence or absence of the bursa of Fabricius; this requires opening the posterior end of the alimentary tract. Its presence denotes a bird of the year.

There is much fighting among the grouse family as summer fades into fall. The birds beaten in these battles often leave the family and go off by themselves; at times their flight is desperate as they seek to escape their tormentors. They may fly much farther than is their normal habit, and wind up in strange surroundings; some of them even fly into buildings, and into the streets of cities. This phenomenon has been called "crazy flight," and has been attributed to the nervousness brought on by the falling leaves from the trees and to irritations from internal parasites. Though the dropping of the foliage may contribute to their nervousness, this activity is actually a part of the normal fall shuffle that takes place with most sedentary game birds; it signifies the breakup of the families and the adjustment to fall territories.

There comes a time in the autumn when the placid and comfortable life of the grouse is suddenly broken by showers of lead pellets; when the hunting season opens, the grouse changes from a protected bird to legal game. Most grouse of the year then have their first experience with the human species. They have no trouble recognizing him as a danger, and after successfully dodging a few blasts of shot become more wary. Not all escape the hunter; and his toll makes the first big dent in the adult population; most of his bag is composed of young birds, especially in years of high populations.

Autumn is a time of high living for grouse; they love many of the fruits and nuts that ripen at this season, and have no trouble in getting enough of them. Some are preferred over others, and their availability often determines where the birds will be; beech nuts, white oak acorns, thorn apples, apples, and flowering dogwood are some of the foods that attract grouse in the fall, when these crops are good. Since many of these are found in open brushy areas and hedgerows, balmy fall days may find the birds far from their usual cover. Expert hunters know about these habits, and seek out the birds in these locations.

By the end of autumn the cover has shrunk some around the edges, as the hardwood foliage drops and the rank herbaceous ground cover is laid low by frost. The easy picking of fruits is soon over, and less choice foods must satisfy. As temperatures drop, winds drive cold rain and finally snow through the open cover, and cause the birds to seek more protective shelter. In most of the bird's range the evergreens furnish the best winter cover. Then one day comes the first big snow of the winter to cover the landscape with a deep white blanket. This new discomfort brings with it the means of escape; instinctively the birds take to snow roosting. This is a rather unusual habit, that brings them both comfort and danger. A cozy hole in the snow avoids the wind, and is warmer than the open air, even though surrounded with subfreezing material. It is also an easy place for a fox to pick up a grouse dinner; these snow roosts are easily spotted on the surface by the slight rise in the level of the snow, and by the little breathing hole. Then, too, grouse tracks often lead to the spot, or wing marks in the snow show that a bird alighted there. Foxes seem to be able to figure this out, just as a man does. With care a man can catch a grouse in its snow roost; it is easy to understand, then, why so many grouse are picked out of the snow by the wily fox.

Grouse often ride out a storm for several days in snow roosts, and seem none the worse for going without food that long. Snow roosting seems to be used more in early season than later; we may presume that the birds become accustomed to the cold and snow and do not mind it so much. Then they roost in evergreen trees more than any other place; in fact, much of the winter is spent in this dense cover. The hardwoods are used in balmy weather when they forage for food. Since their winter food is mostly tree buds, they can usually feed fairly well without leaving the shelter of the woods.

Grouse are more gregarious in the winter than at any other season; after the breakup of the families in the fall they tend to regroup in the winter. These new coveys are not ordinarily families, but merely the birds of a given locality that gather for companionship. In the spring they become solitary again.

Late winter is a time of great losses from enemy attack; much of this mortality is associated with the vulnerability caused by bad weather. The predators themselves are hard pressed at this season, and have to work harder for their food; this increases the pressure on secondary food species like the grouse. As spring approaches the vulnerability of the grouse to predation increases, as they expose themselves by their courtship activities; the rate of death of the male grouse goes up, particularly during the drumming period. Later this differential in mortality between the sexes is offset by an increase in the rate of loss of females during the nesting and brooding season. It is well to note that practically none of the winter losses of grouse are due to starvation or direct exposure to the elements; the partridge is well adapted to the rigorous climate in which it lives.

Thus the round of the seasons is completed, and spring brings the exuberance of another breeding season. There may be more or fewer grouse than there were the year before, but this much is reasonably sure: if there are fewer, another year will probably reverse the trend and there will be more grouse again; if there are more, another year may well reverse this trend and there will be fewer grouse again. Grouse populations are a dynamic resource, always changing; they never go one way for very long.

Individual birds have a daily traveling range of but a few hundred yards in spring and summer; they tend to gravitate to the drumming log, the nest, the choice summer food area, and similar territorial nuclei. In the fall grouse travel more than at any other season; young birds especially may go several miles in the process of the fall shuffle. In winter the movements are once more restricted to a few acres. The adjustment from winter to spring cover may require a trip of half a mile, more or less.

ADAPTABILITY TO ARTIFICIAL PROPAGATION

MAN has tried for more than 200 years to raise the ruffed grouse in captivity, but success today is not much better than it was when this was first tried. After the severe decline of ruffed grouse in 1916–18 the American Game Association persuaded Dr. A. A. Allen to undertake scientific experiments to learn how to raise the bird (Allen, 1929); he spent 12 years at these experiments, and was able to learn much about the problems involved. He placed the birds in wire-bottom pens to avoid diseases spread by the droppings; he learned the requirements for breeding—so essential to getting fertile eggs. But these were only a few of the needs. Gardiner Bump picked up where Allen left off, and conducted large-scale grouse propagation work in New York for more than a decade (Bump, *et al.,* 1947). He raised more than 2,000 grouse, and these included some birds that had been ten generations in captivity. Despite the great gain in knowledge and techniques that this work gave, it remains true that the propagation of ruffed grouse in captivity is expensive and impractical. The breeders do not lay enough eggs, the eggs laid have a high rate of infertility, and the techniques of obtaining high hatchability are imperfectly worked out. The biggest stumbling block of all is getting a high rate of survival of the hatched chicks, especially in the first two weeks after hatching. These are some of the many reasons why grouse breeding and raising have not been a practical success; and it is doubtful if these problems will be solved—at least not for a long time. Fortunately the stocking of ruffed grouse is not essential in its management; it is probable that it would not play an important part in managing the species even if we could raise them practically on game farms. Where the cause of their disappearance has been removed, there are opportunities to re-establish them by the stocking of wild-trapped birds.

THE SHELTER REQUIREMENTS OF THE RUFFED GROUSE

TYPES OF RANGE

ANY species as widely distributed as the ruffed grouse is sure to have a great many types of range. Because "type of range" is a broad concept, it is desirable to avoid breaking it down finely into a multiplicity of areas; thus it becomes somewhat arbitrary in the case of the ruffed grouse, since there are so many variations of

COURTESY SOIL CONSERVATION SERVICE, USDA

PLATE 45. *Coniferous woodland makes the best winter cover for ruffed grouse. The alder run in the foreground of this Adirondack Mountains, New York, scene is good summer brood cover.*

range that *could* be recognized. Considering management and hunting conditions, four divisions in the entire range seem warranted: (1) the Appalachians; (2) the northeastern forests; (3) the lake states forests; (4) the Rocky Mountains-Pacific Coast forests. These are shown with their approximate boundaries in Figure 17 (p. 198).

The Appalachian range includes the Appalachian Mountains proper, their northern extensions through Pennsylvania, New York, and into western Massachusetts, and the forested portions of the coastal plain from southern New Jersey into Massachusetts. It merges on the northern edge into the northeastern forest zone along the lower fringes of the Adirondack, and the Green and White Mountains. It is clearly separated from the lake states forest zone on the west by the agricultural areas of southern Ontario, western Ohio, and southern Michigan. The Appalachian zone includes much of the better eastern grouse-hunting areas. The terrain is hilly except for the coastal plain portion; forests are well interspersed with farming areas, except in some of the southern mountains. It has a moderate climate, compared with the other three range types. Land ownership is generally in small parcels, and lumbering is therefore done in small units,

which results in a good pattern of different age classes of woodland. The major forest types found are the hemlock-white pine-beech-birch-maple association in the northern portion; the oaks-hickory-hard pines association in the southern section; the scrub oak-pitch pine association in the coastal plain part. The grouse carrying capacity of the Appalachian range type is relatively high; it is generally lower than that of the lakes states forests, but is better than in most of the northeastern forests and Rocky Mountains-Pacific Coast forest range types.

The northeastern forest type extends from the Adirondack, Green, and White Mountains north and northeast through Maine, the Maritime Provinces, Quebec, and Labrador to the limits of forest. It merges on the west with the lakes states forest zone, and the boundary between them is entirely arbitrary. The terrain is mountainous in the southern portion, but with generally low, rolling land to the north. Forests are extensive and almost continuous, except for the portions of the southern section where agriculture thrives. The climate is rigorous, with very cold winters and heavy snows. Land ownership is mostly in large blocks, largely by lumber companies and governments. Forests are primarily of spruces, balsam, and the most northern hard-

PLATE 46. *Slashings following lumbering are fine summer habitat, abounding in insects and fruits to feed young grouse.*

COURTESY SOIL CONSERVATION SERVICE, USDA

woods; among the prevalent hardwoods are the birches, beech, sugar maple, aspen and willows; tamarack and northern white cedar are additional evergreens found in swampy areas. In the most northern section the stature of the forests shrinks as the limit of trees is approached; lumbering is mainly for pulp, and is conducted by extensive operations. The grouse carrying capacity is relatively low, except for parts of the southern sections.

The lake states forest zone includes the wooded portions of Michigan, Wisconsin, Minnesota, a little bit of North Dakota, western Ontario, and some of the prairie provinces of Canada. On the eastern side it merges imperceptibly into the northeastern forest zone; but the western boundary, while geographically contiguous with the Rocky Mountains-Pacific Coast forest zone, is well separated from the western range by open prairies. The terrain is generally flat. Forests are continuous, except where the scattered forest edges merge with the prairies. Agricultural lands surround this zone on three sides, and intermix with it somewhat; on the northern side the range type ends in the limit of trees and the beginning of the tundra. The climate is very severe; rainfall is lower than in most grouse range. Forests are owned mostly by lumber companies and units of government; cutting is mostly for pulp, and is done in large units. The forests in the southern part are composed of jack pine and the northern hardwoods; white and red pine are less plentiful than formerly; spruce and tamarack prevail in the wet areas. Aspen is plentiful in burned areas for a period after the fires, which have swept over much of this zone since the white man came. In the northern parts spruces, tamarack, and willows are prevalent. The grouse carrying capacity is high in the southern portions, progressively less so to the north. The better portions of this range type are probably the optimum grouse range.

The Rocky Mountains-Pacific Coast forest zone extends over the greatest area of any range type; the southern extremities are in northwestern California and central Utah, while the northern limit is in the river valleys of central Alaska. The birds are found in most of the forest areas in between, including those on Vancouver and other islands off the coast. The terrain is mostly very rugged and mountainous. The climate is severe, except for the coastal mountains section from California to British Columbia. Here the rainfall is high, but the snow is light— except at high altitudes; inland the precipitation is relatively low, except for the winter snows. Land ownership is mostly by government and big lumber companies; lumbering is done by large units. The forests are composed of Douglas fir, western red cedar, Port Orford cedar, Engelmann spruce, Rocky mountain yellow pine, western white pine, lodgepole pine, western yellow pine, and a scattering of associated hardwoods. At the northern fringe of the range the habitable cover is limited to low-altitude valleys, and the occupied range becomes scattered. The carrying capacity of the Rocky Mountains-Pacific Coast forest range type is generally the lowest of all four.

COVER TYPES NEEDED

REGARDLESS of the type of grouse range, the birds require certain vegetative associations for various functions. These *cover types* are substantially the same in all kinds of range, though the plants that compose them vary. The needs of ruffed grouse are met by five different cover types: open land; brushy areas; hardwood woodlands; mixed woodlands; coniferous woodlands (see Table 14).

Open Land. Areas covered with herbaceous plants or with no vegetation at all are the kinds of open land used by grouse. Their usefulness is not so much their intrinsic value, but rather their relation to adjacent cover; for example, a gravel road provides an opening that breaks up the woodland cover and makes it more useful; it lets sunlight into the marginal cover beside the road; more food plants will grow along these edges for that reason. Any other kind of open land, such as field edges, mountain meadows, marshes, beaver meadows, and rocky outcrops

TABLE 14

COVER TYPES USED BY RUFFED GROUSE

COVER TYPE	SEASON OF USE	FUNCTIONS SERVED
OPEN LAND Farm fields; roads; mountain meadows; bare land; marshes.	Summer; some in spring and fall.	Enhances value of adjacent cover; dusting and sunning.
BRUSHY AREAS Overgrown fields; slashings, alder runs; aspen pin cherry burns.	Summer and fall; some in spring.	Brood cover; fall feeding; summer feeding and dusting, some spring and winter feeding.
HARDWOOD WOODLANDS Appalachian hardwoods; northern hardwoods; old aspen pin cherry burns; western hardwoods.	Spring, summer, and fall.	Nesting; fall and winter feeding.
MIXED WOODLANDS Variety according to combination of hardwood and conifer species.	All year.	General feeding and shelter cover, except for summer.
CONIFEROUS WOODLANDS Variety according to predominant species of conifers.	Winter; some in spring and fall.	Winter shelter; escape cover and storm shelter.

serve the same purpose; they make edges, and improve the interspersion of the cover pattern; they increase the food supply in the adjacent cover. Some foods may grow in the open cover itself, as clovers and insects. These are also used for sunning spots and dusting. They are the least important of the cover types, and are not absolutely essential, provided others are well distributed.

Brushy Areas. Cover that is predominantly made up of shrubs, saplings, and young tree sprouts, and without significant numbers of grown trees, is called *brushy*. It is of great significance to grouse for raising broods in summer; and some varieties of brushy cover make the best fall feeding grounds.

The quality that makes brush so useful for the young birds is the combination of good summer shelter and abundant insect life close to the ground; in many kinds of brushy cover the prevalence of summer fruits such as strawberries, raspberries, and blueberries enhances this value. The kinds of brushy cover that make good fall feeding areas are those that have an abundance of wild fruits that mature in autumn; such species include the hawthorns, wild apples, sumacs, greenbriar, dogwoods, viburnums, wild cherries, and wild grapes.

Brushy cover may be of a variety of types that vary in plant composition and in origin. Abandoned farm fields that remain undisturbed for years will gradually be invaded by woody plants; these may be tree or shrub species, but for a period the cover will be brushy. This is a relatively short-lived situation, since on most of these areas tree species ultimately become dominant and develop into woodland. The length of time the area remains brushy depends on soil fertility and on the happenstance of species nearby that successfully invade the area. The commonest brushy cover type is the woodland slashing. When mature trees are cut from a

PLATE 47. *Second-growth hardwoods are a favorite winter feeding and spring nesting cover type for ruffed grouse. These woodlands should be protected from grazing by domestic cattle.*

woodland, the space they occupied is quickly taken over by woody species that develop a brushy cover. Many of the hardwoods sprout from the trunks and quickly re-establish the species that were cut. Where waste limbs are burned, light-seeded species like the aspens come in; blueberries and pin cherry are also germinated by burns. In some cases the understory of shrubs that is released by the tree harvest assumes temporary domination of the site. The alder run is an example of brushy cover that may be a subclimax type, because on certain soils it maintains itself for long periods. It is deficient in food, and is not used much in the fall.

A scattering of young conifers improves any of the brushy types; this element makes protective shelter that is particularly useful in autumn.

Herbaceous as well as woody plants are important in brushy land; those that produce sum-

mer foods include strawberry, sedges, touch-me-not, and buttercup; fall foods are available from sheep sorrel, miterwort, and false miterwort.

Hardwood Woodlands. Woodlands with a high proportion of hardwood species in comparison with conifers make up a large share of the Appalachian range, but much less in the other three range types. It is an important type of cover for the grouse at all seasons, especially from spring through fall; but its lack of protective shelter for winter weather limits its use at that season. In the spring it is the favored cover for nesting; it also has general utility for feeding and loafing; many drumming logs are found in this cover type.

There are several varieties of hardwood forest, according to the species composition. Of particular significance in the Appalachian area is the prevalent oak-hickory tree association; it may

COURTESY SOIL CONSERVATION SERVICE, USDA

PLATE 48. *Stands of mixed conifers and hardwoods are good all-year grouse habitat. Woods roads make desirable edges and openings, especially if kept cut a little wider than just the roadway.*

contain many species of oaks, plus a mixture of hickories, ash, walnut, tulip poplar, gums, hophornbeam, black locust and others. In the Northeast and North-central ranges, the common hardwoods include birches, maples, beech, serviceberries, aspens, willows, cherries, and hophornbeam. The Rocky Mountain-Pacific forest zone has fewer species of hardwoods than the East; some of these are the tree alders, birches, oaks, serviceberries, and aspens that grow in this region.

The usefulness of hardwoods to grouse depends not only on the species composition, but on the age of the stand and its density; mature hardwoods, those with tree diameters that exceed twelve inches, also have sparse understories. At the other extreme is the pole-size stand, with small-gauge trees growing thickly but with little understory; it is just beyond the brush stage.

In between are second-growth hardwoods larger than pole size but not mature; in this age class the understory is moderately dense, which is the most useful to grouse. Any of the hardwood age classes are better if they have been "spot-lumbered," so that there are scattered openings throughout the stand. The ground cover is more luxuriant in the younger age classes, because of the greater amount of sunlight reaching the ground through the canopy; grouse foods are more plentiful with plenty of sunlight.

Some of the important food plants found in the understory and ground cover in hardwoods are: greenbriar; blueberries; mapleleaf, nannyberry, witchhobble, and witherod viburnums; grapes; flowering dogwood; mountain laurel; poison ivy; bunchberry; wintergreen; Canada mayflower; partridgeberry; evergreen woods ferns; jewelweed; skunk cabbage; wood sorrel;

miterwort; false miterwort; shinleaf; hepatica; white clover; violet.

Mixed Woodlands. A woodland with a good balance of hardwood and coniferous tree species is classed as a *mixed* woods for game habitat purposes. Though somewhat arbitrary, it appears that a woodland with 20% to 70% of conifers is in this class of grouse cover; it is an all-year cover type, able to support grouse in fair numbers with little other cover; it has good winter shelter, depending on the age and species of the coniferous element. Food plants are usually varied and well distributed. Its main shortcoming is the relatively poor summer cover. Insects and summer fruits are not as abundant as is desirable for brood cover. Mixed woods is the best place for drumming logs, because of the presence of the evergreen shelter combined with open hardwoods.

The variety of mixed woods depends not only on the species of hardwoods present, but also of conifers. The age of the coniferous element is important, just as it is with the hardwoods. It is desirable to have a good share of young evergreens, so that there will be protective shelter close to the ground. The presence or absence of openings resulting from "spot lumbering" cuttings is as important in this cover as in hardwoods; a good distribution of these open and brushy spots in a mixed woods makes it the ideal single-cover type for ruffed grouse.

Conifer species that are found with the hardwoods are: hard pines, hemlock, and some white pine in the Appalachian zone; white and red pine, hemlock, spruces, and balsam in the northeastern forests; jack pine, and some white pine, hemlock, and spruces in the lakes states forests; Douglas fir, cedars, Engelmann spruce, and ponderosa, and other western pines in the Rocky Mountain-Pacific Coast zone.

Food plants important in the understory and ground cover of mixed woodlands include most of those found both in hardwoods and conifers; their distribution is in accord with the canopy with which they are associated.

Coniferous Woodlands. Woods with a predominance of the evergreen needle-leaved trees belong in this cover type. Its great use to grouse is as protective shelter and thus it is inhabited more in winter than in any other season. It is generally deficient in food plants; but this depends on the age and density of the stand, and on the prevalence of openings and hardwood intermixture. This type is relatively scarce in the Appalachian zone compared with the others, and is the prevalent one in the Far West.

The coniferous forest tends to be more limited in the number of tree species than either the hardwoods or mixed woods. In the Appalachian zone the type is likely to be a hemlock ravine or an old-field growth of hard pines. In the northeast it may be a hemlock-white pine or a spruce-balsam combination. The lakes states forests have the jack pine as the key species in many areas, and the spruces farther north. In the West the Douglas fir and cedar of the coastal forests and the Engelmann spruce-ponderosa pine woods of the Rockies are common types. In all of them the age mixture is very important; an all-age forest is better for grouse than one that is even-aged.

The understory and ground cover of a young coniferous stand is very sparse or wholly lacking; in older stands it is more evident, but is usually composed of but few species. The carpet of needles may be broken by a few brambles, blueberries, ferns, partridgeberry, wintergreen, and others. In the West there are the western serviceberry, western chokecherry, Greene's mountain-ash, mountain snowberry, and Oregon grape, among others.

The Interspersion of Cover Types. In discussing the characteristics of the various grouse-cover types, we have considered only one of the three major aspects of habitat—its *quality*. We have only indirectly considered the question of the *quantities* of the various needed types, and their *arrangement*. The proportions of the several cover types that are needed for good grouse range will be considered shortly, under "Ideal Land-Use Pattern." The arrangement of the various types is mainly a matter of *interspersion*.

Extensive areas of a single cover type do not make good grouse range. There is a near exception to this principle in the case of mixed woodland, but here the reason is that this type actually contains the elements of two types. It is generally true that the more mixed the cover types are the better is the habitat; this provides lots of *edges* among cover types, and the grouse is very much a bird of the edges; it prefers to live in the summer along the margin between a brushlot and a woods rather than in the woods; along the edge of an evergreen forest in the winter rather than deep in the area; and so on. That is why the smart hunter looks for grouse in the fall along the edges, rather than far back in a solid forest.

The explanation lies in the fact that grouse need more than one type of cover each day to supply their needs; one type may serve for night roosting, another for feeding, another for dusting, and still another to make a quick escape from an enemy. It is obvious that if these needs are to be met with convenience, the cover types must be close together; and they are closest together along the edges. The emphasis on cover-type use changes from season to season, but several are needed at all times.

This explains why we emphasize the need for variety of cover arranged in small units when we discuss management of habitat.

Tree and shrub plantings improve cover for ruffed grouse on abandoned farms and on poor parts of operating farms.

PLATE 49. Top. *Steep slope planted to alternate bands of conifers and hardwoods.*

PLATE 50. *Pine planting with shrub border of dogwood.*

THE IMPORTANCE OF PLANT SUCCESSION

NATURAL plant succession is more important in ruffed grouse ecology than it is in the ecology of many other game birds. Most of our game birds are greatly influenced by the farming techniques that closely control the plant succession on farmland; not so the partridge. It makes practically no use of farmed areas or farm crop plants; it will not succumb to artificial propagation, or be influenced by food handouts. Its habitat—hence its welfare—is little allied to short-term cover controls; its cover is largely determined by the slow process of plant succession.

Grouse cover is a dynamic, always changing plant complex; it is never exactly the same two years in a row, yet it does not change much each year; that is, until it grows to a point where man

COURTESY SOIL CONSERVATION SERVICE, USDA

COURTESY SOIL CONSERVATION SERVICE, USDA

steps in to set it back a long, long way. Plants grow, plants die, new plants replace dead ones, and often the new ones are different kinds; the cover thus continually changes in composition and age. Grouse management is based largely on the laws that govern this phenomenon.

Let us consider an example to illustrate how this process affects grouse habitat. We will begin with a poor, hilly New England farm. The last crop on a field beside a mixed woods is a sparse stand of buckwheat. That fall the people move off and let nature take over. Possibly the property reverts to town ownership for nonpayment of taxes. Next year the field has no more buckwheat; it is badly worn out, and its fertility is very low, even though it does not exhibit obvious signs of soil erosion. A few annual weeds appear to provide a sparse cover. The ragweed plants mature at a height of but a few inches; there is also a little smartweed and foxtail. The second season after abandonment there is less of these annual weeds, but a few sprigs of poverty grass and quack grass show up. A little moss here and there indicates a continuing degeneration. In another year the same grasses are thicker, and a few goldenrod and wild carrot appear. Years pass, and the field becomes thickly grown with an association of perennial weeds and grasses. It may be a decade before there is much change in this condition. In all this time it furnishes no grouse cover—merely an edge to the woods.

Ultimately a few woody plants appear, usually along the edges of the field; dewberries, blackberries, aspen seedlings, and a few pin cherry are the most likely first woody invaders. Once these shrubs and trees start to take over the old field, the tempo increases; pines, hemlock, maples, and others may germinate along the field margins; and wild apple, thorn apple, dogwoods, and other long-lived shrubs appear. For a time this early woody plant cover is so sparse that the field is still essentially open land to grouse. Then there comes a season where the growth is such that grouse find the cover useful in the fall, and move out in the brushy spots to feed; then the old field becomes brushy land, and is an integral part of the grouse habitat. This transformation may have taken ten to twenty years.

In the next decade or two the field fills in with shrubs and tree saplings; the briars and the sun-loving herbaceous plants are shaded out. More and more the subclimax and climax forest species become dominant. As the brushlot matures it changes to a pole-size woodland. If there is a good proportion of evergreen species, it becomes a mixed woodland; if not, it becomes a hardwood stand. In the pole stage it is often too dense to be very good grouse cover. As it matures to full-statured woodland it merges with the adjacent woods, and the new edge is pushed across the field, or farther to the nearest open area. It now serves the grouse as nesting cover, for fall and winter feeding, and possibly for winter shelter. By this time the aspen are full grown, and will start dying if not harvested. The pin cherry has been smothered by the larger-growing and longer-lived species; the open-field, sun-loving shrubs have disappeared too, and a new understory of shade-tolerant species develops. More kinds of forest hardwoods have sprung up, including birches, ash, and beech. By now some four or five decades have passed since the natural plant succession began after the buckwheat crop.

During the next 50 years the woods reaches its climax. It loses the short-lived species, and is completely made up of the climax kinds. As the crown grows higher and more complete, the woods loses much of its value to grouse; only lumbering or some other act that sets back the succession, like fire or a wind storm, can return it to productive grouse use.

This is but one case of plant succession, from a very early stage to climax. It could have taken various other courses, and could have been set back at times by the interference of such agents as fire, livestock, plowing, and so on. Grouse habitat is made up of the great variety of cover that results from plant succession.

IDEAL LAND USE PATTERN

THE "perfect" cover pattern for ruffed grouse would be predominantly wooded land, yet it would be very much broken up by age and species associations. The small portions that are not woodland would be exceedingly important, even though not a large part of the whole.

About 80% to 85% of the area would be in woods; it would be divided about half and half of woods that are largely coniferous and woods that are predominantly hardwoods. The age class would be mixed by a sustained-yield cutting system, maintained by a selective, spot-lumbering type of cropping. It would not be grazed by domestic livestock. The narrow dimension of either cover type would never be more than 600 feet, or about twice the distance a grouse penetrates.

Most of the balance of the area—all but about 2% to 4% would be brushland; this could be overgrown fields, alder runs, or slashings. The 2% to 4% would be open land, either grass or crop strips; or roads with grassy margins. This brush and open land would be in narrow bands, well distributed through the woods. No part of the woods would be more than about 600 feet from an opening—that is, a brushy area or open place.

The ideal arrangement of these cover types would be to have the open strip next to brushy land, which in turn would be next to the hardwoods; then would come the coniferous woods. Continuing on through the evergreens one would come to hardwoods, brush, and open land—successively on the other side. The cover units could be endless strips of the width dimensions mentioned above, or they could be circumscribed patches. The important thing is the proportions and the great interspersion of the units.

It is obvious that such an ideal land-use pattern will rarely exist, or be practical to develop; it does, however, give us an ideal to guide us in developing and managing grouse range.

FOODS OF THE RUFFED GROUSE

THE partridge is practically omnivorous in its food habits within its physical limitations; most

kinds of vegetable foods available above the ground are eaten, including leaves, buds, flowers, seeds, fruits, nuts, and even some twigs. Its animal foods are limited to kinds small enough for it to handle and easy to catch close to the ground; these are mostly slow-moving insects.

The seasonal use of these various kinds of foods varies according to availability and to the degree of preference. The summer diet is made up of fruits and greens, with a considerable amount of insects; all are plentiful then. In winter the greatest amount of food is buds; they are readily available, whereas the other foods are relatively scarce. In spring and fall the proportions are intermediate between these extremes, with a preference for a mixture of greens, fruits, and insects if these are available.

We may conveniently group grouse foods into four kinds: fruits and seeds; greens, including flowers; buds, including twigs; and insects, including other small animals. The proportions of these foods eaten by grouse at different times of the year are shown in Figure 18. These proportions vary somewhat according to range type, but are fairly representative wherever the bird is found.

FRUITS AND SEEDS IN THE RUFFED GROUSE DIET

MANY kinds of fruits and seeds are among the most important of grouse foods, and are chosen by the birds in preference to most foods. The earliest ripening fruits come in June; strawberries are very important in the early summer diet of both young and adults. Later the blackberries, raspberries, and blueberries are heavily utilized as they ripen. Several species of cherries are important summer fruits, and are also eaten throughout the fall and winter—as long as they can be found. Sedge seeds are eaten in summer and fall; other available fruits are taken in lesser quantities.

Fall is the season when fruits are most plentiful—at least in the number of kinds. Several kinds of dogwoods furnish fall fruits. Those of the little bunchberry and the gray dogwood are most

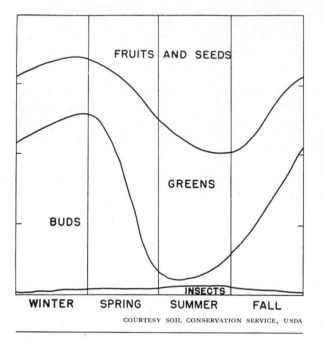

FIGURE 18. *Types of food used by the ruffed grouse by seasons.*

used in the northern range, and those of the flowering dogwood farther south; all the other dogwoods furnish some food too. A number of viburnums are important producers of fall fruits for grouse, especially mapleleaf viburnum, witherod, nannyberry, blackhaw, and highbush cranberry. Thorn apples, wild apples, and all the wild grapes are used in the fall and well into the winter, depending on their availability above the snow. Fruits that are eaten in the fall, and that are also dependably available in the winter, include those from greenbrier (mainly cat greenbrier and common greenbrier), sumacs (mostly flameleaf, smooth, and staghorn), and the closely related poison ivy and poison sumac, and wild rose hips. Three important woodland ground cover plants that provide fall fruits are the wintergreen, partridgeberry, and Canada mayflower. Important dry seed foods in the fall include the nuts of beech and hazel; both are preferred foods, but vary greatly in availability from one year to the next. One of the most important fall

and winter foods in the southern range is the oak mast from all the kinds of oaks.

All these fruits and nuts are taken by grouse as long as they are available; as winter progresses they are harder and harder to find, because they are used up or are covered by snow. The supplies that are snow-covered become more available in the spring as the snow melts, and this explains the surprising amount of this kind of food the birds find at this time of year.

GREENS EATEN BY RUFFED GROUSE

A GREAT variety of leaves and other succulent plant parts are taken by grouse, though most of it comes from a relatively few kinds of plants. Greens are most important in the summer diet, and least important in winter; they make up a somewhat larger part of the spring than the fall food supply.

The leaves of a number of species of the *Carex* sedges are eaten in quantity, from spring through fall. Strawberry and partridgeberry leaves are eaten throughout the year, and the strawberry flowers are taken in the spring. Summer greens include the leaves of thorn apples, apples, and a great number of other plants. Fall and winter greens of importance, in addition to those mentioned above, are leaves of wintergreen, mountain laurel, sheep sorrel, blueberry, brambles, and the fronds of several evergreen ferns; most important among the latter are the shield ferns—especially spiny-toothed and marginal shield ferns—and the Christmas and polypody ferns.

BUDS AS GROUSE FOOD

THE ability of the ruffed grouse to utilize tree buds for food is the key to its success in the rigorous northern climate. It means that at all times, except under the most catastrophic circumstances of the ice coating of trees, the bird can easily find food; thus there is practically no such thing for this species as starvation.

There is little doubt that buds are eaten mainly to supplement the limited supplies of other foods; but the birds do seem to desire some buds in fall and spring, even when they could find an adequate supply of food without them. Clearly the season of greatest importance for this kind of food is winter; practically none are eaten in summer.

Not all tree buds are acceptable to the grouse as food; in fact, some of the dominant species in most woodlands are worthless for this purpose; the conifers and beech in the northern range and the oaks and hickories in the southern range are examples. The important bud-food species are rather few, though they are generally plentiful. They are the following: the birches (yellow, black, and paper birches mostly); apple; hop hornbeam; the poplars, especially the quaking and large-toothed aspens; cherries, mostly the black cherry, pin cherry, and chokecherry; and blueberries.

In the mountains of southern Idaho Marshall (1946) found that grouse were budding western chokecherry, willow, Douglas maple, western serviceberry, Greene's mountainash, and California poplar.

ANIMAL FOODS OF THE RUFFED GROUSE

INSECTS and other small animals found close to the ground or on the ground are eaten by adult grouse at all times, but because of their varying availability the volume is small except in summer; even then it makes up but a small portion of the total diet; it is probable that the dietary significance of this type of food is much greater than the frequency of its use would indicate. There is no doubt that insects are vital to the young grouse in the early weeks of their lives; from half to three-quarters of all their food in the first month is insects. In July the volume of insects eaten by the chicks drops to about 10% to 15% of the diet, and by August their diet is like that of the adults.

The variety of animal foods eaten is evidenced by the fact that 580 kinds have been identified from New York grouse alone (Bump, *et al.,* 1947). Most commonly eaten kinds are ants, bees, wasps, beetles, moths, and grasshoppers; also other insects and spiders and snails. The volume rarely exceeds 4% or 5% in summer and 1% the rest of the year, for adult birds.

The plant foods discussed above, though only a small number of all that grouse are known to eat, make up from about 60% to 90% of the diet in different seasons and different sections of range; together with the animal part of the diet, they cover almost the entire food supply of the juveniles. Thus they compose the substance of the diet, while the great number of other foods eaten add variety. Altogether between 400 and 500 kinds of plants provide food for the grouse, and many of these furnish two or more kinds of food.

VARIATION IN JUVENILE AND ADULT DIET

THE high proportion of insect food used by the young chicks in comparison with the adults was mentioned above; there is also great variation in the amounts of different plant foods used by the youngsters as compared with the adults. The chicks in their first two months of life use few different kinds of foods, whereas the grown birds use many. The young birds use far more raspberries, blackberries, and strawberries than do the adults; the bramble fruits often make up more than half of their midsummer diet after they have slackened off in the use of animal foods. Their use of greens is less than with the adults, but they do take leaves of sedges, strawberries and some other plants regularly.

FOOD SUPPLIES IN DIFFERENT COVER TYPES

THE five major cover types used by the ruffed grouse each have different value as a source of food, and their use as feeding areas changes with the seasons. In general, the food-producing rating of each cover type is as follows.

Open land often has good supplies of insects and seeds in summer and early fall; at this time its food-producing value is high, especially for very young grouse in early summer. Its usefulness depends on its proximity to other cover types though, since the birds will go out into open fields only a few feet from the edges. From late fall until early summer its food-producing rating is very low.

Brushy land is particularly useful for feeding; in summer and fall both slashings and overgrown areas have an abundance of fruits, seeds, greens, and insects; at these seasons the food-producing rating is very high. In winter and spring the rating is lower, from medium to high, depending on the presence of species with palatable buds.

We may consider the food attributes of hardwood woodlands and mixed woodlands together, since the difference is only a matter of quantity. Because mixed woods have a considerable proportion of conifers that produce little food, these areas will have less abundant food supplies of the kinds coming from trees than will the hardwoods stands. Both these cover types rate low to medium on the production of summer and fall foods; insects are relatively scarce, fruits much less abundant than in sunnier cover, and many of the most desired species are largely absent. Blackberries, raspberries, and strawberries are examples of the important summer fruits that are lacking in the older woodland types. The ground-cover fruits and greens are chiefly used from fall until spring. The very great use of these types for feeding grounds comes in winter and spring, when their rating is high to very high for most hardwoods, and medium to high for mixed woods. Tree buds are the major type of food produced, with fruits and nuts also important.

Coniferous woodland is the poorest of all types for feeding. A few plants of the ground cover, such as wintergreen and partridgeberry, grow fruits that are eaten in winter and spring when not snow-covered, and greens that are eaten at all seasons. For the most part the food grown in conifer cover is proportional to the amount of hardwood tree and brush cover that is interspersed through the stand; only when the type deviates from standard does it have much food-producing value to grouse; then it is used as feeding cover in winter and spring. The foods grown are the same as in the other woodland types.

COURTESY SOIL CONSERVATION SERVICE, USDA

COURTESY SOIL CONSERVATION SERVICE, USDA

Abandoned farm fields grow into brush that makes fall feeding areas for ruffed grouse.

PLATE 51. Top. *Food producing plants such as the wild apple (shown), hawthorn and dogwoods are plentiful.*

PLATE 52. Bottom. *An old white pine seed tree adds evergreens to the brush cover.*

WATER REQUIREMENTS

THE ruffed grouse inhabits humid lands where water is easily found in many forms. The succulent fruits, greens, and insects eaten through most of the year have enough water for the bird's needs, without recourse to drinking open water. Either dew or snow is available most of the time; and both young and adult grouse can live their entire time in cover wholly lacking free water. When grouse are found close to water areas, like springs or swales, it is because of the food or cover rather than the water.

THE ECONOMICS OF RUFFED GROUSE FOOD HABITS

FEW grouse foods are of economic importance to man; the insects eaten are taken mostly from nonagricultural lands, and therefore are of little benefit to farming. Probably as many insects are eaten that are beneficial to man's interests as those that are harmful; thus the insectivorous phase of grouse food habits is neutral.

There is one grouse food the loss of which sometimes causes damage to a farm crop—namely, apple buds. Where a commercial orchard lies next to good grouse cover the birds may invade the orchard and bud the trees in winter. If not overdone, this does not affect the next year's crop; but occasionally the budding may be severe enough to cause appreciable damage. In New Hampshire and Massachusetts damage claims resulting from grouse apple-budding have been paid by the states as recently as the late 1930's. Few commercial orchards today are situated where grouse can use them, and complaints of this damage have virtually ceased.

The net appraisal of grouse eating habits in relation to man's economic interests is *neutral*, and show little benefit and little damage.

THE EFFECT OF THE FOOD FACTOR ON GROUSE NUMBERS

FEW game birds are as assured of an adequate year-round supply of food as is the ruffed grouse. When its preferred foods are used up, or become unavailable, it can always turn to tree buds, the supply of which is virtually inexhaustible, since few other animals eat them; starvation is practically unknown in this species. Even when winter sleet covers everything with ice the birds can go without food for several days without harm; they frequently do this voluntarily during stormy weather. It is hard to conceive of ice conditions so protracted that the grouse would starve; such conditions have been conjectured, but no case has ever been authenticated.

The starvation situation that is most likely affects the young grouse in their first few weeks of life; during this period they are almost wholly dependent on insects for food. A very cold, rainy period at this time could reduce the supply of insects to a point where the chicks could not get enough food, and would starve. Yet if this happened the youngsters would also be unable even to search for food, since they must be brooded by the mother during wet and cold spells. If in desperation they did go looking for food while cold and wet, they would almost certainly die of exposure before they could die of starvation; thus it is academic whether or not they starve. The vital factor in this instance is the weather.

The distribution and abundance of foods has a great effect on the distribution of grouse, and has considerable effect on their numbers. But if the range is suitable in other respects it usually has an adequate food supply.

WEATHER AND CLIMATE IN RELATION TO RUFFED GROUSE

TAKEN as an individual, the ruffed grouse is a hardy fellow. The lowest extremes of winter temperatures are little more than an inconvenience; the hottest days of summer mean no more than a time for loafing. Deep snows are turned from danger to benefit, for he uses them for roosting, as an Eskimo uses his igloo. Heavy rains, high winds, and the worst that nature can offer in other ways are taken in stride. The partridge probably enjoys balmy weather as much as any animal, but it manages to live well enough in bad weather—as long as it has good habitat. Rarely is an adult grouse a direct victim of the elements.

In marked contrast with this encouraging picture is the fact that weather conditions and the climate are the biggest factor in determining grouse population levels; weather conditions predispose more grouse losses than any other thing. This seeming inconsistency is resolved by the fact of the very great difference between the hardiness of an individual animal and the hazards it faces as a species in its relation to its environment.

THE INFLUENCE OF WEATHER ON NESTING

As the hours of daylight lengthen in March the long-dormant ovaries of the hen grouse begin to grow. The rate of their development depends on the amount of sunlight to which the bird is exposed; an unusually sunny spring will cause egg-laying to start early, whereas a cloudy season will delay it. There is often a ten-day difference in egg-laying time from one year to another. This relationship is almost wholly independent of temperatures and precipitation, but is directly related to the quantity of sunny daylight in the period from early March to mid-April.

Once egg-laying begins it continues at a rate of about an egg every day and a half until the clutch is finished. The only protection from the elements these eggs have before the start of incubation is the lining of the nest and the covering, both made of dead leaves. The eggs may be subjected to temperatures in the low 20's, and yet they are rarely if ever frozen; after incubation begins they are kept at constant temperature by the hen bird, except when she leaves the nest usually twice daily, and for periods rarely exceeding a half-hour. Even late season snowstorms do little damage as far as is known; egg losses seem to be little affected by weather. I have known of eggs well along in the incubation period to be exposed for two whole days after the death of the hen grouse, and yet hatch when placed in an incubator. How much the vitality of the chicks had been affected could not be told, but the tolerance of the eggs to adverse temperatures is remarkable.

BROOD LOSSES IN RELATION TO WEATHER

THE most critical time in the life of a grouse is the first month after hatching. It does not have a feather coat adequate to protect it from the elements; its diet is exceedingly restricted; it cannot even fly for the first two weeks—it must rely completely on its protective coloration to escape attacking enemies. It is not surprising, then, that mortality is high in this period. In normal years the loss of young birds is 30% to 40% in the first month, and in bad years it may be much higher.

The primary key to this situation is the weather; it is the one time of the year when grouse may actually be killed by exposure. Chicks that are lost from the brood are chilled the first night spent alone, and soon die. If there is a protracted period of cold, wet weather after the hatching, the chicks are prevented from feeding as they should; or if they do feed they are exposed to wetting and chilling; the result is accelerated mortality. If they are long prevented from feeding by bad weather, when they finally do go foraging they are abnormally vulnerable to predation because of the urgency of their feeding.

There is little doubt that the weather in this first month after the grouse chicks hatch is the single biggest factor in the determining of grouse populations. In years when the weather is reasonably good the effects on grouse are moderate, and hunting is good the following fall; when the early brood period is cold and rainy, the mortality of the young birds rises, and hunting the following fall is poor. This adverse weather may occur as a protracted period of cold and wet days, or it may come as a short, violent, stormy period. An example of the latter was observed in 1935 in south-central New York. During the first week of July a storm dropped over ten inches of rainfall in 48 hours, most of it the first day—this is normally a whole summer's rainfall. It caused unprecedented floods and damage. It was immediately evident that it had also caused a sudden and drastic decline in the numbers of young grouse; the usual 60% summer brood loss was over 80%, which meant that the survival was less than 20% instead of 40%—a drop in survival of 50% caused by a single storm (Edminster, 1947).

The best evidence available indicates that the principal cause of the periodic declines in grouse numbers is associated with a failure to produce the crop of grouse in the summer; this is more closely related to weather conditions than to any other matter. When this crop failure happens two years in a row, the grouse population takes a serious drop. This seems to happen about once every decade.

WEATHER AND THE SURVIVAL OF ADULTS

Grouse frequently adjust their behavior to changes in the weather; they seek coniferous shelter during extremes of heat, cold, wind, and precipitation; they come out into the open-cover types when the weather is balmy. Their roosting place in pleasant weather may be in hardwood trees or on a log; or during cold nights in conifers. When the wintry blasts bring deep snows with the wind and cold, they often seek shelter beneath the snow, where they ride out the storm. At no time is their health or vigor seriously impaired by exposure to weather; they never (or at least practically never) die from direct exposure to snow, sleet, and cold, as do quail and pheasants. They are always able to get food regardless of the depths of the snow. Even when the trees are coated with ice they can easily go without food for several days without discomfort; it would be a rare catastrophe for such ice conditions to last long enough and be severe enough to cause grouse to starve.

The very behavior adjustments they make as a result of weather conditions may make them vulnerable to predation, or to gunshot; for this reason weather conditions are exceedingly important in the determining of the losses of adult grouse, even though there is another killing agent.

When a grouse suns itself in the open along a wood's edge and becomes a relatively easy target for a gunner, the balmy weather is instrumental in setting the stage for the bird's demise; if it is a Cooper's hawk that swoops down and picks the bird from its sunning spot, the relations are still the same. It makes no difference what the killing is done by; the conditions that predispose the setting are fundamentally important. This case is a normal and expected situation, one that may be counted on to happen to a certain proportion of grouse each year; some are taken by hunters, many by natural predators, a few die from physical accidents and other causes, but the species still thrives. These cases of mortality are important in game management only in so far as it may be possible to shift the conditions so that a higher proportion of the inevitable losses are from hunting, and fewer from other causes.

Beyond the normal grouse losses that are related to weather conditions are the occasional very high losses brought about by very abnormal weather. These deaths almost always happen in late winter—February and March; they are predisposed when extremely severe winter weather is sustained for long periods. Even under these circumstances the birds can manage to survive in good numbers even though losses are high, provided their population is good at the winter's beginning. When the extremely bad winter weather comes in a year that follows a bad production season, and the population is already below normal, the added losses may reduce the population to a very low level. If then another poor production season ensues, and another bad winter with high losses follows, the breeding population in the next spring will be decimated to a critical point. This then, is the extreme low of a population cycle.

It is this compounding of weather troubles in successive summer and winter seasons for a couple of years that really causes the grouse serious trouble. Any single season of poor production or high winter mortality can be overcome the following year, if conditions are favorable. A study of the weather records and grouse population trends in New York for over half a century shows clearly that every time a two-year period occurred with extreme snows and low temperatures in late winter, and a cold June each year, the grouse suffered a severe decline; corollary to this analysis, every severe grouse decline that occurred was accompanied by this length and combination of weather conditions (Edminster, 1947). It is fortunate that this does not happen often; it does seem to occur about once every decade. That regularity of grouse declines has led to the belief in a cycle phenomenon; and though the correlations are imperfect, the close tie between grouse losses and the two kinds of extreme weather conditions seems to be the soundest explanation.

PREDATION ON THE RUFFED GROUSE

PROBABLY the most prominent thing in grouse ecology is predation; it is a stark reality that seems to spell disaster at all seasons of the year. When one studies the life of the grouse in detail, the work of its natural enemies is repeatedly evident. Even in normal times some 40% of the nests are failures, and almost all this loss is caused by predation. The early mortality of young grouse has little predation involved, but as the chicks grow up they are common prey of the accipitrine hawks. As adults, grouse are forever threatened with sudden death from their enemies. Whatever may be the conditions that favor effective attack by predators, the evidence always convicts the flesh eater; in ordinary years half or more of all the grouse are eaten by other animals—and this does not include those taken by man.

It is not surprising, then, that predation has received prominent attention as a factor in grouse welfare; the general tendency is to condemn the predators as the reason that grouse are not more abundant; the predators are easily convicted by common testimony, and their sentence is constant persecution. Yet, despite the most intensive efforts at control of these animals, there has been no evidence that the grouse has benefited;

the populations of grouse continue their ups and downs in an almost inexorable fashion, regardless of whether any predator or group of predators is abundant or scarce.

The effectiveness of intensive predator control on grouse numbers was studied in the New York investigation of the ruffed grouse (Bump, *et al.*, 1947; Edminster, 1947). It was concluded that even intensive effort to reduce all predators to as low numbers as possible had no effect on the mortality of young or adult grouse—though it did have some effect in reducing nest losses. This was a temporary benefit, and was effective primarily in years when grouse numbers were low; since the population was increasing anyway at those times, the reduced nest losses were of little value. These results confirmed the modern view that predation is an effect more than a cause, and that the basic reasons for grouse populations not rising higher than they do lies in the habitat and climate; predation is merely the tool that nature uses to bring the prey down to the numbers its environment can care for each year. If this agent were to be entirely removed, some other would take its place, and the result would be essentially the same.

THE PREDATION OF NESTS

AMONG the many egg-eating predators that live in grouse habitat, the red and gray foxes are by far the most destructive of grouse nests; nearly half of all predator-destroyed nests in New York were attributable to foxes (Edminster, 1947). Other nest predators that are common eaters of grouse eggs include skunks, weasels, raccoons and crows. Many others take grouse eggs occasionally; not that they would not take many more than they do were they more efficient at it; these include the red squirrel, chipmunk, woodchuck, dog, black snake, and others. Eggs are sometimes lost when predators kill the hen bird; horned owls and accipitrine hawks thus become egg destroyers indirectly, even though they do not eat the eggs.

Most destruction of grouse nests occurs in late May and early June, after incubation has progressed well toward its completion. The hens rarely make another nest under these circumstances; only if they are broken up early in the incubation period are they likely to renest. Thus most grouse nests that are destroyed mean broodless hens for that year; nest destruction is therefore more serious with grouse than with birds like the pheasant and bobwhite quail, which readily make second nests.

Predation is the only important cause of nest loss. A few grouse nests are deserted, and a few are destroyed by fire, flooding, and disturbance by man or livestock; but these are a small part of the total number destroyed. In no other phase of grouse mortality is predation so pre-eminent.

THE DESTRUCTION OF YOUNG GROUSE BY PREDATORS

Less than half of the young grouse born will reach maturity in an average year; yet this period in the bird's life is the only one in which predation is not the most significant cause of loss. For the first six to eight weeks of their lives the young grouse chicks are well cared for by their mother; they are completely responsive to her wishes. Few are caught by enemies through this period, even though many of their number will succumb to exposure, accidents, and other means of death. Then the youngsters begin to grow up and to become independent of their mother's control. When this time comes, the mortality curve rises; this change is due to predation—mainly by the Cooper's and sharp-shinned hawks, and in Canada the goshawk. These accipitrine hawks are very skilful at catching reckless young grouse that have not yet learned to respect their enemies. By the time fall comes and the chicks are full grown, some 60% of their original numbers will have perished; in years of poor production the figure is more likely to be 80%. In average years somewhat less than half the loss is due to predation; in the years of low survival predation plays a smaller part, with an eighth to a fifth of the birds taken by predators. It should be noted that the predation mostly *follows* the other losses of chicks; thus the few birds taken by predators in the poor-production years are much more important than usual, since they add to an already excessive mortality.

The accipitrine hawks are the most destructive predators of young grouse, but there are others; the great horned owl, the red and gray foxes, and the weasels take young grouse regularly. Those that occasionally take young grouse include the marsh hawk, red-tailed hawk, barred owl, house cat, crow, and black snake.

PREDATION ON ADULT GROUSE

The partridge is a common prey of several very capable kinds of predators. Under most circumstances the grouse is successful in evading capture, and consequently these predators do not eat grouse very regularly; the only exception to this generalization is the goshawk. This large accipitrine might well have been named *grouse-hawk*; it is the only predator that can consistently pursue a grouse and overtake it by sheer speed and dodging superiority. It may be fortunate that its range is largely confined to the northern wilderness country.

The most significant grouse predators are the horned owl, the red and gray foxes, the goshawk, and the Cooper's hawk; taken together they are a major decimating agent of adult grouse, effective from fall through spring. Most of the grouse that die as prey will be meals for one or another of these five species. Yet despite this none of them eats grouse so frequently that it makes up very much of the predator's diet; even the goshawk, so famed for its destruction of grouse, has only 10% to 20% of its food in grouse. Grouse rarely exceed 5% of foxes' winter diet— and winter is the season of their greatest predation on grouse. The great horned owl and the Cooper's hawk may eat enough grouse to make up 1% or 2% of their fall-to-spring food supply —rarely more; it is clear then that the grouse is an occasional delicacy to these predators rather than a staple item of food—with the exception of the goshawk. It should be emphasized, though, that it makes little difference to grouse ecology what percent of the predator diet is composed of grouse; the important thing is what proportion of grouse are lost.

In addition to the five prime predators of adult grouse, there are many others that catch grouse occasionally; the New York weasel, and less frequently the smaller species of weasels, are fairly efficient grouse predators. Where the bobcat is plentiful, it takes a fair number. The barred owl, red-tailed hawk, and marsh hawk will sometimes catch full-grown grouse, but not very often; also house cats that roam in grouse cover occasionally catch them.

Predators hunt for their food all the year round, and there is no reason to suppose that those capable of taking grouse are not willing and anxious to catch them at any time. There are several reasons, though, why the incidence of predation varies greatly at different times of the year. The birds at some times make themselves vulnerable to predation by their special activities —notably during courtship and nesting; the use of open areas for feeding, dusting, or sunning also increases the hazard of predation. Most significant of all is their habit of snow-roosting when the winter weather is bad; they are specially vulnerable to fox predation while under the snow; in this instance their danger is conditioned by the weather. The number of grouse killed by natural enemies is partly determined by the abundance of predators. The urgency of the predator's food-seeking also may sometimes play a part; it is generally felt that animals hunting to feed a whole family are more efficient than at other times. The abundance of the common prey species—the so-called "buffer" animals—makes some difference in the pressure on grouse; if mice and other rodents are plentiful, there is little urgency for the predator to work hard to get the less easily caught foods; contrarily, when mice are scarce the predator must work harder and take more of the harder-to-catch kinds of food than usual if it is to eat well. It has been shown, for example, that there is a clear inverse relationship between the abundance of buffers and of fox activity (Bump, *et al.*, 1947). Thus the intensity of predation on grouse is not only a seasonal mat-

ter, but it also varies greatly in different years.

The loss of grouse to enemies is very low in the summer, when they are not especially vulnerable, and when food for the enemies is abundant; the rate of loss increases in the fall, and still more in early winter. In areas where man's hunting takes many grouse the population is already lowered in autumn, so that by the time winter comes the pursuit of grouse is less profitable for predators than it would otherwise be. As the winter progresses the situation worsens for the grouse; they are more vulnerable than earlier, and especially so if their population has remained high. The predators are pressed harder and harder to get enough food as the deep snows shelter the rodents; so by February grouse deaths from predation increase greatly; sometimes they reach the peak of yearly mortality in this late winter period.

The end of winter would seem to offer respite for the grouse; but its own activities prevents this, due to their increased vulnerability on account of their courtship and mating behavior. The mortality rate of the male birds in particular often rises higher in April than the high winter loss rate. Then when this period is over the predation on cock grouse drops off; but the hens are still vulnerable through the nesting and early brooding period. Their losses at this season tend to equal the losses of the males in the drumming period. Therefore the year's total mortality from predation is about the same for the two sexes.

The drama of predation is the stark realism of nature that is difficult for many people to accept; yet the more one studies the lives of these animals the clearer it is that predation is not only natural but necessary. It assures that most of the surplus of each year's production will be consumed. In the struggle for survival it helps evolve better creatures—the old survival-of-the-fittest principle. To those sportsmen who may feel that predation deprives them of some of their sport, let me point out that they have their hunting opportunity soon after the summer production season is over; there is little predation on the year's crop up to that time; man has practically the entire crop to hunt. The serious predation comes later, and concerns only the vulnerable surpluses that man's hunting did not take in autumn. Thus nature takes care of her own.

DISEASES AND PARASITES OF THE RUFFED GROUSE

IT would be rare indeed to find a ruffed grouse entirely without parasites; it is normal for them to carry a variety of internal and external organisms through their lives. Though these parasites sap some of the bird's strength, the effect most of the time is inconsequential. The big question is, how important in the ecology of the species are these occasional times?

In the studies of the ruffed grouse in the first three decades of this century much attention was paid to the possibility that disease was important in causing declines in grouse populations. Woodruff (1908) concluded that " . . . an epidemic of some disease or parasite, or both, just which we cannot now determine," was one of three factors that occurred in an "unhappy combination" to cause grouse scarcity; the other two factors were winter predation and adverse spring weather. Stoddart (1918), after studying the next big decline in grouse numbers depreciated the importance of disease. Allen and Gross (1926) studied the diseases of grouse by actual examination of specimens for several years after the minor decline of 1924. They were unable to prove that disease was a prime cause of the fall in grouse numbers, but did demonstrate that some diseases of grouse could kill individual birds, notably the stomach worm (*Dispharynx spiralis*).

Several investigators in the 1930's delved into the problems of grouse diseases. Clarke (1936) studied the problem in Ontario, and found a protozoan blood parasite. (*Leucocytozoon bonasae*) very common, and concluded that it " . . . is most probably the organism responsible for the dying-off of grouse." Boughton (1937) made examinations of grouse from Minnesota, but was unable to make definite conclusions as to the

part played by disease in grouse declines. In studying Michigan grouse Fisher (1939) wrote that " . . . parasites and diseases of the ruffed grouse appear to be a major factor in the decimation of these birds. . . . "; but he also noted that further study was needed to prove the matter. The New York study (Bump, *et al.,* 1947) examined 1,728 adult and 1,119 immature grouse from that area. It was evident, in correlating the autopsies with field studies of populations, that the incidence of many organisms rose as the grouse population increased. This relationship of disease organisms to the host species is fundamental, and was suspected, but had not before been demonstrated in grouse. The commonest cause of death from disease was found to be the dispharynx stomach worm; but the study " . . . revealed no disease of epizootic proportions which would account for the sudden and widespread disappearance of ruffed grouse."

At least 61 different kinds of organisms, of four types, are known to infect or infest the ruffed grouse; these are grouped for convenience as helminths, protozoans, infectious disease organisms, and ectoparasites.

The helminths are internal parasitic worms of three sorts: nematodes or roundworms; cestodes, or tapeworms; and trematodes, or flukes. Fourteen species of roundworms are known to occur in the grouse; they are found in many parts of the bird's body, including the windpipe, crop, gullet, proventriculus, gizzard, caecum, small intestine, in the body cavity, in the blood plasma, and under the nictitating membrane. The group includes some of the commonest parasites of grouse, and one of them is an important species that can cause death—the stomach worm, *Dispharynx spiralis,* already mentioned. It is found mostly in the proventriculus (or saccular stomach), and causes lesions in the walls of this organ. In severe cases it impairs digestion, with resulting emaciation; and it may perforate the walls of the organ and cause fatal peritonitis. The area where it is known to occur extends from New England to Michigan. It may build up to rather serious local epidemics, and has been suspected of being a factor in major grouse declines; but the evidence does not support this conclusion.

Other common roundworms besides the dispharynx stomach worm are the intestinal worm (*Ascaridia bonasae*), which is the largest (two to four inches) of grouse parasites; the caecal worm (*Heterakis bonasae*); and the gizzard worm (*Cheilospirura spinosa*), all of which are found generally where the grouse is found. None of the three is of any consequence in affecting grouse populations.

Seven species of tapeworms are found in grouse from New England to Minnesota, and probably elsewhere in the bird's range. They are common in the adult birds, and somewhat more common in the juveniles. They are found in the duodenal section of the small intestine. They rarely occur in numbers large enough to cause death, and are of no significance in affecting grouse populations.

Flukes are the third kind of helminths found in grouse; at least eight kinds have been found in various parts of its range from Labrador to Minnesota, but only one species (*Harmostomum pellucidum*) is known to be widespread. They are imbedded in the bird's tissues in various locations, such as muscles, skin, rectum, intestine, gall bladder, cloaca, and bursa of Fabricius. Autopsies do not generally reveal them in abundance; but since they are easily overlooked they are no doubt more common than the records show. Since they are of no importance in grouse mortality, it is not necessary to take the time to find them all in autopsies.

Protozoan organisms of at least 10 kinds are responsible for infections in grouse; one has been of some significance in causing grouse mortality. Three of the protozoans are coccidia that reside in the cecum and small intestine. Though potentially dangerous, these organisms have not been shown to be a significant cause of mortality in wild grouse. They are found everywhere the grouse is found. Five of the protozoans found in the grouse are flagellates; all but one are apparently a normal part of the internal fauna of the bird, and are not actually associated with any disease. The exception is *Histomonas meleagris* (see below), found in the intestine, cecum, blood plasma, and liver; its occurrence has been reported only in the eastern part of the range.

Two malarialike protozoans have been found in grouse in Ontario, Michigan, and Minnesota; both are blood parasites that live in the red blood cells. One of them, *Leucocytozooan bonasae*, has been shown capable of causing considerable mortality of grouse, especially of young ones (Clarke, 1936). Despite the capacity of this organism to kill grouse, no substantial evidence has been found that it is importantly connected with sudden or widespread die-offs of this bird.

Another group of disease troubles that may plague the ruffed grouse is caused by organisms of miscellaneous nature, but which have the common charcteristic of being infectious; five of them are worthy of mention. One belongs taxonomically with the protozoans, and was mentioned above; it is the organism that causes "blackhead," *Histomonas meleagris;* it is known to occur only in captive grouse, but circumstances indicate the great probability that it may occur in wild birds where they use range also used by domestic turkeys. If wild grouse were to be exposed to this disease the action would be so rapid and lethal that it could well wipe out local groups. Again it should be noted that this possibility is mentioned here only because of the great potentiality of the disease, not its known importance.

A disease of the lungs and air sacs of grouse is caused by a fungus organism, *Aspergillus fumigatus*. It can be lethal, but is so infrequent that it is of little significance as a mortality factor; it has been found only in the northeastern states. Another infectious disease that has been known to occur in grouse is bird pox; it is caused by a filterable virus, and has been reported in wild grouse only a few times in New England (Bump, *et al.,* 1947).

A potentially dangerous disease of both mammals and birds, tularaemia, has been reported to have been found in ruffed grouse from the Midwest (Green and Shillinger, 1934); it is caused by a bacterial organism, *Pasteurella tularense,* and must be transmitted through an intermediate host, the tick *Haemaphysalis cinnabarina.* Where the disease is rampant in populations of hares, the incidence of ticks is very high. This condition never occurs in the East, and may explain why the disease has not been found there. Though the contention that tularaemia may be important in causing grouse declines has not been demonstrated, its potentiality should certainly not be overlooked. Another infectious disease that is potentially dangerous is the so-called "quail disease," or ulcerative enteritis; it has been very troublesome in captive ruffed grouse, but has been reported only once in wild birds from Minnesota (Green and Shillinger, 1934). The organism was unidentified for a long time, but was finally isolated by Morley and Wetmore (1936) as a type of bacteria; it was later identified by Bass (1941) as an anaerobic bacillus. It must be pigeonholed along with tularaemia as a potentially destructive agent, but not yet shown to be an important mortality cause in wild grouse.

The fourth group of organisms that infest ruffed grouse are ectoparasites, those that live on the outside of the bird; there are 16 species known to attack the grouse, and they are of five types. The mites and ticks belong to Acarina, while the fleas, flies, and lice belong to Hexapoda. They are not significant directly in grouse mortality, but ticks may be important in carrying tularaemia (see above), and very heavy infestations of any of them may be a drain on the bird's vitality. Four species of ticks have been found on grouse, with the greatest abundance reported from the Midwest. Two kinds of louse flies occur on grouse, four species of lice, one kind of flea, and five kinds of mites—all reported only from the eastern parts of the range, except for one Western mite. No importance is attached to any of this group in connection with grouse losses.

The full significance of disease as a factor in grouse ecology cannot be gauged by simply considering the effect on the grouse of each in-dividual afflicting species; there is a cumulative effect of compound infections. This may well be illustrated by comparing the incidence trend of individual disease organisms with that of the total disease and parasite prevalence; in no case does the rate of occurrence of any one organism parallel the curve of abundance of the grouse itself. But when all organism occurrences are added together, the curve of occurrence-rate makes a rough but true parallel to the grouse population curve. How much significance this has is difficult to say, but it almost certainly is not a mere happenstance; it is entirely logical that the total effect of all disease and parasitic organisms on an animal is more significant than any single disease. But whether this means that disease is a prime factor in influencing grouse populations is still very uncertain; more probably it is a secondary contributing factor, or in some instances one of two or more co-ordinate factors that determine grouse population levels.

MAN'S RELATIONS TO THE RUFFED GROUSE

ONE has only to consider the great areas of original grouse range from which the bird has been exterminated by the white man to appreciate how vital has been man's impact on this species. The large contiguous area from which the grouse was eliminated is the Mississippi Valley section from central Ohio to Iowa and Arkansas. Equally important are the sizable farming sections still surrounded by grouse range, such as the agricultural valleys of the northeastern states. It seems probable that this clearing of the forest for agriculture has largely run its course in most of the range of the ruffed grouse, and that this great influence of man on the partridge is history; the present-day effects of man on the grouse are much less drastic, even though still very important. Man's activities constantly influence the welfare of grouse populations for better or for worse, as he pursues his business and pleasure of hunting, trapping, farming, lumbering, and conservation. These works can result in more favorable conditions for grouse; but the grouse is not nearly as dependent on man for satisfactory living conditions as are the truly farm game birds like the bobwhite quail and the ring-necked pheasant.

GROUSE HUNTING

THE ruffed grouse is one of our most important upland game birds north of the range of the pheasant. In the northern states where the pheasant is hunted the grouse furnishes much less volume of sport than the pheasant, but makes up in quality of sport what it lacks in quantity. In the Appalachians the grouse is much less hunted than the bobwhite. In some areas of the eastern states turkey or woodcock hunting may outrank grouse hunting in the amount of participation, but these places are not prevalent in the good grouse range. The kill of ruffed grouse in good years will run from 3 to 4 million birds, about three-quarters of them in the United States; in times of poor grouse abundance this total may drop to 2 million or even less. Most grouse are taken in the lake states—Michigan, Wisconsin, and Minnesota; the northeastern states, from Pennsylvania to Maine, and the eastern Canadian provinces compose the other major area of good grouse hunting. The Western area in the Rocky Mountains and the coastal region is much less intensively hunted.

The hunting seasons for ruffed grouse usually run from one to two months in the fall. Since the sexes cannot be easily distinguished, both are hunted. Daily bag limits are generally two or three birds, and season limits ten to fifteen.

Grouse are hunted either with or without dogs. Before the advent of the ring-necked pheasant bird dogs were trained on grouse or quail, but now there are very few well-trained grouse dogs; most hunting dogs in the north are used on pheasants, which makes them of little use in grouse hunting; as a result most grouse hunting now is done without dogs. Since grouse lie well to approach, it is feasible to hunt grouse on foot, and most hunting of these birds is now done this way.

Fabulous stories of hunter's bags of grouse are recounted in the literature of the 18th century; but since the era of sport hunting the individual hunter has little chance to make such kills. The legal bag limits alone prevent it, but even without them it would be difficult to run one's bag into the dozens per day or hundreds per season. Few get even the present limit of about a dozen birds a year; the average for those who hunt grouse is less than a bird per day and less than two per season. The best grouse hunters do considerably better, but they are a select few.

The effect of hunting on grouse populations has been studied in a number of states. All results show consistently that the proportion of the fall population that is bagged is about 15%, often less, and rarely over 20%. About a quarter more are killed, but lost as cripples. The total kill then is about 20% of the preseason population—sometimes as high as 25%. In local areas it may run higher than these general averages, but few coverts will have over half of the birds killed by man's hunting. When grouse are plentiful these losses from hunting are of little importance in affecting the trends of grouse numbers; when grouse are scarce the hunting take tends to drop considerably, so that even then the effect on the next year's crop is slight. It seems very clear that man's hunting is a secondary factor in controlling grouse numbers.

THE EFFECTS OF FARMING AND LUMBERING ON GROUSE

WE have already noted the tremendous effect on the grouse of the white man's original clearing of the eastern forests for farming. The first effect was to improve the variety and distribution of cover, to the benefit of the bird. As the elimination of the forest progressed on the better soils, the amount of open land exceeded what the grouse could use, and even the small blocks of woods that were left became too small to sustain them; thus great areas of once fine grouse range became uninhabitable. In the eastern range only the rougher terrain and higher altitudes were left uncleared; in the lower Midwestern range, where the grouse had only marginal habitat anyway, it was eliminated.

In the past century, as the marginal farming areas reverted to forest, much of the Eastern and Midwestern grouse range has improved; the period of transition from open fields to woods on these lands benefited the grouse, because of the large amount of brushland intermixed with the forest and fields. This transition is still in progress in many areas, but when it is completed the resulting habitat pattern will probably be less productive of grouse than the present one.

Farming preserves the intermixture of fields and woodlands, and aids in maintaining good cover-type distribution where the open areas are not too extensive; where there is 40% or more of the farm land in woods and brush, the land may support more grouse than does continuous forest. The plant crops that the farmer grows have practically no effect on grouse; none of the grains or cultivated crops are important grouse foods. Apple trees near woodland cover provide good food, and clover growing along field edges and in woods roads is eaten as greens; otherwise the grouse largely depends on wild plants for its sustenance.

Farm livestock often affect grouse; cattle-grazing in grouse habitat may destroy the ground cover and undergrowth to such an extent that the usefulness of the cover to grouse is reduced or destroyed. The practice of allowing stock in woodlands is lessening, as farmers develop better pasture management. Dogs and cats that are allowed to roam freely on farms cause some predation of young grouse. Where poultry use the edges of grouse cover there is the possibility that they may spread disease to grouse, but this is not known to be of any importance.

Man's most important land management activity in so far as grouse are concerned is lumbering—or any other form of wood cutting; all forms of wood-product harvest directly affect the habitat, and in one way or another almost all grouse forest habitat is cut. Whether the cutting is for lumber, pulp, poles, posts, or toothpicks makes no difference; what the cutting does to

the woods is all that is important to grouse welfare.

Man *can* either destroy grouse habitat or make it much less productive of grouse by either of the two extremes of treatment, namely: clearing off all forest and preventing its regrowth; or leaving the forest entirely alone to grow back into maturity. He actually does neither of these except in a few cases. Cutting is done at intervals when a profit can be made, and the type of cutting depends on the species and sizes of trees, the markets available, and the attitude of the owner toward woodland management. What he does will largely determine the quality of grouse habitat. If he is interested in grouse, he can deliberately take their needs into consideration in planning his cuttings, as we shall see when we discuss the management of grouse.

FIRE IN RELATION TO GROUSE

ONE of the prominent effects on grouse of modern man's use of the forest has been the great increase in forest fires; this has resulted in both improvement and destruction of the habitat. One direct effect is the occasional destruction of nests and birds in fires; but this mortality is rarely significant. Wild fires of great extent have the immediate effect of destroying the habitat more or less completely in the area burned. After the burned land grows back to brush it may become good cover, especially for the young birds; if not too large in area, this brushy cover, combined with unburned woods, may make excellent habitat. Hence small fires often are a benefit to grouse cover. With modern forest-fire prevention and control systems in operation, few fires burn a large enough area to be detrimental to grouse.

The favorable effects of fires on grouse habitat were summarized by Grange (1948). While these benefits apply more to the prairie chicken and sharptail in the early stages of plant succession after fires, they also apply to the ruffed grouse then—and still more in the later succession stages. These are the benefits that Grange lists: the control of forest growth; the stimulation of new food supplies; the greater availability of food; the elimination of "rough"; the fertilizing effect of ashes; and the control of insect parasites and disease organisms. The first three are of most significance to ruffed grouse; the last item is strictly theoretical. In a later work Grange (1949) expressed the view that forest fires are the dominant long-time influence on wildlife populations in the northern forest zone, and are correlated with cycles of the abundance of species like the ruffed grouse. His arguments on the great influence of fires on animals are very convincing, but the correlation with cycles is inadequate to explain this phenomenon.

MAN AS A GROUSE CONSERVATIONIST

THE history of man's interest in the ruffed grouse in the last 50 years has been unique, in that the greatest emphasis has been on conservation rather than on exploitation; before that time the only effort made on behalf of the bird was to enact laws to limit the freedom of the hunter in harvesting them. Commercial hunting was virtually eliminated by making the sale of grouse illegal; sport hunting was restricted to a period in autumn, and bag limits were lowered; the use of snares and traps in taking grouse was banned. The attitude of vast numbers of hunters became one of concern for the bird's welfare.

The alarm over the future of the ruffed grouse gave rise to a series of studies to determine the causes of decline in grouse numbers, and what might be done about it; at first these were questionnaires to obtain sportsman and naturalist opinion. Forbush conducted the first of these in Massachusetts after the minor grouse decline of 1903–04; Woodruff (1908) made the first of several studies in New York. Stoddart (1918) reported on his analysis of the 1916–17 grouse decline, the last of the questionnaire studies. The scientific approach to the problem began in the early 1920's, when Allen (1929) studied methods of artificially propagating ruffed grouse; and later with Gross the diseases of grouse (Allen and Gross, 1926). The decade of the 1930's saw the full blossoming of the comprehensive investiga-

tion of the complete ecology and management of ruffed grouse as well as other game species. Among the more significant reports made on these studies are: Bump, *et al.,* 1947; King, 1937; Clarke, 1936; Fisher, 1939; Grange, 1948. As a result of all this attention there is probably more known about the ecology of the ruffed grouse than almost any other game species.

While the conservation era has necessarily emphasized studies as a prerequisite to intelligent action, there has also been much effort at management. Some of these efforts aborted when they were found to be ineffective; artificial propagation of grouse for restocking was given up, because it could not be done effectively or economically, and because it was found to be unnecessary. Refuges established for the protection of grouse proved to be of little value and are now largely abandoned (Edminster, 1937). Predator hunting and trapping is mostly for fur harvest and sport, but some is done in the name of game management; it has little influence on grouse welfare, but as long as it is limited to the important grouse predators it will do little harm.

The most significant effort of man as a conservationist is the management of land for grouse and other natural resources. Some progress has been made in this field, particularly in the acceptance of sustained-yield woodland harvest methods, which are sound grouse management as well as sound forestry. In a more limited way land-use practices are being followed specifically for grouse benefits. State and Federal forest and game lands are managed according to plans made for the best harvests of plant and animal crops. Private lands are more and more receiving good conservation treatment in connection with soil and forest conservation programs. This is aimed at the management of ruffed grouse along with other game and tree crops, and will be discussed in some detail in the chapter on management. Though the greatly needed work in land-use practices lies mostly in the future, we can say that at least a good start has been made; man is rapidly growing up to his destined role as a conservationist.

REPRODUCTION AND POPULATIONS

REPRODUCTIVE POTENTIAL

THE ruffed grouse is promiscuous in its breeding habits. It breeds in the spring following the year of hatching. The female never has more than one brood a year.

The sex ratio is even among the newly-born young, but by fall there is a slight tendency toward a majority of males; among the adult birds there is a small preponderance of females from spring to fall. The total fall population has in most years close to an even balance of the sexes. A differential mortality resulting in a high loss of males in the spring is associated with their vulnerability from courtship activities. The unbalance in the proportions of the sexes in the spring may be as much as 60 to 40, but 52% to 55% females is more common.

Productivity is measured by the ratio between the prehunting season fall population and the spring breeding population; it gives the same information as the ratio of young birds to adults in the fall population. These ratios are typically much lower in the ruffed grouse than in the bobwhite and ringneck. When the production ratio exceeds two to one, productivity is high; and if the spring breeding population was reasonably high, fall hunting should be good. Production ratios of three to one are indicative of rapid recovery, usually from low spring breeding populations. When the ratio is below 1.5 to 1, a decline in population usually results; this happens most often when populations are at high levels.

Grouse population records on two New York areas showed a variation of from 0.96 to 3.04 in the productivity ratio over a period of 13 years, but not including a year of major decline (Bump, *et al.,* 1947). In 13 years of records on an area of semifarming country in south-central New York the ratio exceeded 2.0 in six years, and fell to 1.5 or lower in four years. On an area of continuous forest cover in the Adirondacks the ratio exceeded 2.0 in six years out of eleven, fell below 1.5 only once. In periods of major decline the ratio of production is close to 1.0,

which means that the production of young birds is practically zero; when this happens two years in a row the grouse populations hit bottom, and a "cyclic" low is reached.

Inversity is clearly shown in the productivity of the ruffed grouse; this phenomenon is revealed in three phases. High breeding populations usually have a low productivity or "recovery rate"; low breeding populations have a high productivity—if they are not too low. Very low breeding populations have a low productivity rate; the latter may happen for one or two years, after a major decline. Then follows a period of two or three years of high productivity, until the peak of the population is reached. An alternation of years of good and poor productivity are then likely to follow during the period of generally good populations, until the next major decline comes.

These ratios may be obtained in either or both of two ways: summer censuses of the broods and adults; fall age identification of harvested birds. The latter is done easily and accurately by the observing of the shape of the outer two primary feathers; in an adult bird these feathers are rounded at the tip, but in the bird born the previous spring they are pointed.

Grouse hens normally lay a clutch of 11 or 12 eggs; occasionally 13, 14, or 15 eggs. Those having still more eggs are usually the result of two or more hens laying in the same nest. Clutches of fewer than ten eggs are commonly those of hens that have had their first clutch broken up before the start of incubation or very early in incubation. Under these circumstances renesting commonly occurs, but always with a smaller clutch than in first nests. Hens that have their nests destroyed during the second half of incubation practically never renest; thus there are very few late broods of grouse, especially in comparison with the bobwhite quail and ring-necked pheasant. This means that the proportion of hens that manage to hatch a clutch of eggs is less with grouse than with the other two species. In good years 60% to 70% of grouse hens hatch their eggs.

The proportion of first-clutch eggs that are infertile is very low—2% is normal; in second clutches it is somewhat higher. Embryos that die during incubation are also few in early nests; 3%, or about one egg in three nests, is usual. It is somewhat higher in renests. From these figures it will be seen that the average grouse brood starts out with ten chicks at hatching time.

The reproductive capabilities of the ruffed grouse that we have reviewed above are clearly high enough to produce good populations if mortality is not excessive. If there were no losses, a pair of grouse could become 14 the first season, 110 the second, 782 a year later, and 5,486 birds by the fall of the fourth year. But such tremendous increases never occur, for a variety of reasons. One is that man shoots some of them each fall. Suppose we assume that a big hunting harvest of 40% is taken; let us see what effect this would have on the population in these same four years. Six birds would be harvested from the 14 present the first fall. Assuming an even sex ratio and 12 fertile eggs per hen, all of which hatch, the population the second fall would be 56 birds; of these 22 would be harvested by hunters. The population the third fall would be 238 birds, with a harvest of 95. At the beginning of the hunting season the fourth autumn, there would be 995 grouse and 398 of them would be shot, leaving a net of 597 birds to go into the winter. Thus the two original grouse become 597 in four years, and during this time they have enabled a harvest of 521 birds. It is clear then that even a high hunting harvest by itself is not a serious deterrent to a rapid rise in grouse numbers. This little theoretical exercise shows clearly that other mortality factors are vital in preventing the grouse from skyrocketing in numbers.

MORTALITY OF THE RUFFED GROUSE

THE environment in which the grouse lives greatly affects its productivity; all the organic and inorganic parts of its physical world—plants, animals, soils, water, sunshine, air, and topography—play their parts in influencing grouse numbers. In part they condition the birds so that they are more vulnerable to the decimating agencies than they would otherwise be; in part they are the killing agents themselves—the predators, man, organisms that infect or infest, and obstacles that cause accidents.

It is desirable to discuss these matters both individually and collectively. We have considered them in the previous chapters as separate entities; now we shall discuss the mortality of the grouse in the three periods of life—egg, juvenile, and adult, and bring together the influencing factors as they affect each period. In spite of our best efforts to show these relationships, the complexity with which they occur is such that the drama is bound to be only partly told. The grouse is a dynamic resource, living in association with many other equally dynamic creatures; their condition is never static, and therefore the fortunes of each are forever changing.

Nesting Losses. Almost all hen grouse nest, but rarely do more than two-thirds of them succeed in hatching their clutch of eggs; most of those hatched are the first clutches laid. Only those few renest whose nests are destroyed before incubation or early in the incubation period. Thus the proportion of hens that hatch a clutch is raised but little by late nests.

In average years in most areas about 40% of the nests are lost; it seems to be a little higher in mixed farm-forest habitat than in continuous forest cover. This is probably due to the higher population of effective ground predators in the mixed cover—notably foxes. Occasionally the nest loss rises far higher than normal; this excessive nest loss is usually local, rather than a widespread occurrence. The mortality of nests is the least variable of all losses.

Predation is responsible for about 90% of grouse-nest destruction; most of this loss occurs late in the incubation period. Several other causes of nest failure are each of little significance, but all together make up about 10% of the total. They include man's activities as a farmer and lumberman, fire, desertion, and flooding.

Losses among Young Ruffed Grouse. The most difficult phase of grouse mortality to appraise is that of the young. In most years a third of their number die in the first month of life; most of this occurs in the first three weeks, and the biggest part of the deaths come still earlier. Sometimes this early summer loss is as high as 50% or even more. Very little of it can be attributed to predators; yet of the few remains of young grouse found in field studies almost all have been predator work.

Great attention to the question of juvenile mortality has been given in grouse studies, since it seems to be one of the most vital phases of grouse ecology; despite this attention, little concrete evidence has been turned up to explain clearly these losses. Even the circumstantial evidence is inconsistent, though it does point to a plausible solution.

At the outset of the grouse family's life we find a mother bird with ten little chicks. No father bird is around to help with family chores, and so she must take care of them all by herself. When they leave the nest some hours after birth there are almost surely some chicks weaker than others; they may not have been incubated quite as well as the others, or they may simply be inherently weaker. In the travels of the first few days some of these chicks may get lost, fall in holes from which they cannot get out, or simply fail to keep up with the crowd. Mother grouse have no time to search for stragglers, even if they were inclined to do so. They take care of the chicks that are *with* them, not those that are somewhere else. How many baby grouse are lost this way it is impossible to say, but some are. Then comes a very cold night, or a rainstorm, or both; the well-brooded youngsters manage all right, but when there are many to keep warm and dry those around the edges may become chilled or wet. Almost certainly a few are lost this way, for very young grouse cannot stand much exposure to adverse elements. As the number of chicks in the brood decreases, brooding is more adequate, and after the first couple of weeks the chicks are better feathered; then they can stand more exposure. Hence the most likely time for losses of this kind is in the very early brood period.

Young grouse have infections and infestations of internal and external parasites almost from the first day of life. How many die from disease cannot be said, but the evidence indicates that in normal circumstances it is very few. Some are captured by predators, but we know that this source of loss in the very young grouse is not high. That about accounts for the various agents that cause young grouse to die. They add up to a normal first month's loss of about a third of the chicks—a loss which, even though *normal,* is a tremendous cut from the possible fall hunting season population.

If these normal early brood losses are bad, then the corresponding losses in *bad* years are hard to describe with phrases less strong than catastrophic or disastrous. The ordinary losses of chicks from exposure are compounded when a protracted period of exceptionally bad weather occurs early in the brood period. The critical time is from the last week of May through the first three weeks of June—the exact time depending on the predominant hatching time; brooding cannot overcome the problem, no matter how well done. The little chicks can go just so long without eating; then they must forage or die, regardless of how nasty the weather is. The result is that they die from exposure instead of—or in addition to—starvation. Several days of rainy, sunless, cold weather in the first few weeks of life of young grouse can result in death for most of them. Those few that hatch ahead of the normal time, or very late, may escape, and thus permit a small number of youngsters to live through the summer and grow up.

The picture of heavy infant mortality described above is *probably* the way it happens in such years. The concept is based on all the evidence available; which, however, does not include very much actual clinical data. One of the most revealing instances that bears on this subject occurred in New York in the summer of 1935 (Edminster, 1947). A three-day rain that caused the worst floods in history in a ten-county area included the Connecticut hill grouse study area of the New York Ruffed Grouse Investigation. As a result of that one storm, the juvenile mortality on the area was more than double the normal mortality; it totaled 77% for the season. It gave a good illustration of what bad weather can do to young grouse. It was particularly impressive, because its terrific effect came at a time when most of the chicks were about five weeks old—past the time of great susceptibility to losses from exposure. It is probable that had it come a month earlier hardly a grouse chick would have survived.

After the early period of heavy brood mortality, the losses drop off to a low rate for several weeks. When the chicks are about eight weeks old the rate of loss increases a little; at this time the youngsters are beginning to become independent of their mother's care, and are a bit reckless. Some are picked off by predators, particularly by sharp-shinned and Cooper's hawks, and all the rest become educated to this danger. In a short time the mortality curve flattens out again, and there is little more loss until autumn. Then the young join the adults as hunting-season targets of sportsmen. The total juvenile mortality averages about 60%.

Adult Grouse Mortality. Soon after the grouse crop of the year reaches full growth, a period of sudden and considerable mortality arrives— the hunting season; the hunting harvest is the biggest source of grouse loss in the fall. About a quarter of the population perishes, and four-fifths of them are shot; the rest are taken by predators, except for a few that die of accidents of their own making. October is the time of the fall shuffle, of which the "crazy flight" is an aberration; birds that fly off on these crazy flights sometimes crash into obstacles like buildings or electric wires, and thus end their careers.

Winter losses are mostly from predation; in early winter it is a slow attrition, the amount of loss depending mainly on the size of the grouse population and the amount it exceeds the carrying capacity of the range. Toward the end of the winter the rate of loss accelerates; the agent is still the predator, but much of this loss is conditioned by weather and by the birds' habits. Both snow-roosting and the onset of the courtship season play a part in this. In exceptionally severe winters the losses may be so large as seriously to limit the production of the following summer.

Spring is a period of high losses from predation; the male birds particularly are susceptible, because of their intense drumming activities. In contrast, the summer period is one of very low mortality; seldom is the rate more than 5% of the population at this season.

The usual mortality of adult grouse from all causes for the full year is about 50%; variation in different years may be from slightly below 30% to over 60%. The higher the fall population the higher the rate of loss. The killing agent in almost all this mortality is either man or predation; accidents and disease are secondary factors, which in average years may account for 10% of the total. Occasionally the disease factor may be more significant.

LIFE EQUATION

THE annual cycle of production and losses tends toward an equilibrium, with the same number of birds at the end of a year as at the beginning. It rarely happens exactly that way, but the birds cannot increase very many years in succession before there must be a reversal; likewise they cannot decrease for long without running into serious trouble. Some of the factors in the varied annual "equations" are constant, while others are variable. As a general rule these are the constant factors: sex ratio; proportion of females nesting; number of eggs laid; proportion of infertile eggs and dead germs; and nest mortality. The variable factors are the juvenile and adult losses. Table 15 shows the life equation of 100 grouse for a single year when the equation runs true. In years of net increase in population, the figures for the mortality of chicks and of adults will be lower than shown. In years of net decrease in population the losses of young and adult grouse will be higher than that shown in the table.

TABLE 15

LIFE EQUATION OF 100 RUFFED GROUSE FOR A YEAR*

TIME	ACTIVITIES	NUMBER OF GROUSE	
		young	adult
SPRING	(1) 50 males mate with 50 females		100
	(2) All females nest, average 11.5 eggs in first nests, 8 in 2nd nests. Total first clutch eggs, 575		
	(3) 60% of females (30) hatch 1st clutch, or 30 × 11.5 = 345		
	6% of females (3) hatch 2nd clutch, or 3 × 8 = 24		
	2% of first eggs infertile = 7		
	8% " 2nd " " = 2		
	3% " first " die = 10		
	8% " 2nd " " = 2		
	Or, eggs fail to hatch = 21, and 348 hatch (av. 10.5)	348	
	(4) 20 adults die from predation (20%)		80
SUMMER	(5) 4 " " " " (5%)		76
	(6) 209 chicks die from accidents, exposure, disease, predation (60%)	139	
FALL	Surviving chicks become adults		215
	(7) 43 are killed by hunters (20%)		172
	(8) 10 " " " predators, accidents (5%)		162
WINTER	(9) 62 " " " " (38%)		
SPRING	(10) Breeding season population		100

* In a year when increases and losses actually balance.

POPULATION FLUCTUATIONS AND CYCLES

THE annual cycle of gains and losses usually results in more or fewer birds than in the previous year. When the same change is general for a region there is a noticeable change—especially in the fall, when the birds are observed by many people. Over the length of a decade these changes tend to result in trends up and down, which make a population curve; these curves show a consistency greater than the erratic annual changes. In fact with the ruffed grouse these trends seem to show about one major peak and one major trough of population level each decade. This regularity has led to the suspicion that the ruffed grouse, along with many other animals of the northern hemisphere, follows a pre-destined cycle. These animal cycles seem to be correlated primarily with climate.

Population levels vary in all kinds of habitat, but the peak populations reached depend on the carrying capacity of the habitat. Where the habitat is of superior quality the high population reached may be limited by the saturation point for the species; this seems to be about four acres per grouse. Spring breeding populations rarely if ever exceed this figure; fall populations have been known to reach densities of a grouse per two acres or even more, but they are clearly untenable. Under these conditions there is an intense dispersion of birds, and a high rate of predation.

The minimum grouse population commonly found seems to be about a bird per fifty acres of occupied range. When the density is lower than this the range is either unsuitable or unoccupied; the few birds that exist must group in the better coverts or breeding will be unsuccessful. Even in good grouse range the number of birds may drop to this density in the low period of a cycle. Recovery from such low densities requires more than a single year. On the Connecticut Hill grouse study area in south-central New York the grouse population varied from a bird per 17 acres to one per five acres in 14 years; it had been somewhat below the 17-acres/bird level for two years before the study. On a continuous forest study area in the Adirondack Mountains the grouse population varied from a low of 20-acres/bird to a high of 11-acres/bird over 12 years; these were early fall populations, the highest of the year. Breeding densities ran from a low of 22-acres/bird to a high of 8-acres/bird on Connecticut Hill, and from 38-acres/bird to 21-acres/bird on the Adirondack area (Bump, *et al.*, 1947). These are typical of the two major kinds of range in the northeastern states and eastern Canada. In the better cover sections of the lake states range the grouse densities average somewhat higher in times of maximum abundance. In the Appalachian Mountains range and in the Far Western areas the levels of abundance are generally somewhat lower, both in periods of abundance and scarcity.

It is not surprising that a popular game species that fluctuates in numbers as widely as does the ruffed grouse would cause great concern among sportsmen. At times its numbers drop to 20% to 30% of what they had been a year or two before; these declines almost always occur precipitately, and thus emphasize the event. As they have been watched over the years, with the subsequent recoveries following inexorably, a remarkable periodicity seems evident. The cycle of decline and recovery is about ten years, and it seems to be too regular to be a happenstance. Could it be that some all-pervading influence causes the populations of ruffed grouse to rise and fall regardless of habitat and the ordinary environmental effects? The same question is asked about many other creatures of the northern

hemisphere, particularly some of the mammals of the far north; lemmings, hares, arctic foxes, and others seem to exhibit very prominent cycles of abundance with regular periodicity.

A great deal of attention has been given to this phenomenon of cycles; it is believed to pervade such widely divergent things as salmon numbers, tree growth, wars, and business levels. These studies continue, for there is no explanation yet known that clarifies the causes of the observed changes and the relations among them. Climatic conditions have been suspected to be at the bottom of the whole matter; changes in the influences of the sun on the earth have been suggested as a possible cause; the phenomenon of sunspots in particular has been mentioned as connected with cycles, since their prevalence also is cyclic.

Simpler answers may explain some cycles of animal abundance. The prolific lemming increases in numbers until it consumes its food supply, then starves en masse; this dislocates the food supply of predators like arctic foxes, snowy owls, and goshawks. They then die or migrate southward in search of food, and cause further upsets. This simple cause and effect certainly does not answer the case of the ruffed grouse.

Major grouse declines happen to peak populations; the density of these populations may vary greatly in different habitats, but they are generally the highest for each place. This places some suspicion on the very population itself as being connected with the decline. Both predation and disease are highest at such times; the vulnerability of the birds is also greatest. These influences by themselves ordinarily result in only moderate reductions in numbers. At least one more reducing factor is needed: that seems to be provided by periodic combinations of very bad weather. These are of two types, and occur at two seasons. Very cold and wet and cloudy periods for a week or two at the critical hatching time in June are the ones that curtail production; exceedingly cold periods, with prolonged deep snows in late winter, are the ones that reduce the population to a low level for the breeding season. When these occur in succession, so that both production and survival are hit in a single year's time, the result is a serious decline; two successive years with such events and the birds drop to a very low populations level.

Such great declines may occur regularly if the drastic weather conditions happen that way. The intervening time is adequate for the bird to rebuild its numbers and provide the periodicity. This explanation is an oversimplification of the matter, since it is not hard to find all kinds of exceptions; this merely points out the complexity of the many factors bearing on the question. At least the theory offers a plausible answer that fits the facts as known. The reader who wishes to delve deeper into the question of grouse cycles may consult Bump, *et al.,* 1947; Grange, 1949; Edminster, 1947; and others cited in those works.

THE CARRYING CAPACITY OF GROUSE RANGE

THE concept of carrying capacity as applied to the ruffed grouse involves characteristics of both the habitat and the species. The usual meaning of carrying capacity refers to the ability of habitat to sustain a limited number of a game species; food and shelter are the main elements concerned with establishing the level of carrying capacity. When the carrying capacity is exceeded—as it frequently is in the fall—the excess birds are vulnerable, and will ordinarily die before spring. With grouse the immediate cause of death is commonly hunting or predation, but this is not important; vulnerable birds will succumb to some decimating agent—if not predation or hunting, then some other.

In good grouse range the tolerance of the birds to their own kind often sets the limit of survival; this is the so-called "saturation point," and is about four acres per grouse in the spring. On such range the food supplies are adequate to support many more grouse than one per four acres; also the quality and pattern of the shelter cover is often good enough to support more grouse than the birds themselves will allow. In such cases the carrying capacity is set by a species consideration that is commonly called *intraspecific tolerance.* Where the saturation point is not reached, the survival limit is set by a combination of environmental conditions, with food and cover the basic elements, and with predation, disease, and weather all serving as modifiers. Thus the carrying capacity for ruffed grouse is less dependent on habitat alone than with many other game species.

THE MANAGEMENT OF THE RUFFED GROUSE

SINCE it is a bird of the woodland, the ruffed grouse must be managed by woodland practices. The primary products of most woodlands are wood products, and therefore the grouse must be considered as a by-product of the land use. There are some exceptions, such as private game preserves and public game lands, but these are a very small part of the total grouse range. A prime question thus arises, namely: can the interests of the grouse be made compatible with those of forestry? Many people have felt that the two could not be harmonized, but I think they were wrong. If theoretical, intensive forestry could be applied on a wide scale there might be some cause for concern, but such is not the case in practice. The fundamental requirements of sound forestry and sound grouse management are about the same.

The forester recommends the protection of woodland from grazing by domestic livestock, from fire, and from insects and disease. He generally wants a mixed woodland, with a variety of species of trees. He advocates a woodland made up of a good balance of trees of all ages. With such a woodland sustained yield management is possible, by the taking of a small crop at short intervals rather than a complete crop at long intervals. The needs of the ruffed grouse are compatible with all these principles.

The conflict between grouse management and forestry comes in connection with attitudes to-

PLATE 53. *Woodland cuttings are the mainstay of ruffed grouse habitat management. A small clearing made by sustained yield, "spot-lumbering" woodland harvest.*

COURTESY SOIL CONSERVATION SERVICE, USDA

ward various species of trees. The forester has a concept of "weed" trees—those which in current markets have little wood product value; but many of these so-called "weeds" are among the most important in providing food for grouse. Examples are the beech, the birches, flowering dogwood, hop hornbeam, and wild apple. Theoretical forestry may visualize eliminating these species from woodlands and replacing them by pines, oaks, and others that are preferred; but this is not only impractical but is not even thought desirable by most foresters today. Ironically, much of the lumbering of the past has resulted in precisely the opposite, namely, a regenerated stand with more "weed" species than before. This has not always been good for ruffed grouse either, for they need the "good" wood product species as much as the others. Since these unbalanced woodlands are a result of cutting methods, both the forester and the game man now agree that sustained-yield methods are best.

HABITAT DEVELOPMENT

THE development and care of woodlands for a combination of wood products, grouse, and other game crops requires that the needed cover types be provided in the right quantities, quality, and arrangement. This can be done with a variety of tools and techniques, including fencing, cutting, and planting.

Woodland Protection. In the portions of the grouse range that are intermixed with farmland, many woodlands are grazed by domestic stock. The damage that these animals do to the habitat depends upon the intensity of their grazing; it varies all the way from negligible to complete destruction. Since the understory of northern woodlands seldom becomes too thick for grouse use, it can be said categorically that grazing should be excluded from wooded cover and confined to good pastures. This often means building considerable fence, but fortunately it pays the owner to do it; the increased yields of milk and meat obtained by keeping the animals on good pasture makes it a good practice economically.

The exclusion of fire from woodland in the range of the ruffed grouse is generally accepted as good conservation. There is no doubt about the wisdom of this policy as concerns the production of wood products; but the relation of fire to grouse is not so simple. Fires that destroy the cover completely over large areas do great immediate harm to game, including grouse; yet small fires and light surface litter burns may be very beneficial to grouse. This is particularly

PLATE 54. *Lane clear-cutting 30 feet wide to provide edges and brush cover.*

COURTESY SOIL CONSERVATION SERVICE, USDA

true in areas of extensive forest that are not frequently cut for crops; here the fires help break up the uniform cover of the forest and provide openings and food. Since controlled burning in these kinds of forests has not been made a practical technique it cannot be recommended, no matter how advantageous it might be to grouse. On the other hand, those fires that do happen, and that are mostly confined to small dimensions by our efficient forest-fire fighting systems, may be looked on as God-given benefits to grouse.

The protection of woodlands from insect and disease damage is sometimes very important in forestry, but is seldom of much significance to grouse. The use of DDT and other insecticides on forests in order to suppress outbreaks of forest insects has not been shown to harm grouse, and probably does not affect them.

Woodland Improvement by Cuttings. The system of cutting is much more important than the details of what species and sizes are cut. Extensive clear-cutting is not recommended. One recommended method is by sustained-yield harvest, handled as scattered spot cuttings of one or a few trees in a group throughout the woodland. Another way is by small blocks clear-cut in a rotation that divides the woods into 10, 20, or more units, to complete the coverage in from 50 to 100 years; instead of blocks these units may

be long, narrow strips, in the manner of a shelterwood cutting. All three of these methods are good grouse management, and good forestry practice.

Selective cutting to improve the quality of grouse cover concerns the species of trees in the stand. In small woodlands, such improvements are most important in the outer 200 feet of the woodland next to open fields; in extensive woodlands it makes no difference where the cuttings are made, since the openings themselves must also be made by cutting. One objective in selecting trees to cut is to free specially desirable food or shelter trees from competition; it is often desirable to encourage apple, crabapple, hawthorn, hemlock, and other valuable species by cutting out other less useful trees that are overtopping them. Where a thinning is needed the species least valuable to grouse may be removed and the better ones kept. Where there is little winter shelter present, trees may be half-cut and toppled, so that the tops continue to grow lying on the ground. Any cutting that opens the crown enough to let sunlight through to the ground stimulates the growth of brambles and other ground-cover plants, which improves the food supplies.

Where the woodland cover is uniform and it is desirable to break it up more or faster than can be done by such ordinary improvement or harvest cuttings as discussed above, limited cuttings for game may be in order. These should be in the form of lanes of clear-cut area well distributed through the forest; to the greatest extent possible they should be woods roads that are also needed to get out wood products and for other access. It is desirable to keep such lanes a little wider than is ordinarily done just for road purposes; fifteen- to thirty-foot-wide lanes have proved to be excellent openings for grouse.

Another type of cutting that is frequently needed and justified is the improvement of the woods border; this applies most commonly where the woods border farm crop fields; here there is an adverse effect of the trees on the crop in the edge of the field. This can be overcome, and a valuable shrub cover developed that is useful to grouse—either by planting the edge of the field, or by cutting the edge of the woods. Here we shall consider the cutting method. All the trees are removed from the woods edge, back to a depth of about 25 or 30 feet; shrubs growing in this zone naturally are favored, and encouraged to take over the area. Where the trees cut are hardwoods that resprout, they must be recut at intervals before they grow too large. An alternative to this recutting that is helpful in reducing maintenance costs is the poisoning of the stumps and sprouts of the cut hardwood trees; modern brush-killer herbicides like 2,4-D plus 2,4-5-T are suitable for this purpose.

Plantings to Improve Grouse Habitat. The place of plantings in grouse habitat improvement is not nearly as important as that of silviculture. Several types of plantings, however, may be used to advantage in some situations; these apply mostly where submarginal farms have been abandoned, and where farm fields and grouse woods join.

The development of shrub borders by cutting was discussed above; the same result may be obtained by the planting of selected species of shrubs in the field edge instead of cutting the woods edge. This is done most effectively when a good job of site preparation can be made by plowing and harrowing the area before spring planting; otherwise each planting spot should be well scalped. Species of shrubs and small trees that can be used for such plantings in much of the range of the grouse include: multiflora rose, silky dogwood, gray dogwood, crabapple, autumn olive, bayberry, tatarian and amur honeysuckles, hazelnut, arrowwood, and highbush cranberry. The spacing of the larger species may be about four feet apart, and the smaller ones two to three feet apart. The taller kinds should be planted in the rows next to the woods, and the lower ones next to the open field; four or five rows are usually needed to make an adequate border.

When old fields are to be planted for the development of new woodlands, the pattern of the planting should provide for good grouse cover. Most tree planting is of coniferous species. It is important in extensive plantings that these evergreen stands be not too extensive, and with other types of cover to diversify them; about 600 feet across the narrow dimension is the most that should be planned in a unit. Plantings of hardwood trees, shrub bands, and open lanes may be used to provide the needed interspersion. The natural regeneration of hardwoods will often aid in developing this type if allowed to do so. Hypothetical patterns for such plantings are shown in Figure 19.

These are the conifers recommended most highly for field plantings to benefit grouse: hemlock; white, red, and Scotch pines; Norway, red, and white spruces; arborvitae; and Douglas fir. Hardwood trees that may be used in plantings on good sites include: sugar maple; white oak; red oak; and black locust. These plantings should follow standard forestry practice, though it is preferred that the spacing be eight feet instead of the usual six.

Where there are extensive hardwood stands that lack good winter shelter, the interplanting of shade-tolerant conifers may be done; this requires more work for good results than open field planting, and growth will be slower. Open glades in the woods should be used for such plantings where available; otherwise it is advisable to plant in open stands, or to kill some of the hardwood competition by poisoning. The conifers that grow best in such plantings are hemlock, white pine, and any of the spruces; arborvitae may be used in wet sites. The spacing should be the same as with other plantings.

OTHER ENVIRONMENTAL PRACTICES, AND RESTOCKING

SEVERAL game-management measures commonly advocated for some species of game birds have no value in ruffed grouse management. The establishment of refuges to protect a part of the population from hunting is of no value to this species. The growing of food patches of annual grains and the placing of grain in winter feeding stations for ruffed grouse are wasted effort; they do not need this food, and will not use it very much. The restocking of coverts with either game-farm reared or wild-trapped birds is impractical and seldom needed. Predator control cannot be justified on the basis of benefits to ruffed grouse.

CONTROL OF THE HARVEST

THE grouse is not seriously reduced in numbers by modern sport hunting; hence the laws that govern the taking of grouse should be liberal, in comparison with those that apply to some game species. Overshooting is unlikely, because of the nature of the bird and its habitat, and because most of its habitat is not located close to large concentrations of hunters.

Open seasons in years of good abundance may well extend from one to two months; bag limits at such times may be from three to six birds per day, and 15 or more per season. This is somewhat more liberal than most states now allow. In the years when grouse are scarce the season should be curtailed to a week or two, and the bag limit cut to about two per day. This is preferable to a complete closure, which is not of enough benefit to the species to make up for the inconvenience and loss of recreation that it causes the hunters. The limited kill that will be made on low populations will not have very much effect on the

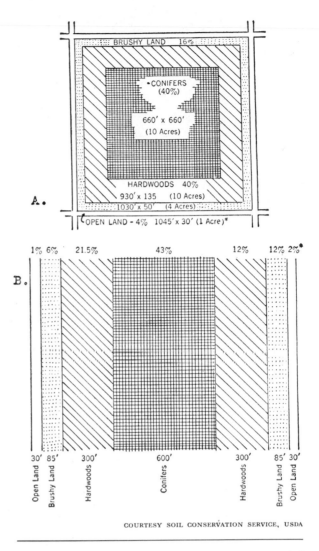

FIGURE 19. *Hypothetical patterns for planting ruffed grouse cover.*

A. A square unit of a checkerboard pattern, 25 acres in size.
B. A linear unit for continuous strips, 1400 feet wide.
* The open land strips are shown double since each serves two adjacent units.

bird's recovery, and it will permit the continued training and use of grouse dogs. It will also provide an opportunity for grouse hunters to obtain some recreation, even if they do not get much shooting; they will be in a position to know the reason for the restricted hunting.

The setting of seasons and bag limits should be a responsibility of the state wildlife agency, without having to go to the state legislature for legal action. The seasons should be established after systematic censuses have provided the needed information on the population level. These censuses are not as easy with the ruffed grouse as they are with many game birds; they must be made in summer, preferably in July and August. A system of standard census areas may be used as a sample for the whole state. Two figures are needed to keep track of the trend in population—the brood size, and the brood density.

The sample units used for censuses should be predominantly summer cover, and the amount of total cover that the summer types represent should be known. Two or more men cover the ground thoroughly on days of moderate, somewhat sunny, near-windless weather; fifty acres per man-day is adequate coverage. An average brood count of four, excluding the hen, indicates average productivity and probably little change in population, other things being equal; a larger count indicates a higher than average productivity per brood, and a lower count indicates a declining productivity per brood. A record of two broods per man-day in summer cover is about average density. Thus a total count of about 12 birds per man-day—two average broods with hens and two separate males—would be the norm from which to gauge population levels. A comparison of the figures of the year with those of previous years would show the trends. The accuracy of the census depends not only on how well it is taken, but upon the adequacy of the sample; about four or five units of several hundred acres each in each major range type in a state should be enough. A maximum sample of 1% of the total cover may be required, where greater accuracy is needed to set limits of the kill on controlled hunting areas.

>>> CHAPTER 7 <<<

The Bobwhite Quail

THE family Perdicidae, the partridges and New World quails, includes seven species native to the United States: the bobwhite quail; masked bobwhite; mountain quail; scaled quail; California quail; Gambel's quail; and Mearns' quail. Two species of Old World partridges that have been introduced successfully in this country also belong to this family—the Hungarian and chukar partridges. All these species except the masked bobwhite and Mearns' quail will be discussed in the next five chapters.

ORIGIN AND CLASSIFICATION

THE bobwhite is a native American, the most widespread of the nonforest game birds that inhabited the continent east of the Rockies in precolonial days. It is one of the two members of the genus *Colinus*, which belongs in the family Perdicidae, the partridges, New World quails, and bobwhites. The second member of *Colinus* is the masked bobwhite (*C. ridgwayi* Brewster), which is found in parts of southern Arizona and adjacent northern Mexico.

Three subspecies of the bobwhite are recognized: the Eastern bobwhite or just plain bobwhite (*C. virginianus virginianus* Linnaeus), the variety found over most of its range; the Florida bobwhite (*C. virginianus floridanus* Coues); and the Texas bobwhite (*C. virginianus texanus* Lawrence).

HISTORY OF THE BOBWHITE

EARLY settlers all along the Atlantic coast quickly became acquainted with the bobwhite; it was one of the staples in the meat supply of the early settlements, and later of the pioneers as they reached over the Alleghanies into the Northwest Territory. According to all early accounts these birds were very plentiful where natural grass lands occurred with the forest, and where the forest was burned by the Indians—possibly for bison grazing. The clearings of the Indians no doubt helped too in providing the field cover that the bobwhite needed to go with the woods.

As the cities of the colonies developed, the commercialization of the bobwhite followed naturally along with other game species. The prices paid for these delicious table delicacies in those days seem ridiculous to us now—a cent apiece, twenty-five cents a dozen, and so on, gradually increasing as the demand exceeded the supply and the value of money declined. It was said that a good day's market hunting by a single skilled hunter would often be 100 to 200 birds; those who used nets in the late 18th and early 19th centuries would sometimes get that many in one haul—so the stories say.

The bobwhite thrived despite the market hunting. Conversely to the story of the diminishing habitat of the turkey and ruffed grouse, the opening up of the forest rapidly extended the habitable range of the bobwhite. The crude cultivation of the newly cleared fields combined with the great fertility of the soil—the accumulation of topsoil for thousands of years under the forest cover—resulted in luscious growths of weeds and grasses as well as crops. Fields were not "clean farmed," for land was plentiful and markets limited. The result was wonderful habitat for the bobwhite, and it responded accordingly; there was no need even to talk about such things as predator control or re-stocking.

The bobwhite extended its range even into the prairie states, where formerly the vast expanses of grass severely limited its usefulness for quail. The cultivation of new crops and the planting of osage orange fence rows greatly improved the cover for these birds. In the Southwest the extension of range and spread within range was an accompaniment of over-grazing, and the resulting invasion of weeds and brush on grasslands. Here the birds were originally limited to wooded river bottoms, and brushy canyons and hillsides.

As long as their habitat was good the birds thrived throughout their newly extended range; as the decades passed, however, farming methods changed, and many of these changes were detrimental to the bobwhite. The era of intensive cultivation and "clean farming" reduced the weedy cover that gave quail both food and shelter; increases in domestic livestock, and particularly the growth of dairying, were specially effective in curtailing the rank herbaceous cover.

The progressive depletion of the habitat had the most drastic effects in the northern periphery of its extended range. Severe winters caused a mass starvation of quail in places where the same weather a few years before would hardly have affected them; without ideal cover they were decimated in these years of bad winter weather, and their range limits pushed back southward toward more optimum environment. If we can assume that intensive agriculture is here to stay, and that is a practical certainty, then it is probable that the extension of quail range attained in the 19th century will never again be reached; it is more likely that further restrictions of the bobwhite's habitable range will occur in years to come, as farming becomes still more intensive.

Bobwhites were stocked in areas even beyond the naturally extended range; these were mostly wild-trapped birds, and in some in-stances the plantings were successful. In Montana, for example, the bobwhite was stocked for a number of years early in this century; shortly after World War I it was fairly common there in some localities. Then came severe winters, and the birds disappeared completely. Other efforts to re-establish it in areas of its former extended range from which it had disappeared have been made generally through the northern states, and continue to some extent today; they have been uniformly unsuccessful. I was in charge of such an effort in New York in 1931, when the state attempted to re-establish the bobwhite in the best agricultural valley near Ithaca, New York; but despite every care and precaution taken to afford the birds the best possible chance, they disappeared within a few years.

As the bobwhite declined from its zenith of prosperity in the middle of the 19th century, laws governing its hunting became more and more restrictive; market hunting was outlawed, and sport hunting limited. Ohio prohibited the hunting of bobwhites in 1912, and placed it on the "song bird" list. Though this was a fine gesture, and was a sincere attempt to save it from extirpation in that state, it has been ineffective for the very simple reason that hunting was not the reason for the bobwhite's decline in Ohio. The bird remains a scattered remnant of its once great numbers there despite its total protection from man's hunting. What the bobwhite needed, still needs, and will probably never get, is protection from soil depletion, improper land use, and very intensive farming. The first two of these may come about through soil conservation programs, but the third seems destined to stay with us and severely limit the bobwhite's usable habitat in the northern states.

There is still another reason that the bobwhite is unlikely to "come back" for any length of time in its northern range: the ring-necked pheasant. In its heyday the bobwhite was the only gallinaceous bird that occupied that particular kind of habitat over most of its

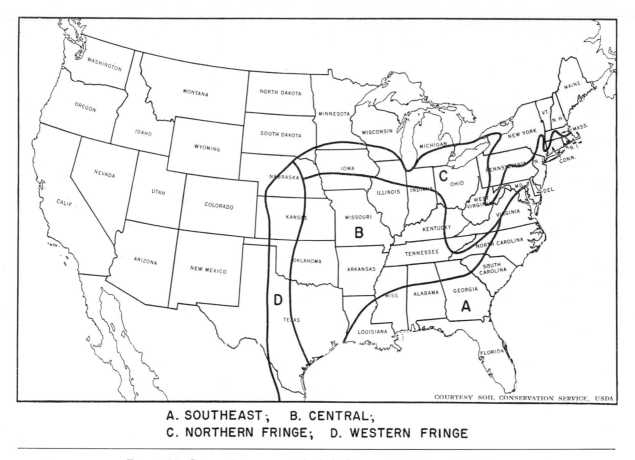

A. SOUTHEAST; B. CENTRAL;
C. NORTHERN FRINGE; D. WESTERN FRINGE

FIGURE 20. *Geographic range of the bobwhite quail showing subdivisions.*

range; but since the successful introduction of the pheasant north of the Mason-Dixon line the bobwhite has a tough competitor. Just how the competition between the two species works is not entirely clear; but it does seem that where the pheasant is established the bobwhite is unable to occupy the same area to the degree that would ordinarily occur. The carrying capacity for this habitat seems to apply to the total of the competing gallinaceous game birds, rather than to each species separately. This is theoretical to be sure, but there does seem to be something to it.

Strenuous efforts have been put forth to increase the numbers of bobwhites throughout its range, and particularly in states having high hunting pressure. Millions of game-farm reared quail have been stocked year after year, mostly in coverts that cannot support them; large numbers of Mexican bobwhites have been trapped and imported for stocking in the northern states. Though almost wholly a failure, to the extent that these southern birds have succeeded they have likely infused a weaker strain into the indigenous northern bobwhites that has done more harm than good. These importations have now been discontinued for the most part, but the rearing and stocking of game-farm birds continues. Every shred of evidence indicates that these stockings are futile as an aid in building up a bigger population of quail in the northern part of their range.

Other developments of the last two decades offer greater hope that man may aid the bobwhite successfully in maintaining its numbers at good levels. Research studies, beginning with the monumental work of Herbert Stoddard in the southeastern states, and buttressed by later work of state game agencies, the Soil Conservation Service, Fish and Wildlife Service, and others, are showing the way to methods of land management that will enable this fine bird to thrive, both on lands managed for game and on farmlands. The effectiveness of these practices will be best in the optimum portions of the bird's range, and progressively less productive toward the periphery of its present area of distribution.

GEOGRAPHIC RANGE

THE precolonial range of the bobwhite extended from southwestern Maine along the coast all the way around to Mexico; it was also found in the fringe forest-grass country from Texas up through the center of the continent to the upper Mississippi River valley. In between it occurred in the open forests, where the bison was also found, and in and around Indian settlements.

Its greatest extension of range in the middle of the 19th century took in all the area from the Atlantic westward to eastern New Mexico and South Dakota, and south of a line running from central Maine across central New York, southern Ontario, and southern Minnesota.

The present geographic distribution of the bobwhite is somewhat more limited. The northeastern limit is eastern Massachusetts; it occurs near the coast from there to New Jersey, up the Hudson Valley a ways, and southward from a line across southern Pennsylvania, below the Great Lakes through southern Wisconsin to southeastern Minnesota. The western limit runs through western Iowa, eastern Nebraska, and south through the panhandle of Texas to Mexico. The constriction of range is even more severe internally than along the outside; in many areas within its general range the quail

have either been exterpated or reduced to remnants (see Figure 20).

All this range is occupied by the type subspecies, or eastern bobwhite, with the exception of two limited areas: the Florida bobwhite replaces the eastern form in Florida except in the northern part of the state; the Texas bobwhite occupies the area from southern Texas into northeastern Mexico.

DESCRIPTION

THE bobwhite is one of the smallest of our upland game birds; a shade larger than the woodcock, but much smaller than any of the grouse. Its length is about 10 inches. It has a large, plump body, and short beak and tail. The short, rounded wings are typical of birds that have rapid but short-distance flight. Its weight is from six to seven ounces—rarely up to nine. The legs are medium long, about in proportion to a chicken's, and adapted to quick spurts of running.

The plumage of the sexes is nearly alike. The general impression is that of a brown bird, somewhat on the reddish side, with some blackish and whitish markings. The back is mostly brown, slightly reddish, and with some mottling of blackish-brown. This same color prevails around the neck and on top of the head, and extends down in front to the upper breast—somewhat farther on the female than on the male. In the male the forehead, chin, throat, and a wide line from the beak running back just above and behind the eye are white with blackish edging. These white parts of the male are buff on the female, and its upper head color is more of a rusty brown. The flight feathers are a plain, grayish color, while the scapulars and wing-coverts are medium brown in the middle and lighter brown around the edges of each feather. The under parts are a grayish white, with many of the feathers having black tips, which make a pattern of cross bars. The flanks and sides have reddish brown stripes

PLATE 55. *The bobwhite quail.*

laterally, which are bordered in black. The tail feathers are bluish gray with fine darker markings. The under-tail coverts are brown, streaked with darker and lighter markings. The beak is black or dark brown; the eye is brown; and the feet are bluish to brownish-gray.

The natal down of the newly-hatched chicks is chestnut brown above, grayish-buff below, with the sides of the head buffy, and a black streak through the eye. The juvenile plumage begins to develop in two weeks, the upper parts being mostly reddish-brown and the under parts grayish-brown. At four weeks the body feathers are well converted to juvenile plumage, but the top of the head holds some of the natal down for two or three weeks more. By the eighth week some of the adult feathers begin to appear on the breast, but the sexes cannot be distinguished until the adult feathers of the throat and head appear. By 15 weeks the plumage is almost perfectly adult.

The eggs are pure white, ovate in shape, with a somewhat pointed small end and blunt large end; the length is 1.1 to 1.2 inches, diameter .9 to .95 inches, weight from 8 to 10 grams.

IMPORTANCE AS A GAME BIRD

To many hunters the bobwhite is our most important game bird; there is good reason to concede this claim, but before doing so we had better consider what we mean by "most important." If numbers harvested is a measure of importance—and it is certainly one of the criteria—then the bobwhite is close to the top; probably more bobwhites are bagged in most years than any other kind of game bird; only the ring-necked pheasant in its years of greatest abundance provides a bigger yield. Judged by the quality of the shooting, the bobwhite may have to defer to the ruffed grouse, turkey, or woodcock for the "king" title, though ardent quail hunters swear that the bobwhite offers the finest kind of hunting. The amount of hunting furnished—that is the total hunting hours—is surely an important criterion too; and again the bobwhite may have to take second place behind the ringneck.

Probably these are the three best gauges of importance, though there are others too—such as the amount of food furnished by the game harvest, the quality of that food, the size of the area over which the species is hunted, the money spent for the sport, and so on. It is easy to see that the bobwhite's only rival for the "best" title is the ringneck, if we exclude the waterfowl from comparison (though taken as individual species they too would be also-rans). I rate the bobwhite as our most important game bird, even conceding that in some ways the pheasant is a close second. If we use as a basis of judgment a combination of the quality of shooting, the numbers bagged, and the amount of sport furnished, it seems to me the bobwhite gets the nod.

Its shooting qualities are excellent; the ringneck is hardly in the same league with the bobwhite in this respect. The bobwhite lies well to pointing dogs; it can be hunted by many methods, including pursuit on horseback, and presents a fast, elusive target.

The total legal bag of bobwhites is somewhere between 10 and 15 million birds a year—probably averaging about 11 million. Most of the harvest comes from 17 states, that each shoot over 100,000 a year—the area from Virginia west to Iowa and south to Texas. They are pursued in longer hunting seasons in most states than prevail for other species; the span of the quail season over all the states is longer than for most other game birds, and notably longer than the composite pheasant season. It is the major upland game bird in most of its range, and it provides sport for the majority of hunters in that area.

The fact that much of the bobwhite quail hunting is done on large estates, many of which are held mainly as hunting preserves, is evidence of the high economic value of quail hunting. No other game bird shooting uses the number of fine hunting dogs that bobwhite hunting does. Only waterfowl shooting and deer hunting may have a higher business cost than quail hunting.

The bobwhite is a legal game bird in 30 states, from Masssachusetts to Minnesota, to Texas and Florida; only Ohio among the states with a reasonably good quail population does not permit hunting it. In the northern fringe of this range it is rarely plentiful enough to furnish really good hunting. Connecticut and Rhode Island in the northeastern corner, and Minnesota and Wisconsin in the northwestern extreme of its range, each harvest fewer than 5,000 birds a year. In contrast, hunters in several states in its optimum range kill over a million birds a year each, notably the south-central area of Alabama and Mississippi and the central area of Illinois, Indiana, and Kentucky.

The bobwhite is the perfect game bird as far as the farmer is concerned. It has no bad habits; it damages no crops; it doesn't attract hordes of city hunters in unwelcome concentrations. Every one likes the bobwhite, and most folks agree that it is a fine game bird.

HABITS OF THE BOBWHITE

COURTSHIP

THE bobwhite is a gregarious bird during most of the year. When spring arrives with its lengthening days and rejuvenation of all living things, each bobwhite loses interest in the congregation of its fellows; by ones or twos they leave the covey with which they have spent the winter, and wander off.

In the South this breakup of the covey begins in February, but farther north it is somewhat later. Cock birds start calling "bobwhite." Signs of impending change come when the cocks begin to get pugnacious toward one another. When one male bird meets another feeding, he will puff up his feathers and make a "pass" at his companion by running toward him with head lowered. Nothing serious happens from this scuffling, for soon they have gone their separate ways to take up their spring breeding territories. During cold spring nights pairs often recongregate in fours or sixes for the warmth of group roosting.

As they settle into their spring coverts, the males call the familiar "bobwhite, bob-bob-white" notes from some vantage point atop a fence post or similar place. At this season the cock quail are relatively unafraid of man, and seem almost to choose close association with him. Their repeated clear whistles make them evident to farmers, who are then beginning their spring work in the fields.

If two cocks attempt to take up their singing posts too close together they will clash. This time the fighting is serious, but rarely results in injury to either of the contestants. These fights happen most commonly when a hen is nearby, ready to encourage the advances of the winner. After the beaten bird retreats, the victor has the field to himself. Seemingly the female always chooses the winner.

The courtship display of the male is much like that of the wild turkey or grouse, but on a smaller scale. The advancing bird puffs his feathers, lowers his wing tips so that they drag the ground while the wing elbow is held high, has his tail spread wide, and head held sidewise. He walks or rushes toward his mate in quick thrusts. At first she keeps her distance, urging him on, until finally it seems to become a game of "try and catch me." He always does, and she submits to copulation with a low note that might be interpreted as a "sigh" of relief.

Once mated the birds remain so; there is considerable evidence that if both live through the next year they remain a mated pair. An already mated pair usually drops out of the winter covey ahead of the others in the spring; for them the courtship and selection of a mate is not necessary. Even though paired from the previous year the male always appears to be gallant to his mate, and she in turn is gentle and ladylike. Bobwhites are not known to be polygamous in the wild—a distinction they have to themselves among eastern gallinaceous birds.

NESTING

Two weeks to a month or more after the beginning of courtship the mated pairs make their nests. During this time the two birds are always together, joining in their feeding forays, following one another in all their activities, the hen usually in the lead.

In their southern range nesting begins in April, usually in the latter half; farther north it is somewhat later, starting in May. Nests that are destroyed are sometimes followed by second or even third or fourth nests; this may carry the nesting period for these birds far into the summer, or even fall—October. A few November nests have been reported (C. O. Handley, letter).

The nest is made in a shallow depression in the ground, and is lined with grass or other convenient vegetation. If not in an open field it is almost always close to one. Egg-laying usually consumes two or three weeks; the number of eggs varies from 7 or 8 up to 30 or more. Large clutches—those over about 18 eggs—are often laid by two or more birds; the average clutch size is about 14.

The cock stays in close touch with the hen during egg-laying and incubation; throughout this time he sings his "bobwhite" calls. The hen leaves the nest every day, usually once; her respite for feeding and exercise is usually from late morning to late afternoon though this varies with the weather. The eggs hatch about 23 days after the start of incubation.

The nesting period is one of great danger from natural enemies. Many nests are found by marauding egg eaters, some of which are hunting with unusual vigor because they have their own young to feed. If an attack occurs early in the setting period the bird is apt to desert, even if the eggs are not destroyed. As incubation proceeds, the setting bird is more and more likely to defend the nest, and to sit tight in the face of danger; it is then that many of the breeding birds are killed, as well as their eggs destroyed. The birds seem well aware of these dangers, and behave accordingly. The cock keeps a good distance away from the nest; there is no unnecessary walking close to the nest, or even any appreciable amount of motion by the setting bird that might give off scent; a bird dog can walk right by a nesting quail and not pick up the scent. The birds seem to have an uncanny ability to distinguish an enemy from a mere intruder; they pay little attention to a grazing cow, but react instantly to the presence of a hawk or fox. If in spite of all precautions the setting bird is forced off her nest, a great effort is made to draw away the intruder; the bird feigns injury by fluttering its wings and dragging them, all the while uttering a squealing note, " t-s-i-e-u, t-s-i-e-u." By good luck, perseverance, and great skill, most nesting quail ultimately bring off a brood. Then a whole new kind of existence begins for the parents, as well as for a covey of new quail that are hardly bigger than bumblebees.

THE BROOD PERIOD

QUAIL that successfully incubate their clutch of eggs hatch most of them; in the average full clutch there is likely to be one infertile egg, and one more that dies during embryonic development; the rest, some 85%–90%, hatch. If the nest is a second or third attempt after the loss of previous settings, the number of infertile eggs may be greater.

In the southern states hatching time is in

early May; a few nests are completed in April, and a good many hatch in late May and early June; many, mostly renests, come off still later. In the northern part of the quail range nests hatch about three weeks later, mostly in late May and early June.

The first few days of life are a time of great hazard for bobwhites; much of this danger is from bad weather. The dozen—more or less—active little chicks are a big chore for the parents to handle. They sometimes fall into holes in the uneven ground while foraging for food; they are left behind and perish. Quick rainstorms, sometimes very cold, may catch them suddenly before they all get in under their mother's sheltering body; even some of those that do reach mama in time may be chilled,

for the brooding of such a large and active group of youngsters is likely to be imperfect. Protracted drizzles are even worse, for then the chicks must feed; they get wet and chilled, and may fall behind the rest and die.

The loss of a few chicks in this manner is the normal thing; but if adverse weather continues for several days without letup it may be disastrous. The majority of the brood may succumb before they have developed enough to withstand the rigors of cold, wet weather. The years when this happens over large areas will have poor quail hunting, for the young birds compose most of the normal hunting harvest.

Weather is not the only cause of death for quail chicks, even though it is the most important. Some are captured by predators, mostly during the late summer; blue darter hawks, the Cooper's and sharpshin, are the bobwhite's most deadly enemies at this season. Some may die of disease.

Quail chicks develop their flight feathers rapidly, so that they start to fly when between two and three weeks old. Most of their first feather coat is developed in six or seven weeks; by then they can roost safely without brooding, in a tight little circle, all heads pointing outward, so typical of the bobwhite. By their 15th week the youngsters closely resemble their parents.

COURTESY SOIL CONSERVATION SERVICE, USDA

PLATE 56. *Winter snows in the northern range force the birds to expose themselves in search of food.*

COURTESY PENNA. GAME COMMISSION

PLATE 57. *Nesting time is one of great hazards. Predators and farm machinery are two common causes of nest destruction.*

Throughout the juvenile period parental care is most attentive. Any of the duties may be performed by either father or mother. Discipline of the chicks is strict; a continual "conversation" of low clucks and cheeps goes on, but when a parent gives the danger call every youngster freezes in its tracks. If the threat materializes in an attack, the old birds try to draw the intruder away from the young ones by pretending injury. After the danger is past, the gathering call is sounded and the family quickly reassembles and goes about its usual activity.

As the youngsters mature, their gregarious nature becomes more and more evident; individuals that have wandered away from their own brood may meet and join another covey; two coveys that meet may travel together for a time. There is a progressively greater interchange of individuals and groups from one covey to another, so that eventually the coveys are seldom a family group, but simply a group of quail.

FALL AND WINTER MONTHS

AUTUMN brings the ripening of many seeds and fruits liked by bobwhites, and they turn to them with a will. Seeking these newly available foods takes them into new coverts with brushy land and woods edges that to a considerable extent, augment summer grass fields. They may roost as well as feed in shrubby cover, especially if their usual grass and weed fields have been thinned by drouth. The birds still use farm fields for most of their activity in autumn—feeding, dust bathing, and roosting—especially fields having good cover. As winter approaches and frosts cut down the herbaceous cover they resort more to woody cover.

The interchange of birds among coveys continues all through the fall and winter, and is accelerated by the loss of birds during the hunting season; as a covey is shot down to low numbers, it may join another similarly reduced group. This regrouping is the reason the size of a covey is not a good measure of the number of birds taken by hunters; by this shuffling process the number of coveys declines, but the size stays moderately large.

Life is easy for the bobwhite through the late summer and fall months. Food is plentiful both in variety and abundance; weather is seldom troublesome, and even attacks by predators are relatively few and cover adequate for easy escape. The 20% or so of birds bagged by gunners is a considerable reduction in quail numbers, but the remaining birds still live well. But there comes a time in late fall or early winter when life changes—often quite abruptly; in snow country the advent of the first big snowstorm marks the point. If the change is not accentuated by a snowstorm, a combination of other events serves the same end. The once lush food supply is consumed by the competing songbirds, rodents, and other creatures as well as by the quail. Cold weather drives the rodents underground, which forces the carnivores to hunt harder for other foods. Farmers have harvested their crops, and their livestock are cleaning up the remnants of palatable herbs.

Add it all up, and it often means a rather grim existence. The birds are pressed to get enough food, even of the poorer kinds, harried by enemies, driven to find protective shelter by harsh weather and the loss of what had just recently been adequate cover; it is little wonder that winter is severe on quail. The habitat reaches its yearly low point—which is *the carrying capacity* for the area. If there are more quail and quail competitors than space, food, and shelter afford, then the numbers must decline. Decline they do in most areas, and usually at a steady pace as winter progresses. Late winter is often the crisis period; food supplies are then at their lowest level, predators are most hard pressed to obtain their own food, and protective cover is the poorest of any time of the year. By spring less than half the fall quail numbers will ordinarily remain; if a catastrophe of very stormy weather has hit, the survival may be much lower than half the fall population.

It makes little difference what actually kills

each quail that dies; most will be food for man or some animal, as nature intended. Some will succumb to disease, freezing, or starvation, and a good many will die from accidents. The determinant of how many die is the amount of food available to sustain them all winter, combined with the quality of shelter present where needed; lacking these essentials they are doomed, and it is just a question of whether man, beast, or parasite gets them before they starve or freeze to death. Surely death by bullet, talons, or fangs is more merciful than slow starvation and freezing; there is no escape from this judgment; only the size of the excess population and the time and cause of death vary. The great majority of the quail that are grown each year must die before spring comes; that is the way with wild creatures. To be most useful to man, the greatest possible share of these inevitable losses should be the harvest of man's hunting.

With the advent of spring and the impending breeding season, the year's balance sheet is drawn. If there are as many quail as the year before, they have broken even; if there are more, it may reflect an increased carrying capacity—possibly the result of a better food-producing season, or changes in farming practices. All too frequently the quail balance sheet has been in the "red" in previous decades, with fewer quail remaining each spring compared to the previous year. There is one thing of which we can be sure: any decreases in quail numbers from year to year are no fault of the quail; given good environment they will populate it to full capacity. We must look to that environment—the climate, soils, waters, plants, and animals that the bobwhite lives in, on, and with—for our explanation of its numbers. The bobwhite's habits are by long evolution well adapted to take full advantage of the opportunities offered.

THE IMPORTANCE OF EDGES

THE bobwhite is the classic example of a species whose activity is closely associated with edges—those lines, bands, or spots where two or more distinctive types of cover come together. Since different kinds of cover provide for different functions, it is evident that the portion of each that is along the boundaries will be most useful, since two or more functions can be satisfied with very little travel. Thus the bobwhite can feed in the edge of a corn field and escape hawk attack by flying quickly into the adjacent honeysuckle thicket, an escape that might not be possible if the bird was in the middle of a cornfield. This relationship of convenience is exceedingly important, for the quail must feed, rest, roost, dust-bathe, nest, court, escape enemies, and avoid heat, cold, and wind to a considerable extent concurrently. Obviously many of the cover requirements for performing these acts must be in close proximity to one another if the bobwhite is to use them; when they are, we say there is lots of "edge" cover, or that the needed cover types are well "interspersed."

The management of habitat for the bobwhite takes into account the *kinds* of cover needed, the *amount* of each needed, and also the *arrangement* of these needs. The arrangement of the cover types makes the habitat pattern, and is related to the principle of edges, namely: the greater the edge between essential types of cover in a unit of range the more game it can support—within limits, of course.

THE INFLUENCE OF FARMING CHANGES ON THE BOBWHITE

THE bobwhite is not wholly dependent on farming for his habitat, since the species had thrived in parts of the eastern and central United States for thousands of years before the white man and his farming system arrived. It is also true that the white man's opening up of the forests and prairies for farming greatly extended and improved the bobwhite range for more than a century. The more recent trends toward the mechanization and "clean farming" of the land have turned the tide in the other direction, ever more unfavorable to the quail;

the great increase in cattle, hogs, and sheep in much of the bobwhite's range has likewise had a detrimental effect on the bird's welfare.

The original bobwhite habitat is gone—replaced by farms, and in some places by abandoned farms. The cover on this abandoned land bears little resemblance to the original habitat, and is more and more unlike the farmed land. Unless it is acquired and deliberately managed for quail and other game it is likely to become poor in quail productivity. Thus the species is now very largely a by-product of farming and woodland management. Many of the methods of farming and lumbering affect the quail, some being beneficial and others injurious. The growing of tilled crops is the greatest benefit; but the detailed methods of handling the crop, and the land it's grown on, often materially cut down those benefits. Very clean cultivation (no aftermath of weeds), the use of corn for silage rather than grain, or the clipping of cereal grain stubble, are examples of methods that remove practically all the values of crop fields to quail in fall and winter when they need them most. On the other hand, methods of tillage that allow aftermath cover, and ways of harvesting that leave much waste grain are very advantageous—provided these fields are not "hogged off" by livestock in the fall.

Practically every adjustment in farming practice will influence the bobwhite to some degree. This process of change has been going on for decades and will continue; new crop plants, new insecticides and herbicides, tillage methods, types of machinery, crop rotations— these and other types of change will be made, and each one will add to or detract from the carrying capacity of the land for quail. The vital question is: will the net effect of these changes make possible more or fewer of this favorite game bird?

Probably the most promising adjustments in our farming system that augur well for the future prosperity of the bobwhite are changes associated with the movement to "conservation farming." The adoption of such land-use prac-

tices as contour tillage, strip cropping, terracing, living hedge fences, tree and shrub planting on areas not physically suited for tillage or grazing—these are a few of the many adjustments that benefit quail.

Too much stress cannot be placed on the vital importance of farming changes to a game bird like the bobwhite, that spends so much of its time in crop and grass fields. Many adverse effects are inevitable in a changing agricultural world, and we may as well accept them and make the best of them. As long as our people want more beefsteak, for example, we must increase the beef animals, and raise our pasture and range capacity to take care of them; such changes as this will almost inevitably harm bobwhite habitat. On the other side of the story it is equally true that many changes are needed in our agricultural system that will benefit quail; and conservationists may well place their energies behind these helpful changes, rather than bewail the losses from those things that cannot be helped.

ADAPTABILITY TO ARTIFICIAL PROPAGATION

AMONG our native game birds, the bobwhite quail is the most easily raised in captivity; it is much more suited to game-farm production than any of the grouse, or the turkey; other upland species like doves, pigeons, and woodcock are not at all adaptable to game farming. The mallard duck alone among its kind is easily bred in captivity, but usually does not retain its wild game qualities in the process.

Of the exotic species, the ringneck pheasant is more easily raised on game farms than the bobwhite, whereas the Hungarian and chukar partridges are about as well suited to life in captivity as the bobwhite.

Tens of thousands of quail are raised and stocked each year, mostly in the Eastern states from Long Island southward. These birds retain their wild characteristics very well, but there is much doubt as to how adequate their stamina for survival is after they are placed on their own resources. Probably there is much variation in this ability to survive, depending on the origin of the stock and on the game-farm methods. Most studies of the results of restocking have shown very low survival, and generally poor success in getting the game-farm birds established. How much this is due to the quality of the bird and how much to the deficiencies of the habitat is a subject of much debate; the more important fact is that the species can populate its environment to capacity without restocking, and hence the introduction of game-farm birds into most habitats is a useless and wasteful business. Stocking before the gun on shooting preserves is another matter, for here the participants can afford the high costs of the ventures, whereas these costs are out of the question for public shooting.

THE SHELTER REQUIREMENTS OF THE BOBWHITE

TYPES OF RANGE

The bobwhite's range can conveniently be divided into four parts. Two of these, the Northern cold zone and the Western dry zone, are the marginal periphery, where quail are relatively scarce in most years and their populations rather insecure; the Southeastern and Central zones are the real quail country. These four portions of the quail range are shown in Figure 20; the dividing lines are only approximations.

The Southeastern zone includes the famed plantation country; it extends from the eastern shore of the Delmarva peninsula through the coastal plain and piedmont plateau of the south Atlantic states, across the black belt and the Gulf coast through Louisiana. It is characterized by a mild, humid climate, and a good mixture of farmed land and forest; the forested land includes extensive stands of pine woods of loblolly, longleaf, and associated species. The major farm crops are cotton, peanuts, sugar cane, and citrus fruits. Domestic livestock are relatively few in the best quail sections.

The Central zone is the heart of the quail range, much of the central and lower Mississippi Valley and the lower portions of the major tributary valleys are included, along with eastern Texas. The climate is moderate and fairly humid, the soils generally fertile, and the farming intensified and mechanized. Woodland is relatively scarce in portions of this zone. The major crops are corn, cotton, tobacco and hogs.

Quail populations in these two zones nowadays average a bird for every 8 to 15 acres of land in the early fall of the year; in the best portions of range, where the majority of the quail are to be found, the population density is two to three times these figures, or a quail to every five acres or better.

The northern cold zone is delimited by an inhospitable climate. Cold, snowy winters prevent the bobwhite from maintaining good numbers; occasionally very severe winters will extirpate the birds from considerable areas of this zone; it frequently takes decades for these sections to be repopulated. This zone is not homogeneous agriculturally, since climate is the limiting factor. The types of farming range from the mixtures of vegetable fields and scrub oak-pine thickets of Long Island and New Jersey, through the dairy farms of southern Pennsylvania, northern Maryland, and Ohio, which have a good mixture of corn, grass, and wooded areas, to the Midwestern corn belt and finally including the southern fringe of the Wisconsin dairyland. The mechanization of farming and increases in domestic livestock have made a normally precarious existence still more difficult for quail through most of this northern territory.

The key characteristic of the Western fringe area is the dry climate. The farther west bobwhite is found, the more uncertain is its tenure; and finally the climate and the habitat that goes with it become intolerable. There is little woodland cover in this zone; the stream courses are about the only areas that can support trees. Farming is mostly dry-land grain or livestock raising.

Quail coveys in these two periphery zones are apt to be widely scattered, and confined to the best habitat. Populations will rarely reach a bird to 15 acres, counting all the land; the more normal density would be 50 acres per bird—where they are actually found. Quail populations in the western fringe zone occasionally irrupt to high numbers, but then decline very quickly.

Of the 850 million acres in the entire quail range nearly half is in the central zone; about 200 million acres are in the southeast, 140 million in the northern, and about 100 million in the western.

COVER TYPES NEEDED

Four kinds of cover are important to bobwhite quail. Most superior quail habitat is a judicious mixture of these four types, and they will be of high quality. This does not mean that quail cannot exist without all four cover types within each covey range; some coveys get along with three, or two, or occasionally even a single one of these types of cover; but the number of birds per square mile is proportionate to the adequacy of these four cover elements. Table 16 summarizes quail cover types.

TABLE 16

COVER TYPES USED BY BOBWHITE QUAIL

COVER TYPE (AND VARIETY)	SEASON OF USE	FUNCTIONS SERVED
GRASSLAND Hay: alfalfa; clover; lespedeza; special grasses; grass and legume. Pasture: grass-legume; mixed grasses. Roadsides and other odd areas. Range: tall grass prairie; short grass prairie.	Spring and summer mainly.	Nesting; roosting in good. weather; some feeding
CROP FIELDS, ETC. Corn and small grains. Cotton, tobacco, vegetables, etc. Weed fields and fallow. Stabilized dunes.	Summer and fall mostly; some in spring and winter.	Feeding; also for loafing, dusting; some for roosting.
BRUSHY AREAS, ETC. Vine tangles. Thickets of shrubs, briars, or rank, tall herbs. Hedges. Scattered shrubs, as sagebrush and mesquite.	Fall and winter; some in spring, less in summer.	Escape cover, fall and winter feeding; roosting; loafing.
WOODLAND Northern oaks or oaks and conifers (oaks, tulip, beech, white pine). Southern pines (longleaf, slash, loblolly). Oaks, oak-hickory, post oak. Southern oak-pines. Southwestern bottomland hardwoods (cottonwoods, willows, oaks).	Fall and winter; some in spring.	Roosting; escape cover; winter and fall feeding.

The primary cover types used by quail are: grassland; crop fields and other areas of herbaceous plants besides grasses; brushy areas and other cover of low woody plants or tall perennial herbs; and woodland. There are varieties of each of these types, depending on the species of plants involved, and sometimes their age; the quality of any of them may also vary widely. The value of any particular type of cover depends on the adaptability of its plants to the climate and the soil, and to the use or abuse given it by fire, livestock, man, or weather. The esteem that quail may place on any specific piece of cover may also depend on its size, and on the kind, quality, and size of other cover types that adjoin it; this involves the principle of interspersion that we shall discuss shortly.

Grassland. The fringes of the original prairies and savannahs, the natural coastal grass areas of the Southeast, and open forests were the bobwhite's ancestral home. They inhabited the great forested areas sparsely except at the edges; not until the white man extended the areas of grass and croplands was the quail able to broaden its habitable range. It seems clear

COURTESY SOIL CONSERVATION SERVICE, USDA

PLATE 58. *Bare fences and large clean-tilled fields have little cover for quail.*

PLATE 59. *Living fences and strip-cropped fields make a good cover pattern for the bobwhite, as these hunters found.*

COURTESY SOIL CONSERVATION SERVICE, USDA

that grass is as essential to this species as one sort of cover can be; yet crop fields serve its functions to a considerable degree. One or both of the two open land types is important, though not absolutely necessary, in each covey's area.

Grass is the best nesting cover; two-thirds to three-quarters of all quail nests are in grass cover of one sort or another. Hay and fallow fields are the commonest nesting location in the Eastern and Central zones, with broom sedge fields and grassy roadsides often used. Frequently the nest is in the edge of a hedge row at the side of a grass field. In the Western range bluestem prairie and other similar grasslands serve the purpose.

Summer insect food is plentiful in good grass cover, and so the young quail spend much time there. The quality of grass cover is as important as its amount; mixed grass and clover fields seem to be preferred to alfalfa—perhaps because the mixed stand is less dense and more livable. Heavily grazed pasture or rangeland has little utility for quail; newly mowed hayfields also lose their usefulness for a time, and frequently result in nest losses from the machinery. The attraction of roadsides and other marginal grass cover stems partly from its close association with hedgerows or other good protective cover. The fact that this sort of grass cover is grazed less and mowed less than regular pasture and hay fields makes it safer for nesting; nesting success in roadside grass cover is twice as high as in hay or pasture fields. The willingness of quail to utilize these narrow-edge grass strips is a key to the possible habitat improvement practices that we shall later discuss in detail.

Crop Fields and Similar Cover. The white man's tilled fields are a new addition to the original quail habitat, except for very limited maize culture by some of the Indian tribes; the abundance of good food for the bobwhite that soil tillage and grain growing supply is the main reason for the great increase in the range and numbers of this bird during the

18th and 19th centuries. It is ironic that changes in the soil culture practices in recent decades have contributed greatly to the bobwhite's decline. It seems to be a fact that the best food area for quail is a carelessly or crudely cultured grain field; it produces not only an abundance of waste grain, but an equally important abundance of weed seeds nutritious to quail; the lush weedy aftermath also makes good cover. In contrast, the modern very clean tilled cornfield with little weed growth—and often with stalks as well as grain removed from the field in autumn—offers little food or protection for the bobwhite.

To the extent that the quail's prosperity is tied to an inefficient farming system, its numbers are certain to decline in good farming areas. Our farming methods must be efficient in our highly competitive economic world; yet fortunately some of the extremes of "clean" farming now practiced are not only not necessary, but are in some ways detrimental to the best interests of the farmer and his land. The soil needs a protective plant blanket as much of the year as possible, and especially in winter; only by the leaving of much of the plant cover on the ground after harvest can the soil be kept from eroding, and helped to maintain good tilth.

Cornfields that do have an aftermath of ragweed, foxtail, smartweed, wild millet, and similar annual weeds, and that have the cornstalks, shocks, or rough stubble in the field over the winter, are ideal feeding grounds for quail; corn used for ensilage, fall-plowed corn, or cornfields thoroughly clean-tilled and harvested, are of relatively little use to the birds.

Wheat, rye, barley, oats, and other small grain stubble make good quail-feeding fields in fall and winter, provided they are not fall-plowed or mowed. The winter grains have an especially good aftermath growth of ragweed the summer after harvest.

Cotton fields figure prominently in the Southeastern and Southern quail habitat, though they have little to offer other than the plant canopy. Through most of the quail range other tilled crops are grown in some quantity: vegetables in New Jersey, Florida, Texas, and elsewhere; tobacco from Lancaster County, Pennsylvania, to Kentucky and the Carolinas are examples. Some of these crops grow quail food in the form of greens and seeds, but all except tobacco have the annual weeds that escape cultivation and that are so important to the bobwhite. The extent that such fields are used by quail depends on the degree of clean cultivation, and on what is done with the field after the crop is harvested; in this respect they are much like cornfields.

There are other kinds of field cover that serve the bobwhite much as crop fields do. Fallow—a cropfield lying idle for a year or two—is closely associated with tillage, since it results from crop cultivation; often these fields are deliberately let lie "to rest" as a part of the farming system. An example is the tobacco-ragweed "rotation" followed in southern Maryland; the natural fallow cover of ragweed and associated annual plants is believed to be beneficial to the next crop of tobacco.

If a fallow field is not returned to tillage it stays in weeds for several years; the annual weeds that come first are replaced by perennial weeds; the plant composition is then gradually changed by the addition of grasses, and then pioneering species of woody plants according to the natural plant succession. Weedy fields are good feeding places for quail, as long as the annual herbs are plentiful. When perennial plants displace the short-lived ones there is less likely to be a good supply of quail food, though this condition varies according to the species present. In many Eastern fields the plant succession goes from weeds to broom sedge grass, which develops a dense cover that dominates the ground for a long time. It has nesting and roosting value for quail, but little food.

In some of the semiarid Western quail range, as in western Oklahoma, a type of cover called "stabilized dunes" occurs between the river bottoms and the high dry prairie of sagebrush land; it is sandy soil, with a growth of mixed herbs that is fairly good feeding cover for quail.

Soil fertility affects the quail-cover value of crop fields more than in any other of the cover-type groups; fertile soils grow lush cover, heavy seed or fruit yields, and products of the greatest nutritional value. Fertility is most needed on croplands where the plant cover must be regenerated from bare ground each year, or two or three. Quail thrive on high-quality soils if the vegetation is not too dense, or the tillage too clean; more commonly they prosper on areas having moderately fertile soils—not the best and yet not poor. Here the growth of crops is good but not too heavy, and tillage is usually not excessively clean. In contrast, worn-out, eroded soils give sparse cover, low yields, and poor quality food; this is a basic reason that soil conservation programs are fundamental to successful farm game habitat improvement.

Brushy Areas. The word "brushy" used to describe this very important cover type is admittedly an unsatisfactory term, used for want of a better one; the objection is that "brushy" often connotes an undesired situation with farmers, as a pasture overgrown with unwanted woody plants. Other terms, like "thicket," "overgrown land," "bushy," "shrubby," are all equally inadequate for one reason or another. Hence we shall use "brushy areas," and define it as land dominated by small-diameter woody plants or very coarse herbs that tend to make a dense overhead canopy by basal branching or entwined branches. Its growth is higher than most herbaceous cover, yet not like a woodland with an overstory and ground cover. Some brushy areas have little ground cover other than the surface litter.

Individual covert units of brushy areas may be termed tangles, thickets, briar patches, and a variety of other names. Their special use for the bobwhite is in helping it escape from pursuing enemies, and as protection from stormy weather. A number of kinds of brushy areas

PLATE 60. *Two-row hedge composed of multiflora rose on the pasture side and bicolor lespedeza on the crop field side. This arrangement makes a good travel lane that has both food and shelter.*

COURTESY SOIL CONSERVATION SERVICE, USDA

are used by quail, some of them very specific in their plant composition. Vine tangles of Hall's honeysuckle are particularly valuable in the Eastern range; greenbrier and wild grape tangles—when not hung in trees—are excellent cover too, but lack the evergreen leaves of the honeysuckle in winter. All have fruits eaten by quail, but are irregular in fruiting. All are most important as escape cover.

Greenbrier vine tangles have the extra protective asset of thorns that deter pursuing predators; some other kinds of brushy cover are especially valuable because of thorny plants. Outstanding is the new type of living-fence hedge of multiflora rose. Once I observed a covey of quail in a multiflora contour hedge near Lancaster, Pennsylvania. The birds recognized the protective value of that thorny cover so well that they simply refused to flush from it, and chose instead to run along the hedge. The same rose, or other shrubs, growing in clumps on odd areas about the farm, serve much the same purpose—that of a safe hideout when attacked, or in bad weather. Thickets of briars, thorn apples, and other thorny plants are good, though most are not as effective as the multiflora rose.

Thick-growing stands of any low woody plants or rank tall herbs provide fall and winter cover for feeding, roosting, and loafing. Some provide superior food supplies, as does bicolor lespedeza; many add to the provender with seeds, greens, fruits, or nuts. Briar patches of various species of *Rubus*—especially blackberries and raspberries—are useful brushy cover, particularly in summer when their fruit is ripe. Patches of rank-growing herbs like pokeberry are also valuable.

Of the greatest importance to quail habitat generally is brushy cover that extends into and across fields; it brings protective cover close to the food supplies. Those that occur naturally are overgrown field boundaries or fence rows, or sharp breaks in the topography like long, narrow outcroppings that make a short steep rise between two field levels; osage orange living fences, once extensively used in the Midwest, are a good type of this brushy field boundary cover. These old osage plantings are being removed in great numbers now because of the room they take up and the care they require; the more acceptable multiflora rose living fences are now serving the same purpose.

Plum thickets are a common sort of brushy

PLATE 61. *Close-up of the dense, thorny branching of multiflora rose that enables it to turn livestock.*

cover in the central quail range, and somewhat less plentiful in the East and the Southeast. Scrub oak thickets are a common brush cover on certain sandy soil areas in the East, often associated with pitch pine and maintained by periodic fires; shinnery is a similar type in the arid Southwest. In the most arid portion of the bobwhite range scattered clumps of sagebrush and cedar serve the same purpose.

Clear-cut woodland becomes brushy cover for a period of several years during its regeneration; where other brushy cover is scarce these woodland cuttings are very valuable to quail, and are the most useful age class of some woodland types. When the trees—coppice from either cut hardwoods or seedlings—grow to a size that shades out the briars and other low cover it becomes woodland again, and of an age class that often has very little utility for the bobwhite.

The amount of brushy cover needed in a quail covey's territory is not large in acreage, but it is important that it be there. It should be of good quality—not grazed, and generally not burned. It is most valuable when located adjacent to grass and crop fields, and in a sheltered situation with regard to slopes; this enhances its use in bad weather. A small amount of this kind of cover is frequently a "key" to a covey territory without which the birds could not inhabit the area through the winter.

Woodland. The bobwhite range is generally well supplied with woodland, except in the Western prairies area and in southern Florida. Woods serve some of the same purposes as brushy cover, though it takes more acreage. Many woodlands do not have the quality of shelter that brush cover has, that enables the birds to escape their enemies easily and avoid discomfort from storms. Where good brushy cover is plentiful, quail can do without woodland; and to some extent the reverse is true; a covey may not include woods in its living area from late spring to autumn, but then it will usually move enough to have wooded habitat available. In areas of the Southwest, where good wooded shelter is not uniformly distributed, these seasonal travels to use woody cover may be ten miles or more.

Escape cover, winter storm shelter, and fall and winter feeding are the functions served by woods. The value of woodland for these purposes varies greatly with the type and condition of the stand; while variety is endless, five types of woods may be recognized as significant to the bobwhite.

In the Eastern and Southeastern range the woodlands most associated with quail are the southern pines. From southern Delaware and Maryland southward through Virginia and the Carolinas loblolly pine woods are the best woodland habitat for quail. In the deep South the woods of longleaf and slash pines are best. In the piedmont zone the shortleaf pine is important, but does not provide the high quality quail habitat that the coastal species do. As shelter for bad weather and avoiding enemy attack, all the pines serve best in young stands; but the highest use of extensive pine woods for quail comes about in a very different manner.

Mature stands of the longleaf pine can be kept open underneath by means of light burning of the ground cover. This prevents the hardwoods from encroaching, and makes the hunting of these forests convenient; it also helps provide food from ground cover plants, like many of the native legumes. Light burning at intervals of one to three years holds back the normal plant succession, and enables these herbs to thrive. Woods under this type of management have little escape shelter, which makes it necessary to have other protective vegetation of plum or honeysuckle thickets or similar types.

The woodlands of the Northern quail range have good shelter, but cannot be handled to provide extensive quail habitat as the Southern pines can. These Northern stands of mixed oaks, tulip poplar, beech, and some pines are used exclusively in the edges, where they lie next to good grass, crop field, or brushy cover.

In the Central range, particularly from Missouri to eastern Texas and eastward to the Appalachians, the mixed oaks, oak-hickory, and post and blackjack oaks (in Texas) woodlands predominate. They serve quail much as the northern woodlands do; the edges are used mostly, and the interiors of extensive stands are of little value; only when they occur in small units—especially long and narrow ones—or are broken up by interior farmed fields, are these woodlands fully utilized by the bobwhite. The southern oak-pine type may combine the qualities of the oak woods with the shelter value of young pines. The species of oaks in the Gulf states varies considerably from the more Northern areas, for there are more live oaks and fewer of the hill country species.

The Southwestern bottomland hardwoods are important as winter quail cover, even though they are often of poor quality compared to some winter shelter types; in many areas they constitute virtually the only tree stands in a predominantly herbaceous range. They occur in ravines and along stream bottoms, are long and narrow, and are of prime importance to the quail habitat for miles around. Unfortunately many of these oak, cottonwood, and willow bottoms are heavily grazed, and as a result most of their value to the quail is lost.

THE INTERSPERSION OF COVER TYPES

THERE are three aspects of quail habitat, all equally important; two of these have been discussed in the previous section—the kinds of cover as to *quality* and *quantity;* the third consideration is the arrangement of the component cover types, or *pattern.*

Let us say that we have 50 acres of good quail habitat. When we say "good" we mean that the crop fields, grassland, brushy areas, and woods are high in the quality of providing living quarters and sustenance according to their best value to quail. When we specify 50 acres we have indicated the *quantity* requirements of a total of the needed cover types. When we discussed each kind of cover the general quantitative need by quail was given: plenty of crop fields and grassland; rather small areas of brush and woods. Suppose that the 50 acres is made up of 25 acres of grass, 18 acres of crops, 5 acres of woods, and 2 acres of brushy cover. But the number of quail that may live here is still not clear until we know how the fields are laid out.

If the grass and cropland are in a single squarish unit each, and the seven acres of woods and brush are placed together in one corner of the grass field away from the cropland, we have very poor interspersion of the different cover types; quail will have rough going on that 50 acres, despite there being adequate amounts of good quality cover needs. On the other hand, if the grass is in three or four scattered units, the crops laid out between the grass fields and arranged in long, narrow contour strip fields, the woods in two or three widely spaced patches, and the brush

in a mile-long network of hedges, then the interspersion of the essential cover types is excellent; this habitat pattern is a productive one, and one or more coveys will thrive. In each of these instances the amounts and character of the cover types was the same—only the arrangement differed; but it made a tremendous difference in quail-carrying capacity.

The bobwhite is notably a lover of *edges*—those margins where two or more cover types come together, where it can move quickly from nest to feeding area, from food supply to escape cover, from loafing spot to storm protection; changing from one activity to another is but a matter of a quick walk or flight of a few seconds. Good quail habitat then is a well-interspersed arrangement of the different important cover types; management, as we shall see, takes great advantage of all opportunities to provide this broken-up cover pattern.

IDEAL LAND-USE PATTERN

THE proportions and arrangement of cover types in an ideal land-use pattern for quail varies with each type of range; for the better portions of the whole range, excluding the northern and western fringes, a summary of

COURTESY SOIL CONSERVATION SERVICE, USDA

PLATE 62. *Good land use patterns favor the bobwhite. Well-distributed contour fields with woodlands, hedgerows and vegetated gullies are shown in this scene.*

these needs is given in Table 17. The same pattern applies in the northern zone, but is less productive on account of the climate.

A different pattern applies in the Southwestern range—again on account of the climate. More extensive grasslands and grazing range with scattered brush will necessarily compose most of the habitat. Quality will be achieved through agronomic measures and grazing management. Suitable woods usually grow in the river bottoms, but are most effective as quail shelter when protected from grazing. Croplands are properly restricted to the best soils and the better watered areas, and are often improved by irrigation. In the drier parts of the Western quail country water is an important factor in good quail habitat, and should be available in each covey range.

BOBWHITE QUAIL FOODS

THE bobwhite is essentially a seed-eating bird. The seeds that compose its food are of several types, most of them found in farm fields.

At each season of the year except winter other food is also important. In spring bobwhites eat greens; in summer the special foods are insects and fruits; in the fall they are grass seeds, fruits, and mast; winter foods are mostly dry seeds, with grain kernels eaten in quantity.

Since the bobwhite is found over a wide range of country, it is not surprising that its foods vary from one place to another; it is consistently true, however, that a large share of its foods almost everywhere are found in farm fields; thus the bobwhite is generally associated with the tillage of the land. Certain woodland types of the Southeast are a partial exception to this generality.

COURTESY SOIL CONSERVATION SERVICE, USDA

PLATE 63. *Thickets of wild plum make good escape cover for quail.*

PLATE 64. *Good cover for the bobwhite can be developed around water areas. This Missouri farm pond has grass and shrubs planted around it and a fence to exclude grazing.*

COURTESY SOIL CONSERVATION SERVICE, USDA

TABLE 17

LAND-USE PATTERN FOR GOOD BOBWHITE QUAIL RANGE

COVER TYPE	PROPORTION OF TOTAL COVER	BEST UNIT SIZE	COMMENT
GRASSLAND	30%–40%	5–20 acres	Good grass-legume mixtures, with Korean lespedeza where adaptable; full use of opportunities for protected grass in sod roadsides, field boundaries, diversion terraces, waterways.
CROP FIELDS	60%–40%	1–5 acres	On best soils, arranged in narrow contour fields; corn and small grains grown as much as possible, and their culture completed early to get weedy aftermath. No burning or aftermath grazing.
BRUSHY COVER	5%–20%	¼–1 acre	Bicolor lespedeza woods borders, multiflora rose living fence hedges wherever suitable; honeysuckle, grape, greenbrier, plum, briar, scrub oak thickets on suitable odd areas; no fire; no grazing.
WOODLAND	5%–40%	5–20 acres	In small units except for old longleaf pine stands handled with prescribed burning; no grazing; abundance of good mast species like oaks, pines, sweet gum, and fruiting trees.

Quail foods may be grouped into eight kinds: grains; mast; fruit; greens; grass seeds; wild seeds; legume seeds; and insects. There are many hundreds of plants and animals that contribute to this food supply, though in any one locality the birds get most of their meals from a rather limited group. Figure 21 shows the general proportions of each kind of food used at each season, with indications of the major geographic variations.

GRAINS IN THE BOBWHITE'S DIET

FROM late summer to late winter the kernels of grains are important quail food over most of the bird's range; in the northern portion, from Pennsylvania to Nebraska, grains make up the majority of its food through the most critical parts of the year.

This dependence on the grainfield is an adaptation to man's changes in the land; before the advent of the white man's agriculture the only crop fields were small patches of maize. The bobwhite found its food in the prairie grass-lands and in openings of the Eastern forests, the latter made largely by fires. The extension of croplands after the clearing of the forests enabled the bobwhite vastly to extend its original range, largely because of the abundant supply of weed seeds and grain.

The most valuable grain food for quail is corn; where corn is grown for grain, as contrasted to silage corn, it may make up as much as 60% of the bobwhite's fall and winter food. More typical, however, is the 17.4% of winter food it made up in Missouri, according to Korschgen (1952). The farther south the bobwhite lives, the less important is the corn; in the Southwestern range it is little grown, but there the somewhat similar sorghum is eaten in quantity. Wheat, rye, and buckwheat are eaten in fall and winter in the Northern range; wheat is important also in the Western and Southwestern quail areas.

Two crop-field legumes may better be included here with the grains than with the hard-seeded legumes, which are mostly wild plants; these two are soy beans and cowpeas. They are used by quail mostly in the Midwest and Southeast, and may make up as much as 15% of fall and early winter food.

In much of the Gulf area from Florida to Louisiana grains are not generally grown, and hence are not important quail foods there. In the rest of the bird's range grains are a basic food in fall and winter, and generally make up 10% to 20% of its food—much more than this in the northern sections.

MAST FOR THE BOBWHITE

Dry tree seeds are important food for quail in fall and early winter throughout their range.

From November through January 10% to 25% of the birds' diet usually will be made up of acorns, pine, sweet gum, and ash seeds, and occasionally other kinds; the acorns are by far the most abundant of this type of food, and are the most used. Less mast is used in intensively farmed habitat, as in Missouri, where acorns made up only 1.4% of winter food (Korschgen, 1952).

Crops of mast are notoriously erratic, hence the amount consumed varies from little in a poor oak-mast year to a third or more of the seasonal diet when the oaks have bountiful crops. There are many kinds of oaks, and they do not all have their crop failures together;

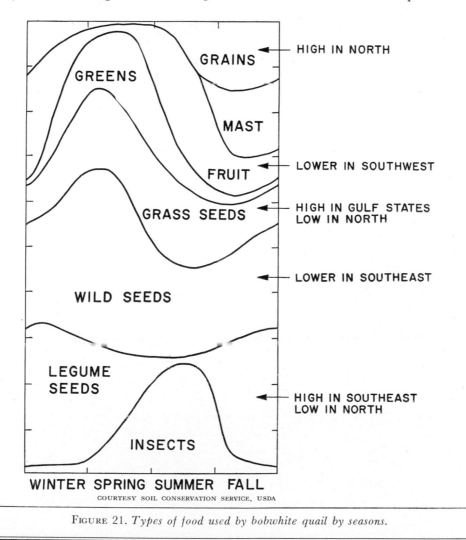

FIGURE 21. *Types of food used by bobwhite quail by seasons.*

some prolific species have a good crop in almost any year, though there are occasional complete blanks.

Bobwhites eat most kinds of acorns, though the smaller sized white oak seeds seem to be preferred when there is a choice.

Pine-seed crops are even more undependable than those of oaks, and there are fewer kinds of them; this partly accounts for the lesser part played by the pines in furnishing quail food compared with the oaks. In years of good pine mast it becomes a very important item in the birds' fall and winter diet.

FRUITS EATEN BY THE BOBWHITE

A VARIETY of wild fruits compose a fairly steady 5% to 10% of quail foods from mid-summer until well into the winter; only in the Southwest is fruit too scarce to provide the bobwhite at these seasons.

Quail are very selective in their choice of fruits; a few kinds seem to be preferred, while many others are usually passed up. Several of the raspberries and blackberries, along with strawberries, are eaten in the summer by both adults and young. During fall and winter the emphasis changes to the autumn-ripened varieties; along the east coast from Massachusetts to Florida the fruits of bayberry and its close relative, the wax myrtle, are used in large amounts in winter. Honeysuckle fruits, particularly those of Hall's honeysuckle, are an important food in the East, from Pennsylvania south to Georgia. In the Southwest hackberry and bumelia fruits are among the kinds most used, while in the Midwest the fruits of plums, grape, rose hips, and sassafras are commonly eaten.

Many other fruits are eaten to a less extent, the amount determined by their local abundance and by the prevalence of other more desired foods. Among them are those of dogwoods, viburnums, gallberry, sumacs, poison ivy, holly, bittersweet, elder, mulberry (in summer), apples, persimmon, pokeberry, and many more.

GREENS IN THEIR DIET

SUCCULENT leaves are eaten by quail in small amounts all year long, probably just as we eat salads; in spring, however, their consumption of greens, particularly clover leaves, increases to a large share of all their food. Whether this is due to the need for "tonic" foods after the long winter, or merely because greens are available in the spring when most other foods are scarce, is hard to say; probably it is a combination of the two.

GRASS SEEDS AS QUAIL FOOD

SEEDS of numerous grasses are eaten by quail all year long, but somewhat more in spring and summer than at other times. In the Gulf states and the Southwestern range grass seeds are used more than elsewhere; there the winter diet also is made up largely of grass seeds; at some seasons and in some years as much as 70% to 80% of all their food comes from this source. In the northern range the grasses are used much less for food, since grain is more available.

Land use determines the type of food available. The grass seeds come mostly from hay, pasture, and rangeland; some, like bullgrass and foxtail, grow in crop fields. Grasslands are particularly prevalent in the Southwestern quail range and in parts of the Southeast.

The large quantities of grass seeds eaten by quail come from a rather small number of species; among them are some grasslike plants that are not true grasses but belong to the closely related sedges and rushes.

In the Southwestern range the seeds of Johnson grass are among the important grass foods; they are eaten to a lesser extent throughout the Southern quail range, but there is some doubt as to their importance where better foods are available.

The paspalum grasses, especially bull grass, probably contribute more quail food than any other group of grasses. Other valuable paspalums of the Southeast include slough grass and Florida paspalum. Bull grass is a weed of cultivated fields, while the other two are found in lowland woods and grass fields.

Many of the panic grasses provide seeds that the bobwhite eats; in the Southwest the Texas panicum often makes up a considerable share of the fall and winter diet. Panicums are common range grasses, and some species are found throughout the quail range in waste places, especially along the coastal plain.

Crab grass seeds are eaten frequently in the South, and foxtail in the North; many other grass seeds are eaten occasionally. It is doubtful if many of these are high quality foods, but rather are eaten probably because better foods are scarce.

The nut rushes (*Scleria*, especially *S. Brittonii*, *S. triglomerata* and *S. setacea*), which are really sedges, are important sources of bobwhite food in Florida and along the Gulf area. They are found in wet, waste places and in pastures.

WILD SEEDS EATEN BY THE BOBWHITE

THE most important source of food for quail for much of the year and over much of their range is a miscellaneous group of wild plants that can probably best be described as "weeds." The seeds of these uncultured plants provide quail with 20% or more of their food through most of the year, except in the Southeast; there the legumes furnish the most food, and this group of wild plant seeds are less used.

These plants are mostly annuals, and the majority of them are found in the aftermath of cultivated fields or in open waste spots. Most notable among the group is common ragweed, which is prevalent in most crop fields and waste places throughout the bobwhite's range; it is one of the bird's best and most dependable early winter foods. Missouri studies (Korschgen, 1952) showed that 24.4% of winter food came from two species of ragweeds; the crotons (mainly woolly, Texas, and glandular croton) are plentiful throughout the Southern quail range, and are fairly important in the quail diet. Others in this group are: poke-berry; beggar tick; jewelweed (a plant of wet areas); sunflowers (annuals important in Western range); skunk cabbage (a wet-ground perennial species of importance in the North); smartweed; stargrass; hemp; sumpweed; and many more.

LEGUME SEEDS IN THE QUAIL DIET

THE most distinctive fact about the bobwhite's tastes is its liking for seeds of leguminous plants. This fabulous family, the Leguminosae, includes many that harbor root nodules of bacteria that possess the invaluable ability to convert nitrogen from the air into a form usable by plants; this capacity makes these legumes soil builders, since nitrogen is an essential food of all plants. The seeds of many—but not all—legumes seem to have particular attraction for quail. Among them are a few that are also used by people (soybeans) and livestock (cowpeas); the ones most used have high nutritional value, especially in proteins.

Probably the most important legumes of all to the bobwhite are a pair of exotic plants now widely used by Southern farmers for hay and pasture; from Maryland and Missouri southward to East Texas and Georgia the seeds of the Korean and common lespedezas, two very similar species, are a prime quail food from early fall to spring; from 10% to 40% of the bird's diet at these seasons may come from this single source. These plants are also valuable in conservation farming—a most fortunate circumstance for quail.

Among the wild legume seeds regularly eaten by quail are several wild beans (*Strophostyles*, *Galactia*, *Phaseolus*), partridge peas, tick trefoil, hog peanut, sweet clover (especially in the Northwestern part of the range), mesquite and rhynchosia in the Southwest, peanuts in the Southeast, and many others. Taken together the legumes furnish 15% to 20% of the annual food supply in the Southeast, somewhat less elsewhere.

Some of the legumes are among the most manageable of the quail foods. Cultural practices like the prescribed burning of certain lands induce some to grow, while others may be used in conservation farming or specially planted for quail use. Among the latter is a food not even mentioned above, since its introduction is too new to make it prominent in quail food studies; it is bicolor lespedeza, a perennial shrub belonging to the same genus of plants as the annual forage lespedezas. Used in borders between crop fields and woods, and in woodland clearings and odd areas on the farm, it can produce large quantities of first-rate bobwhite food for fall and winter seasons. We shall hear more of this plant when we discuss quail management. Black locust is a tree legume whose seeds are of value to quail.

INSECTS AND ANIMALS EATEN BY THE BOBWHITE

ADULT quail are almost wholly vegetarian except during the summer; then insects, along with spiders and other small animals of similar type, make up about a quarter of their diet. For the quail chicks the "bugs" furnish an even bigger share of their food, especially when they are very young; for their first few weeks the youngsters are mainly insectivorous.

Insects are most plentiful in summer, when many other quail foods are not yet available; this may explain their use of animal foods at that time. They do eat some insects throughout the year and their limited use of them from fall through spring is simply the lack of supply; except in summer, insects add up to only 1% to 3% of the foods taken; this seems to be quite consistent throughout the birds' range.

Most catchable forms are eaten; these are the ones that live on or close to the ground; probably some of the coarser insects, like beetles, may be avoided. Grasshoppers and soft-bodied flies and bugs seem to be liked.

THE WATER NEEDS OF THE QUAIL

THE bobwhite inhabits mostly humid lands, where moisture is plentifully available in succulent foods, from dew, and from generally dependable rainfall; on these parts of its range ample water is generally available to the birds without a special need of flowing or impounded waters. As the western edge of the range is approached these sources of water are less plentiful and dependable, and the lack of water may finally set the limit of habitability for the bobwhite. Thus if water is inadequate the range itself (its vegetation and food supplies) is unsuitable; the bobwhite quail cannot live there.

In drouth years the normally inhabitable range may become a dry death trap for quail; dew and succulent vegetation are not available, and territories lacking open water become untenable; nesting cover dries up, and production fails. A study of the wildlife use of farm ponds by Greenwell (1948) showed a marked contrast in quail numbers per acre of land in fenced pond areas in a southwestern Missouri drouth area compared with the rest of the state; the quail density in the dry area aided by ponds compared to the rest was double in June, over four times in August, over 17 times in October, and three times in the following April.

It is clear that water is no problem in most of the bobwhite's range in most years, but when drouth strikes it may become the limiting factor in its survival.

THE ECONOMICS OF THE BOBWHITE'S FOOD HABITS

PROBABLY no other game bird stands as high in the esteem of the farmer as the bobwhite; his behavior, including his eating habits, are in full accord with the landowner's best interests. He damages no crops, commits no nuisances, helps consume destructive bugs and weed seeds, entertains with his sweet music; and thus is entirely on the favorable side of man's ledger.

THE EFFECTS OF WEATHER AND CLIMATE ON HABITS AND NUMBERS

CLIMATE and weather conditions are known to be prime limiting factors with most of our game birds, but this is particularly true with the bobwhite quail. The northern limits of its range are set by the winter temperatures and snow conditions; nesting success is often cut low by excessive drouth or excessive rain.

A succession of mild winters permits increases in bobwhite numbers in its Northern range, and is accompanied by an actual extension of that range. Valley farming areas farther north than the bobwhite is ordinarily found harbor them, to the delight of farmers and sportsmen alike. Then their hopes that the bobwhite has come to stay are rudely shattered; periodically a severe winter reverses the trend. If it is an especially bad one—like 1917–18 or 1935–36—practically the entire quail population is decimated, and the limit of inhabited range is pushed sometimes hundreds of miles southward.

Except under very severe winter conditions a heavy, well-fed quail can tolerate very low temperatures—even to 20° below zero or more —without trouble; it can go without food for a day or two in order to "ride out" a storm, and the loss in weight may not exceed 10% to 15%; but if the bird continues to go without food a third or fourth day the loss in weight accelerates and a crisis comes. The danger begins after the bird has dropped to about 75% of its plump, early-winter weight; it may drop to 65% of normal in four days without food, whereupon it will almost surely succumb; most birds dropping below 150 grams are doomed. The same result happens over a longer period of time if the bird is forced to subsist on inferior foods, such as many of the wild fruits, chaffy seeds, and the like.

The usual pattern of starvation in a poorly fed covey during bad winter weather is for one or two of the weaker birds to succumb first, followed by others in quicker and quicker order. But a quick drop to subzero temperatures—especially if accompanied by high winds and drifting snow—may catch a weak covey so quickly as to result in complete loss within a day or two.

Sustained periods of low temperatures, deep snows, and high winds, extending for a week or more, are likely to be disastrous; whereas the same amount of adverse conditions occurring in occasional single days through the winter would not be serious. The later in the winter the bad weather comes, the worse is its effect on quail. Recovery from exposure and loss of weight is probable if the bird does not drop below 65% of normal, provided it then gets good food and tolerable weather.

Heavy, healthy quail may die suddenly of freezing by getting wet; this is known to happen at times to birds feeding on steaming farm-manure piles in very cold weather.

Mortality through the winter months is generally from 30% to 60% of the fall population; when exceptionally severe winter weather occurs the losses may mount to 80% or more. The farther north in the bird's range, the more disastrous are the consequences.

Covey roosting of quail in their compact little circle helps to preserve body warmth, and is a big factor in helping them survive the winter. As the number in the covey drops, this warming arrangement is less and less effective, until with groups of about six or fewer they are unable to keep warm enough on cold nights; unless two such coveys merge without delay the birds are doomed.

The vulnerability of the bobwhite to winter weather depends in part on the habitat; with good food supplies that are available close to protective cover the birds manage very well; lacking either good food in adequate amounts or satisfactory shelter, they are vulnerable to exposure and starvation. The poorer the proximity of food and shelter, the farther the birds must travel and expose themselves, and the less likely they are to survive. This vital problem is obviously closely related to our farming methods; exploitive farming may produce few quail because of the lack of winter security.

There are two degrees of winter quail losses. Those that occur as a result of the limited carrying capacity of the habitat are predictable, and are to be expected; the occasional catastrophic losses from exceedingly severe winters are unpredictable, and are not preventable even with good habitat.

It would be difficult to say whether winter or summer weather troubles are most serious to bobwhite; both are disastrous when extreme. The winter conditions are the more troublesome in the Northern range, and summer problems certainly the more damaging in the South.

Winter weather affects the survival of the birds already produced; summer weather mainly concerns the production of the annual crop of young birds. The latter begins with the nesting season, and ends when the youngsters are four to six weeks old; since many quail broods are hatched late, the critical period extends into August.

Quail eggs need a moist climate in which to develop and hatch; excessive drouth may cause the death of the embryo, either before or during incubation; this is most likely to occur in upland habitat and on sandy soils. High ground temperatures of 120° to 140° sometimes cause quail to desert their nests; this happens most commonly in the Southwest. At the other extreme too much rain may drown out the nests or beat down the nest tops, and cause desertion (C. O. Handley, letter); this happens most frequently in lowlands, flatwoods areas, and especially in such localities with heavy soils. These contrasting conditions may exist at the same time in areas close together, since summer weather often varies greatly from one locality to another. According to Stoddard (1940) the best continuous hatching of quail nests occurs on areas with a diversity of soils and topography.

Widespread serious drouths may wipe out practically the entire year's hatch. Errington (1935) reported this situation in southern Iowa in 1934, and Jackson (1950) found substantially the same thing in north-central Texas in 1948. Under such extreme conditions the environment also is badly affected; food crops are short, and the surviving adult birds may have difficulty in finding enough food during the following fall and winter. Faced with starvation, they leave the security of their usual cover in their search for food, and thus become vulnerable to predation and other decimating agents. If the dry summer is followed by a cold winter with heavy snows, the result is a major decline of quail over the area affected. The regular summer food shortage appears to be the limiting factor in southern Texas.

Occasionally adverse weather may result in improved habitat, and may temporarily increase the quail numbers. Jackson (1947) reported such an instance in northwest Texas on range land where the normal grass cover supports few quail; he said that " . . . contrary to established principles of quail management, the irruption of bobwhites which occurred in 1942 was brought about by a background of drouth and hard range usage. Mesquite brush came in after the advent of grazing, and more recently, the drouth which began in 1934 resulted in grazing to the point of destruction of the grass turf. The weed growth of 1941 was essentially a tillage succession, not less so because it was produced by hooves of range cattle rather than the plow."

Very wet summers are as bad for quail as very dry ones. Nests may be inundated; but the most critical time comes just after hatching. The little chicks are very susceptible to trouble from chilling if exposed in a cold or prolonged rain; as they grow up they are able to stand summer exposure increasingly well. Heavy rains of short duration and widely separated are not nearly as bad as a single long period of rain, with cool, cloudy weather lasting for several days.

Hurricane winds occasionally cause heavy quail losses; in the Gulf states the summer crop of bobwhites may be reduced as much as half by late summer storms coming north out of the Caribbean area.

PREDATION; DISEASES AND PARASITES

The life of a bobwhite is perpetually harassed by a host of enemies. Those individuals that fate has located in good habitat usually fare well, despite the ever-present dangers; like the urban jay walker, they have many close calls but few succumb. This security of good habitat presumes, however, that normal weather prevails, and that the number of quail in the coverts does not exceed the carrying capacity of each unit of range.

If the carrying capacity—which is usually determined by the late winter conditions—is exceeded there will be almost certain losses. Some of the birds may move out and seek other territories; if they find suitable cover not already filled with their kind, they are fortunate; if they do not they become even more vulnerable than before. The commonest agent in reducing coveys to the carrying capacity of the range is predation. A natural process, it is important in maintaining the vigor and character of the birds; it rarely decimates quail numbers below a point from which they can quickly repopulate. It does reduce their numbers so that the remaining birds can fare better with the available food supplies.

All the rules of survival may go awry when extreme weather conditions prevail; when winter snows and low temperatures persist for weeks, even normally secure birds may succumb; the population may decline far below the ordinary carrying capacity of the habitat. Many of these birds meet death from the claws or paws of a predator, even though the basic reason for their demise is bad weather.

Bobwhites are an esteemed food of an imposing array of natural enemies; since they are small and have little defensive strength, they *can* be eaten by a number of creatures that are not themselves very imposing; some of the egg-eaters are especially trivial.

We may rank quail predators by their size, efficiency, or importance; the latter is the most significant consideration, though it varies greatly in different parts of the quail range. It is difficult to say whether the worst nest destroyer or the worst eater of the grown birds is most important; this too will vary in different areas and in different years.

THE PREDATION OF NESTS

Among the nest predators the skunks, fire ants, cotton rat, snakes (chicken, coach whip, and black), self-hunting dog, coyote, and foxes are among the most important—at least they are the most destructive. The coyote and stray dog are the largest, while the fire ant, mice, and chipmunk are among the smallest. The most efficient is probably the horrid fire ant, which waits for the eggs to pip, and then, when the embryos are first exposed, swarms over the pipped eggs in such numbers that the parent quail are helpless to protect their almost-hatched young ones; the ants consume the embryo as completely as would a skunk or fox. The peeping chicks at hatching time may attract the attention of a passing fox or house cat, which pounces on the closely setting hen quail, and the result is the loss of a whole potential covey.

Other nest predators, usually of little account but which in some instances may become seriously destructive, include the house cat (which does not eat the eggs themselves but may cause their loss by killing the parents), opossum, raccoon, weasel, mink, crow, blue jay, king snake, chicken snake, pine snake, white-oak snake, and coach-whip snake; even the wild turkey and other gallinaceous birds have been known to destroy quail nests.

Of the various causes of the loss of quail nests, predation is by far the biggest. Normally from 60% to 70% of quail nests fail to hatch; of these losses one-third to four-fifths are attributable to egg-eating enemies, with the average well over half. The second major source of nest loss is from farming operations —plowing, mowing, harvesting crops, trampling by livestock; this problem is increasing in importance as more and more farms are mechanized; tractors are faster than horse-drawn equipment, and much more destructive of ground-nesting birds. Nest losses from farm machines are more frequent in the Northern states than farther south; a study of quail in southern Pennsylvania revealed that 29 of 41 nests destroyed were by farm tools (Latham and Studholme, 1952). This difference will no doubt equalize as Southern farming becomes more mechanized.

Other causes of nest loss are desertion (which is usually the result of disturbance by either man or predator), flooding, drouth, fire, and poaching.

LOSSES OF CHICKS TO ENEMIES

DESPITE high mortality among quail broods, few succumb to flesh-eaters. It is not that the quail's enemies do not relish eating young bobwhites—they catch every one they can; but the good cover that prevails in summer makes the hunting hard. Predators usually have an abundance of easier-caught food at this season, which takes much of the pressure off the game birds.

The only group of predators that is of much consequence to young bobwhites comprises the blue darter hawks, the Cooper's, and the sharpshin. These fast-flying fellows are well named as "darters," for they plunge on to their prey with speed and dexterity; even so, many of the young birds taken by the darters are made vulnerable by the sudden loss of cover from farming operations, or the withering of protective vegetation in drouths.

Almost any of the other quail enemies may take a chick now and then, but it is usually a matter of accident rather than efficient hunting. Compared to the effects of weather and farming operations, the predation of quail chicks is ordinarily insignificant.

PREDATION ON ADULT QUAIL

A LARGE proportion of the bobwhites that survive the fall hunting season are destroyed by natural enemies before spring comes; while not true every year, this is the typical course of events. At first thought such a sweeping statement might seem to stamp predation as a critical matter in quail survival. That this is not actually so is explained by two facts: (1) the bobwhite can thrive even with rather large losses—in fact, it *must* sustain high losses in the annual cycle of life; and (2) most of the birds that become food for flesh-eaters are made available by exposure to adverse weather or starvation. Thus the true cause of these losses relates to the luck of the weather and to the quality of the habitat; habitat, as well as weather, is a matter of luck to the quail— but man can assure that it will be good luck, if he wishes.

Winter mortality progresses steadily from autumn to spring; most losses come in the worst weather, often in February and March. This may be caused directly by bad weather, but is more often due to the increased vulnerability of the birds as their food supplies dwindle; their vitality is lowered, and they must expose themselves in search of the food that is more and more difficult to find.

Among quail predators the Cooper's hawk and great horned owl are probably the most efficient; they occur throughout the bird's range, and are destructive under almost all weather and cover conditions. When snow makes the birds specially vulnerable the foxes, coyote, and marsh hawk may be added to this "first team." Occasional quail eaters include the house cat, stray dog, sharp-shinned hawk, redtail, prairie falcon, barred owl, goshawk (rarely found in quail range), crow, mink, weasel, skunk, raccoon, and various snakes.

Since the amount of winter predation under normal conditions is directly tied to the carrying capacity of the environment, it obviously will vary with the number of birds remaining after the hunting season. Let us assume an area with a carrying capacity of 100 quail. If at the end of hunting 200 quail remain, 100 will probably die before spring—a loss of 50%; if only 125 birds remain after hunting, about 25 will die through the winter, or 20%; and in either case predators will take most of these vulnerable birds. In the one instance, predation will appear to be 2½ times as big as in the other; but actually the same function was performed in each case, and the result was the same: 100 birds in the spring. The *real* difference lay in the relation between the quail population and the environment.

Studies of quail throughout its range show losses in average winters running from 20% to 50% of the late fall populations. Occasionally, in especially favorable winters, the losses will be very small, as for example the 6% loss reported in Wisconsin quail in 1946–47 by Buss, *et al.* (1947). Contrasting are the tremendous losses observed under extreme conditions. In Fulton County, Pennsylvania, 90% of the birds succumbed in the winter of 1944–45 (Latham and Studholme, 1952). In northwest Texas Jackson (1947) reported a crash decline of bobwhites in the winter of 1942–43 from a high concentration of 1½ birds per acre down to a bird per five acres in the river bottoms and a bird per 15 acres in the uplands; this was a quick decline of from 87% to 96%. Both of these disasters were accompanied by heavy predation—in Pennsylvania by Cooper's hawks, foxes, and horned owls; in Texas by marsh hawks, Cooper's hawks, redtails, and horned owls. In Pennsylvania the predation was predisposed by prolonged deep snow, low temperatures, and starvation; in Texas it was set up by drouth, overgrazing, and starvation.

In local instances predation by Cooper's hawks may be unrelated to the carrying capacity and the level of the quail population. Latham and Studholme (1952) cite an instance where a single Cooper's hawk took six birds from one covey in ten days; in another case a hawk took all eight birds, one a day; and in a third instance all twelve birds succumbed to the vigilance of a big blue darter. These cases illustrate the ability of some of these fellows to decimate a covey when they keep the quail under constant watch.

With all the testimony on the destructiveness of predators to quail, what is their true importance? Mr. H. L. Beadel (1939), who operated a 2,000-acre quail preserve in northern Florida, concluded " . . . that an above-average quail population can not only be maintained but is more easily maintained by leaving hawks unmolested than by killing them." In a review of the trends in quail abundance over the decade 1939–48, Goodrum (1949) summarized the results of a professional appraisal by technicians in 39 quail states; of 11 reasons cited 78 times to account for quail declines, predation was not mentioned once! Most of the opinions laid the blame for reduced quail numbers on habitat changes that involved farming problems. As Errington and Hamerstrom (1936) put it, "Predation . . . depends more upon the presence of something vulnerable as prey than upon the . . . predilections of the animals which may do the preying . . . Within ordinary limits there is no evident relation between kinds and numbers of predators and the severity of predation upon bobwhites under natural winter conditions." With these opinions I agree.

DISEASES AND PARASITES OF THE BOBWHITE

BOBWHITES may harbor a variety of organisms that cause disease or irritations internally or externally; but none are known to be a significant mortality factor in wild quail populations. Several have been troublesome with captive quail on game farms, but that is outside our purview.

Among protozoan parasites the most common are coccidia of the genus *Eimeria;* chronic coccidiosis is fairly common, but acute cases are rare. A caecal parasite, *Trichomonas gallinarum,* causes an occasional chronic case of trichomoniasis. The malarial parasite, *Plasmodium praecox,* is frequently harbored, and though potentially dangerous is not known to be so in the bobwhite.

Internal worms are common in the bobwhite; nematode roundworms are frequently found, and are occasionally abundant, though always chronic. About 13 species are known to occur in the bobwhite (Stoddard, 1932), and are found in the body cavity, trachea, esophagus, proventiculus, gizzard, crop, small intestine, and caeca. Tapeworms are occasional—always chronic when present. Flukes are rare and not known to be of any significance.

Nonparasitic diseases are rare in wild quail; various infections are found associated with physical injuries, but are not in themselves important. A form of "bird pox," a warty growth on the feet, occurs occasionally (Stoddard, 1932). Most of the serious game-farm diseases are nonparasitic.

Ectoparasites of several sorts occur on quail, as with most birds; lice, ticks, and mites (chiggers) are common, and are no doubt irritating even though unimportant. When they are found in severe infestations the birds involved are those initially weakened from some other cause. Fleas are rarely found on quail.

It is clear that disease is almost always a secondary factor in quail mortality—when it is a factor at all; mostly it is a minor irritant or an unfelt associate.

MAN'S RELATION TO THE BOBWHITE

Probably no other important game bird is tied so intimately to man's works and activities as the bobwhite; many of the factors that limit quail abundance are the result of his operations as farmer, lumberman, and hunter. The opportunities to improve quail conditions are likewise predominantly in his hands.

The pioneer farmers aided the quail tremendously by their cutting of the virgin forests and development of farms; the bobwhite responded by extending its range and increasing its numbers. At the same time—but most particularly in recent decades—the farmers' techniques of land use and management have become the major limiting factors of quail populations, excepting climatic influences; both the major functions of the land manager, farming and lumbering, are involved. Man as a hunter is a major decimating agent of quail, and the only one that is effective regardless of environmental conditions.

QUAIL HUNTING

In the southeastern quarter of the United States the bobwhite is the most important game bird; most quail hunters also consider it the *best* of all game birds. There is much to support their view, despite the claims of those who say the turkey, or mourning dove, or ruffed grouse, or woodcock is superior as a sporting bird. In terms of the total kill, the bobwhite is second only to the pheasant. The total annual harvest approximates 10½ to 11 million birds; of this total 10¼ million or more are taken in the 17 states that have the best range—this is the area from Virginia to Iowa and Texas, and south. The 13 fringe quail-hunting states shoot fewer than a quarter of a million birds in an average year; this group includes southern New England, the middle Atlantic states, Wisconsin, Minnesota, Nebraska, and Kansas.

Quail-hunting seasons are long compared to those for other upland game birds; except in the Northern and Western fringe states, hunters may shoot quail for one to two months in the fall and early winter; the daily bag limits are usually five to 10 birds per hunter. In the better quail-hunting states about half the licensed sportsmen hunt the bobwhite; in the fringe states few hunters hunt specifically for quail—they usually take them as opportunity comes while they are hunting all small game.

In good quail country an average man hunts 2 to 4 hours for each quail he bags and returns with 1 to 4 per trip; these averages obscure the occasional full-day's bag got by many hunters, and the regular high take of a few highly skilled shooters. For the whole season from 3 to 12 birds is the usual bag for an individual. Here too there are exceptions, since the fellows who bag very few birds are balanced by those who take many times the average;

PLATE 65. *A bobwhite rises for hunter from tree and shrub plantation.*

PLATE 66. *Hunting dog assures that the bird will be retrieved, if downed.*

PLATE 67. *Safety zone marker in cooperative farm game project in southeastern Pennsylvania. An area around each farmstead becomes a refuge for wildlife by this arrangement which prohibits hunting inside.*

the latter are the expert hunters who are privileged to shoot in the best coverts. Those who hunt with good dogs may anticipate bagging a quarter more to twice as many birds as the fellows hunting without a trained dog.

Hunters from metropolitan areas are generally less successful than those from small urban centers and rural areas; the urban quail hunter goes less often than the rural hunter, hunts fewer hours when he does go, flushes fewer coveys, bags fewer birds, and has a higher proportion of cripples. He also confines his hunting more to holidays and week ends more than does his rural competitor (Bennitt, 1945).

The effect of hunting on quail populations varies some in different areas and in different years. In the better quail range, the loss of birds from hunting is a secondary population factor, and rarely influences the subsequent year's population. Baumgartner (1944) had this to say about quail hunting in Oklahoma: "Reduction of the autumn population by hunting to approximately the normal breeding density did not result in a decline in numbers of birds from year to year. For example, . . . the removal of approximately 20 to 55 per cent of the birds each autumn did not result in any conspicuous change in the breeding population from year to year. . . . " In the fringe states, where the population is more likely to fluctuate widely from year to year, hunting may sometimes contribute to slowing the recovery of low density populations. Latham and Studholme (1952) observed that in Pennsylvania a hunting loss of 40% of the birds in good years was no deterrent to their quick recovery, but that a kill of only 20% or 30% of the quail in years of scarcity might retard recovery.

Studies of hunting losses have been made in a number of states in recent years on controlled areas, and summarized in the *Pittman-Robertson Quarterly* reports. The bag in most of these areas was from 20% to 50% of the preseason populations; of this from 10% to 15% of the bag was the loss from crippling. Where trained dogs were used the crippling loss was about half what it was without them.

Davison (1949) said that an average annual harvest of 10 quail per 100 acres is to be expected on well-managed Southeastern preserves; on such elite quail lands he says, 15 to 20 coveys may be located in a six-hour hunt over 1,000 acres. These are reasonable figures for good quail environment where the bobwhite is really managed—that is, where the bird is looked upon as the preferred crop of the land; on general farmland the average yield of quail is more likely to be from 2 to 5 birds per 100 acres.

The methods of hunting quail differ, according to locality and the presence or absence of hunting control. On Southeastern preserves the quail shoot is a formal affair; the dogs are handled by a trainer, while the hunters cover most of the ground on horseback or in a wagon, and dismount to approach the pointing dogs for the actual shooting.

The most widely used method is to follow the pointing dogs afoot, and hunt only as far from the house or automobile as is convenient for a few hours walk. Others tramp the woods and fields without dogs to jump-shoot quail and other game alike.

The etiquette of quail hunting requires that coveys once flushed and shot into should not be molested again for several days; but this is possible only on lands where the hunting is effectively controlled. When a covey is reduced to about half size, or a minimum of 6 to 7 birds, it should be exempted from further shooting; thus the harvest is held within the safe limit of a 50% harvest. Again, on uncontrolled shooting areas such restraint is not to be expected by various hunters using the area who are unfamiliar with the coveys, their size, and their previous exposure to gunning. Only the ability of the birds to dodge shot prevents their near-extirpation in heavily gunned areas. Fortunately the bobwhite is a resourceful fellow, and can stand heavy gunning and still bounce back to good numbers the next year under conditions of favorable habitat. Man's hunting is a big decimating agent of quail, but it is a chronic, and not the critical one that weather and poor habitat sometimes present.

THE EFFECTS OF FARMING AND LUMBERING

PRACTICALLY every land-management operation in quail country has its effect on the birds for good or ill. Agriculture is a mixed blessing to the bobwhite; without farming and lumbering it could exist only in small numbers, in scattered areas of naturally suited habitat. The basic things that farming brings and that quail thrive on are a variety of cover and abundant foods from annual weeds and waste grain. On the other hand modern farming also brings changes that offset many of the benefits derived by quail from earlier farming systems. Clean farming, or the avoidance of woody cover outside of woodlands, reduces the variety of cover provided by small fields and hedge rows; this makes much of the open-field area uninhabitable for lack of shelter, especially in winter. The trend toward an increase in domestic livestock that results in more and bigger grass fields and fewer cropped fields and in more grazed woodland cuts down the amount of bobwhite foods grown and the amount left available to the birds.

In many areas the depletion of the topsoil through erosion has impoverished the land, and with it the capacity of the land to grow quail as well as farm crops.

Farm dogs and cats add to the army of enemies the birds must avoid; if the birds lack good food and shelter they are easy prey for enemies, whether domestic or wild.

It would not be difficult, from these trends, to paint a dreary picture of the future for the bobwhite. Goodrum's (1949) summary of quail trends from 1939 to 1948 showed that they had declined in population in 25 of 39 states whose wildlife agencies answered his questionnaire. All the major quail-shooting areas were included in the 25 states that reported the quail declining; this occurred despite reduced hunting pressure during the war years and increased restrictions on hunting. Clean farming and increases in domestic livestock were the two primary reasons ascribed for these declines. These trends continue today, and in some parts of the quail range at an accelerated pace. In fact the growth of the livestock industry in the Southeast is barely reaching its full stride as it replaces a part of the cotton-tobacco economy.

It is probable that quail numbers will decline further before the trend changes; the hopeful aspect of the problem is that *conservation farming* is gradually "taking on." In it lies hope for the development of a permanent farming system that will include adequate provision for good crops of quail.

The early Southern agricultural system was ideal for quail. The fields were small, and provided a variety of cover and plenty of edges. The cultivation was imperfect, and the aftermath of weeds in corn, cotton, and tobacco fields yielded abundant food. The mules used for "horse power" destroyed few nests, and had little effect on quail cover. Land not in woods was cropped or left idle, and there was little pasture. The prevalence of idle or fallow fields provided good quail cover. This agriculture we now know to be an exploitive one that leads to land impoverishment; it is an anomaly that the bobwhite should seem to be tied to such an economy.

In extricating itself from the scourge of this "one-crop" system, Southern farming is indeed changing in ways detrimental to quail. It may be well for us to review the main ways: increase in field size, with the consequent reduction of edges; the reduction of tilled land and increase in grassland, with the consequent drop in quail foods grown; the great increase in numbers of domestic livestock, which cause loss of both food and cover; and the advent of fast, efficient farm machinery that raises nest destruction, and often curtails foods through the clean cultivation and harvesting of field crops. All these things have been and are working to the detriment of the bobwhite. Yet bad as this situation seems, there is good evidence that the trend will end, and will be amended in many ways by conservation farming that will benefit quail; certainly the cause is not lost.

The reader may have concluded that these changes in agriculture are *wholly* bad for quail, but such is not the case. For example, though grassland produces little quail food, and little shelter of a protective sort if well grazed, it does make a useful quail cover type for a short distance next to woods or other usable cover. Most hay and pasture make good nesting cover, despite the hazards of hooves and mowing bar. Common and Korean lespedezas used in hay and pasture seeding mixtures offer some food, even when rather intensively farmed. The short sod of a well-grazed pasture is the best place to sun after a rain—a use which is occasionally important to quail.

Stoddard (1932) points out that the grazing of swine in fall and winter turns up such foods as chufa and peanuts not ordinarily available to quail; the hogs' eating habits leave considerable waste that the birds can use. This rooting habit of swine also exposes spots of mineral soil, where annual weeds grow the next year; some of these weeds, like ragweed and foxtail grass, produce quail food. Stoddard (1942) later emphasized the detrimental effects on quail of the growing livestock industry, but "also that livestock may be advantageous to a game program if stock is confined *to improved pastures* and the grain for supplementary feeding is raised in small fields that are well distributed over the shooting grounds. . . . " These improved pastures are an integral part of a sound soil conservation program.

Woodland as well as farm-field practices vitally affect quail habitat; though essentially a bird of open cover, it depends on woodlands and thickets for protective shelter. Some woodland types, like the longleaf pine of the Southeast, may support quail with little or no farm land. Whatever the woodland type its value to quail is dependent on the way man handles it.

The longleaf pine woodlands offer a particularly clear example. Given protection from fire, the hardwood species invade the understory and then the crown, and develop a dense forest cover of little value to quail. In contrast, given a periodic controlled ground fire—or even under the old customary annual land burning—the forest is kept open, the pines hold their domination of the stand, excess ground cover is destroyed, and quail food grows more abundantly. With a reasonable amount of scattered dense cover in unburned spots, such woodlands support good quail populations. The dense hardwood cover has only shelter for the bobwhite, and can be used only where it is close to fields that have good food supplies.

In this instance man's use or nonuse of fire in handling the woods made a vital difference in its value as quail habitat. It may seem contradictory that fire in the forest, which is

usually thought of as bad practice, is in this instance beneficial; even foresters who have long preached the gospel of "no fire in the woods" now realize that under some conditions the use of fire can be a useful tool of management for timber as well as for quail; it all depends on how it is used. Wild fire is of course not condoned.

The grazing of livestock in woodlands has a marked effect on its habitat value; for the most part it is detrimental to quail, since the stock graze the ground cover and destroy the bird's food supply. There are some exceptions that modify this rule. Woodlands having very dense undergrowth may be opened up by limited grazing and made more usable for quail. Here it is a matter of degree; if the useless dense woods are heavily grazed they become an equally useless open woods, and there is no gain for quail.

Lumbering continually alters the plant succession, and causes major adjustments in the habitat character; as a general matter, the sustained-yield harvesting of wood products in mature woodlands creates a pattern of brush and forest cover that is better quail habitat than the solid mature forest. Severe burning also sets back the whole plant succession in most woodland types, but has a different species composition of regrowth than follows cutting. In observing the effects of woodland cuttings on quail in eastern Texas, Lay (1940) found that the lumbering of a mature stand improved its value to quail, and that quail habitat on the cut-over area got better as the plant succession advanced through the weeds, grass, and brush stages; it reached its best condition about eight years after cutting; after about ten years its habitat value declined. It is abundantly clear that quail require a certain stage of plant succession. In part this is accomplished by growth toward maturity, and in part by being set back through lumbering or fire.

Lay (1940) points out that a woodland that is submature as to timber is "mature" as far as quail are concerned. The desirable woodland habitat has a continuous addition of new openings to replace the older ones growing up; this can be accomplished through sustained-yield tree harvest by spot-lumbering.

MAN AS A QUAIL CONSERVATIONIST

WITHIN the species optimum climatic range the bobwhite quail can be increased on almost any lands. When landowners want more quail, and do those things that are needed to produce more quail, they are practicing conservationists. Though husbandry is not the only aspect of being a conservationist, it is the most satisfying—the fullest fruition of conservation effort.

It is probably true that most landowners who are familiar with the bobwhite are quail conservationists in philosophy; at least the bird is universally liked, and most folks wish there were more of them. But there is often—all too often—a wide gulf between these theoretical or part-way conservationists and the practicing ones. Many landowners who wonder why there aren't more quail and who also desire more quail at the same time practice cleaning out fence rows, pasturing wood lots, overgrazing pastures, and cropping their fields more than the soil can stand. Not only are they failing to do constructive things to help quail, but they are doing things that damage quail habitat; they are not practicing quail conservation—merely dreaming it. Much of this malpractice is done through lack of understanding rather than from greed.

Because there are many things the landowner can do to benefit his land and his income that will also benefit quail, we may reasonably expect that more and more of the theoretical conservationists will practice their beliefs, once they understand the needs and learn the methods.

REPRODUCTION AND POPULATIONS

REPRODUCTIVE POTENTIAL

THE bobwhite is monogamous, a rather unusual characteristic among gallinaceous birds.

It breeds the year after it is hatched, and if fortunate produces one brood in a year—never more.

The balance of the sexes is even at birth, but it does not remain so; by the time the young birds are 3 or 4 months old the males predominate by a slight margin, 51 or 52 out of a hundred or occasionally a few more. But this is only a start toward the distortion that follows; the adults in a fall population (birds more than a year old) almost always have a markedly unbalanced sex ratio; from 55 to 65 of each 100 birds normally will be males. In the northern range it may be even more distorted. Since this condition is so extreme, approaching a 2 to 1 ratio, and so consistent, there must be an explanation; it evidently lies in the differential survival that favors the cocks in times of stress.

The proportion of birds of the year to adults in the fall population is an important measure of productivity. It is not a complete measure of good or bad hunting season populations, but in a limited way it serves that purpose. Ratios of young to adults that are below 3 to 1 (75% young birds) usually indicate low numbers of birds; a 4 to 1 ratio is about normal, and indicates a healthy production of 8 or 9 chicks per female; it usually—but not always—signifies good hunting. A very high age ratio, say of 5 or 6 to 1, means a high yield per breeder, but it frequently happens when the number of breeders is low; then the total number of birds may or may not be exceptionally high.

A phenomenon called "inversity" is a fundamental aspect of quail reproduction. In simple terms it says that a high spring breeding population tends to have a low reproduction rate, whereas a moderately low breeding population tends to have a high reproduction rate. This tends to equalize the fall populations from one year to another, and makes for greater stability of numbers. It explains why quail can bounce back to good numbers so quickly after a bad year, and why a large breeding population often fails to produce a still larger stand.

As C. O. Handley wrote me, "Why? I know it is true, but why?"

The aging of quail in fall and winter is most accurately done by means of the characters of the wing feathers. Compared to those of an adult bird, the outer two primaries are relatively pointed in a bird hatched the previous spring or summer; on the juvenile birds the primary coverts are spotted, especially the inner ones, while on the adults they are even-colored.

Quail lay an average of 14 or 15 eggs in their first spring clutch. If the first effort is for any reason a failure—and it often is—they try again; the second clutch may have fewer eggs than the first, often 11 or 12. Birds that lose their second nest will usually persist in trying a third time, or even a fourth. About two-thirds or more hens eventually manage to hatch a clutch of eggs in normal years.

Of a hundred quail eggs that are incubated the full period about 90 to 94 hatch, 1 to 3 are infertile, and 3 to 7 die as partly developed embryos. Late clutches differ little from first nests in hatchability. From these data it will be seen that quail coveys ordinarily start with 12 to 14 chicks.

The reproduction attributes of the bobwhite that we have just discussed are somewhat higher than the average of all gallinaceous birds; taken as a whole, they are adequate to populate quickly any environment to its carrying capacity, if a few breeders are present. Theoretically, a cock and a hen quail mating in the spring and hatching 13 of a clutch of 15 eggs would contribute a covey of 15 birds to the fall population. By next spring, presuming no losses and a 50–50 sex ratio, this group of eight males and seven females would make seven pairs and one unmated cock. Continuing as with the first year, there would be 106 birds the second fall, 15 adults and 91 young. By the third autumn the original pair would become 795 quail, 106 adults and 689 young. Obviously it is very unlikely that an area that had only a pair of quail one spring would have

795 only two and one-half years later; to make it a little more realistic, let us add 40% hunting take to this problem.

Hunting would take six of the 15 birds the first fall, leaving nine, perhaps five cocks and four hens. These birds would increase to 61 the second fall, of which 24 would be shot, leaving 37. These 19 cocks and 18 hens would then increase by the third autumn to 271. A harvest of 40% would then mean a kill of 108 birds, and would leave 163 for the next year. Thus there is the theoretical possibility that a single pair of quail would provide a hunting harvest of 138 birds within three years and still leave a rapidly increasing population. The 40% hunting harvest each season would reduce the theoretical productivity by more than half, yet still leave it high.

The point of all this discussion is to illustrate clearly that the bobwhite has a high potential for increasing its kind; and that it can stand a high hunting harvest *if* production and survival factors are favorable. These factors are never perfect, as we assumed in the illustration above, but vary immensely. As far as its own capacity is concerned, if the bobwhite is given good environment it can maintain good populations.

THE MORTALITY OF THE BOBWHITE

DEATH from a great variety of causes threatens the bobwhite throughout its life; losses are suffered at all stages of life and at all seasons of the year. This constant attrition prevents the numbers of quail from skyrocketing, and keeps them within the carrying capacity of their range. Even the normal losses that can be expected in the egg, juvenile, and adult phases of life are high; when climatic factors occasionally become seriously adverse, the losses become catastrophic; then the population declines. Soon it rises again, for quail populations are dynamic—they are never the same for long. We may discuss this mortality conveniently according to the three stages of life: egg; juvenile; and adult.

Nesting Losses. Most hen quail hatch a clutch of eggs each year, yet most of them have their nest destroyed; this seeming paradox is resolved through the habit of renesting. Rarely are fewer than 60% of quail nests destroyed, and sometimes the proportion is 80% or more. Despite this, so persistent are the birds that 50% to 70% of them manage to hatch a clutch of eggs in most years. If it is not a first spring nest, then it may be a late spring nest; or if not that, then possibly a midsummer nest or even a fall nest; they do not give up easily. A fairly high proportion of the birds still nesting in midsummer may be successful; cover is better, and the mowing of hay crops is less intensive than in early summer. The hen quail is more persistent and the cock is more likely to adopt deserted nests or lost chicks. Thus is perseverance rewarded.

The causes of the destruction of quail nests are mainly three: predation; farm machinery; and desertion. Predation results in the greatest nest loss in all areas except where cattle farming predominates. Where dairying is the major enterprise, the mowing of hay and other farm machinery activities take a high toll of quail nests. The total nest loss from predation and machinery is about the same everywhere, since one is a larger factor where the other is less important. The third major cause of nest loss is desertion; its causes include accidents to the hen, floods, drouth, trampling by livestock, intrusion of fire ants, and human interference.

The proportion of nests deserted is commonly from 10% to 30% of all destroyed; predators take from 20% to 80% of those lost, while farm machinery losses range from zero to 50%.

Juvenile Mortality. Through most of the quail range in normal seasons the losses of young birds are low. Predation by accipitrine hawks is a small factor, and some are lost through accidents. Some may succumb from chilling in cold, wet weather and in long wet spells. The total loss for the 16 weeks of growing up is generally 25% to 40%.

Seasons of excessive drouth or excessive rains increase the mortality to half or more of the youngsters; these abnormal losses contribute materially to periods of declining populations.

Most of the losses of chicks occur soon after hatching; the closer they are to maturity, the more able they are to care for themselves. Thus the juvenile mortality curve starts high and drops rapidly as the summer progresses.

Losses of Adult Quail. The population of adults is swelled in October by the addition of the young quail; then it is not long before the first period of high mortality comes—the hunting season; in most places this occurs in November and December. By late fall, then, on hunted areas, the population may have dropped anywhere from 10% to 70%; most commonly the loss from hunting is between 20% and 50% with an average of about 30%. In good quail range in years of good abundance the loss of 30% or even 50% of the birds to gunners is not a serious threat to the population; they not only repopulate fully the next year after such losses, but it may even be better than having a low hunting take; reduced numbers in the fall give the remaining birds an easier time finding adequate food and shelter through the winter.

Mortality from October to early spring is from 30% to 60% of the October population in average years, with a norm of about 40%; some years it may be as low as 10% in places, or as high as 80% or more. In ordinary winters after an average hunting-season kill the additional loss is low; the normal expectation is a loss of not more than 10% to 20% of the early fall population. This winter loss is mostly by predation. On protected areas where there is no hunting the winter loss is higher, the total fall and winter toll on hunted and unhunted areas being equal; the predators then have more insecure birds to attack. Occasional winters of great severity cause large additional losses from freezing and starvation; these catastrophic drops are more prominent in the

Northern range than elsewhere, and the birds recover more slowly there.

Spring and summer are periods of considerable mortality because of the increased vulnerability of the birds during courtship and nesting. The male birds lost are primarily victims of predations; hens incubating nests are frequently killed by farm machinery, and sometimes by predators—cats and foxes in particular.

Adding the losses together for the twelve months beginning with October, the total annual decline is 80% of the birds in ordinary times, a little more or less in some years.

LIFE EQUATION

THE balance sheet of quail numbers through the annual cycle tends to end with about the same number of birds it started with, the "life equation"; actually it varies from year to year, as the bobwhite's fortunes wax and wane. If conditions of habitat and weather do not change, the numbers of quail vary but little each way from the "equation" in different years; the changes tend to be first one way and then the other, like the swings of a pendulum. We can see what this life equation is like if we follow a hypothetical population of 100 quail and their progeny for a year, as shown in Table 18.

The year illustrated is one when the production exceeds losses and the population is higher the following spring.

FLUCTUATION IN THE QUAIL POPULATIONS

THE oversimplified "equation" of numbers discussed above is rarely a true state of affairs; since conditions change, the populations of the bobwhite also change. On a local basis the

---

TABLE 18

LIFE EQUATION OF 100 BOBWHITE QUAIL FOR A YEAR*

TIME	ACTIVITIES	NUMBER OF QUAIL	
		young	adult
SPRING	(1) 40 males mate with 40 females; 20 males do not mate		100
	(2) Females nest, average 14 eggs, or a total of 560		
	(3) 75% of females (32) eventually hatch a clutch: 30 × 14 = 420; Of which: 17 are infertile (4%); 34 die in shells (8%); 369 hatch (av. 12.3)	369	
	(4) 15 adults die from predation and farm machinery (15%)		85
SUMMER	(5) 5 adults die from predation, etc. (6%)		80
	(6) 111 chicks die from accidents, exposure, predation (30%)	258	
FALL	Surviving young become adults		338
	(7) 135 killed by hunters (40%); 34 succumb to predation		203
			169
WINTER	(8) 51 die from exposure, predation, and starvation (30% of post hunting season population)		
SPRING	(9) Those remaining are the new breeding population		118

* A year of slightly increasing population.

quail in a given area may increase or decrease year after year, depending much on fortuitous circumstances at the time; adjustments in farming, in the weather, in food distribution, in hunting pressure, in predator pressure may bring these changes. A rainy period that delays haying and allows more early nests to hatch is all that is needed to permit a temporary increase in quail numbers that fall. An influx of several Cooper's hawks in the fall may offset the earlier "break," or even reduce the fall population below average. These are examples of the minor ups and downs of a dynamic resource.

There are two other sorts of fluctuations, both more serious than the ones just discussed. Catastrophes may decimate the birds far below the ordinary carrying capacity of the land. Such precipitous declines may be preceded by exceptionally high (and therefore vulnerable) populations resulting from a particularly favorable production period, or they may not; in any case they are almost always brought on by such violent climatic phenomena as drouths, floods, extreme cold, and deep snows; these we have already discussed. Given time, the bobwhite recovers from these tragedies, but it may take several years—especially in the Northern range.

The second serious type of change is more a one-way adjustment of population level than it is a fluctuation; if it does have a reversal it is a long-time swing, rather than a quick annual change. These are trends caused by major land use changes. For decades in the early history of this country, as the forests were opened and the prairies broken, quail were favored, and a long upward course in quail numbers took place; more recently the tendencies toward clean farming, mechanized farming, and the increased hunting intensity have resulted in a long, slow decline in quail numbers. The era of conservation farming ahead of us may reverse the trend again; time will tell.

It may be well to mention here another relationship that has had a big influence on the bobwhite in its Northern range: the exotic ring-necked pheasant has been successfully established in the same ecological niche used by the bobwhite—that is, the farm fields and adjacent woody cover. They are both gallinaceous birds, eat much the same foods, nest in the same kind of cover, seek shelter in much the same places; they are thus competitors. They rarely engage in physical combat, yet it seems clear that to the extent that the ring-neck has entrenched itself in quail range, it has largely displaced the quail there. Thus the presence of the ringneck in much of the northern quail range is a factor in preventing the bobwhite's full repopulation there.

The question inevitably arises in the discussion of game-bird fluctuations, "Is the species cyclic? does it rise and fall in numbers in a rhythmic pattern?" As to the bobwhite, the answer is that in most of its range it probably does not; in its northern range there is considerable evidence that it may. If this situation is true, then the influencing factor is almost surely associated with the rhythmic climatic peculiarities of the northern part of the north temperate zone.

POPULATION DENSITIES AND CARRYING CAPACITY

THE saturation point for bobwhite quail is usually considered to be about a bird per acre; another way of saying it is that the largest number of birds on a given area of range that the species will tolerate is equal to the number of acres in the area. Though such a stand of quail is a desirable objective of management, it is not possible except under ideal habitat conditions, aided by very favorable climate. A more practical goal of management would be a quail to three acres of range in the fall in optimum range; this would be a density of about three coveys per 100 acres. It is suggested as a target of bobwhite management in the Southeast by Davison (1949).

Actual population densities of quail vary with the quality of the range and with the weather for any specific period. Autumn prehunting populations may be from 2 to 10 acres per quail in the best range, from 10 to 50 acres per bird in the medium good to marginal range, in average years; in years of poor production the density will be somewhat lower—especially in the fringe of the species range. Fall coveys commonly have from 10 to 14 birds each.

Spring population densities are commonly from 4 to 20 acres per quail in good range, from 20 to 100 acres per bird in the medium to marginal sections; exceptionally severe winter weather sometimes reduces the birds below these levels, especially in the Northern fringe states. Covey size is somewhat smaller in late winter than in the fall, usually from 6 to 12. As coveys decline in size they may regroup in order to maintain adequate numbers for survival; it has been shown (Gerstell, 1939) that the covey must have a fair number of birds in order to maintain body heat while roosting in cold weather.

The concept of *carrying capacity* in the relations of environment to wildlife poulations has been intensively studied with the bobwhite quail; the work of Errington in particular has defined and clarified this very difficult subject. He says, " . . . carrying capacity . . . is . . . the upper limit of survival possible in a given covey territory as it exists under the most favorable [weather] conditions . . . [I]t is . . . more exact for groups of adjacent territories than for single territories" (Errington and Hamerstrom, 1936). It is essentially a matter of habitat—the pattern of land use; the agricultural and forestry crops grown and the practices followed; and the condition of the soil. It is ever-changing, since its components are never static; every time a field is plowed, a woodland cutting made, a crop harvested, a calf born, the actual carrying capacity of that area for quail is affected. These routine matters are taken into account, however, in computing the number of quail that can survive the winter in a given area. The more radical changes that are relatively permanent are a different matter; when a farmer changes from cotton farming to livestock farming, when he removes his hedgerows to gain more land or to rearrange his field boundaries, when he clears off a woodlot to make pasture—these long-time changes greatly alter the carrying capacity of the area for the bobwhite.

A study of two areas in Missouri (Murray, 1948) to analyze the factors influencing quail survival revealed that " . . . the occupied ranges [compared] with the remaining lands within the study areas . . . contain[ed], per unit of area, more than three times as much fence row cover, 50 percent more corn, 25 percent more lespedeza, and nearly nine times as many quail." Some of the other factors that directly influenced the carrying capacity on these Missouri farmlands were these: whether the lespedeza crops were limed; the proximity of hedgerows to corn and lespedeza fields; and whether crop fields had the aftermath grazed.

Another example of the changes in carrying capacity brought about by habitat alteration is described by Lay (1940). The woodlands of eastern Texas may be favorable for quail or poor range, according to their plant succession stage in relation to cutting. Beginning with a timber harvest, the new sprout growth is just fair habitat for about four years, and supports about a covey per 140 acres. Then rather suddenly it changes to good quail range, as it enters the early-intermediate stage of growth; this lasts from about the 5th to the 10th year after cutting, and may have a covey per 77 acres—nearly double the carrying capacity of the first stage. From the 11th to about the 15th year in the growth of the stand, the late-intermediate stage, it declines a little in carrying capacity; still it is rather good, and may carry a covey per 95 acres. Then another quick change occurs; the woodland begins to mature as a tree-dominated stand from about the 16th year on; the quail-carrying capacity drops way down, and there may be only a covey per 500 acres; it is then definitely poor range. Some years later, when it is cut again at maturity, the cycle repeats. These changes in carrying capacity in wooded range take longer to consummate than changes in farm fields, but they are more predictable.

The carrying capacity can be used to gauge the expectation of winter survival. If the post-hunting-season quail density is close to the carrying capacity, there will be little additional winter mortality from predation or from ordinary winter weather; those quail are said to be *not vulnerable;* they have a favorable relationship between their own numbers and their habitat. On the other hand, if an area has been little or not at all hunted, and the early winter population is well above carrying capacity, these extra birds are vulnerable; their numbers will almost surely be decimated by one cause or another before spring.

Exceptional weather occasionally alters this expectation; extremely severe winters sometimes result in freezing and starving birds even though they were not "vulnerable." At times a very mild winter may allow survival in excess of the carrying capacity for a season. These abnormalities occur about once in a decade.

Errington (1941) points out another variable in the determination of quail-carrying capacity. Though basically a matter of habitat, it is sometimes conditioned by what the birds themselves make it. Older birds in a covey may stick to certain territories simply because that was where they were brought up; they have a "tradition," as Errington says, that urges them to remain there, regardless of whether it is overstocked or understocked with quail, and regardless of food and shelter conditions. Often these older birds will dominate the action of the covey; this may at times result in greater winter losses than might have occurred had the covey been more mobile, and utilized the more favorable habitat available to it.

THE MANAGEMENT OF THE BOBWHITE QUAIL

THE bobwhite is our most easily managed game bird; it is relatively sedentary, and thus can be cared for on a small acreage compared to most game birds. In its optimum range as little as 100 acres provides a satisfactory unit of management; Murphy and Baskett (1952) suggest four square miles as the minimum unit for management in central Missouri. At the fringes of the bird's range it may take many hundreds and even thousands of acres to assure good development and control.

Until recently most bobwhite management was on Southeastern shooting preserves. These lands were mostly nonagricultural—made up of woodlands, brushy land abandoned from cotton farming, and broomsedge fields interspersed with patch farming by tenants. This crude mule farming was fine for the bobwhite; both the small size of the fields and the abundance of annual weeds in them made for good habitat. Apart from the quail benefits that this kind of farming gave, all habitat improvements were made as game management measures aimed specifically at quail production. Quail management is now much more widespread, and to a large degree is an adjunct of farming. The trend away from small fields, mule power, and crude cultivation, and toward large fields, power machinery, and clean cultivation has hurt the quail seriously. Offsetting it somewhat, and offering hope for the future, the trend to conservation farming has helped the bobwhite.

These are the background trends that most strongly influence the management of the bobwhite. We shall discuss first the production phases of management—its relations to land use, farming practices, and woodland measures; then we shall take up the special techniques of quail management needed to supplement agriculture and forestry, and to control hunting.

HABITAT DEVELOPMENT

ALMOST all land in the bobwhite quail range is managed by man for either farm or forest crops—except that managed principally for game. Any that is naturally ideal quail habitat is an uncommon accident. Most of it can be improved as a part of the job of making the land produce better sustained crops of food and fiber products. Where more quail are desired than result from strictly agricultural and forestry practices, some additional measures are practical.

The basis on which quail habitat can be developed while improving the land for its major uses is a sound program of soil and water conservation. In discussing the management of the ring-necked pheasant in Chapter 1, we described the techniques and procedures for developing such a program. The inventory of the land resources and its interpretation, the conversion of the use of lands in accordance with their capabilities, and the planning of conservation practices adaptable to each land use are the same, regardless of the kinds of wildlife involved. We shall not repeat that discussion here, but begin with the different kinds of land use and the measures for improving them as bobwhite habitat.

At the outset we need to emphasize that the program must be based on good farming; practices opposed to the best interests of the farmer are not practical. Also it should be clearly understood that moderately fertile farmland has a greater *potential* for producing quail than poor land—though very fertile soils often have poor quail habitat because the cover is too dense. The limitations of opportunity in the northern and western periphery of quail range as compared to the more southern and eastern sections should also be recognized. Regardless of how well the habitat is developed in the fringe zones, there will be great fluctuations in quail numbers; the closer an area is to the edge of the geographical range of the species, the less dependable quail management will be.

Cropland Practices. Quail depend on the farmers' crop fields for much of their food; hayfields are favorite nesting places; the borders of open fields serve as sunning areas and loafing spots. But most vital is the food they obtain in his fields; the proper use of fertilizers, lime,

and manure adapted to each crop grown is important in determining the amount of quail food produced, as well as the amount and quality of the crop. Crop rotations that assure the maintenance of good soil structure are equally important. The use of green manure crops and winter cover crops are desirable where they fit the crop rotation. Methods of harvesting and fall plowing that keep the crop residues on the surface of the ground—the so-called "stubble mulching"—are widely recommended, especially where a winter cover crop cannot be grown. The organic remains of harvested crops should never be burned. Aftermath grazing is not advisable on most crop fields. Cutting grain crops high to leave as much stubble as possible is another way of keeping organic matter on the field surface. All these soil-management practices that are a part of good farming help in a general way to provide good supplies of quail foods.

The arrangement of the crop fields is important in assuring good erosion control. It is fortunate that the best erosion control system, contour strip-cropping, is also the best crop-field pattern for quail; instead of growing his crops in a few rectangular fields with straight-row culture and its attendant erosion, the farmer lays out his crop fields in a system of long, narrow "ribbon" fields that have their edges on contour lines. To illustrate, on a 400-foot-long, gentle slope there might be a 100-foot-wide strip of corn, then another equally wide strip of hay, then below that a band of wheat, and at the bottom another strip of hay. The length of these fields might be a few hundred feet, or a mile or more, depending on the lay of the land and the farm boundaries. Such an arrangement of fields aids in the control of erosion by keeping the cultural operations on contours, and by placing the erosion-resisting hay crops in between the grains that tend to induce soil loss. It helps improve quail habitat by providing for the maximum interspersion of the three cover types. By the addition of a fourth type to provide protective shelter (which we shall discuss shortly), the needs of one or more quail-covey territories would be met.

Some crop fields need additional erosion control treatment, beyond soil management and proper crop-field layout: long slopes may require diversion terraces to gather run-off water and dispose of it in nearby pasture or woodland. These channels are kept permanently in grass, and are safe nesting places (outside the bottom of the trough where water flows after heavy rains). The grass on the berm, channel and on the filter strip above the channel are usually mowed but once a year, after the regular hayfields are finished; quail nesting there have a good chance of hatching the eggs before mowing time. The channel itself is a good cross-field travelway except for a short time after mowing.

Cultivated crops on gentle slopes are sometimes farmed on cropland terraces, which enables a wider field to be used in a single tilled crop than with strip-cropping. This system has a succession of shallow channels over which the crop is grown, with the cultivation following the direction of the channels. This is less advantageous to quail than the strip-cropping and diversion-terrace arrangement, but it does furnish some protection to the birds in the channels themselves.

Poorly drained soils in crop fields can often have the drainage improved; if the topography permits the development of an outlet to get rid of the excess water in a nearby stream or ditch channel, the drainage may be accomplished by the use of a network of shallow, open ditches or underground tile lines. Where ditches are used, the modern broad V-shaped channel with farmable slopes is preferred to the steep-sided U-shaped channel. While many crop-field drainage channels are farmed, those that have to carry very much water, or are dug to a considerable depth, have to be kept in permanent vegetation; this ditch-bank vegetation is almost always good cover for quail. If it is kept mowed—as it should be—the grass cover is allowed to grow until midsummer or

later, until the regular hay mowing is finished. The purpose of mowing is maintenance of the grass rather than its harvest; it may even be done biennially rather than annually; but if allowed to go longer than two years the banks develop woody cover, and become brushy and more troublesome to manage. Some ditches are deliberately allowed to develop brush, and are managed by periodic cutting. The brush-covered bank is not as good nesting cover as grass, but does give good protective shelter; some of the woody plants may also provide some food. The seeding and planting of these banks with species of grasses, legumes, and shrubs to control erosion and improve quail cover will be discussed later.

The Care of Pasture and Rangeland. It can be said as a general rule that grazing land is poor quail land. This is not always true, for conditions vary greatly; much of the Western quail country is range land, and some of it is productive of quail. It depends on the intensity of grazing, the kind of stock, the condition of the grass, and the nature of the associated vegetation. Severe overgrazing reduces the value of the range for quail, but moderate overgrazing is beneficial; this benefit comes from the prevalence of weeds that develop on range that is grazed rather heavily—some of the weeds furnish quail food. The more drouthy the season, the worse it is for quail, as well as for the livestock.

The change to more livestock and more grassland farming in the East and South in recent years has had very adverse effects on quail; but pastures that are managed in the best way for livestock are also the best for quail. All pastures should be *improved;* this means that the land is prepared and seeded to the best adaptable grass-legume mixture; land not worth improving is usually not good enough to be used for pasture. Liming, fertilizing, annual mowing before weed-seed maturity, and periodic scattering of droppings are some of the cultural practices needed. The number of livestock grazed should be kept within the carrying capacity of the pasture. Range land likewise should be stocked with only enough animals to utilize the forage without seriously damaging the plants.

Grazing should be confined to land devoted to that purpose; woodlands, orchards, streams, ponds, thickets, and crop fields should be excluded from grazing, in so far as it can be done. In the East the stock can well be confined to pastures, and most of the unsuitable land within the pastures fenced out; Western range lands cannot be so easily separated from woody cover areas, and habitat for quail can best be maintained by limiting the grazing intensity.

On lands in Texas and Oklahoma that are managed especially for quail, mesquite grassland can be improved by half-cutting the mesquite plants; this makes better cover close to the ground, and protects from stock-grazing some of the ground-cover plants beneath. Disking strips of mesquite range land in the spring brings on the growth of partridge pea and doveweed—both good quail food plants; fertilizing the strips and excluding them from grazing will assure the best results. The disking of saw palmetto rough on Florida grazing lands induces volunteer quail food plants like nut rush, small partridge pea, and small-seeded paspalum; here too the best results come with the strips fertilized and fenced from livestock.

Even the recommendation to protect quail shelter areas from grazing has exceptions; there is no simple rule that applies everywhere. The moderate grazing of dense thickets and thick woodlands may make them more useful to quail by opening the ground cover. Not all quail foods will be eaten by the stock if the browsing is not too intense, and the birds may inhabit areas that would otherwise be impenetrable. Foraging by hogs is another exception; though often bad soil conservation, the *rooting* of swine exposes mineral soil that is often covered with annual weeds the next year; it is like spotty fallow plowing. Many of these

weeds grow quail foods. Sometimes hog rooting will expose the underground "nuts" of chufa and make them available to quail—to the extent that the hogs waste them; bobwhites, unlike turkeys, do not scratch out these nuts themselves.

As a general rule, pastures and range lands should not be burned; many good pasture plants and prairie grasses are damaged by fire; nesting cover is lost by spring burning. There are, however, exceptions. Stands of broom sedge or wiregrass in the Eastern states are poor stock forage, and may become too thick for quail use; they may be burned to advantage if safety precautions are taken. The best time is on quiet nights in late winter. Fire breaks should be prepared to limit each burn to a small area; the rough is removed by this light burning, and the new cover is open enough to be suitable for quail use; it also will have some annual food plants among the grasses. This type of management is recommended only where the renovation of such fields by plowing and reseeding is not appropriate.

The rotation of pasture use and the division of grazing among several units of pasture are both good livestock management and helpful to quail; the periods when the stock are off pasture permits grass growth that provides usable quail cover. The smaller the pastures the better is the interspersion of their grass cover with other adjacent cover types, and the more useful they are to the bobwhite.

Woodland Management for Quail. Woodland cover may range all the way from uninhabitable to excellent quail habitat; the extent of the woods, composition by species, age class of trees, condition of understory and ground cover, and the diversification of cover types both within and adjacent to the woods are the key considerations. Small woodlots with irregular shape and a high ratio of edge to area are better than extensive ones. Young stands from a year or two after cutting up to ten years old are the best age class for quail use on most sites; older stands are progressively less useful to quail unless manipulated on their behalf. Ground cover should be fairly open, though not heavily grazed by livestock. An understory of shrubs and saplings in scattered thickets is desirable, but most of the ground should be open; woodlots that are broken up with openings are better for quail than those of a uniform type. Any type of woodland may have value as shelter, but the longleaf pine type of the Southeast has greater possibilities for management than most others; under proper management it can produce good food supplies as well as shelter.

The major techniques of woodland management for quail are cutting, burning, grazing, and tree planting.

Cutting practices should be consistent with recommendations for the improvement and harvest of wood products; the harvest of trees by rotating cuttings of small blocks at about five-year intervals, to achieve a complete cycle of the whole area in the maturity time of the species involved, is generally a good system; strip-cuttings or shelterwood cuttings are other satisfactory ways of arranging a cutting rotation. The spot-lumbering of small groups of mature trees over an entire tract, as they reach harvestable size, is an excellent way of achieving a sustained yield of both timber and quail.

All these techniques distribute cut-over with the uncut or middle-aged portions to achieve a variety of age classes, hence a mixture of types. If quail are a prime consideration in managing woodlands, some of the cut-over areas may profitably be cleared of stumps and kept permanently open; these areas can then be plowed and seeded to food-producing crops; this should be done only on portions having fertile soils and topography that is suitable for cultivation without serious erosion. We shall discuss these seeding techniques again under plantings. Stoddard (1932) recommended such cleared areas to be from 40 to 60 feet wide and spaced at frequent intervals. Davison (1949) suggests that the strips be 15 to 20 feet wide and 400 feet long, using one strip for 25 acres of woods, or .05% of the whole area in such plots.

In the making of woodland cuttings, the species of trees that are important in producing quail food should be preserved in adequate numbers; for most food trees mature specimens are most productive, and some should be left uncut until they begin to deteriorate; this is most effective close to the woodland edges. The oaks, sweet gum, wild black cherry, flowering dogwood, and black locust are some that warrant being favored; the evergreens should be favored for their shelter value, especially in the understory.

Controlled burning—or *prescribed* burning, as it is sometimes called—is a very important tool of quail management in certain kinds of woods. It was first practiced and recommended for the longleaf pine woodlands of the Southeast by Herbert Stoddard. Although a controversial practice for years, since it was diametrically opposite to the usual recommendation completely to exclude fire from forest, it has now received the approval of most foresters as well as game managers; actually it is a wildfire preventive, and is now used as such in the oak-pitch pine woodlands of New Jersey as well as in the longleaf pine stands of the Southeast. It functions much as does an inoculation for disease prevention; the woodland is given a light, nondamaging burn in order to get rid of the most inflammable material that under favorable fire weather could cause a serious forest fire.

Thus the controlled burn reduces the danger of serious fire. In the longleaf pine type it also maintains the dominance of the subclimax pine by suppressing the hardwoods; this improves the woods for quail, or keeps them in good condition by preserving the relatively open growth. The heat on the ground and the reduction of ground litter induce the germination of many dormant seeds, especially some of the wild legumes that grow quail food; among these are native lespedezas, partridge peas, beggarweeds, milk pea, and butterfly pea.

PLATE 68. *A light controlled burn in southern pine woods when properly handled benefits quail and maintains the dominance of the pines over hardwood trees. Good game and forest management are combined.*

COURTESY SOIL CONSERVATION SERVICE, USDA

On damp ground the nut rush, panicum and paspalum grasses, and jewelweed are stimulated. It has also been found that the organic matter in the soil is increased by fire-stimulated root growth, and that nitrogen in the topsoil increases for the same reason (Greene, 1935). Thus the controlled burning of longleaf pine woodland is a sound management practice.

Management burns must be done with care. Firebreaks around the area to be burned should be planned wherever natural breaks, such as roads, streams, and plowed fields, are unavailable. Late winter is the best season, and clear weather is the best time. The fire should be set in the quiet of the evening, or when there is a light wind of not over 10 miles per hour; the fire is set on the leeward side of the area like a backfire, and burned into the wind. The U. S. Forest Service has developed a fire-setting can with a long tube through which the fuel is poured in an even, fine stream along the starting line as the man walks along; this aids in getting an even fire, for better control. The fire may be set in a series of spots a few hundred feet apart; each burns a small area, and goes out quickly when the dew falls. Burning should be repeated at least every two or three years; some believe that an annual burning is better because it is lighter.

Longleaf pine resists fire damage best of all the pines; loblolly ranks next. Young slash pines are apt to be killed by fire unless they are over four inches in diameter. Slash pines with turpentine scars are very inflammable, and should not be burned. Burns that do not reach the crown rarely damage these three species of pines, except as noted.

Since the burns destroy hardwood understory plants, some of which are desired for quail shelter, small thickets should be excluded from burning by plowing firebreaks around them. Some of the species suitable for these thickets are wild plum, Hall's honeysuckle, blackberries, and other briars, saw palmetto, wax myrtle, sumac, bayberry, and chinquapin.

At the present time controlled burning is recommended for quail management only in the Southern longleaf pine forests; the burning of woodlands is not recommended in the Northern or Western parts of the quail range. Lay (1940) points out that in East Texas the quail problem in the forest is one of controlling brush and trees by cuttings; hot fires of the sort that can occur there change the habitat so that little quail food is available for a decade. Afterward a burned area may have better food supplies than an unburned area of the same type, since at that age the latter becomes very dense. Lay does suggest that spot-burning of slash from cuttings may be advantageous, with due regard for safety precautions. It should be done in the winter. Such burns can be made to continue growing quail food plants for several years by biennial fallow plowing or disking.

The heavy grazing of woodlands destroys its suitability for quail; but in some situations light grazing by cattle, horses, or swine is beneficial. Where the hardwood understory has become so thick that quail cannot use the area, light grazing will help it. This condition can be judged fairly well by the ease with which a man can traverse the cover; if he has to push his way through the underbrush then it is too dense for quail. Lay (1940) says that grazing not more than a cow per 30 acres in Texas cut-over up to 15 years old helps keep it open enough for quail without doing very much harm; in older stands the grazing should not exceed a cow for each 40 acres. Any food plots in these lightly grazed woodlands should be fenced or grazed lightly enough so that a quarter to a half of the range indicator plants like vetch, bur clover, and lespedeza will set seed.

Woodlands in the Northern quail range should not be grazed.

Recommendations for tree planting may be made: (1) where land physically unsuited for cropping or grazing is being so used; this is usually Class VII land by the Land-Use Capability system of the Soil Conservation Service; or (2) where new woodland cover is needed and wanted for quail or other wildlife, or for growing wood products; this may be any class of land. Species used in tree plantings should be locally adapted to the climate and soils of the area, and of a type suitable for the purpose planned. Most plantings in the East are of conifers, while in the semiarid West they are hardwoods. In their early years they serve as brushland for quail; as they mature they should be managed like other woodlands.

Wildlife Areas on the Farm. The term "wildlife area" as applied to farmland has come to mean any area that is not cropland, grazing land, woodland, homestead, or roads, and that has value as wildlife habitat. They are usually of three types: brushy cover or thickets; herbaceous cover that is not harvested; and aquatic areas. More and more these places are being recognized as opportunities for wildlife habitat management, and are being improved for that use. They often represent the chance to develop good habitat patterns as an adjunct to good farming.

There are a number of situations where brushy cover is appropriate on the farm. First let us discuss the woodland border, since we have just finished our section on woodlands in quail habitat management. The border is the transition zone between woods and field.

It is well recognized that the woodland trees on the edge next to a crop field have an adverse influence on the crop in the outer 20 feet or more of the field; root competition, and to some extent shading, explain this phenomenon. The net result is that little or no crop is grown in the affected zone. This trouble can be corrected in either of two ways: (1) cutting the trees from the edge of the woods, killing their roots by recutting or by poisoning with herbicides, and developing a cover of native shrubs, supplemented if necessary by planting; or (2) by planting the edge of the field with a border of shrubs and/or perennial herbs. If the crop-field area is short, the best method is to cut the border from the woods; if the loss of the crop-field edge (which has already been out of production anyway) is not serious, the unproductive zone may be planted.

The techniques of cutting a border are simple. All large trees, and small specimens of kinds that grow large, should be cut for a depth of 20 to 30 feet into the woods; small trees like flowering dogwood, crab apple, and sassafras should be cut only from the field half of the border. The native shrubs present should be carefully protected from damage in the cutting. Usable wood from the cutting can be removed, and will often pay the cost of the operation; the remaining brush should be piled along the woods edge of the border, and preferably over stumps. If the border had a good understory of shrubs and vines they will quickly respond to their release from shading and take over; if few shrubs are present, some may be planted to fill in the open spaces (see below).

Hardwood trees that are cut often sprout about the base. Some species, like beech, maple, and oaks, usually sprout with great vigor, and can quickly redominate the border if left alone; they should be either recut, or preferably treated with herbicide. Either the stumps or the young sprouts may be treated with good results; a mixture of the herbicides 2,4,5-T and 2,4-D carried in oil is effective for this purpose.

An advantage of planting borders in the field edge is that the species used are chosen rather than being merely nature's bounty. Of greatest significance, in border plantings for quail, are the shrub lespedezas. All these shrubs and sub-shrubs of the lespedeza genus are Oriental in origin; approximately 20 species are known. Only a few have so far proved useful for quail or other wildlife; of these the bicolor is best known. It is adaptable for use from Georgia to

eastern Texas and Oklahoma north to New Jersey and Missouri. The early-maturing strain of bicolor called *Natob* (Crider, 1951) is suitable for use somewhat farther north (but *not* in the South); it will mature seed in average years in Massachusetts (except the Berkshires), the lower portions of the lake states, and Iowa (probably). Thus this species (regular bicolor and Natob) is suitable for use in all the bobwhite quail range except Florida, the Western fringe, and the Northwestern fringe. It should be noted, however, that the Natob strain shatters its seed early in the fall, and is thus of very limited use as a winter food plant in the snow zone; efforts are now being made to develop a variety of Natob that is not only early maturing but also has persistent seed.

Japan lespedeza is a subshrub suitable for use in the zone from Virginia to New Jersey, and possibly as far west as the central Mississippi Valley; because of its lower stature it may be used to advantage in the field side of a border. Cyrto lespedeza may be used in the area from Virginia to southern New England. It is somewhat smaller than bicolor but larger than Japan lespedeza; it is slightly earlier in seed maturity than common bicolor, but not nearly as early as Natob. Seeds of all these lespedezas are excellent quail food for fall, winter, and early spring use.

Another lespedeza suitable for use in borders is sericea; it is an herbaceous perennial, and has the same range for use as common bicolor. Its seed is fair quail food, but in moderately dense stands it makes good roosting and nesting cover. It is a fine erosion control plant, and makes a good turning area for farm machinery when used in the field side of the border.

PLATE 69. *Planting seedlings of bicolor lespedeza in a prepared border strip with a planting machine.*

All these lespedezas can be established by direct seeding with unhulled, scarified seed; all but sericea may also be grown by setting out year-old seedlings. The use of seedlings is more certain of success, and is the only practicable method in sandy soils. Borders established successfully by seeding are more certain of achieving a dominant stand of plants than when seedlings are used—but there is more chance of failure through poor germination. The seeding rate for the woody species is 10 pounds per acre if broadcast, five pounds per acre if drilled. Drilling is preferred; and the rows should be 30 to 36 inches apart, with 15 to 20 seeds dropped per foot and covered about one-quarter inch. The seeding rate for sericea is 20 to 30 pounds per acre.

Whether the border is seeded or planted with seedlings, the site should be prepared by plowing and harrowing. Seeding may be done in early spring; or, if it is to be fertilized and cultivated, as late as May 1 in the South, June 1 farther north. Fertilization is the same as locally for clovers or annual lespedeza. Acid soils should be limed to 6.0 pH. Planted seedlings should be spaced in rows three feet apart, with the plants two to three feet apart in the rows. They should be mowed off an inch or less above the ground at the end of the first or second season, to force the plants to bush out. Shrub lespedezas recover well from burning, but burning is not recommended. Cultivation of a new planting is desirable for at least the first season.

Where the existing border zone has Hall's honeysuckle growing, this vine should be killed out by poisoning before the border is planted, or else kept out of the planting by later treatment with herbicide; otherwise it will eventually destroy the lespedeza.

Lespedeza borders should be wide enough to consume the unproductive crop-field edge, usually 20 to 30 feet. Border plantings may be established between pasture and woodland where this is desired, but here the border must be excluded from grazing. Shrub lespedezas are not suitable for growing in poorly drained soils.

Sericea stands tend to grow very dense; then the growth becomes poor quail cover, but good for cotton rats and mice. This can be remedied by thorough disking; thin stands of sericea are benefited by a light disking.

The shrub lespedezas are also recommended for use in quail food strips through woodland (see "Woodland Management for Quail," above), on ditch spoil banks, next to vegetated stream banks, on highway fills, and across fields in hedges or windbreaks; in all these areas the plantings must be protected against grazing. When they are used in hedges and windbreaks it is desirable to have some shelter along with the lespedezas; evergreen trees are commonly used in windbreaks in the East, and black locust, Russian olive, osage orange, and other hardwoods in the West. Multiflora rose may be used in rows parallel to the lespedeza on one or both sides in hedges; where this is done the hedges will consume a width of about 20 feet. This extra width over and above the usual hedge-fence width must be charged to quail management.

It should be emphasized that while the shrub lespedezas are very important in bobwhite quail management, they are not a panacea; these lespedezas do not *produce* quail; they can only support them with food in fall, winter, and spring. Lespedeza borders are used some in the summer for brood cover and food, and are better for this purpose than unimproved woods edges. In the winter they are most important; then they are used many times as much as most natural borders; they produce 200 to 400 or more pounds per acre of good quail food that is largely available to the quail since it is not much eaten by competitors.

Borders can be planted with other species besides lespedezas, though the lespedezas are best for quail where they are successful; few other perennial plants adaptable for use in borders provide high grade food. Bayberry, flowering dogwood, and autumn olive may be

COURTESY SOIL CONSERVATION SERVICE, USDA

PLATE 70. *Field border of bicolor lespedeza next to the woods and sericea next to the corn crop provide cover and food for bobwhite.*

PLATE 71. *The bicolor has an abundance of seeds eaten by quail from fall through spring.*

COURTESY SOIL CONSERVATION SERVICE, USDA

used, and their fruits are fairly good quail food; other shrubs that can be used to fill in for their shelter value or for other wildlife values include multiflora rose, silky dogwood, and Russian olive (in the Western range). One-year seedlings are adequate planting stock of these species, except for bayberry, which should be grown two years in the nursery before planting. The two species of "olive" (not true olives) and flowering dogwood are tall plants suited for the woodland side of the border. Silky dogwood, multiflora rose, and bayberry are low enough for use on the field side.

Herbaceous perennials other than sericea suitable for seeding borders include: slough grass, switchgrass, weeping lovegrass, Florida paspalum, and tall oat grass. The slough grass and Florida paspalum are adapted for use in the Southern states from Florida to Texas, tall oat grass in the Northern states, the others throughout the quail range. Seeding rates of 10 to 20 pounds per acre are suggested, except for love grass, which needs only two pounds per acre. All make good nesting cover. The seeds of the slough grass, Florida paspalum, and switch grass are fairly good quail food.

A managed hedge between crop fields, or between crop and pasture fields, is one of the most important elements of farm quail habitat. It is a lane of protective cover across the open fields that enables travel between coverts, and access to food supplies that would otherwise be too far from cover. Natural hedge rows that develop along field boundaries can be kept in good condition for quail, and with a little care are unobjectionable to the farmer; close plowing and mowing are needed to prevent the growth from widening to an excessive size. The judicious removal of trees or shrubs that grow too high or are otherwise undesirable should be done every few years; cutting followed by poisoning of the stubs with brush-killer is easy to do if not put off too long.

Hedges can be planted along field boundaries to improve the wildlife cover pattern, to maintain contour guide lines, for living fences, and to aid in conserving soil and water. The use of multiflora rose for living fences has been in recent years the most common hedge-planting activity; osage orange used for this purpose for many decades has declined in popularity, owing to the high upkeep costs necessitated by annual trimming.

Multiflora is adapted for use throughout the quail range, except in the Northwestern and Southwestern fringes where it becomes too cold or too dry, and in Florida. In the Southeastern and middle Atlantic states from Ohio and New Jersey to the Gulf of Mexico it sometimes spreads, and requires good maintenance to assure that it will not become a nuisance; most of the spread is brought about by birds carrying the seeds into idle areas and fence rows, and may not be objectionable. Some plants may come up in pastures, and should be repressed by annual mowing and other good pasture-management practices; it can be killed with sprays containing 2,4,5-T. Where pastures cannot be mowed but will continue to be used for pasture, multiflora should not be used along the boundaries unless some spread and the consequent control work is acceptable.

Where used for living fences, multiflora should be planted in a single row, one foot apart, in a well-prepared seed bed. Fertilization and cultivation are important during the first year or two; mulching with a heavy layer of sawdust, wood chips, peat moss, hay, or other suitable materials may be substituted for cultivation.

Other kinds of shrubs may also be used in hedges, either alone or in combination with multiflora rose; the shrub lespedezas, bayberry, Tatarian honeysuckle, California and Amur privets are some of them. The combination of shrub lespedeza flanked on one or both sides with multiflora rose is especially promising for quail use where a width of 20 feet or more can be devoted to the planting; this is practical only where the quail (and other wildlife) are very important to the landowner. To complete the cover improvement in such a planting, a strip of perennial grass, ungrazed and unmowed (except for maintenance), should be included either on one side or in the middle.

Another conservation practice that makes safe cover available across crop fields is the windbreak. Where plantings are made in a continuous line across many properties, as in the semiarid plains states, they are called *shelterbelts*. Windbreaks are planted in straight lines across the direction of damaging winds. They may be used to prevent soil blowing, to conserve soil moisture, or to protect buildings, livestock, roads, and railroads from damage by wind or blowing snow. Farmstead buildings frequently have windbreaks on two or more sides to give full protection. All these plantings afford shelter to quail.

Windbreaks are composed of from one to ten rows of trees and shrubs spaced close enough together to give a solid wall of vegetation when full grown. A triangular cross section is best, with shrubs planted next to trees on at least the windward side. The distance between windbreaks to get the most practical protection for farm fields is computed as 20 times the mature height of the planting; but the plantings are sometimes made half this distance apart to obtain more complete protection sooner. The extra lines of plants are then removed later when no longer needed.

Trees used in windbreaks in the East are mainly conifers, and in the West mostly hardwoods. Among those that may be used where adapted to soil and climate are: white, Scotch, Austrian, Banks, loblolly, and red pines; white, Norway, and red spruces; Douglas fir, arborvitae, black locust, osage orange, cottonwood, Russian olive, and Chinese elm. Shrubs useful in these plantings include: Tatarian and other upright species of bush honeysuckles, California and Amur privets, purple-osier willow, multiflora rose, and Japan lespedeza.

There are often other areas on the farm or ranch that can best be used and improved for quail food and cover; odd areas that are unsuited for cultivation or grazing, like gullies, knolls of thin soil, rocky outcrops, spoil banks from ditching or mining, steep breaks between level fields, and roadbanks are found on most farms. Sometimes there are small areas of good soil that do not fit into the cropping pattern, and that can therefore be devoted to wildlife use; these can be developed as cover "islands" or connectors. Stream banks and ditch banks are other examples that may require special treatment for erosion control or channel maintenance.

The pattern for planting islands of cover is to use shelter species in the center, and surround them with bands of shrubs and grass according to suitability. If the area is adjacent to a woodland or other permanent cover, the improvement planting may be confined to food species and nesting cover; if good nesting cover is adjacent, then this element may be omitted from the plan. Each case has to be designed to fit its surroundings.

Some of these areas need only to be managed with quail benefits in mind. Roadsides in perennial grasses, to take a common example, should have maintenance mowing deferred until midsummer or later. Portions away from the road itself may need mowing only every two or three years instead of annually—just enough to prevent woody plant succession; this in most years preserves good grass cover throughout the year.

Existing brushy cover in areas devoted to wildlife habitat may be retained or improved by protection from damaging grazing and fire, and by improvement cuttings. Types of thickets especially suited for this purpose are those dominated by such plants as wild plum, Hall's honeysuckle, blackberry, wax myrtle, bayberry, mesquite, and yaupon.

Seriously eroding stream banks may require mechanical as well as vegetative treatment; where this is true the services of a skilled soil conservationist is needed to design the structures. For the vegetative treatment of stream banks, adapted shrubs include purple-osier willow, silky dogwood, and red-osier dogwood.

Drainage ditch banks across crop fields should be kept in perennial grass cover in order to simplify maintenance. One suitable seeding mixture that has done well for this purpose is weeping love grass and sericea.

All these small wildlife areas on the farm should be protected from wildfire and overgrazing.

On some farms, where the entire area is composed of good agricultural soils, cover developments with woody plants other than hedges and windbreaks are not needed as a matter of proper land use; any other tree or shrub plantings desirable for quail would have to be done just for game management. There is one small exception: the homestead area of the farm can be landscaped with tree and shrub plantings that will also benefit quail; such plantings are often of the greatest use to quail in the prairie states.

Ponds can contribute importantly to quail cover, especially in the West and Southwest. Except in drouth periods it is not the drinking water that attracts the birds to ponds as much as the vegetation around the pond; thus a pond without cover around it, and heavily grazed by livestock, will be of little use to quail. A pond with ungrazed grass and woody cover close to the water may be the key to a quail covey territory. Whatever the major purpose of a farm pond— livestock water, irrigation, fire protection, or recreation—it should be improved for wildlife too; it costs little extra to do so, and the value of the pond is greatly enhanced. Livestock watering tanks can be provided below the pond (except with dugouts) and the animals excluded from the pond area by either a mechanical or a living fence. The water the animals drink is better if they do not muddy it. Plantings of trees and shrubs may be made around the pond, to landscape the area as well as provide quail cover. The grass area next to the water, and the shrub plantings farther back, should both include species that grow quail foods. Hedges or other protective cover should connect the pond area wherever possible with nearby woodland or other woody cover.

A rather special opportunity to improve wildlife habitat, including quail cover in the quail range, is on the vast network of utility company rights of way. The strips of land under cross-country electric lines and over pipe lines have to be kept in a low cover of herbs or shrubs to maintain the facilities; where these strips cut through forest cover they can be made especially useful to wildlife by being covered with vegetation that controls erosion and also grows quail food. Some of the plants that offer possibilities for this work are the shrub lespedezas, sericea, switch grass, and weeping love grass. This presents an opportunity for co-operative action among the utility companies, state wildlife agencies, and soil conservation districts; projects of this kind have already been started in Maryland.

Food Patches for Quail. The best habitat improvements are those that fit soundly into a system of good land use and soil conservation, and that are harmonious with the farming enterprise. These we have just discussed according to the four major kinds of land use: cropland, grazing land, woodland, and wildlife areas. To a large extent those recommendations are compatible with farming and forestry, and their cost is chargeable almost wholly to the production of farm crops.

Despite the best that can be done with land-use practices, not all farms will have good quail habitat with this treatment alone; this is particularly true on the most level and fertile farms. Both winter shelter and winter food are apt to be short; food is most commonly the short item. It is here that the *wildlife food patch* may be used. By its nature it is mostly applicable on good land that can grow farm crops; it therefore competes with the farming business, and must be justified by the game that it produces. On game preserves this justification is easy; on farms it is rarely economical unless subsidized by the state wildlife agency, or by sportsmen.

Food patches should be placed near good winter shelter cover; they should be narrow and long, and at least one-quarter acre in size. Woodland clearings make good places for quail food patches. These plantings should not be burned or grazed. An acre of food patches for each 100 acres of woodland is suggested.

The sites should be plowed, harrowed, fertilized, and seeded like any other farm crop. One good quail-food plant should be used—or at most two or three in a mixture; complicated mixtures are less productive, and attract more competition from the songbirds and other wildlife for the foods available.

In the Northern quail range, where the winter food supply is most likely to be short, hard yellow corn is the best plant to use. Leaving an edge unharvested in a field of corn is the best way to do it, but if it is grown in a special wildlife plot it must be cultivated like a regular cornfield. Soybeans and wheat are the other recommended food plants for the Northern zone; all three can be used in most other parts of the quail range.

In the Southeast a few other kinds of foods may be grown to advantage—Augusta vetch, Florida beggarweed, cowpeas, and annual lespedezas. Any that can be handled as unharvested crop field edges are best done that way.

In the Southwest the adapted food-patch species are sorghums, guar, blue panicum, and annual lespedezas (Philip Allan, letter).

Fallow plowing or harrowing in early spring to induce the germination of native annual weeds is often an effective way to improve the natural quail-food supply. It has the additional advantage of being less trouble and expense than a planted patch; it has the disadvantage of being less dependable. Ragweed, paspalum grasses, partridge peas, Florida beggarweed, nut rush, and others may respond. This practice is best used in broom sedge fields and other rough areas where the strips are also useful for firebreaks.

THE EFFECTIVENESS OF QUAIL HABITAT IMPROVEMENT

THE question will be asked, "How effective is habitat improvement in increasing quail numbers?" It would be fine if wildlife management were a science exact enough to answer that question with assurance; it is not. This much we can say: habitat determines quail numbers within the limits of climatic conditions. A habitat improvement program that is a sound phase of agriculture and forestry provides the best chance possible for having optimum quail populations.

It is difficult to evaluate precisely the changes in quail numbers that result from habitat improvement; many conditions complicate the problem. Nevertheless there are some guides to indicate what may happen.

Southeastern quail preserves have raised their quail production level (the fall population) to a quail per three acres or even better. Davison (1949) says that three coveys per hundred acres is a reasonable goal, and that four or five may be possible under the best conditions.

Steen (1950) reported that a 2,000-acre demonstration in Missouri resulted in an increase from 13 coveys to 31 coveys in four years. This result was in contrast to that on a similar area unimproved, but heavily stocked with game-farm quail for three successive years, but which failed to have an increase in quail.

The response of quail to individual improvements have been repeatedly observed and reported. For example, bicolor borders have three or more times the quail sign in winter that natural borders have; improved farm-pond surroundings support quail where none were before. These are some of the indicators of the response quail can make when their habitat is improved. Though these bits of evidence are encouraging, and are enough to go forward on, we need much more accurate and complete information on this subject.

SPECIAL QUAIL MANAGEMENT PRACTICES

In addition to the development and care of the habitat, there are a number of quail-management practices that play a large or small part in the whole scheme; these we shall discuss under several headings below.

Winter Emergency Feeding. Sportsmen have long believed that when snows come they and the farmers should get out and feed the birds. Various types of feeding shelters for handling grain have been used for this purpose. At best it is a spotty effort; in full effect it contributes practically nothing to the welfare of species like the bobwhite; it is not recommended.

When discussing food patches we noted that unharvested edges of corn- or other grainfields made the most practical kind of supplementary feeding. Where a grainfield needs to be fall-seeded to a new crop, and the crop must therefore be removed, an alternative to leaving unharvested edges is suggested; shocks of corn may be stacked along the hedge row or woods at the field edge. For those who wish to do so, this is the kind of winter feeding recommended.

Stocking Game-Farm or Transplanted Quail. Restocking each year with quail grown on game farms or with wild-trapped Mexican birds has been standard practice in much of our quail range, especially in the Northern sections; the fact that no one could tell whether any good came from these efforts made it easy for sportsmen and game-department people to be optimistic about the matter. But as more and more trained wildlife men looked into the question, beginning in the 1930's, doubts arose as to the wisdom of haphazard stocking; even worse, the probability arose that infusions of inferior birds from the Mexican subspecies or from game farms might be weakening the native stock.

It was clear that the tens of thousands of quail stocked annually were not halting the general downward trend in bobwhite populations. Game agencies that put leg bands on their released birds found that very, very few were returned by hunters. With this background, a number of the states began careful field studies of released quail, mostly with Pittman-Robertson projects; seven of these states (Indiana, Kentucky, Ohio, Oklahoma, Pennsylvania, Tennessee, Texas) have been reporting on progress with these studies in the

P-R Quarterly, mostly in the past decade. Their findings are consistent, and indicate the following: stocking does not increase the quail population except in unusual circumstances; very few stocked birds survive to the hunting season from late summer stocking, and almost none last until the next spring; birds released in the spring rarely breed that year, and rarely survive until fall; native quail populations seem to do better by themselves than with added stocked birds; spring-released birds are specially vulnerable to predation; there is little difference in results from spring or fall stocking, but there is a slight preference for the use of subadults.

Buechner (1950) reviewed the results of quail stocking, and state game agency policies on the matter, in 17 states, and found that it " . . . is costly and does not materially increase the shootable population of bobwhite." He found that eight of these states had abandoned their quail farms; six more were keeping their production at a low level, retaining a semblance of a game-farm setup for public relations reasons; and the other three retained a large quail-stocking program. Buechner's conclusion is the same as mine, namely, that the only sound place for quail stocking on public hunting areas is where the native population has been almost wholly decimated by some catastrophe, or where there is newly created quail range of good quality that cannot reasonably be stocked by native birds from nearby areas. This would limit the practice to few places and infrequent occasions—obviously not enough to justify state quail-farm propagation.

Stocking quail on controlled shooting preserves, while expensive, can be fairly effective if the releases are made just before hunting and throughout the hunting season.

Where public stocking is to be done regardless of its merits, the best results can be obtained by releasing 10-to-12-weeks-old subadult birds. Release should be in the best cover available—preferably areas known to be lacking native birds; groups of 15 to 20 birds should be released together. This means that the operators should have a good knowledge of both the cover and the local quail coveys. Transplanting Southwestern bobwhites is not recommended.

Control of Bobwhite Predators. Though many quail succumb to predation, it is rarely the limiting factor that determines quail survival. Errington and Hamerstrom (1936) point out that there is no substitute for good habitat, and that any quail in excess of the carrying capacity of the habitat are doomed. Winter predator control to save vulnerable birds is futile, and for nonvulnerable birds is unnecessary. Jackson (1951) observed heavy predation on an irruptive quail population in Texas, yet concluded that predator control would not benefit quail even when predators were very abundant.

An exception to the general failure of predator control to aid quail is the "quail-happy" Cooper's hawk; this large blue darter hawk is widely known as a very efficient quail enemy, but even so the majority of them take their quail at random along with other prey. Once in a while an individual Cooper's hawk will hang around a covey territory and harass the birds until they are decimated or scattered; such a bird should be shot. Quail-preserve operators and farmers who watch such matters can do selective control of this sort; sportsmen are not in a position to evaluate the need for eliminating individual Cooper's hawks, and hence cannot be of much aid. Indiscriminate hawk-shooting in the hope of getting the "bad actors" is not only ineffective, but does harm by hampering nature's rodent control system.

Except for the Cooper's hawk, any other predators should be killed only for reasons other than quail conservation; fur-bearers should be harvested as a crop, and game mammals hunted for sport. This largely takes care of the foxes, skunks, opossums, and other mammalian predators. In a discussion of this question with Herbert Stoddard and Ed Komarek on their Georgia plantations, they explained that they concentrate on trapping foxes and bobcats in early spring; by using urine as the "bait" they take females almost exclusively, and at that time of year their unborn litters with them.

Stray domestic cats and dogs should be eliminated by landowners for a variety of reasons, including quail protection. The control of snakes and fire ants is impractical.

Quail Refuges. Refuges that protect quail from hunting are no substitute for good habitat, any more than is predator control; neither practice produces any quail. In good quail range refuges are not needed; in marginal range they may serve a purpose.

In Oklahoma quail populations in comparable habitat on two areas, one hunted and the other a refuge, were studied by Baumgartner (1944). Quail were slightly more numerous on the hunted area before the open season, slightly fewer than on the refuge in the following January; but the quail numbers were equal by spring. The refuge had served no purpose, and it had deprived some people of quail hunting.

The usefulness of refuges for quail was studied in Kentucky by Gale (1950). He found them to be useless in good quail range; hunting there was simply not a vital factor in quail survival. In marginal areas with high hunting intensity refuges can preserve some brood stock, but they do not *improve* future hunting. Gale notes that improved habitat would make these refuges unnecessary. He adds that refuges are expensive, since they have to be patrolled to prevent poaching; he conceded that they may have some public relations value—in other words, a sop to erroneous sportsman opinion.

Jackson (1947) felt that refuges could play a valuable part in quail management in Texas range habitat; but they are most needed there in drouth times, and under those circumstances the exclusion of domestic livestock from the refuges would be essential. Since the stock are short of forage also at such times, few ranchers would be willing to keep the refuges safe against livestock as well as hunters.

Some state game agencies use refuge establishment in their farm-game programs as a nucleus of co-operation with the landowners in habitat improvement; this has value as a means of establishing working relations with landowners. Maryland has used this technique to good advantage in its work with co-operators of soil conservation districts. Most of these refuges are small, from five to 40 or 50 acres; large refuges are not useful, even for public relations reasons. The setting up of refuges around farm buildings, called "safety zones," as is done on Pennsylvania farm-game projects, is for human protection; but they may have some use for quail, since this state has mostly marginal quail range.

HUNTING CONTROL

GOOD game laws are the framework for the control of the quail harvest; they should be set so as to permit the widest possible participation by the sporting public, and liberal enough to assure a fair take of the harvestable surplus. The procedure for setting them should be flexible enough in operation to permit changes on rather short notice when that is desirable; to do this, the dates of open seasons, the hours of hunting, types of weapons, and daily and seasonal bag limits should be controlled by regulations issued by the state wildlife agency rather than by laws passed in a legislature.

An open hunting season is normally warranted in all good quail range. The periphery —especially in the North—is less likely to justify an annual open season, since quail populations fluctuate more widely there. The hunting season should begin in the fall, as soon as the cover shrinks from defoliation; this comes in late October in the North, and in late November or early December in the Southern states. From one to two months of hunting may be allowed; it makes little difference in the annual kill to have the longer period. Bag limits of from 4 to 8 birds per day are permissible; season bag limits are of little value.

The setting of the hunting regulations in

states with good quail range is a routine matter; the regulations can safely remain the same year after year, even when quail populations change. In the northern and western states, in the fringe of the quail range, where open hunting seasons are not always warranted, a census in midsummer that determines the population level should be the basis for setting the season; this can be done by means of a sample count of whistling cocks (Dalke, 1943). This involves selecting rural road routes throughout the state on which the counts are made at one-mile intervals; each route should cover a single major soil area, and the total of the routes should give proper representation to all quail-inhabited sections of the state. Dalke says that from 1,500 to 2,000 stops are needed in a state like Missouri; replications may be made to get more accuracy in the averages. Days used for the counts should not be stormy or in a period of weather change; it should not be raining, and the wind should not exceed 15 miles per hour. The census should begin one hour after sunrise and continue for two or three hours; each stop should last a uniform length of time, say two minutes.

Whistle counts may be totaled by counties, soil areas, or in relation to particular cover associations. The state total gives a final index figure of the population level. When taken for a succession of years, these figures show trends in the quail population; they do not give actual populations.

Better hunting prospects are indicated by increasing numbers of whistling quail per stop on a given area compared with the year before; a declining "call index" reveals poorer prospects for hunting. Estimates of the year's quail production can be obtained in July and the fall hunting seasons set at that time.

Dalke found that the summer call index correlated well with the quail-kill per gun-hour in the succeeding fall, thus confirming the validity of the method. Trained technicians need experience in using the system for a couple of years, in order to interpret properly the figures

for any particular state. It should be reiterated that these censuses are needed only in states where quail hunting is marginal.

There are many other techniques for making censuses of quail in spring, summer, or winter; these utilize signs of various kinds—such as tracks and droppings—trained bird dogs, landowner interviews, and so on. They are mainly useful in research studies.

The local field control of quail hunting by any kind of a permit system is rarely needed; the hunting intensity on quail is not badly concentrated, either in area or time, as is pheasant hunting. This does not mean that the total pressure on quail is not as great as on other species of game birds; it merely means that it is spread more evenly over the quail range and through the fall months, so that it does not create as much of a problem in hunter control. Actually, according to a recent survey by Henry P. Davis of Remington Arms Company, more shotgun shells are used on quail (14% of the total) than on any other game bird; waterfowl shooting consumes 11% of the shotgun shells, and pheasant shooting 10%.

Private control of quail hunting by the establishment of commercial shooting preserves, or private shooting properties not open to the public, and by land posting to limit hunting, will provide partial hunting control; the latter will continue to increase in the vicinity of cities, as it has for some time. This trend may sometime be changed by co-operative projects arranged by state game agencies or organized sportsman and farmer groups.

The more the landowner engages in quail management by culturing his land in their behalf, the more surely will he insist on more control of the quail harvest. Wise sportsmen will recognize this fact, and through their organizations do everything possible to see that the landowners receive adequate benefits for their work. The landowner holds the future of the quail in his control; he is the one who is in the best position properly to control the harvest.

CHAPTER 8

The California Quail

ORIGIN AND CLASSIFICATION

THE California quail is a native of the Western states, primarily California, though its present range is extended somewhat by transplantation. It belongs to the family Perdicidae of the order Galliformes; its genus is *Lophortyx,* meaning "crested quail," and there are two species in this genus in the United States. The other species besides the California quail (*L. californica* Shaw) is the Gambel's quail (*L. gambeli*) (see Chapter 9).

Three subspecies of the California quail occur in the United States: the type form *L. c. californica* has a restricted coastal range; the valley quail (*L. c. vallicola* Ridgeway) is found throughout most of the species range; Catalina Island quail (*L. c. catalinensis* Grinnell) is found only on Santa Catalina Island. There are two more subspecies found only in Lower California, Mexico. The term "California quail" is used in this chapter to cover all three United States subspecies.

DESCRIPTION

THIS quail is the official "state bird" of California, and a lovely creature it is. It is a small, plump bird with short tail, short rounded wings, and strong, moderately long legs. Its length is from slightly less than 10 to a little over 11 inches in different individuals. Males weigh about 6½ ounces or a shade more, and the females slightly less.

The plumage of the sexes is generally similar on the body, but very different in the head region. The male of the valley quail is colored as follows: the back and wings are grayish brown to bluish gray or olive gray; the rump, tail, and upper breast are plain bluish gray; the wings when folded have a whitish buff line on the inner margins; the lower breast is golden yellow, changing to golden brown with whitish edges below, and all with outer black curved lines on each feather that give the area a scaled appearance; the sides have long brownish feathers with white shaft streaks, shading into buff flanks, belly, and under-tail coverts.

The head region is distinctively beautiful. The most prominent feature is the topknot of black, broad-tipped feathers that are held as one, and usually hang forward at a rakish angle from the top of the head. The crown is smoky brown; the sides and back of the neck are bluish gray with fine white spots, and the outer black feather edgings give a fine, scaly effect; a double band of black and white bounds the crown in front and extends back to above the ears; another white band extends in a U-shape from behind the eyes to under the throat; the chin and the throat are deep black, and the forehead is buffy white with fine black lines; a short white line extends from the eye to the blackish bill. The iris is brown; and the legs and feet blackish.

The female lacks the prominent black and white bands on the head; the lower breast lacks the rich golden cast, being more of a whitish buff ground color; the upper breast is olive gray; the topknot is brown, and smaller than

PLATE 72. *The California quail.*

that of the male; the throat is streaked whitish; and the head color is pale brown. It is slightly shorter and lighter than the male.

The juvenile birds have white markings on the back, wings, and breast that are not on the adults. The two outer primaries and the greater upper primary coverts are carried beyond the postjuvenile molt and thus make age identification possible in autumn. The coverts of the old birds are plain gray, whereas those of the young birds are mottled with buff and white. The outer primaries are more pointed in the young birds than in the adults (Leopold, 1939).

Downy young are whitish, with some brownish above, especially around the sides and back of the head; the head plume is discernible after they are only a week or two old.

The above description is of the valley quail (*L. c. vallicola*); the type form (*L. c. californica*) differs in being more of an olive brown on the upper parts in place of the grayish or bluish cast; the inner wing margin line is dark buff rather than whitish. Its behavior is essentially the same as that of the other two subspecies.

The Catalina Island quail (*L. c. catalinensis*) is larger than the valley quail; darker colored; the scaling is heavier on the lower breast; and the brown streaks on the flanks are wider than on the mainland forms (McLean, 1930).

Throughout the subsequent discussion all three subspecies will ordinarily be referred to as "California quail."

GEOGRAPHIC RANGE AND DISTRIBUTION

THIS commonest of the western quails is predominantly a bird of the Pacific coast states and Lower California. The type subspecies is limited to the humid coastal region from the Bellingham Bay area of Washington and Vancouver Island of British Columbia, south through Oregon and to the vicinity of San Luis Obispo, California. The Catalina Island quail is restricted to that island off the coast of southern California.

The more widespread valley quail is found in interior valleys, desert edges, and lower mountain slopes, from southern Washington, western and southern Oregon, through northwestern Nevada and most of California into Lower California (see Figure 22). The southeastern desert area of California is excluded from this quail's range (where it is replaced by Gambel's quail); the higher mountainous areas, mainly the Sierra Nevada and Cascade ranges, are also excluded; and there it is replaced by the mountain quail. The valley quail is also found in the Snake River valley of southern Idaho, in a small portion of the Clearwater River valley in northern Idaho, and in a small area around Salt Lake City and Ogden, Utah; some are present in portions of the mainland in southwestern British Columbia.

The two additional subspecies, both of smaller size than those above, occupy most of the Lower California peninsula of Mexico.

Most of the range given for British Columbia, Washington, Oregon, Nevada, Idaho, and Utah resulted from successful transplantations; the indigenous range extended northward only to about Klamath Falls, Oregon. The heavily populated areas are largely within the original range in California.

HISTORY OF THE CALIFORNIA QUAIL

THE rapid settlement of California after the gold rush of the mid-19th century required

FIGURE 22. *Geographic range of the California quail.*

quick attention to the problems of conserving the native game, including quail. In 1852 the first game law of that state was enacted; it gave six months' protection from hunting for quail and some other species in certain counties. Then followed a half century of relatively unrestricted harvest; this was the commercial era, when quail-hunting was primarily for the market.

The stories of large numbers of quail and the hunter harvest of those days are hard to envision today. Twining (1939) pieced together a fascinating account of this period, mostly derived from interviewing seven "old-timers" who hunted for a living in the last 20 years of the 19th century. Then there were thousands of men whose livelihood came from hunting quail, rabbits, and ground squirrels; many of these

fellows were excellent field naturalists of a sort, and came to know and understand their quarry with a skill seldom matched by sportsmen today. Some 200 operated in Contra Costa County alone, who sent their harvest twice weekly to the San Francisco market. Two to three dozen was a good day's catch, and they brought from $1 to $1.75 a dozen; quail on toast could be had in most restaurants for 30 cents.

This hunting was done mostly by ordinary shotgun shooting, with the help of a dog and a "quail caller," which was made of a small split stick and a laurel leaf. The birds were so abundant that a day's hunt rarely extended more than five miles from home. In some areas where the birds gathered at water holes they were "ground sluiced" with extra large shotguns; some were trapped with nets. By these methods the kill per hunter occasionally was as high as 100 dozen a week. Some marketers shipped as high as 10,000 birds a year, but the average was about a thousand, according to T. S. Van Dyke as quoted by Horn (1938a); the San Francisco market alone received from 70 to 100 thousand in some years (Grinnell, Bryant, and Storer, 1918). The trapping of quail was outlawed in 1880.

The abundance, according to recorded comments, seems phenomenal: " . . . in good quail country near Lafayette there could be expected to be about 50 quail to each 25 acres," and "Every little canyon was full of birds . . . " (Twining, 1939); flocks of a thousand or more at water holes, and so on. From about 1880 to 1885 a marked decline is said to have occurred. This came at a time of many developments on the land; agriculture was growing rapidly, land was being cleared of brush, water was being piped for controlled use, breach-loading shotguns appeared, squirrel-poisoning on a large scale began. All these events had adverse effects on the quail, but whether they explain the entire decline is not known. In 1901 the commercial sale of quail was prohibited by law, thus ending that era—though some illicit sale continues even today.

Though present-day populations of quail are low in some areas of California compared with those of the 19th century, in other areas of the state their numbers are equal to or exceed these historic numbers. Recent counts of up to 700 birds at one water development give credence to the recorded comments noted above. It is true that environmental changes have brought vast differences in California quail habitats and in local bird numbers; these changes have been generally downward, and are evidenced mostly by a general shortage of free water. "Formerly there were springs at short intervals all over the [Contra Costa] county and many streams ran all year. Now even the largest springs seldom run after July or August, and only in unusually wet years . . . " (Twining, 1939).

The lack of cover on intensively farmed areas and on overgrazed range land, and the other extreme—too dense brush cover resulting from fire prevention—have contributed to the lowering of the carrying capacity of the land for sustaining and producing California quail.

On the other hand, man's agricultural and home-making pursuits have increased quail populations in many sections of California. The irrigated vineyards of the San Joaquin Valley, which now are excellent quail coverts where not too cleanly cultivated, were once bare, dry plains with a quail population of zero.

The adverse comparisons of today's quail populations with those of the "good old days" that the old-timers describe are therefore somewhat more imaginary than real; they referred to local situations rather than widespread conditions. The same sort of stories could be written about today's quail.

Man's interest in encouraging the quail began early. According to Dawson and Bowles (1909), two lots of these birds were transplanted to the vicinity of Puget Sound, Washington, as early as 1857; subsequently it has been introduced with some success into parts of Nevada, Oregon, Washington, Idaho, and Utah in this country, and into British Columbia, Chile, New Zealand, Australia, Hawaii, and a few other islands. It failed to respond to introductions in the eastern United States.

In recent years much attention has been given to improving the environment for quail, and considerable success has been achieved—notably by providing water; the species is now considered to be one of our more manageable western game birds; it competes for popularity with the newly-introduced ring-necked pheasant. It is, however, still rated as the finest western game bird, even though more hunters (43%) now hunt pheasant than hunt quail (33%) in California. The California Wildlife Conservation Board appraises the *food value alone* of the quail in California as $906,591 annually, compared with $552,749 for pheasants (*Cal. Wildlife Cons. Bd. Report,* 1950).

HABITS OF THE CALIFORNIA QUAIL

COURTSHIP

THE first signs of courtship behavior begin in late February in most years. Covey organization has before this been stabilized, and all activity takes place among members of the same covey. A male will take a short, quick run toward another male, his body crouched and plume laid back; he makes a pass with beak or wings as the object bird dodges uninterestedly. As the days pass—and particularly when a warm spell comes—this fighting grows prevalent. If a strange quail encroaches on a covey, the fight becomes a real contest rather than a one-sided skirmish.

As the covey goes about its business of feeding, loafing, dusting, and traveling, there is much vocal communication. Mostly it is a subdued twitting, but there is a distinctive three-part call known as the assembly call; it is "described" in various ways as "ku-kwak-up," "ki-woil-uh," "tuck-ke-tew," "ki-ka-kee," "ka-kow-ka," and so on. This same call given in a low tone by a hen during courting will bring males to her from long distances.

During the mating period and while hens are incubating, males are heard to give a single-noted "cow!" call. The significance of this has been variously interpreted by different authors; some believed it to be the call of unmated males, while others held that it is a call of mated birds whose hens are on the nest. Later workers have observed both mated and unmated males giving this call; it is probably the call of any male seeking female companionship. Some workers believe the "cow!" call to be analogous to the "bobwhite" call of the bobwhite quail.

Pairing takes place within the covey in a very unobtrusive manner. In an unpublished paper, "Pairing Behavior in the Valley Quail," Emlen summarized the process of mate selection as follows: "The choice of a mate by a female valley quail is apparently influenced but little by physical characteristics of size and perfection of plumage, or by behavioral characteristics of social and sexual aggressiveness and dominance. Synchrony of sexual cycles probably does not feature in early mate selection, but could explain certain peculiarities of late pairing. Social factors of acquaintanceship, previous pair relationship, and association under adverse social conditions apparently feature in the formation of certain pair combinations. Such conditions of the social environment may be an important factor in mate selection in the valley quail."

By mid-April some pairs have strayed away, and those that remain are a loose group of pairs rather than a well-organized covey. By the end of April (the time varying somewhat according to latitude and altitude), the coveys have disintegrated; the paired birds wander considerable distances in many directions, looking for suitable nesting territories. Thus the total territory occupied by the former covey members in nesting season is much greater than that used by them as a covey in winter.

At length the pair locate a satisfactory nesting location. The cock defends his mate from intruding males wherever she is, but he does not defend a nesting territory as such. The birds are monogamous when paired; but there is a limit to the males' faithfulness, as evidenced by an observation of Sumner (1935) on two pairs of birds in a large pen enclosing natural cover. He describes the event thus: "The reproductive cycles of the blue [refers to leg bands] pair coincided, whereas those of the red pair evidently did not, as shown by the fact that the red female refused for about a week to allow her mate to copulate (although they later reared a brood of young). Balked in this direction, the red male tried repeatedly during the week to copulate with the blue female whenever both pairs came out of the brush to feed together at twilight. In every instance observed, the blue female refused to accept his attentions, although she received the advances of her own mate, while the blue male was evidently roused to anger (the word is used after due consideration) by these attempts upon his mate."

NESTING

FROM the time a pair leaves the covey they are constantly together, except when the hen is on the nest; then the cock remains nearby. If some emergency separates them, they find each other by calling as soon as the danger is past. At night they roost together side by side on a branch of some suitable tree.

The nesting site may be almost anywhere, as long as there is some partial obscurement. The nest is usually placed on the ground, among annual vegetation with no supplemental cover; some may be found beside or slightly under overhanging shrubbery. It may be in sparse herbaceous cover, or even among bare rocks or under dead wood. Quail occasionally parasitize other birds' nests; they have rarely been known to nest in low shrubs or vines a foot or two off the ground.

The nest itself is a slight hollow lined with dry grass or other plant material; some are not even lined. They are usually "roofed" with some kind of vegetation during the early part of the nesting period. Egg-laying begins in April or May, and is completed in late April, May, or June; the peak of the nesting period is in May. The size of the clutch is variable, ranging from fewer than ten (probably an incomplete clutch or a late nest) to more than twenty (probably laid by two or more hens); the average number of eggs in first nests is from 10 to 12 in different areas and years. Renests have fewer eggs—the later the laying the fewer there are.

The eggs are cream, buff, or off-white in ground color, and are heavily splotched with brown spots and blotches of varying size and shape. They are short ovate in shape, and measure 31 by 24 mm. in average dimensions, but there is considerable variation.

Incubation is performed by the female only, unless she is killed, in which case the male sometimes takes over the task. The male stays nearby, standing watch and loafing. Just before an incubating hen leaves the nest to feed, the male gives his "cow!" call; when the hen leaves for feeding and relaxation, he joins her. She habitually leaves for about 20 minutes in the morning, again in the afternoon; occasionally at other times in between on pleasant days. During the time the female is setting, the cock roosts alone in some nearby tree. The eggs are incubated for 23 days.

THE BROOD PERIOD

WHEN the chicks hatch, both parents share their care. The little ones are led away from the nest as soon as they are dried off and the weather is favorable; they go at once to rather thick brushy cover, where they spend their early life. They are very sedentary unless severely molested. Though they start to fly within two weeks, they seldom make use of their wings in emergencies, preferring to get out of sight or away from trouble by running; they are exceedingly agile afoot, and frequently race into cover so fast that the observer sees little more than a blur of motion. Both parents and chicks seem very nervous, always twitching head or tail and clucking conversationally. When danger is spotted, a warning cry "kur-r" is given, and the whole group "dives" for cover; if need be, the male exposes himself to draw away intruders, all the while keeping the chicks under control with a nervous call, "plit-plit-plit." At times the parents actually attack an intruder; they have been known to chase meadow mice, a thrasher, spotted owl, California jay, snakes, California ground squirrel, roadrunner, and even a dog and a weasel (Sumner, 1935). The parents are solicitous of the youngsters feeding, and call them to partake of any good foods they discover. While the parents lend encouragement to their offspring in all manner of situations, they do not physically aid them out of difficulty; if a chick falls into a hole and cannot climb out, the old birds will "talk" to it and hang around a short while to give it a chance to rejoin the brood, but if it fails it is left behind.

There are always some unmated birds around in the summer; they are mostly males, and are a frustrated lot; as Emlen (1939) says, they assume " . . . an antisocial and noisy behavior. Intolerant of others of their kind, they scatter widely over the nesting grounds to announce their presence and lonely condition with the single 'cow' note or 'crow.' This crowing was almost always directed toward the female of an established pair, much to the annoyance of her mate." Emlen's studies with marked birds showed a remarkably large amount of summer shifting of adult marital status as a result of mortalities. "When the male of a pair was lost, the widowed female, if not nesting, acquired a new mate from amongst the unmated crowers of the vicinity within less than two days . . . or else attached herself to a local brood of chicks. . . . Males which had lost their mates during the nesting season, unless they had chicks to guard, assumed the crowing habit within a day. . . . At least 8 of the 19 marked males spent part (up to 91 days) of the summer in an unmated condition as a result of losing a mate." In fact, of 29 pairings that Emlen was able to check through markings, 22 suffered upsets of one sort or another during the summer, and of these "15 were disrupted by the death or desertion of the female, 3 . . . by the death of the male, and 4 . . . by the disappearance of both members of the pair." This study illustrates the great hazards under which these birds live.

The response of the chicks to parental orders is rather lax at first, and may well be a factor in early mortality; after three or four weeks their response is much better. Up to about four weeks of age they have been brooded on a ground roost each night and during inclement weather, but now they shift to tree roosting along with the parents. Their days are spent feeding, dusting, loafing, and exercising. They practice escape tactics, and learn the various call notes of their species. After about six weeks their diet is changed from being dominantly insectivorous to the vegetarian foods used by the adults. By the eighth week they are fully feathered in the juvenile plumage. At this stage of their life they range over a much larger territory than in their first few weeks, possibly using some 10 to 30 acres.

The latter part of the summer finds the broods developing into coveys. The parents no longer guard and guide the youngsters. For a time they flush in flight more readily than adults, and may perch on exposed places, still unappreciative of all dangers. Some mortality results from predation, and the survivors learn better. The young now give the assembly call, somewhat shrilly at first, as "cu'-cu'-cu' " or "cu-cu-cu' " (Sumner, 1935). As summer ends, broods begin combining to form the fall coveys.

One brood per season is the normal production of California quail; since it is a precocial, gallinaceous bird, one would expect no more, but there is some testimony that they have been known to raise two broods in a single year. McLean (1930) quotes two observers who reported possibly authentic cases based on circumstantial evidence. Though this is theoretically possible, it rarely if ever does. A male *could* care for a first brood alone while his mate hatched and cared for a second lot; or both *could* desert their first offspring half grown and nest again.

FALL AND WINTER SEASONS

FALL coveys are formed by the combination of summer broods and the addition of unattached adults. Sometimes these stray adults join a brood in late summer prior to the fall covey formation; this would not be tolerated early in the summer by the parents of the brood, but these social barriers weaken as the chicks mature. The first aggregations of groups and individuals is usually completed by early October. Emlen (1939) termed these "subcoveys," for they are usually smaller than the ultimate size of coveys in winter. As hunting takes its toll and the amount of roosting cover shrinks with defoliation, there is greater urgency than before for the joining together of the subcoveys; thus the large winter coveys are formed late in the year.

These quail are strongly gregarious. The covey is well organized, and when they are moving or foraging they keep sentinels on watch; different birds, probably mostly adults, take turns in this duty. Thus the natural wariness of the individual bird is reinforced by the alertness of the covey; these characteristics make them very difficult to hunt. Add to this their tendency to run ahead of either man or dog rather than freeze or flush, and it is easy to understand why sportsmen find them so exasperating. Still these ways make them a real challenge to the hunter; the fellow who admires skill in his adversary rates the quail as a first-class game bird.

If they are hunted hard they may move over more territory than otherwise; ordinarily, in areas of uniformly good cover, the fall and winter covey territory is not more than 25 to 50 acres, but if molestation or food shortage is acute they may move as much as two miles. In semi-arid lands of scattered cover, covey areas may encompass several hundred acres.

Coveys go to roost at dusk when visibility becomes poor; this time is usually just ahead of the hour at which most of the songbirds retire. They use rather thickly branched trees or shrubs for roosting, preferring to be some 15 to 25 feet off the ground. If good roosting cover is plentiful at the proper time, they may choose any tree close by; if cover of this sort is scarce, they may return to certain roosts over and over again. The covey may be all in a single tree, or spread out in several trees close together. Each bird squats low in a small crotch when roosting, with head either bent forward with topknot drooping out front, or with head tucked under the shoulder. Before arising in the morning they converse some (in summer the unattached males start their "cow" call early before leaving the roost). They come down from the roost later than

COURTESY CALIFORNIA DEPARTMENT OF FISH AND GAME

PLATE 73. *A typical roosting tree used by California valley quail.*

most birds by some 15 minutes to an hour, depending on the weather (Sumner, 1935).

The size of the covey seems to be governed more by the food supply and adequacy and spacing of shelter than anything else; this assumes that there are enough subcoveys to try to increase the covey size. Once a covey has built up to full size for the area they occupy—that is, to the carrying capacity of that habitat—it is practically impossible for any other quail or group of quail to join it; such strangers are then beaten off, and the covey maintains its size and dominates its territory. Only when its own numbers are so depleted that the "pressure is off" is it possible for further combinations of birds to take place. Winter coveys vary widely in size in different habitats, from 10 to over 200 birds.

RELATIONS WITH OTHER BIRDS

CALIFORNIA quail are found in the same areas with several other species of game birds, including the ring-necked pheasant, mourning dove, Hungarian partridge, chukar partridge, and its own relatives the mountain and Gambel's quails; each occupies a different ecological niche, so that the competition among them is limited. But it is probable that the range-carrying capacity limits the numbers of *all* of them together rather than each independently, since their food habits broadly overlap. The limited supplies of both food and shelter places these species in various degrees of competition in some areas, just as it does different coveys of quail.

The quail take care of themselves pretty well in their relations with other kinds of birds; they are able to beat off the attacks of most other birds. The more efficient predators, like the horned owl and blue darter hawks are exceptions; and marsh hawks and roadrunners in their attacks on quail chicks. The occasional parasitism of other birds' nests by quail has already been noted.

ADAPTABILITY TO CHANGING ENVIRONMENT

VAST changes have come about in the land of the quail in the past century: agriculture has taken over most of the area for growing crops and livestock; cities and highways make a network of completely converted type; brush control, rodent control, predator control, burning, the prevention of burning, drainage, the diversion of water—all have contributed importantly to the alteration of the environment. The usefulness of the land cover for quail habitat has changed with all these activities—mostly for the worse but occasionally for the better. As a result the numbers of quail have generally declined below the levels supported by primitive conditions. Despite this adverse effect on the quail, they have adapted to the new conditions remarkably well. An unadaptable bird might have been exterminated or reduced to remnant numbers; but quail have learned to use orchards, vineyards, and landscaping vegetation for shelter, and some crop fields for

feeding. They have accustomed themselves to living close to man, and yet have remained wary; they have survived his hunting, and have learned to be duly cautious of his highways and machines. They have altered their ways very well, but there are definite limits to their ability to survive under any circumstances. They cannot live on barren landscapes or in solid, extensive, heavy cover, any more than ever; they must have shelter, food, and water that suits their needs.

ADAPTABILITY TO ARTIFICIAL PROPAGATION AND TRANSPLANTATION

THIS quail is easily trapped, transported, and established in new areas that are suitable for it; it may also be grown in captivity on game farms—though not as easily as pheasants, bobwhites, and chukars. Wild-trapped birds have generally proved superior to the pen-reared ones for releasing in order to establish new colonies.

HABITAT OF THE CALIFORNIA QUAIL

THESE quail can live in a wide variety of habitat types, but certain requirements must be met; whether the area be in the coastal fog belt, an irrigated valley, mountain foothills, or desert, it must have good interspersion of herbaceous and woody cover, and it must have water. Quail are notably birds of cover-type edges. Emlen and Glading (1945) have put quail habitat in four classifications: (1) irrigated land; (2) dry farming land; (3) range land; (4) desert. Most widespread and most important is the range-land type.

There are many variations of habitat within each of these major types; they may be appraised by how well they provide the habitat essentials for feeding, drinking, roosting, loafing, escaping enemies, and nesting. These relations are shown in Table 19. It will be noted that the best populations are found in the open brushy range land, but if it is lacking in brush or is solidly brush the quail do not prosper. Medium high populations may be found in the similar but drier brushy desert, but only close to the limited places where water is available, such as canyons. Other habitats where medium high populations may be found are on irrigated lands devoted to certain field crops and vineyards; irrigated areas growing truck, orchard fruits, or pasture forage are generally poor quail range, as are the dry farming areas. Some of these types of habitat are more productive of quail where they exist in close arrangement with other types. For example, an irrigated orchard next to an area of nonbrushy range land would be a better combination than either one individually, since each makes up for some of the other's deficiencies, and between them they meet all requirements fairly well.

Irrigated lands have plentiful water and may have good food supplies, depending on the crops grown and the methods of culture, but they generally lack shelter of all kinds. Some of the crops that provide some of the food requirements are clover, alfalfa, and Sudan grass. The presence of ditches and streams provides some weed and shrub cover, roadsides may have grass or weedy cover, and house yards often have trees and shrubs arranged so that quail can make use of them.

Dry farming lands lack water and shelter as a rule, but abound in food; where water is available along with woody plants, as around

TABLE 19

HABITAT TYPES FOR CALIFORNIA QUAIL*

TYPE OF HABITAT	EVALUATION OF HABITAT†					QUAIL POPULA-TION‡	REMARKS
	food	water	escape cover	roosting cover	nesting, loafing cover		
IRRIGATED LAND:							
Truck farms	—	xx	—	—	—	Low	Quail restricted to borders
Field crops	x	xx	—	—	x	Medium	Variable with crop
Orchards	—	xx	x	x	—	Low	Varies with degree of cultivation
Vineyards	x	xx	xx	—	x	Medium	" " " " "
Pastures	xx	xx	—	—	—	Low	Quail only in brush areas
DRY FARMING:							
Nonirrigated orchards				x	—	Low	Used only for roosts if cultivated
Hay, grain, etc.	xx	—	—	—	x	Low	Limited to brush and water areas
RANGE LAND:							
Nonbrushy	xx	—	—	—	x	Low	" " " " " "
Open brushy cover	xx	x	xx	xx	xx	High	Birds widely distributed
Heavy brush	—	—	xx	x	—	Low	Birds along edges near water
DESERT:							
Brushy	x	—	xx	x	x	Medium	Birds only near water

* From Emlen and Glading, 1945.
† Symbols: — = low value; x = moderate value; xx = high value.
‡ Population density: low, 15–100 acres per quail; medium, 5–15 acres per quail; high, less than 5 acres per quail.

houses and along permanent water courses, quail may be found in good numbers.

The vast range lands in quail country provide the best and some of the poorest of quail habitat; which it is depends on the natural conditions of rainfall, topography, and soils, and on the land management—especially the grazing intensity and the use or control of fire; the range lands that have scattered trees and brush and well-distributed water are ideal. This combination is associated with moderate to light rainfall, rolling topography or foothills next to valleys, nondrouthy soils, moderate grazing of domestic livestock, and occasional burning. The fertile soils of the Coast Range, for example, produce more quail than the poorer soils of the Sierra Nevada foothills, other things being equal. The plant associations on range land may include such trees and shrubs as these: willows, California live oak, interior live oak, silver lupine, California buckeye, mariposa manzanita, blue oak, Rocky Mountain white oak, California laurel, digger pine, sagebrush, coast sagebrush, black sage, tree lupine, deerweed, rabbit brush, quail brush, western chokecherry, gooseberry, California buckthorn, and wedge-leaf ceanothus. Among the herbs and grasses are commonly found tarweed, turkey mullein, mustard, dock, western wheat grass, foxtail fescue, brome grasses, California Croton, Spanish clover, filaree, and smartweed. These range lands sometimes extend up mountains to rather high altitudes; the California quail may be found occasionally as high as 8,500 feet, but at high altitudes it is generally replaced by the mountain quail.

The deserts that support California valley quail are relatively humid, as deserts go. They have a scattering of brush and small trees and a sparse growth of annual grasses and weeds; the kinds found are mainly the most dry-tolerant ones of the group that live on range lands. Various cacti are common, some of which have a high cover value for quail. The key to the usefulness of this habitat for quail is the water supply; where it is adequate there

may be good populations; without it they cannot live here at all, and vast areas are like this. It is on this range that the California and Gambel's quails are both found, with the Gambel's quail tolerating the drier habitats.

The most common nesting cover is open herbaceous growth. The nest itself may be next to or under an overhang of some brush, but is more commonly next to a clump of weeds or grasses. Such sites abound over much of the range and desert lands. It is an open site. Brush land is not acceptable. Vineyards provide a satisfactory nesting place if not too closely cultivated, as do field edges on irrigated lands. Open cover with rocks alone or with sparse vegetation sometimes offer enough protection for nesting. Fields of truck crops, tree fruits, and pasture are of little use.

Roosting cover is composed primarily of trees or large shrubs. If the birds have to use low shrubs for roosting, they have high losses from predators. California live oak and California laurel are examples of the best type of trees for roosting, but any thick-branched tree or tall shrub will do; evergreen species are best in the winter. Roosting sites are plentiful in most of the rangeland and desert habitats except the all-grass range. On other areas good roosting places are likely to be scarce except in orchards, around houses, and along streams and canyons.

Escape cover is any dense growth of shrubs, vines, or rank grasses or herbs in which natural enemies cannot catch the birds easily. It is lower and thicker than good roosting cover, and taller and denser than good nesting cover. It helps the birds to escape hunters without flushing, especially if the terrain is rough. It is generally adequate in all range land except the nonbrushy type, in desert scrub, vineyards, and some orchards. Heavy, continual grazing in certain types may cause escape cover to lose its effectiveness by destroying all cover within three or four feet of the ground under a browse line. It is lacking in dry farming country and in open-crop irrigated fields.

Feeding cover requires a large quantity of

PLATE 74. *Habitat of the California quail in the costal hills of San Benito County, California. It is an interspersion of brush and open grass and weed cover.*

annual herbs that supply the seeds the birds eat. All the brushy types furnish fair to good supplies of food except thick brush. Orchards and truck crop fields are poor sources of wild seeds, owing to intense cultivation. Most pastures and grain fields are good feeding areas around the edges where cover is near.

Loafing cover is substantially the same as escape cover. The birds like to hang around under bushes that are open at the base and around the sides, but with shade above.

Free water is essential during the hot, dry summer in all quail range outside the humid coastal belt; there the birds can get enough dew and succulent vegetation to meet their needs, but elsewhere they must find water to drink every day of low humidity. Since their daily travel radius is so small, the birds can use only habitat that is within about 300 yards of a source of water, and even less in the nesting and brood-raising seasons. In a country that is predominantly dry this is a critical limitation. There are vast areas of range that are suitable for quail use except for the lack of water. On the opposite side, irrigated farm land, so deficient in some of the other needs, is the one habitat where water is uniformly plentiful. In all the other habitat types water is deficient, except in some of the open brushy rangeland.

In our discussion of the types of habitat and the sorts of cover used for different functions, the importance of interspersion has been mentioned several times. This need for different kinds of cover arranged close together to provide habitat for *all* the birds' needs in a small area cannot be overemphasized. Their habitat is like a house they live in; if any vital room is missing the whole structure is untenable.

FOOD HABITS

THE California quail is almost wholly a vegetarian in its adult life. Insects and related forms make up only about 1% to 3% of the annual diet, and that is taken almost all in the spring and mostly by nesting hens. Its plant food diet changes greatly from season to season, chiefly as a necessity. Evidently the bird is a seed eater by choice, but seeds are almost unavailable during the winter months. At that time quail live largely on green leaves that come with the winter rains. Since the greens are available only from fall to spring, one might conclude that they preferred them to seeds. The question of which they prefer is partly academic, since in any case they have to take what is available; that means seeds in summer and greens in winter. But quail fed on steel-cut yellow corn at the Dune Lakes Club in San Luis Obispo County, California, used this alone for over 90% of their food all year long (Glading, Selleck, and Ross, 1945). This indicates that their use of greens for a high proportion of their diet in winter is more a necessity than a choice, and the use of seeds is more often by choice. The proportion of seeds and greens in the total year-round diet is about 60% to 75% seeds and 25% to 30% greens. Fruits of shrubs and oak acorns are eaten some during the fall, but are not made use of in anything like the proportion of their availability in their habitat. The proportions of these different kinds of foods eaten at each season are shown graphically in Figure 23.

The quails' foods come primarily from annual plants. These germinate and grow each winter with the coming of the rains; they go to seed in spring and early summer as the foliage dries up. During the green period the birds feed on foliage, plus such seeds as they can find on the ground left over from the previous year's crop. As the new seeds ripen they shift their eating habits to them. The relationship of food to cover type is thus very clear; it is abundant wherever the ground is bare enough for the weeds to develop. Open brushlands and non-brushy grasslands are the best food-producing cover types. Some cultivated crops also provide food, primarily the small grains and hay. Ground covered by dense brush and intensively cultivated fields have little quail food.

A great variety of plants furnish some seed or leaf food for quail; Sumner (1935) lists 103 kinds of plants and 16 kinds of animals found in 102 quail stomachs examined by him; the total number is no doubt much higher. The great bulk of this food, however, comes from a relatively few species of plants. The most important ones differ somewhat from place to place, but the 29 species or genera that are most significant are discussed below. In most places and most years these compose 90% or more of the birds' total food. These plants are listed in Table 20, together with the season of most use.

Legumes commonly furnish from a quarter to a third of the year's food; it is principally seeds, though leaves of some kinds are eaten too. The California bur clover is a staple quail food where it occurs as livestock forage. The seeds are eaten from October to December, and the leaves from February to May. Seeds of a number of kinds of *Lotus* are eaten from May to December. American deervetch or Spanish clover is outstanding, but foothill deervetch, broom deervetch, and Chilean deervetch are also used. The seeds of this group are *preferred* foods, and are eaten in greater proportion to their total food than the plants exist in the cover. Clovers furnish seeds and greens from

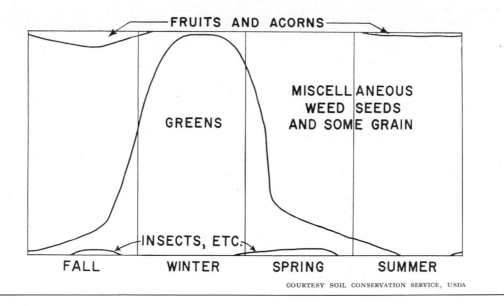

FIGURE 23. *Types of food used by California quail by seasons.* (*After Emlen and Glading, 1945; Glading, Biswell and Smith, 1940; and Sumner, 1935.*)

April to December and are a preferred food; among the species used are the annuals pinole clover, tomcat clover, and puff or sour clover. Seeds of lupines are preferred food from June to January; the species of most importance include lunara lupine (a perennial), partcolor lupine (perennial), arroyo lupine (annual), and bicolor lupine (annual). The seeds of feather acacia, a tree, and occasionally other acacias are eaten from August to March, and are one of the few types of seeds available in winter. American vetch seeds are eaten in October. Many other legume plants furnish smaller quantities of food that may be quite important locally.

Grasses and grains provide both greens and seeds. The leaves of grasses are a staple food throughout the birds' range, but grain seed use is localized, mainly where barley and oats are grown. The amount of the year's food coming from these sources may be a tenth to a quarter of the total. The leaves of many grasses are eaten. But much of this material found in the stomachs of birds used for food

habit studies has been unidentifiable as to species; thus the list of the kinds of grasses in Table 20 is not complete. Many bromes and some fescues, wild oats, wild barley, and others are common range grasses, and are among the kinds eaten from August through the winter to May. The introduced Italian ryegrass provides seeds and greens from February to November. Some annual bluegrass seeds are taken in the spring, but most wild grass seeds are unimportant as quail food.

Seeds of annual weeds generally make up the largest volume of food from any one group of plants, and this is specially true in summer; some also are eaten as greens in the winter. These plants may furnish 20% to 60% or more of the year's food supply. Filaree seeds and greens are staple foods from April to December. Tarweeds, especially *Hemizonia congesta* and *Microseris douglasii*, have seeds that are eaten in late summer and early fall. Seeds of turkey mullein are preferred summer and fall food, and the leaves of gilia are highly selected in winter and early spring. Fiddleneck greens are

TABLE 20

PRIMARY FOODS OF THE CALIFORNIA QUAIL*

GROUPS AND KINDS OF PLANTS	PARTS EATEN	WHEN EATEN
LEGUMES (25%–35% of all food)		
California bur clover	Seeds	Oct.–Dec.
" " "	Leaves	Feb.–May
Lupines (lunara, particolor, arroyo, bicolor)	Seeds	June–Jan.
Deervetches (American, foothill, broom, Chilean)	Seeds	May–Dec.
Clovers (pinole, tomcat, puff and others)	Seeds; leaves	Apr.–Dec.
Acacias (feather and others)	Seeds	Aug.–March
American vetch (and others)	Seeds	October
GRASSES, including grains (10%–25% of all food)		
Barley	Seeds	Aug.–Feb.
Italian ryegrass	Seeds; leaves	Feb.–Nov.
Bromes, fescues, etc.	Leaves	Aug.–May
Oats	Seeds	December
Annual bluegrass	Seeds	Apr.–May
ANNUAL WEEDS (20%–60% of food)		
Filarees (red stem, alfileria)	Seeds; leaves	Apr.–Dec.
Tarweeds (*Hemizonia; Microseris*)	Seeds	Aug.–Nov.
Napa thistle (and other thistles)	Seeds	June–Nov.
Turkey mullein	Seeds	July–Dec.
Popcorn flower	Seeds	Apr.–July
Gilias	Leaves	Jan.–Apr.
Fiddleneck	Seeds	March
"	Leaves	June
California buttercup	Leaves	Jan.; Apr.–May
Pimpernel	Seeds	June–Oct.
Sheep sorrel	Seeds	October
Mustard	Seeds	Dec.–Jan.
Chickweed starwort	Seeds; leaves	Apr.–May
WOODY PLANTS (3%–5% of food)		
Oaks (interior live, blue)	Acorns	Aug.–Dec.
Poison oak	Fruit	Oct.–Nov.
Snowberry	Fruit	October
Brambles (thimbleberry, California blackberry and others)	Fruit	June–July
Christmasberry	Fruit	Oct.–Dec.
Saltbush	Leaves	June–Sept.
(see also acacias under Legumes)		

* Based on food habits records in Summer (1935); Glading, Biswell, and Smith (1940); McLean, (1930); and others.

taken in late winter, and the seeds in early summer. Leaves of California buttercup and chickweed starwort are used in winter and spring. Other weed seeds eaten in significant amounts include napa thistle, popcorn flower, pimpernel, sheep sorrel, mustard, and chickweed starwort.

Woody plants furnish surprisingly little food for these quail, considering the habitat in which they live. Shrubs are usually close by at all times, and many of them yield fruits, leaves, seeds, and nuts that are potential wildlife food. But the California quail eschews most of them entirely, and all of them to a large degree. The proportion of the annual larder that comes from these plants is usually about 3% to 5%. Most of the woody plant foods that are used are taken in the fall. Acorns of the blue and interior live oaks, which are small, are consumed then. Fruits of the snowberry, California and other blackberries, thimbleberry, poison oak, and Christmasberry are others eaten in summer and fall as available. Leaves of the saltbush provide some summer and fall greens on range and desert areas at a time when greens are scarce.

The food of young quail is practically the same as that of the adults, except for the first few weeks; the proportion of insects and other small animals may be a third or more of the diet at that time. This is much less animal food than most young gallinaceous birds eat. When the chicks are small they avoid some of the larger seed foods, such as bur clover pods and lupine seeds (Sumner, 1935), but otherwise their foods soon become the same as those of their parents. There is some evidence that the food of laying hens is similarly high in insects, thus satisfying a possible dietary need (Glading, Biswell, and Smith, 1940).

The water requirements of this quail have already been discussed under "Habitat," since it is such a critical factor. The water need is for ingestion, and must be met daily all year long. These birds are just about as able as bob-

white quail to substitute succulent foods for free water, and they do so to some extent when suitable greens and fruits are available. At such times they may go several days without visiting a water source. The trouble is that such foods are not available in much of the species range during the dry months of the year. Thus the presence of free water is an essential for habitable quail cover.

Quail need grit in order to grind their seed foods in preparation for digestion; this is obtained as gravel and small bits of stone, and rarely is scarce enough to be a problem. They occasionally use hard seeds such as those of the rose as a substitute for grit—or at least it works that way (Beer and Tidyman, 1942).

The relation of cover type to food has already been discussed, but it should be noted further that the management of food-producing cover is as important as the type itself. Chief among the influences that affect quail food supplies in California are the degree and type of grazing, the degree and timing of cultivation, and the degree and timing of burning, controlled or otherwise. Weather may supersede all these, but more of that later. Quail foods on range lands generally are favored by moderately heavy grazing use, or lacking moderately heavy use, a light fire at the proper season will foster filaree, bur clover, and other preferred foods over some of the nonpreferred, coarser grasses. Likewise, on irrigated pastures moderately heavy use fosters good conditions for California quail. Extreme use of course results in erosion and consequent loss of food values.

Cultivation has a vast effect on quail foods. Most high-producing California vineyards and orchards are kept so free of weeds as to be completely without quail foods. In other situations early spring cultivation may actually foster the production of late summer annuals like turkey mullein or tarweeds, both of which furnish ample supplies of late summer and early fall forage for quail and doves.

Weather conditions have a greater influence

on the food supplies of this quail than with most game birds. The yearly development of the crop of annual weeds, and later the maturity of their seeds, are both dependent on a small but vital amount of fall and winter rain; when this fails to come in adequate amounts, quail are hard pressed to find enough to eat. When drouths are prolonged the birds may starve, their reproduction is affected, and their populations decline.

Quail regularly feed twice a day—early in the morning for several hours after sunrise and for a couple of hours before sunset. They do not travel far in search for food if it is plentiful; a few hundred feet may be the extent of a day's movement, and this largely because they always keep moving while eating. When food is scarce, or widely scattered as in deserts, they move faster and spend a longer time eating than otherwise, and they travel farther. The distance they move is largely governed by the food supply, the spacing of cover, and how much they are harassed by enemies. They pick their food off plants or off the ground surface, and scratch in the ground surface like chickens to turn up seeds. In a day's time they may consume 20 to 25 grams of food, or about 13% to 15% of their weight. This amounts to 19.3 pounds a year, based on calculations by Sumner (1935).

Quail food habits are economically almost wholly neutral. The grain they take is waste, and the greens that come from cultivated crops are of negligible importance to the farmer; the rest is from wild plants. They do not consume enough insects to be of any account as an aid to agriculture. The California Department of Fish and Game reports that quail cause only minor depredations on crops; these depredations are confined largely to succulent fruits like grapes, plums, and strawberries, and to small garden plots in the spring. Under certain circumstances quail eat these crops in lieu of free water; depredations generally can be controlled by furnishing free water (Glading, letter).

THE EFFECTS OF WEATHER AND CLIMATE

THE distribution of the California quail is limited by the combination of temperature and snow, and by aridity. They are not well adapted to living in freezing temperatures, and when snow lies three inches or more deep for very long they become very sluggish and suffer heavy mortality. The quail is not found in areas where those conditions are common in winter. In the East and South its range is limited chiefly by aridity. It is not the dryness itself, but rather the drinking water, food, and cover conditions associated with the very dry desert lands that make them untenable. High humidity does not affect them where it is common in their geographic range.

Within the occupied range, weather exerts a major influence on the quail's welfare; this is specially true in the drier habitats. The delicate balance between plant growth and the very limited rainfall has already been noted; when the rains fail the food supply is impaired. When this condition is severe, there may be starvation mortality; but even when the birds survive, their condition is so poor that reproduction may be affected. In very dry years few birds even nest. Drouth reduces the quails' limited water supplies and causes them to congregate at the remaining water holes, where they become easy prey to natural enemies and possibly to disease. In years of plentiful winter rains and good food conditions almost all the birds nest, and there is evidence that they even lay larger clutches than usual (McLean, 1930). The onset of the hot, dry summer brings nesting to an end, even for birds whose early nests have been broken up. In exceptionally cool summers renesting may continue through August.

When dry years are combined with hard winters, the production of quail is very low. This happened in much of the California range in 1949; there was no succulent vegetation, and the birds failed to nest. Examination showed that the ovaries of hen quail had not developed to breeding condition (*P-R Quarterly*, Oct. 1950). Then, when this condition was followed by a bad winter, survival was low, and the population declined below its ordinary spring level.

Wet weather during the early brood season is not very common, but may cause considerable loss of young chicks when it occurs. McLean (1930) describes the fates of two broods he observed in a coastal area. One hatched 12 chicks on May 26, the other 14 on May 27. Heavy ground fogs rolled in night after night. By June 5 the broods numbered 5 and 7 chicks respectively. The fogs continued, and the chicks showed "dumpiness." Heavy rains followed, and by June 11 the first brood was reduced to one youngster and the second was annihilated. A third and later brood of 16 dropped to 8 after a severe rainstorm; a search of the area revealed that four of the water-soaked chicks died.

There is little doubt that weather is a primary factor in determining the changes in quail-population levels; the habitat sets the carrying capacity, but weather conditions have a vast effect on the number of birds actually present within that carrying capacity.

PREDATION; DISEASES AND PARASITES; ACCIDENTS

PREDATION

PREDATION is the most obvious source of natural quail mortality. The greatest amount of predation over most typical California ranges is on nests. Most losses of young and adults to natural enemies are conditioned by the habitat.

At least 18 kinds of birds, mammals, snakes, and insects are known to have eaten quail eggs; most of them eat quail eggs rarely, and find them largely by accident. A few of them may be of real consequence in affecting production.

Ground squirrels, particularly the Beechey's and Douglas ground squirrels, may cause high nest losses when and where these rodents are abundant; of 96 nests observed by Glading (1938) in 1937, 31% were raided by them. In this same study Glading compared the quail populations on an area on which the squirrels were poisoned with one where they were not molested. The February quail population rose from 90 to 229 the first year and was 220 the second following year on the poisoned area, whereas the quail numbers on the nonpoisoned area went in the same time from 90 to 135 and down again to 90. Horn (1938b) recounted the evidence against the ground squirrels, and concluded: "From these instances of destruction of quail eggs by ground squirrels and the marked increase in quail on large areas following the reduction of these animals, it is strongly indicated that they are a factor influencing the density of quail populations."

Ground squirrels become important predators only when they are abundant; there were about 10 per acre on Glading's study area. They find quail nests simply by stumbling on them. At a density of 10 per acre, each squirrel has a plot only 66 feet square to cover in order to reach every square foot. Some of the other quail nest predators achieve their results with more stealth. The house cat, bobcat, coyote, skunk, and fox may be locally destructive, and between them account for a large number of eggs. Of the 96 nests checked by Glading (1938), 17, or 18%, were taken by these mammals. Other predators known to account occasionally for a quail nest include Cooper's hawk (by killing the hen), California jay, crow, raven, shrikes, magpie, dog, gopher snake (*Pituophis*), king snake (*Lampropeltis*), milk snake (*Lampropeltis*), and rattlesnake (*Crotalus*), and the red fire ant (*Solenopsis*).

Few predators are able to take adult quail with any regularity. Young quail are vulnerable for a few weeks after hatching, but they are well guarded by the alert parents. A few of the hawks are the most destructive of the quail eaters, particularly the Cooper's, sharp-shinned, and marsh hawks. Where the marsh hawk is very common on quail range it is sometimes the most frequent cause of chick predation, but the blue darters generally rate this title. Quail pay little attention to many of the less efficient bird-catchers. Observers working on a California Pittman-Robertson project report that bobcats drank at a watering station within 15 feet of quail without attempting to bother them. These birds paid little heed to buteo hawks or eagles flying overhead, but were severely harassed by blue darters (*P-R Quarterly,* January, 1952). Other predators that may be of local importance in quail mortality are the horned owl, road runner, house cat, bobcat, coyote, and fox. Weasels, prairie falcons, and rough-leg hawks occasionally catch a distressed bird. Some of the snakes have been known to catch quail chicks.

In summary, predators cause a high loss of nests, may take considerable numbers of adults (usually under conditions of poor habitat or bad weather), and account for a small number of chicks. In the total it is an important mortality factor. Its effects can be lessened by good habitat management on range and farm, and under some circumstances by the judicious reduction of certain species of rodents and predators.

DISEASES AND PARASITES

Post-mortems have been performed on several hundred California quail, and thousands of blood smears and fecal samples from live birds have been studied; despite this, we know relatively little of the importance of disease as a mortality factor. A number of kinds of parasites and disease organisms have been found in wild quail (and others in game farm and aviary birds), but few natural deaths have been confirmed from this source, and no significant epidemics observed.

A local March die-off of quail on 140 acres was observed by Sumner (1935). A total of eight birds died a natural, nonviolent death, but autopsies failed to reveal the cause. Four more quail were trapped from the area and examined without uncovering any clues; as Sumner says, " . . . the epidemic, whatever its nature, had subsided." But this event does indicate that disease is a potential mortality factor.

A common disease of this quail is caused by a protozoan, malarialike blood parasite, *Haemoproteus lophortyx.* It is transmitted to the bird by the bite of a hippoboscid fly, *Lynchia hirsuti,* which is a common ectoparasite. According to O'Roke (in McLean, 1930), about 45% of the birds in California were parasitized. Herman and Glading (1942) checked the blood smears of 503 birds from one area in central California and found 84% infected. Very acute cases of this disease may be fatal, or cause the bird to be so weakened that it succumbs from some other mortality agent; the vast majority of cases are chronic. It has been shown that once a quail is infected with this organism it remains infected for the rest of its life (Herman and Bischoff, 1949). This fact, combined with a high incidence of infestation of the alternate host fly (Sumner [1935] found one quail out of five with the hippoboscid fly), indicates how easily this disease is transmitted. It is a potential source of serious epidemic, but so far is not known to have caused one.

Five species of protozoan coccidia of the genus *Eimeria* have been identified from quail by Herman and Chattin (1943). They examined some 3,500 fecal samples, and found the incidence of coccidiosis to be very variable geographically; the lowest incidence was 20% and the highest over 90%. The intensity of infection was low in birds from all areas except one. No mortality has been noted resulting from this disease, though it is potentially dangerous. These authors concluded, " . . . it is impossible to state how much of the coccidia found was of importance pathogenically, or had any effect on the health of the wild birds."

Flagellate protozoans of the genus *Trichomonas* are common in quail, but are not pathogenic and may be commensal. Internal parasitic worms are not prevalent, but some round-worms and tapeworms have been found; so far as is known they are of no significance. Other ectoparasites known to occur in this bird are a bird louse of the genus *Gonicotes*, occasional ticks and mites, and another hippoboscid fly, *Stilbometopia impressa*, in addition to the one already mentioned (O'Roke in McLean, 1930). From the present evidence the California quail is relatively free from serious disease.

ACCIDENTS

MORTALITY from a number of kinds of accidents is common. Nests are occasionally destroyed by fire, flood, mowing, plowing, trampling by live-stock, disturbance by workmen, and other molestations. Farm machinery damage to nests is relatively low in this species, since it does not ordinarily nest in hay or grain fields. Some such losses do occur along roadsides and in field edges. Five of the 96 nests checked by Glading (1938) were lost in accidents, four from the trampling of stock and one by a construction crew; 18 of the other nests were abandoned, 13 before laying and 5 after, some of which may have been caused by similar events. On irrigated lands some nests are de-stroyed by flooding.

Young quail succumb from accidents of several sorts. Their quest for water commonly results in drowning. Large irrigation ditches are specially bad, because of the steep banks and fast flowing water, which can easily trap a careless chick. They sometimes drown while drinking at tanks and other watering places. Hay mowing and the cultivation of vineyards and orchards catch a few chicks unawares.

Farming operations also kill adult quail; setting hens, along with their eggs, are oc-casionally victims of mowing. Brush fires that run wild trap many quail that do not attempt escape by flight. Flight collisions with fences, moving vehicles, buildings, and other obstacles are fairly frequent. During Sumner's (1935) quail study he encountered 14 cases of col-lisions, 10 of which resulted in death. Drowning in water tanks kills a few adult quail as well as young.

Poisons used in rodent and insect control are a source of some trouble. How much mortality results from poisons cannot be gauged, but in some places it may be considerable. The use of thallium in rodent-control work is dangerous to quail and other birds, as well as to the squirrels it is designed to kill. These quail, however, are quite tolerant of the two principal rodenticides currently employed in California, namely, Compound 1080 and strychnine; in recent years this problem has been minor. The fumigation of citrus orchards with cyanide gas under tents at night may trap some roosting quail (Emlen and Glading, 1945).

Accidents cause a year-round attrition of quail numbers. It is not usually spectacular, nor very great at any one time or from any single cause, but adds up to a major source of decimation.

MAN'S RELATIONS WITH THE CALIFORNIA QUAIL

THERE is no doubt that man was the major factor that caused the populations of quail to decline after about 1880. Sumner (1935) names the chief reasons in the order of their importance for this long-term decrease: over-hunting; the destruction of food and cover by clean farming, overgrazing, and fire control; and the exclusive use by man of water sources. Today man remains the chief determinant of the land's carrying capacity for quail; he is also responsible for a large share of quail losses as hunter, farmer, and rancher. Glading (letter) disagrees with the hypothesis that hunting has or has had any long-range effect on quail numbers; he feels that, given equal habitat conditions, quail numbers are as great as ever in historical times. The market hunting take, though admittedly vast, had no more effect on populations than modern hunting. Where habitats are unchanged, or restored to capacity, quail populations are present in numbers commensurate with former times. Wallace Macgregor, game biologist for the California Department of Fish and Game, reports counting concentrations in the summer of 1953 as high as 700 birds in restored habitats.

AS A HUNTER

THIS quail is one of the most popular upland game birds in California; about a third of the licensed hunters find part or all of their sport in its pursuit, and bag an annual harvest of some 1,200,000 or more in most years (*California Wildlife Conservation Board Report,* 1950; Emlen and Glading, 1945). It is also hunted in Oregon and Washington and in a few localities of Nevada and Idaho.

Sportsmen find this bird a real challenge in hunting. Its wariness and tendency to run rather than flush is exasperating, but is at the same time a challenge to the hunter's skill. Hunting with trained dogs is preferred over walking them up, even though the birds frequently refuse to lie for the dogs. At least the dog can circle them when they are running, which is more than a man can do by himself. Another habit of quail when pursued is to go up into the foliage of dense shrubs or trees and freeze while the dogs and hunters go by. When flushed they make a speedy target, sometimes flying as fast as 51 miles per hour (McLean, 1930). If not too scared, the covey holds together, and on alighting takes off at top speed on foot, preferably uphill. The daily visit to water holes provides one way by which many are killed. By merely concealing himself nearby the hunter can kill the birds easily, as they approach or leave the drinking place. Obviously this is not a very sporting way of hunting.

Despite their ability to elude the hunter, the hunting harvest is on a par with that of most other gallinaceous species. On an experimental hunting area of 720 acres in central California the kill in four successive years, 1938–9 to 1941–2, was 26.5%, 25.3%, 18.6%, and 24.1% respectively (Glading and Saarni, 1944). Kill records were kept on a hunting club property along the California coast for a number of years, and population censuses were made in 1941 and 1942. These counts showed that out of a total population of 2,240 birds in 1941, 598 (27%) were bagged and 359 more crippled; thus the total loss from hunting was about 43% (Glading, Selleck, and Ross, 1945). In 1942, a year of lower populations and lighter hunting, the bag was about 16% to 18% of the population, and the total hunting loss between 27% and 30%. Emlen and Glading (1945) state that "On many unmanaged ranges, hunting annually removes 10 to 25 percent of the quail without bad effect."

The crippling loss of 60% of the bag found by the observers on the managed club grounds is rather astounding. The crippling loss on the Madera County experimental area in central California was considerably less, but still high; it varied in four years from 27% to 42% of the bag, and averaged 37% (Glading and Saarni, 1944). A very interesting point in connection with crippling revealed in this study concerns the effect of using dogs; the crippling loss by hunters using dogs was less than one-third that of dogless hunters!

The hunters on the Madera County study area bagged an average of about six birds each, and took 1.2 hours of hunting per bird. A later California study showed that 119 hunters bagged 713 quail or six per hunter (*P-R Quarterly,* April 1952). The total state harvest divided by the number of quail hunters reveals a surprisingly large annual bag of nine birds per man, even though it includes some Gambel's quail (*Cal. Wildlife Cons. Bd. Report,* 1950).

AS A FARMER AND RANCHER

WHEN the white man took over the lands of the West and developed them for agriculture, the changes he wrought had tremendous effects on the quail. Not all the changes damaged the land cover as quail habitat, but many of them did. And even if overhunting caused the first big declines in quail numbers—which is doubtful—it has been agriculture (including livestock grazing) that has prevented recovery.

Where the soils were adapted to growing crops, and water was available, the original grass, brush, and forest land was cleared. Under intensive crop production and clean farming methods these lands lack adequate shelter for quail, and the interspersion of cover types so essential to good habitat. Much of this land is valueless for quail, and the rest is poor to medium.

The sections that could not be watered and cropped were stocked with cattle, sheep, and other domestic livestock. Excessive numbers of animals were grazed on much of this land, and deterioration of the cover resulted. This alone damaged its habitat quality, but more than that, it set other events in motion. Rodent populations increased tremendously as the plant composition of the badly overgrazed land was altered in their favor; in areas where these rodents were abundant they became a severe deterrent to successful quail nesting. To overcome the rodents, which ranchers believed were the *cause* rather than the *result* of range deterioration, great poisoning campaigns were undertaken. Strychnine-treated grain was spread far and wide, and though it did little direct damage to quail, it caused much loss of other wildlife. In fact the relief from squirrels robbing their nests greatly benefited the quail in many areas. Then in 1928 was begun the use of the new and more effective rodenticide, thallium sulphate. It proved to be poisonous to quail as well as to rodents, and a new mortality factor was added. Government agencies also carried on intensive predator-control work against coyotes, mountain lions, and bobcats, in order to protect domestic livestock. None of these animals is of much importance as a quail predator; but their reduction in numbers did complicate the rodent problem, since they (the predators) live mainly on small mammals.

The clearing of brush from range land and the cutting of forest cover benefited quail as long as it didn't go too far. Opening up woodland or solid brush stands created a more varied habitat; but complete clearing eliminated quail almost entirely. Man has been responsible for causing very destructive fires in some of the brushlands. More recently, however, he has contrived to prevent and control fires to such an extent that many range areas that were once good quail cover have grown into useless thick brush. Because this dense brush cover is poor stock range as well as poor quail habitat, something may be done to correct the mistaken view that *all* fire on these lands is bad.

Great changes have been made in the natural water distribution because of the water demands of agriculture and of cities. Where water sources useful to quail have been appropriated for man's exclusive use, quail have been eliminated. On the other hand, man has developed water that quail can use in many places where it did not exist before. For example, in the Kettleman Hills of Fresno and Kings Counties, California, the country was barren and had a low quail population. Then oil was discovered. "With the advent of the . . . oil development, water was spread virtually throughout the North Dome, and a consequent boom in the quail population resulted" (Glading, Enderlin, and Hjersman, 1945). Interestingly, the oil company men took the trouble to fix their water pipes so that here and there quail would have water. Water is often a miracle-worker for quail, as it is for farm crops.

In all these ways, and in many other smaller details, man has altered the Western landscape. The changes have been complicated, but the net result has been a lowering of the carrying capacity of most quail habitat.

AS A CONSERVATIONIST

SOON after the beginning of the 20th century, laws were enacted that made the California quail exclusively a sporting bird. Hunting was limited to a relatively short period in autumn, and daily and seasonal bag limits were established. This was man's first deliberate effort of great significance to conserve this species. Restocking with wild-trapped and game-farm-reared birds was practiced soon after, and there were instances of predator control and artificial feeding carried on by sportsmen's clubs. Some of these efforts were quite successful (Glading, Selleck, and Ross, 1945). In recent years a great deal of work has been done on habitat improvement, particularly with water developments and artificial shelters on arid range land. The quail has proved to be a rather easily managed species, and man is more and more demonstrating an ability to be a conservationist as well as a destroyer of quail.

PRODUCTIVITY AND POPULATIONS

PRODUCTIVITY

The California quail has a high reproductive potential. It is rather loosely monogamous, in that new mates may be acquired very quickly during the reproductive season if one member of a pair is killed. They breed the year after birth, and normally have but one brood each year. There is some circumstantial evidence that rarely a pair may have a second brood.

Young quail have an even sex ratio, but among the adults there is usually a small excess of males. Emlen (1940) summarized the records on sex ratio for 15,728 birds gathered from hunter kills, banding records, and field observations, and found an average of 53% males. There was little variation in the results from the different sources of data. He found that the ratio follows a definite annual cycle, being lowest in males in early fall (when the young are first included), at 51% males, and highest in late spring and summer, at 56% males. There is much local variation in different years, as one would expect, and also some indication of continuing differences in various sections of the range. For example, a three-year average of birds from foothill range lands of central California was barely over half males, while birds taken at the same time from the

Sacramento Valley had a predominance of 58% males. The shortage of females was attributed to their higher mortality during nesting season (Emlen, letter).

According to Emlen and Glading (1945), "Nearly all the adult females lay at least one set of eggs during each nesting season, except during extreme drought." But there are indications that the proportion of hen quail that nest is less than with most gallinaceous birds. McLean (1930) also pointed out that "During dry years . . . California and valley quail do not nest in large numbers, and locally perhaps not at all." He then goes on to say that "Certain adult birds do not nest apparently even in good years, as often flocks of birds high up on ridges are encountered that are extremely wild and show no sign of having paired off." McLean collected some of these birds in June 1928, dissected them, and " . . . came to the conclusion that they were very old and sexually spent." If this condition is typical of California quail, it is an exception to the general rule in gallinaceous birds. At any rate, whatever the reason, evidently there is imperfection in the completeness of breeding by hens, and this is very acute in years of bad drouth.

The birds that nest but are broken up usually try again. In cool summers renesting may continue even into August, some birds trying a third time. If the usual hot, dry summer comes early, renesting is reduced.

MORTALITY

The mortality of quail nests is high. Of 96 nests checked by Glading (1938) on a study area in the foothills of the Sierra Nevada in central California, only 17 hatched—a mortality of 82%; this included 13 nests abandoned before laying. Without these the loss was 79%, still very high. Predation was the main cause of destruction, with ground squirrels doing well over half; accidents and desertions accounted for the rest.

A two-year study on a coastal area with a

high quail population revealed a nest loss of 60% in 1941 and 82% in 1942 (Glading, Selleck, and Ross, 1945); here, too, abandonment played a large part in the loss. In some of the abandoned nests two or more hens had laid a large number of eggs; others were due to molestation. The rest of the nests that failed were destroyed by predators, with the exception of one that was burned. A factor that may have been involved in the great change in mortality from one year to the next was a program of predator control that was not carried out intensively the second year.

Sumner (1935) computed a nest loss of 60%. If we discounted the importance of abandonment on the basis that the birds involved renested early, the figure of 60% would be reasonably consistent with the records noted above. Because of the persistence of quail in renesting as long as weather is favorable, the ultimate proportion of hens that hatch a brood is probably from 30% to 60%.

No data are available on the infertility of eggs or the number that fail to hatch because of incomplete embryonic development, but according to Sumner (1935) it " . . . appears to be comparatively rare."

The first two weeks after hatching are the most critical period in the early life of a quail. They are flightless, completely without experience, and have little feather coating to protect them. Their fate is dependent on the weather, on how many accidents befall them, and on what enemies spot them. According to Emlen and Glading (1945), a loss of about 25% is to be expected in this period. Sumner's (1935) studies indicated mortality of the young in the first week to be around 22%, and in the first month about 40%; if the weather is very rainy the loss may be much higher. Mc-Lean (1930) tells of three broods he observed that suffered losses of 11 out of 12, all of 14, and 8 out of 16 in the first weeks, as a result of fogs and rains. Some chicks fall into holes, ditches, and tanks from which they cannot escape, and a few get lost and die from exposure. Some young quail are caught by predators, especially the Cooper's and sharp-shinned hawks. After the first two or three weeks after hatching, the mortality curve levels off, and their rate of loss from then on is not very much different from that of the adults.

The total loss of young quail from hatching to early fall is 45% to 60% in normal seasons. An indication of the year's production may be obtained from the fall age ratio. If the juvenile loss is about 45%; and half the adult hens succeeded in hatching a clutch of eggs, the early fall age ratio will be about 2:1, young to adults. If the loss of young is about 60%, and half the females had broods, the ratio will be around 1.5:1. When the age ratio is 2:1 or higher, productivity is good to very good. When it is 1.5:1 or lower, a fair to poor yield is indicated. Emlen (1940) found the age ratio to be 1.46:1 in 4,257 birds checked from a variety of sources, including some winter and spring birds. Autumn ratios were about 2:1. In three successive years on his own study area the November age ratio was 1.5:1, 2.35:1, and 1.4:1.

The loss of adult quail goes on the year round at a rather even pace, except at a few periods when some particular decimating agent is effective. The primary period of exceptional loss is the hunting season; at this time a drop of some 15% to 40% of the birds may occur in a period of a week to a month where they are hunted. The nesting and early brood seasons bring high losses of hens, due to their greater than ordinary vulnerability at that time. At other times there is a steady drain from predation and accidents, and possibly at times from disease. Emlen and Glading (1945) found the steady attrition to be about 7% a month in one population they studied. Sumner (1935) reported a drop of 19% in a group of quail from November through February, or about 5% a month. Emlen (1939) counted the birds on a 760-acre tract for a year and found the adult mortality to be 83%, or about 7% a month. Several of the birds were lost on account of trapping and banding, which may have made the mortality a little above normal. Most of the nonhunting losses are from predation, and are a normal, healthy adjustment in the annual population cycle of birds of this type. In some severe winters in the higher and colder parts of the species' range there are periods of accelerated loss from exposure. In Modoc and Lassen Counties, California, quail built up to high levels in the mild winters in the late forties, only to be decimated 1950–51 and 1951–52 (Glading, letter).

The total mortality is indicated by the probable length of survival of quail at any period in life. Emlen (1940) concluded from his studies that with quail in that area " . . . average survival from potential egg to birds of one year of age is 8.5%; from 6 months to 18 months of age it is 31%; for birds over 12 months it is 50% per year; . . . The mortality rate is higher in females than in males, particularly during the summer." According to Sumner (1935), " . . . out of 100 quail raised in a given summer, 26.8% will be alive at the end of the first year, 7.2% at the end of the second, 2.0% of the birds at the end of the third year, and 0.5% at the end of the fourth. From this average life expectation is seen to be about eight months."

LIFE EQUATION

IN a period of stable populations the gains and losses for a year balance each other; such a theoretical example is illustrated in Table 21. This shows the typical changes that might happen in a unit of 100 quail in a year that ends with the same number it began with. In years of decline the extra loss may be due either to high mortality of birds or to low production; population increases necessitate reasonably good production and high survival. In eight years' records of quail populations from four localities, Emlen (1940) found that " . . . population decline was attributable largely to low survival in one instance, to low replacement in one, and to a combination of the two factors in three. High survival was responsible for population increase in one instance; a combination of high survival and high replacement in two." Periods of population increase and decrease alternate, and with this species they are usually short.

POPULATION DENSITIES

THE distribution of quail over areas of some size, such as whole counties, is nearly always very spotty; this is true even where the cover and food conditions are uniform, and is due in considerable measure to the locations of water. Thus if there are any quail in a location, there must be water; and therefore there may be a good many quail. The population-density data include only the portions of the range that coveys of birds actually use.

California quail can tolerate rather high concentrations; hundreds sometimes use a single watering spot. A very high population, up to 4.8 birds per acre in late fall, has been maintained for several years on about 450 acres of a sportsman's club property along the California coast (Glading, Selleck, and Ross, 1945). The annual harvest for three years from 1939 to 1941 exceeded a bird per acre of the occupied range. This was accomplished in naturally poor habitat by means of hand feeding and predator control—a very artificial situation. On a small area of very good habitat in the Santa Cruz Mountains south of San Francisco, Sumner (1935) determined that the density varied from 1.1 to 3.9 quail per acre at different times of the year. These examples are representative of the best populations, and are not general. An example of a low-density population was studied by Emlen (1939) at Davis, California, where he found the year's highest density was .15 birds per acre, or about 7 acres per bird. The low spring density was .06 birds per acre, or about 16 acres per bird. Late-winter densities on an area in the Sierra Nevada foothills of central California over a six-year period ranged from .26 to .59 birds per acre (3.9 to 1.7 acres per bird) (Glading, 1941). These figures are prob-

		NUMBER OF BIRDS	

TABLE 21

LIFE EQUATION OF 100 CALIFORNIA QUAIL FOR A YEAR

SEASON	ACTIVITIES	NUMBER OF BIRDS	
		young	adult
SPRING	(1) In a population of 52 males and 48 females, 44 females mate with 44 males		100
	(2) 44 hens lay av. 15 eggs in 1st nests, 11 in renests; total 1st eggs—660		
	(3) 32% 1st nests hatch, or 15 × 14 = 210; ⅚ of hens broken-up renest, or 25 × 11 = 275; 32% of renests hatch, or 8 × 11 = 88; 2% eggs in 1st clutches do not hatch, or 4; 5% " " 2nd " " " " " 4 Thus 8 eggs of 298 are left in nests and 290 hatch (av. 12.6)	290	
	(4) 25 adults die from accidents and predation, or 25%		75
SUMMER	(5) 18 " " " " " " " 24%		57
	(6) 116 young die from accidents, exposure and predation, or 40%		
FALL	Surviving young become adults		231
	(7) 69 are killed by hunters, or 30%		162
FALL & WINTER	(8) 62 " " " predation and accidents, or 38%		100
SPRING	(9) Breeding season arrives again with same number of birds as the year before		

ably typical of the quail densities on much of the range.

THE MANAGEMENT OF THE CALIFORNIA QUAIL

MANAGEMENT of the California quail presents two kinds of problems, according to who owns the land. Much of the desert and dry range lands habitat is public land, and the job of management is up to the public agencies, both state and federal, that operate it. Much of the southern California coastal quail habitat, and that in the valleys through the central part of the state, are privately owned farms and ranches; most of these lands are very high-priced, and there is not very good opportunity for practical habitat improvements. The private ranch lands in the mountain foothills offer the best chance for quail developments, but here too the social problems of landowner-sportsman co-operation are difficult (Glading, 1946). The practices and techniques discussed below may be used on both private and public lands wherever they apply, but the problem of financing is obviously different.

LAND USE AND DEVELOPMENT

MOST of the developments and techniques for improving quail habitat and aiding the birds' survival are primarily applicable to range land; this may be arid desert range, or semi-arid grass-brush areas. Some practices are also practical on farms, where they can be harmonized with the land use. According to a recent California state report, "There is more potentially good quail habitat in California than for any other species, except probably deer." (*California Wildlife Conservation Board Report,* 1950.)

In a consideration of the need for the improvement of quail habitat on any area, the three essential requirements must be judged as to their presence, adequacy, and arrangement: these are water, food, and shelter. Shelter must serve the functions of feeding, nesting, roosting, escaping enemies, and loafing. The ways of arranging for water, food, and shelter will be discussed in that order.

Providing Water. Water for drinking may come from springs, streams, ponds, tanks, seeps, irrigation channels, wells, pipe lines, or special catchment arrangements. In irrigated farming areas there is adequate water; on all other kinds of range there are usually areas that lack quail because they lack water. An artificial water development may be considered for any area more than a half mile from an existing source of water.

Advantage should be taken to improve the existing sources of water for quail as far as possible before considering the expense of a new development. Many springs, wells, pipes, and tanks are inaccessible or unsafe for quail use. By the use of shallow troughs, ramps, and valves as they may be needed, the facility can be adjusted to provide quail drinking places. An example of this sort of improvement was at the Kettleman Hills oil field. According to Glading, Enderlin, and Hjersman (1945), "Water used for fire protection at the wells and drilling sites was made available to quail by means of a 'cracked valve' or drip, often supplemented by an open, concrete basin to hold limited quantities of water. Employees of the Standard Oil Company of California developed a standard, concrete drinking trough, and placed these at many of the wells." Where the loss of water by the "drip" method is objectionable, a float valve can be installed in a trough or basin to shut off excess flow.

Where springs or seeps are unimproved and the water mostly wasted, they can be dug out and boxed in with concrete or redwood. It is better not to expose such a water hole to direct animal use, but instead to pipe it to a trough. Here again the water flow should be controlled by a float valve; the trough should be covered except for the access end. A sloping ramp is needed to enable the birds to walk to the water edge safely. If domestic stock are common on the area, the trough and a small area around it should be protected by a fence. The same sort of pipe and trough arrangement can be used in connection with wells and tanks (see Figure 24). All that is needed in some stock troughs or tanks is the addition of a ramp to enable the birds, especially the young ones, to reach the water without falling in. Emlen and Glading (1945) recommend " . . . a wooden ramp with cleats up to the edge of the trough (from the ground) and a ramp of wire screen down into the water. A plank floating in the trough can serve as a convenient platform for the drinking quail." Shallow concrete basins or troughs should be protected by a surrounding ring of flat rocks or concrete to keep rodents from getting dirt into them.

If no active water source is available in an area where water is urgently needed in order to make otherwise suitable quail range habitable, an automatic, self-filling "gallinaceous guzzler" can be built. This catchy title can be made even more alliterative by adding the name of its inventor, Ben Glading, the eminent California wildlife management authority—"Glading's gallinaceous guzzler!"

This device has undergone several improvements and model changes as a result of production installation by members of the California Department of Fish and Game. Descriptions of various developmental models may be found in Glading (1947) and Emlen and Glading (1945). Blueprints of current production models may be obtained by writing to the California Department of Fish and Game at Sacramento, California.

FIGURE 24. *Float-valve watering trough for quail and other game birds. The trough is supplied from an existing water supply, as a well or tank, or from a storage tank specially provided. The inset figure shows the details of construction, the cover being raised to show the ball float and valve.* (*From Emlen and Glading, 1945.*)

Currently (1953) the cost of a permanent type of installation is in the neighborhood of $200 to $300, depending on the site in which the device is installed, and its nearness to the sources of construction materials. Though the installation costs are large, maintenance costs are negligible. Installation costs amortized over a life expectancy of at least 25 years are extremely low. Depending on where it is located, it will serve other game species as well as the California quail, including the mountain quail, Gambel's quail, the mourning dove, the white-winged dove, the chukar partridge, and the cottontail rabbit.

California has installed some 2,000 of these guzzlers (1953). Other arid Western states, including Nevada, Utah, Arizona, and New Mexico, have—or have had—active Federal aid in Wildlife Restoration programs that include the installation of guzzlers. They have been found, by Charles W. Schwartz, success-

ful in improving California quail habitats in Hawaii, and have been used—at least experimentally—in Puerto Rico for habitat improvement.

The principle of the guzzler is to collect winter rainfall and store it for summer use in climates characterized by long summer droughts. Currently, the California Department of Fish and Game is using two production models, the choice of which is determined largely by the accessibility of heavy equipment to the site of location. In easily accessible places the model used has a subsurface rectangular concrete tank five feet wide and about twelve feet long. The bottom of the tank slopes gradually from about halfway back up to the surface, to form a sloping ramp from ground level down to the bottom. Its water capacity is 650 to 700 gallons. The tank is covered with a reinforced concrete roof, which is subsequently covered with earth for added insulation. This

COURTESY CALIFORNIA DEPARTMENT OF FISH AND GAME

PLATE 75. *A "gallinaceous guzzler" watering facility, showing tank with opening, apron, fence, and brush cover. The birds are California quail. These devices are also used by Gambel's, scaled and mountain quails, Hungarian and chukar partridges, band-tailed pigeons, and mourning and white-winged doves.*

guzzler is filled with water from a rain-collecting apron placed on a slight slope about its mouth. The apron area is cleared of any brush and stones, smoothed over, and then surfaced with a three-inch coating of concrete, or cement and soil mixture; on sandy gravel soils an asphalt emulsion and soil mixture is used. The surface of the concrete, if that is used, should be sprayed with asphalt emulsion while it is still green, which provides a bond for future repairs with asphalt compounds. The size of the apron should be such that half of the minimum annual rainfall for the area will fill the tank. For a 700-gallon tank the apron area in square feet is equal to 2,250 divided by the minimum annual rainfall figure in inches; thus, in an area with ten inches minimum annual rainfall, the apron should be 225 square feet.

In site locations that are difficult to reach with building supplies, the California Department of Fish and Game regularly installs fiber-glass-reinforced plastic guzzlers. These devices are tanks of about the same general dimensions as the concrete one described above, but are constructed of about ⅜ inch fiber-glass-reinforced plastic. Firms equipped to manufacture so-called "glass" boats have fabricated these tanks for several Western game departments. The over-all weight of the current model used in California is from 80 to 100 pounds; they thus can be packed easily by two men.

The plastic guzzler is installed by digging a

PLATE 76. *Close-up of entrance to guzzler with a group of quail loafing about.*

hole, dropping in the tank and lid, and, after covering them with dirt, connecting it to an asphalt-earth apron. The basic manufacturing cost of the plastic guzzler is $185; installation costs bring the total cost up to the same figure as for the concrete type.

Guzzlers should be located in low areas like valley floors and along washes, but not on ridges. They should be placed close to trees or brush that will shade them and cut down evaporation wherever possible. Good roosting cover and an ample supply of good food-producing plants should be close by. If livestock grazing is at all intensive, the guzzler and apron should be fenced.

The distribution of these water developments should generally be at least one mile apart; in some types of cover half-mile intervals produce optimum effects.

Experience shows that quail respond to new water developments quickly if native birds are within a mile or two. Their full use may require three years, by which time they may have as many as 300 birds using them (*P-R Quarterly,* April 1951). Recent reports (1953) indicate that in favorable years concentrations up to 700 may be expected.

Developing Food Supplies. Deficiencies of food may be corrected in some types of quail range, though the methods may be difficult and expensive. Before measures are taken *especially* for this purpose, it should be clearly ascertained that there is a need for more food. The majority of important quail foods are wild annual plants, and the best way to increase the available food is to encourage these weeds by various management methods. It should be noted here that the word "weed" is used in a broad sense, to include a wide variety of broad-leaved herbs that are not cultivated and that are mostly not noxious on range and desert lands, although a few of them may be considered as pests.

Of first importance on range and desert lands is the *control of grazing* by domestic stock. The stocking of animals in numbers that results in denudation of the cover should be avoided, not only because they destroy quail food but because they seriously damage the land itself. The understocking of grazing animals should also be avoided. Inadequate consumption of the range forage results in dense stands of the native grass and brush that suppress quail-food plants and that may even become too dense for shelter use. The proper use of the range for domestic stock is thus a key to good quail management.

Brush control can be profitably undertaken on much range land to improve the natural growth of quail foods. Dense brush shades out the herbaceous annuals; and so, by clearing lanes or spots or by thinning the brush, the ground may be exposed enough to induce the germination and growth of native food plants. This may be aided by grazing, as noted above; or it may be done by mechanical clearing with bulldozers or special brush-clearing machines. Stands that are big enough to provide firewood can be thinned by cutting if either the commercial or home supply cutting of fire wood is economically justified. Fire may be used to thin brush stands; it is often the cheapest method where conditions are safe for its use. Appropriate caution is necessary to choose the right time and atmospheric conditions, assure natural or plowed firebreaks, and provide adequate personnel to guide the burn. Care should be taken to confine the burn to strips or spots where food plants are needed, and to leave adequate amounts of brush for escape and roosting shelter. The best season for burning is just ahead of the winter rains. The use of chemical herbicides is currently being explored as a means of opening up dense brush stands.

The germination of food plants on areas clear of all or much of the former brush cover can be stimulated by disking; this is most effective just before the winter rains. Places selected for this treatment should have good soils that are neither extremely acid nor extremely alkaline. Improved growth can be obtained by applying superphosphate at the rate of about 100 pounds per acre. No seeding is necessary in most areas, but certain food plants can be assured by seeding. Bur clover seeded 15 pounds per acre in the fall is one of the best to use; it should be planted next to cover and close to water. It is adapted to all but desert range, and reseeds readily after it is once established. Where cover and summer succulents are absent on dry range, saltbush can be seeded after the first fall rains; ten pounds of seed per acre may be used, or transplants can be set (Emlen and Glading, 1945).

American and purple vetches are suitable to seed for green food in the coastal regions (Sumner, 1935); seeding is at 40 pounds per acre in the fall after disking. On irrigated lands, a variety of food plants may be seeded along field borders and next to brush patches; foxtail or proso millets and Sudan grass are among the best. They should be seeded in spring in disked ground, using 10 pounds per acre.

Feather acacia trees planted for landscaping along roads, around house lots, and on other areas are used by quail for both roosting and feeding; seedlings should be planted in the fall.

Artificial Feeding. The hand placing of grain can be of some value in managing this quail. On one private preserve year-round feeding with steel-cut yellow corn, combined with the vigorous reduction of certain predators, resulted in maintaining quail populations as high as 4.8 birds per acre (Glading, Selleck, and Ross, 1945). They used some 500 sacks a year on about 450 acres, feeding heaviest in summer and least in spring; this area was deficient in

PLATE 77. *An artificial quail roost of a type suitable for Gambel's and California quails.*

COURTESY CALIFORNIA DEPARTMENT OF FISH AND GAME

natural foods. An experiment on the Kettleman Hills area showed that " . . . a small but consistent increase of quail has been obtained by feeding quail on scratch feed" (Glading, Enderlin, and Hjersman, 1945). But this was an area abounding in natural foods, and the authors concluded that the benefits from feeding were not worth the cost.

Emergency summer or winter feeding can be used on areas where owners, sportsmen, or professional game men are organized to go into action quickly. Covey locations must be known ahead of time. Summer seed crop failures during drouths may be offset by hand feeding, which must be continued for the season in order to be effective. When snow comes the feed should be placed in open spots cleared of snow and next to escape cover. Regular or emergency feeding may be done with any mixture of small grains, cracked or cut corn, and small wild seeds of varieties that they eat. Regular feeding is justified only on areas deficient in natural foods, and where conditions or facilities do not permit the efficient development of natural foods; even then it is an expensive business. It is also suggested that

where feeding is to be done regularly a judicious program of predator reduction accompany it. Birds concentrated at cafeterias are exceptionally vulnerable to predation.

Improving Shelter. Some of the suggestions given for improving food supplies also apply to the development of shelter. Controlled grazing and brush reduction by means of part-clearing, burning, or cutting to develop feeding areas also result in good nesting and loafing cover. Only escape and roosting shelter require extra attention in such areas.

Where a scattering of roosting trees already exists, they should be avoided in any brush-control operations; patches of thick brush should also be left for escape shelter. Thus results a pattern of open strips or patches, scattered brush, scattered trees, and patches of thick brush.

Areas deficient in trees for roosting, or thick brush patches for escape shelter, may need more treatment than just grazing control, though this alone will often do the job. Fencing out small areas will help on heavily grazed land. By the selection of gullies and other eroded spots for grazing exclusion, no good forage will

PLATE 78. *Habitat improvement for western quails. Tamarisk and pampasgrass planted in Kettleman Hills area of California to provide shelter.*

COURTESY CALIFORNIA DEPARTMENT OF FISH AND GAME

be lost and erosion can be controlled. Fencing out small areas adjacent to water sources is specially desirable.

Thicket plantings to provide escape shelter may be made where natural establishment is inadequate even with grazing exclusion. The planting of saltbrush on dry lands for food and escape cover, and of feather acacia for food and roosting cover, have already been mentioned; acacia plantings also make good shade at watering places. Other plants that can be set out for roosting cover include California live oak (on all but deserts), willows (on all lands), evergreen tamarisk (all lands), and osage orange (irrigated lands only); the evergreen tamarisk and willows also make good shade at water. In addition to saltbrush, plantings for escape cover may be made with willows, osage orange, Scotch broom (all but deserts), blackberry (all lands), bush buckwheat and California buckwheat (all but irrigated land). Fine escape cover can also be developed with some of the grasses. Pampas grass may be used for this purpose in good soil on all but desert lands, and European beach grass on range and desert sand dunes; both these grasses must be established by setting crowns.

Artificial roosting shelters have demonstrated their value in quail management where natural roosting shelter is inadequate and quick results are desired. One way is to make simple brush piles by pushing together scattered brush from an area being cleared; such piles should be about 20 feet in diameter and 10 feet high (*P-R Quarterly,* April 1952). More substantial roosts can be made of a pole framework with a netting top covered with brush. Early trials with this device used a slanting roof with one edge of the roof close to the ground (Dill, 1939). It now appears that a flat top well off the ground is better; it helps avoid predation, and the birds take to it better. Three or four wood posts or iron pipes are set in concrete some 8 to 16 feet apart in a triangle or rectangle; they should extend 8 to 12 feet above the ground. The top frame is also made from wood or pipe bolted to the uprights. Sheep wire is stretched across the top to hold the brush, which is piled on at least three feet deep. Branchy material should be used, so that the brush will remain fairly open, but it should be wired down tightly enough so that it will not blow away. These shelters should be built some 200 yards to half a mile from a watering place.

In some areas an open tree may serve as the framework in which to build brush shelter above the ground (Macgregor, 1950).

PREDATOR AND RODENT CONTROL

THE indiscriminate killing of predators is a wasteful, expensive and unnecessary activity that sometimes does quail more harm than good; no conservationist in his right mind who is familiar with the ecology of predation would advocate it today. This is specially true in the use of predator control to reduce losses of California quail. The greatest predation is on nests; and some of the rodents, notably the ground squirrels, are among the worst quail-egg eaters. A careless program of hawk- and owl-killing might well boomerang by increasing the ground squirrels, and thereby result in greater quail-nest loss.

On areas where quail are to be managed intensively, selective predator and rodent control may be followed. A fur-trapping program to harvest the majority of foxes, raccoons, opossums, skunks, and weasels during the prime pelt period each year is one phase. Feral cats should be taken all the time, and coyotes and bobcats also *if* they are known to be plentiful enough to be troublesome. Hawk and owl reduction should be carefully limited to the Cooper's and sharp-shinned hawks, and in some areas also the horned owl. Where marsh hawks are very abundant they may warrant reduction locally. All this hawk- and owl-killing should be by shooting only by individuals who are expert on field identification and in conformity with state laws; no pole traps should be permitted. In fact the small owls may well be encouraged, by supplying them with nesting boxes placed in suitable trees.

Ground squirrels should be kept down to low numbers. If natural means (predators, habitat) fail, strychnine poisoning or carbon disulphide gassing may be used; thallium poisons should not be used in quail areas.

Snakes, jays, magpies, and other minor predators can be ignored, unless in some local situation any of them should become so abundant as to be really destructive.

It should be remembered that the limited use of predator control in quail management as suggested above applies *only* on areas of intensive management. Any general shooting of predatory birds or mammals in the name of quail management is unwise, inefficient, and uneconomical; it is never a good substitute for providing satisfactory habitat.

REFUGES FOR QUAIL

REFUGES posted against hunting are not generally an effective tool in quail management. In areas of heavy hunting pressure, hunting should be prohibited within about 200 yards of occupied buildings and around water holes; this is about as far as land posting need go in behalf of quail. In extremely arid regions, where quail concentrate at guzzlers or other water holes during the hunting season, refuges may be established to prevent "ground sluicing."

THE RESTOCKING OF QUAIL

RESTOCKING is rarely needed; if quail exist in an area of satisfactory habitat, they are capable of quickly populating it to carrying capacity; adding other birds does not help. If areas of unpopulated range have been made habitable for quail by some development (such as water), and there are no quail within several miles of this habitat, introduction may be worth while. It should be done with wild-trapped birds liberated in groups of at least 100; game-farm reared quail are not as satisfactory for stocking as are wild birds (Richardson, 1941). The state of California recently recommended stopping the game-farm production of California quail (*California Wildlife Conservation Board Report*, 1950). The area where any quail are stocked should be protected from hunting for at least one year.

CONTROL OF THE HARVEST

THE California quail endures modern sport hunting well except in the most heavily gunned areas. Modern hunting laws and regulations usually provide for a season of ten days to six weeks, and daily bag limits of five to ten birds; such safeguards are adequate protection for the species. In some areas, particularly in marginal range, it would be desirable to be able to adjust the regulations to provide for an adequate harvest in years of plenty, and the curtailment of hunting in years of scarcity. In order to be able to make such adjustments, an annual census would be required to determine the population level in time to publicize the regulations ahead of the hunting season; no technique is yet satisfactory to do this.

Counts of quail can be made in arid country by observing the numbers coming to each source of drinking water; this may be done easily from a blind. By knowing the number of water sources in an area, sample counts may be projected to estimate the quail population.

The only area-wide census method presently in use for this quail is designed to determine the population on controlled hunting areas; it is used just before and during the hunting season, and is an accurate way of keeping track of the bird population. It may be adaptable to summer use on sample areas to give data for setting state hunting seasons, but has not yet been developed that way. This census technique is described by Emlen and Glading (1945): "In relatively open country, the horseback method is recommended. Two to four riders, arranged side by side, and spaced about 200 feet apart, cover the area as a unit in much the same manner as a man mowing a lawn; when the riders reach the end of a strip, they wheel about, pivoting on the outside man, and return on the adjacent strip. This procedure is followed over the entire area. Three men can cover about 1,000 acres per day on flat lands or low hills with scattered cover.

"When a ranch of several thousand acres is to be censused, it is best to count the quail on several scattered sample strips, estimate the acreage covered, calculate the number of birds seen per acre, and then multiply this figure by the total number of acres on the ranch."

This method is not accurate where cover is dense; censusing such areas in research studies may be done by live-trapping and marking birds, and then making visual covey observations through binoculars. This technique is not suitable for management work.

Operators of controlled shooting areas should keep records of the harvest as the season progresses. Knowing the quail population, they can safely allow enough hunting to take 20% of the population as bagged birds. By using a rule of thumb of six quail per hunter-day, the number of hunters who may safely be allowed to hunt on a given area may be determined.

CHAPTER 9

Gambel's, Mountain, and Scaled Quails

THE discussion of these three quails will be handled to some extent by comparing their characteristics and needs with those of the California quail and with each other. This will save some duplication, since the ecology and management of these species are similar in many ways.

ORIGIN AND CLASSIFICATION

ALL three species are native to the United States and Mexico. The ranges they occupy today are essentially the same as formerly, though both the Gambel's and mountain quails have been successfully established in some new areas.

All three belong to the same order and family as the California quail. Gambel's quail is also classified in the same genus, and bears the name *Lophortyx gambeli gambeli* Gambel. It is also known as desert quail and Arizona quail.

The mountain quail is named *Oreortyx picta* Douglas. The type form, *O. p. picta,* is also known as the plumed quail. Another subspecies that inhabits the humid coastal range is *O. p. palmeri* Oberholser, also known as mountain quail, but sometimes called painted quail. A third form, the San Pedro quail (*O. p. confinis* Anthony), is found only in Lower California, Mexico.

The scaled quail is *Callipepla squamata pallida* Brewster, and is also known as the Arizona scaled quail. Another subspecies, the chestnut-bellied scaled quail (*C. s. castanogastris*

Brewster), is found in the lower Rio Grande Valley section of Texas and Mexico.

DESCRIPTIONS

THE Gambel's quail is similar to the California quail in size, form, and general coloration. The male has the same knobbed topknot, though a little longer, and the same black and white facial markings. The crown is reddish-brown instead of the smoky-brown of the California quail. The upper belly is white, and below it is a large black patch, whereas in the California quail the whole belly is a scaled yellow-brown. The color of the back is paler than in the California quail, perhaps a reflection of its desert habitat. The legs and feet are olive-gray rather than blackish, as in the California quail. The hens resemble California quail hens in general pattern, but are lighter in color and more brightly marked along the sides.

The mountain quail is slightly larger than the California and Gambel's quails, but has a similar form and body appearance. The males and females have the same body form and markings, and are indistinguishable to the eye. The topknot or plume is made up of two long, pointed feathers, much longer than in the other species and not knobbed at the tip. The throat is chestnut, instead of black as in the other two. The flanks and sides are prominently barred in black, white, and chestnut. The legs and feet are horn color.

337

PLATE 79. *The Gambel's quail.*

The scaled quail is about the same size and form as the others, but it lacks the head plume. It does have erectile crown feathers that form a crest when raised; the crest is distinctive for its white-tipped feathers. It is a bluish-gray bird with olive-brown wings and back. The breast and whole neck region are prominently scalloped with black-tipped feathers, which give the bird a scaly or shell-like appearance. The flanks are brownish, with prominent white stripes. It has no prominent facial stripes and marks, as in the other species; in fact it resembles the bobwhite more closely than it does the other Western species, and its range overlaps that of the bobwhite.

GEOGRAPHIC RANGE AND DISTRIBUTION

THE Gambel's quail is found from southern Nevada and southeastern California through Arizona (except the northeastern part), southwestern New Mexico, and far-western Texas to northwestern Mexico; small transplant colonies are located in western Colorado and east-central Idaho.

The mountain quail is found in the higher altitudes of western Washington, Oregon, and northern California, south-central California and northern Lower California, eastern California and Oregon, southeastern Washington, western and central Idaho, and western Nevada.

The scaled quail is found in southeastern Arizona, most of New Mexico, southeastern Colorado, western and southern Texas, and northern Mexico.

These geographical ranges are largely exclusive, except where the Gambel's and scaled quails are found together in southeastern Arizona, southwestern New Mexico, and northwestern Mexico. Even here the occupied habitat is generally different, the Gambel's quail being on desert range and the scaled quail on grassland. See Figure 25 for map of the geographic ranges of these quails.

The geographic range of the mountain quail overlaps that of the California quail to a large extent, though the habitat used is mostly different; the mountain quail use the more heavily forested and heavy brush areas of higher altitudes, while the California quail use the light brush cover of the lower elevations. The mountain quail use these lower brushlands also, mainly in the winter in the Sierra Nevadas. There is also some overlap of the ranges of the Gambel's and California quails in southeastern California where the desert and rangelands meet.

HABITS

COURTSHIP

PAIRING takes place in the winter coveys; the dissolution of the covey usually comes in March. Most pairs select a nesting territory within or close to the winter range just occupied by the covey. Many mountain quail—probably a majority of them—go through a spring altitudinal migration, and follow the retreating snow to higher elevations to select a nesting territory. Other "nonmigratory" mountain quail remain in their winter areas to nest.

On the upward travels of the mountain quail the birds walk in single file along roads

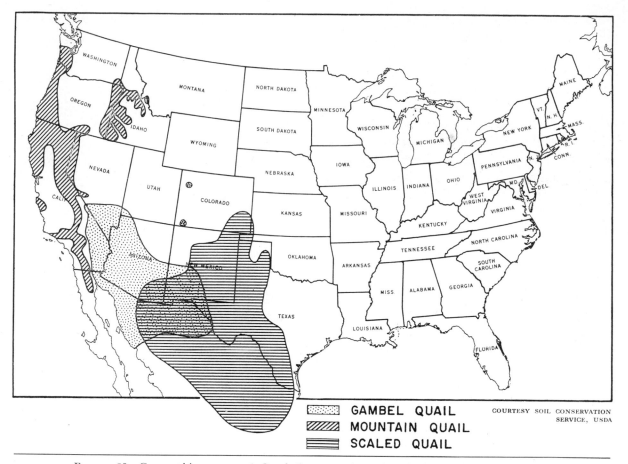

FIGURE 25. *Geographic ranges of Gambel's mountain and scaled quails. (After McLean, 1930; Gorsuch, 1934; Bent, 1932; and others.)*

and ridges until they reach suitable nesting localities above the heavy forest belt. These journeys may be a few miles, or as much as 20 miles; and sometimes end at altitudes as high as 6,000 feet. Here they establish nesting territories of some 5 to 50 acres that the males defend. Mating begins in early April.

Fighting among male Gambel's quail is vigorous during the competition for mates. After the pairing is completed and the breeding territory is decided, the cock defends it against other males, and picks a perch from which he whistles to his mate. On occasion he goes through a display as she approaches. This may consist of a slow, deliberate circling of the hen with chest expanded and wings trailing, all the while carrying on a low-voiced conversation (Gorsuch, 1934). Mating begins in early April and is at its height by mid-April.

NESTING

ALL these quails locate their nests on the ground. Those of the Gambel's and scaled quails are placed beside or beneath desert scrub vegetation or grass clumps where concealment is good. The mountain quail nests in rugged, brushy terrain where the nests are difficult to find; they are usually shaded and obscured with shrubs, roots, rocks, clumps of grass, or an overhanging bank (McLean,

1930). The average clutch sizes for Gambel's quail is 12, for mountain quail 9 to 11, and for scaled quail 12 to 14. The incubation period is 21 to 23 days for Gambel's, 25 for mountain quail, and 21 for scaled quail. Gambel's quail eggs are a dull buffy or whitish color, and heavily marked with irregular-shaped blotches of reddish-brown; those of mountain quail are a cream color to pinkish buff and unspotted; scaled quail eggs are ivory to cream color, and sparingly marked with small brownish spots.

The Gambel's cock shares some in incubation duties, but these are mostly done by the hen; the cock spends much of his time standing guard some 50 feet or so away from the nest. Both sexes of the mountain quail share the incubation duties, whereas only the hen of the scaled quail does this chore.

The hen birds follow the usual habit of leaving the nest for feeding and resting twice a day, early morning and early evening; otherwise they or their mate stay on the nest, unless some accident or attack causes a breakup. Renesting is habitual in the Gambel's and scaled quails after such a nest loss, but is infrequent with the mountain quail.

THE BROOD PERIOD

MOST nests hatch in May or early June, but some Gambel's and scaled quail renests may come off in July or even later. The chicks leave the nest as soon as they are dried off and the weather is favorable. Both parents attend the brood unless one is killed, in which case the survivor carries on. Development of the chicks is similar to that of the California and bobwhite quails; flying begins at about two weeks, plumage is well developed in about four weeks, and the juvenile coat is completed in eight weeks.

During the early weeks of life the activities of the chicks are largely directed by the adults. The hen guides the young in catching insects, dusting, and responding to her calls. The cock guards the family and warns of approaching danger, then attempts to draw intruders away from the brood by attracting attention to himself. The hen broods the chicks frequently at first, then only at night after the first few days; after the young are two or three weeks old, they roost independently on warm nights. After their feathers are well developed, the Gambel's and mountain quail broods take to roosting in shrubs and low trees.

All these quails have but one brood a season. Some observers have suspected Gambel's quail of sometimes having two broods; this may have resulted from their habit of adopting stray chicks, so that a family is occasionally seen with young of two ages. However, Gullion (letter) found circumstantial evidence that under suitable conditions with nesting starting in February and early weaning of the first brood, two broods may be produced.

FALL AND WINTER SEASONS

BOTH the Gambel's and scaled quails have strongly gregarious instincts. In early fall the coveys are mainly families, but sometimes are augmented by stray broodless adults. As the season advances and the number of birds in a group is reduced by mortality, the family units join together to form larger coveys. These are largest in late fall and early winter, and may number from a dozen or two up to 40 or 50 or even hundreds of birds. The very large groups are commonly associated with watering places during times when succulent vegetation is absent. The size of coveys may vary widely from day to day, depending on the amount of grouping or separating that takes place in response to changes in feeding conditions and the weather.

The mountain quail has little of the covey instinct; the groups stay together somewhat as families through fall and winter, but the aggregations seldom exceed 10 or 12 birds. The amount of grouping depends on water availability in dry periods, but the gatherings around water holes are related to the water need and are not true flocking.

With the Gambel's quail it is common for a

cock bird to drop out of the roost first in the morning to check any possible dangers. When he begins to stretch and loosen up, the other birds come down and join in the exercise (Gorsuch, 1934). They may then go to a drinking place, if one is nearby, or otherwise start feeding. When the weather is pleasant the birds spend much time feeding; as much as three hours following sunrise may be devoted to foraging. The middle of the day is spent loafing, usually beneath the open shade of woody plants. Here they rest, dust, and "converse" in low chuckles. The evening feeding period is shorter than the morning one, and comes just before dusk; after this they go to roost as darkness settles.

The daily movements of the Gambel's and scaled quails depend on the availability of water or succulent vegetation, and on the food supply. When living is easy they travel little. Because of the poorer distribution of food and water in the higher portions of the Gambel's quail range, the hill birds move around much more than those in valleys or canyons.

When fall frosts come, the mountain quail that spent the summer at high altitudes start their migration down the mountains. As in the spring, they move on foot in single file, and often take advantage of roads and trails. When thus traveling they pay little heed to vehicles or people, which is in contrast to their usual shy nature. They usually reach their winter range by the end of October. Autumn distribution is often associated with oak woods when acorns are plentiful. They do not forage far afield, but when such staple food sources are gone they may move around from a quarter to half a mile a day in search of food.

These birds remain very mobile all winter, and tend to move up and down a mountainside as the weather changes. This wandering ends with nesting in the spring. They are sometimes caught in deep snows despite their ease of travel, and at such times they may remain beneath brush that holds the snow above the ground. During such times they often feed in the snow-free places along streams and around water sources of other kinds.

VOICE

THE repertoire of the Gambel's quail is more varied than that of the California quail, according to McLean (1930). When they are foraging or moving, the covey members converse in low chuckles and twitters, much as does the California quail, but " . . . more excited in style and in a higher, more metallic pitch. The alarm note is a *clink, clink* or *clinkit, clinkit,* which is also given in a slightly different pitch as a flock call. A call commonly heard during the mating season is a clear, and rather loud, *killink-killink. . . .* " A harsh, screeching note is often given on flushing.

The male mountain quail has a mating season call that he gives repeatedly from some prominent perch. As described by McLean (1930), " . . . the head is drawn down, the plume laid back, then suddenly the head is thrust upward and thrown back, the plume stands upright, and the loud, clear, far-carrying *quee-ark, queerk,* or *plu-ark* issues from the bird's throat. The sound has definitely been known to carry more than three-quarters of a mile down an open valley." When a covey scurries off into the bushes on being disturbed, the birds give a call described by McLean as "*ca-ca-ca-, cree-a-a, cree-a-ca-ca, cree-a-a, cree-a.*" When the birds rally again they whistle "*kow, kow, kow.*"

The call of the scaled quail may be described as *chek-churr, chip-churr,* or *chek-ah,* and is given as a single note. When it is alarmed, the same note is given in fast repetition. A guttural *oom-oom-oom* is also given when the bird is worried (Bent, 1932).

ADAPTABILITY TO CHANGING ENVIRONMENT

As a general thing there has been less change in the environment of these three quails as a result of man's occupation of the land than for most game birds. The desert habitat of the

Gambel's and scaled quails, and the mountain wooded cover of the mountain quail, have changed less than most of our land. Further, some of the changes that have occurred have been beneficial to the birds.

Overgrazing of the desert range by domestic livestock has damaged quail habitat in many areas, particularly that of the scaled quail. This has been most destructive during drouth periods. On the other hand, the development of watering places for livestock has made more of the desert habitable for the birds; they quickly accustom themselves to making use of water from tanks and other facilities.

In some of the flat valleys, land leveling and brush elimination have destroyed the Gambel's and scaled quail habitat. Irrigation, and the development of farming that followed it on such lands, have provided some quail benefits, especially water and food. Crops of succulent plants like lettuce, cauliflower, and other vegetables are relished by the Gambel's quail. Both desert species commonly feed on waste grain around farmyards. Gambel's quail have also learned to perch on stalks and eat from heads of maize and similar crops. Where these farming operations are extensive and cleanly managed there is little that quail can use except the edges. Nevertheless, they have adapted their ways well to these habitat changes.

The primary effect that has changed mountain-quail habitat has been from lumbering. The birds have benefited from cuttings where the resulting cover was not too extensively uniform and the new growth not too dense. The roads and trails associated with lumbering have improved the interspersion of cover types and aided the birds' migratory tendencies. Thus the mountain quail has proved its adaptiveness to changes that have affected its environment.

HABITAT

GENERALLY speaking, the Gambel's quail inhabits the brushy desert; the scaled quail, the grassy-brushy near-desert; and the mountain quail, the steep, brushy-wooded mountain slopes. Fitting into this picture, the California quail occupies the open brushy range land below the range of the mountain quail and west of the desert range of the other two.

The Gambel's or desert quail occupies desert land primarily, yet its best habitat is not the driest type of desert. Few birds are found where the annual rainfall is less than 10 inches, though drier areas with dependable water supplies may support good populations. Some of the valleys have good desert quail populations, but much of the good habitat is on rolling, upland terrain at elevations between 2,000 and 4,500 feet. A classification of habitat types in southeastern Arizona (*P-R Quarterly,* January 1941) recognizes six types used by the Gambel's and scaled quails, five of which are used by the Gambel's and four by the scaled quail. These are:

(1) *Mesquite brush association*—scattered plants and dense clumps of mesquite with mixtures of catclaw, Spanish bayonet, blackbrush, and prickly pear. It occurs where rainfall exceeds 10 inches a year. In other parts of the range this brush type may have somewhat varied composition, including such species as thick-leaved hackberry, western hackberry, quail brush (*Atriplex*), desert ironwood and paloverde. Along water courses, willow, cottonwood, and quail brush are common. In the open ground among these woody plants grow annual herbs and grasses and some perennials in varying amounts. This is the primary type of the Gambel's quail habitat.

(2) *Creosote bush association*—scattered brush on the most arid desert range. Some other associated plants are black brush, snakeweed, mortonia, and prickly pear. This type is used by the Gambel's quail only in the edges where it mixes with other types.

(3) *Tall grass association*—tobosa grass and alkali sacaton mixed with Spanish bayonet, squawberry, catclaw, Mormon tea and lotebush. Other grasses and plants are found in this type in other parts of the range; it is an important habitat type for the Gambel's quail.

(4) *Short-grass association*—grama and three-awn grasses mixed with beargrass, Spanish bayonet, catclaw and prickly pear. It is poor habitat for Gambel's quail.

(5) *Oak type*—Emory and Mexican blue oaks with a mixture of bear grass, Spanish bayonet, squawberry, and thick-leaved hackberry associated. It is used by the Gambel's quail mostly along the edges. Other species of oaks are included in parts of the range.

(6) *Irrigated farmland*—crops of truck, fruit, grain or alfalfa; used by the Gambel's quail mostly along the edges.

All these types except creosote bush were used by the Gambel's quail in the Arizona study, but 79% of the birds were in the mesquite and tall-grass types; the short-grass type lacks escape and nesting cover. The oak type is used only along the edges, and in extensions of the type along streams into the mesquite and tall-grass areas. In other parts of the range in the Upper Sonoran zone, associations of California scrub oak, cherrystone juniper, pointleaf manzanita, desert hackberry, and lotebush support fair numbers of the Gambel's quail (Gorsuch, 1934). Dense stands of mature brush and tree types are not good quail habitat. Farmland edges are used to some extent by the Gambel's quail where other desired cover is close by. Extensive areas of thickly grown herbaceous cover of any type are not good for this quail, except along the margins.

The Gambel's quail need moisture for ingestion at all seasons. Whenever and wherever succulent plant growth is available, they can use the range regardless of the presence or absence of free water. During dry seasons, and on range that lack succulent plants, they must have free water available at four-mile intervals or closer to utilize the cover fully.

Scaled-quail habitat overlaps that of the Gambel's quail, but the optimum conditions for the two species are quite different. Of the six habitat types noted above for the Gambel's quail, all but the short-grass association and the oak type are used by the scaled quail; but creosote bush desert and irrigated farmland are generally used very little. The tall-grass association is the key to scaled-quail habitat. In the Cochise County, Arizona, study (*P-R Quarterly,* January 1941), 70% of the scaled quail were found in this type, and most of the rest—27%—were in the mesquite brush type. Thus the primary cover type for scaled quail is the secondary type for the Gambel's quail, and vice versa. In southern Texas Lehmann and Ward (1941) found the chestnut-bellied scaled quail " . . . most abundant on densely grown tasajillo-prickly pear flats," and associated with rather dense brushy cover, where grass and weeds were scarce.

Scaled-quail habitat is associated more with sandy soils on flat and gently rolling land than on other soil conditions, though in southern Texas they thrive on relatively heavy, tight soils (Lehmann and Ward, 1941). Their water requirement is perhaps more exacting than that of the other quails; they make relatively less use of succulent greens than the other species, and are rarely found more than a mile from free water in dry times; during wet periods they spread out through the cover more widely.

The habitat of the little Mearns' quail overlaps that of the scaled quail along the lower mountain slopes in southeastern Arizona.

Mountain-quail habitat is entirely separate from that of the scaled and Gambel's quails except in a few parts of southern California, where they use the same desert-mountain land as the Gambel's quail; it overlaps that of the California quail in southeastern California. The mountain quail come down to middle-low altitudes in winter, and some of them live there the year round. Some California quail range up the foothills in these same latitudes from 2,000 to 4,000 feet in summer. In between the high and low ranges of the mountain quail there is a heavily forested belt that is little used except when they are traveling to the other side.

Mountain quail prefer moderately open brush and tree cover on slopes 20% or steeper. Woody cover that shades from one-quarter to

PLATE 80. *Typical summer range of the scaled quail in the Texas Panhandle. The cover is grass with scattered low shrubs.*

one-half the ground is best for nesting and brood cover. Small trees help to open the understory cover, and make good roosting places. Roads and trails serve as openings, as also do patches of bare ground or herbaceous cover; roads make particularly good places for dusting, and for drying off the young chicks when the vegetation is wet.

The summer highland cover may be mixed associations of such trees and shrubs as white-leaf manzanita, mariposa manzanita, California juniper, western yellow pine, incense cedar, and canyon live oak. Canyons that have water close to nesting cover usually have good summer populations; heavy pine stands with dense undergrowth are avoided. Lowland nesting and brood cover is mostly the chaparral association (golden bush, baccharis, ceanothus, etc.). Much of this cover is unusable because of the lack of water.

In autumn, before the downward migration, the birds frequent the oak-pine stands to feast on the mast crop; here they tarry as long as the food lasts and the weather permits.

The winter range of the mountain quail is in the low-middle and middle altitudes below the heavy forest and above the valley foothills. The cover is mixed brush and herbs. The brush may include such species as chamise, Fremont silk-tassel, manzanitas, scrub oaks, and others.

The birds living in the northern coastal zone are often found in the understory of the open redwood forests. In the western Sierra Nevadas they inhabit open woodlands that have combinations of western yellow pine, mountain misery, incense cedar, California black oak, white fir, manzanitas, and madrone.

Mountain quail need free water close by, in the summer brood period; few broods are raised more than a quarter of a mile from a water source. The chicks must have water soon after hatching, and at regular daily intervals. This need is easily met at the higher altitudes, but is a very limiting factor in the lower summer range. At other seasons they will travel farther for water, and in late winter and spring they make use of succulent greens to provide some of the moisture they need. They nearly always choose an area of green vegetation in which to nest.

The best populations of mountain quail are found at elevations of from 2,000 to 4,000 feet; few live above this range and up to 6,000 feet. Climax plant associations not severely changed by burning, grazing, or lumbering are generally more productive of quail than others.

FOOD HABITS

THE food habits of the Gambel's quail are similar to those of the California quail; a few of the important food plants are the same, and the types of foods eaten are much alike. They are primarily vegetarians; the proportion of animal foods—primarily insects—is 1% to 7% of the total annual food consumption, though it may be as much as 20% for short periods in early summer and early fall.

The vegetable foods are mostly seeds. Greens are eaten in winter and spring, and fruits are used in summer and fall as they ripen. They consume more fruits than the California quail.

Legumes are the most important group of food plants, with the mesquite being by far the most used single kind. Gorsuch (1934) reported that in 316 Gambel's quail stomachs analyzed 19% of their contents were mesquite beans; this food is eaten throughout the year where it grows. Seeds of deervetch, milkvetch, Coulter lupine, alfalfa, and bur clover are other legume foods commonly eaten in summer and fall, and the greens from many of these plants are taken in winter and spring.

A number of weeds combine to make the second most important group of food plants. Gorsuch (1934) found that the seeds and pods of Menzie's tansy mustard were eaten in quantity in the spring, and were the second largest item in the food used by the Arizona birds he studied; this species composed 8% of the total food. The new shoots of alfileria are eaten throughout the bird's range in the spring and fall, and the seeds are eaten in the fall. A large percentage of the food of quail taken in December 1951 near Oracle, Arizona, consisted of new growths of this plant, locally called "filaree" (Wendell Swank, letter). Other weed seeds eaten in considerable amount include those of the Watson spiderling (summer), Arizona euphorbia, pigweed, Russian thistle, rock daisy, pepperweed, chickweed, wild sunflower, Wright's Dutchman's-pipe vine, Arizona evolvulus (summer, fall), golden crownbeard (winter), and bassia (fall and winter).

Grasses and grains are important sources of both seeds and greens for the Gambel's quail. Seeds of barley, wheat, corn, and oats are utilized in summer and fall, where the birds live next to irrigated or dry-farmed grainfields. The tender new shoots of many grasses are eaten in winter and spring as they appear. Grass seeds are used some in the summer; and Gorsuch (1934) mentions Hall's panicum as one species whose seeds are eaten in Arizona.

A few cultivated plants in addition to grains provide some food; these foods include flax seeds, and leaves from lettuce, cauliflower, and other truck crops. Occasionally the quail's depredations on these crops are serious enough to make farmers complain. A special hunting season for the Gambel's quail was held in Yuma Valley, Arizona, in 1949 to reduce the damage to lettuce crops (P-R Quarterly, April 1950).

Woody plants furnish more food for the Gambel's than the California quail; they are mainly fruits, seeds of fruits, and dry seeds. Some of those commonly taken are fruits of the desert hackberry, lotebush, and mesquite mistletoe, and seeds of quail brush. The use of mesquite seeds has already been noted under legumes as an important food, and is the most important one from woody plants. Foods of this type are also obtained from the fruits of several cacti, including cholla, prickly pear, and barrel cacti.

Greens from many plants not already mentioned are taken in quantity, especially in winter and spring, but these materials are hard to identify in stomach-content studies. A large variety of other plants furnish small quantities of seeds and fruits that are significant in the total.

Grit requirements are high, as with other quails; Gorsuch (1934) found that grit composed 10% to 30% of the total stomach contents of the Gambel's quail. It was highest in February, March, and August; lowest in June, July, October, and November.

Young Gambel's quail eat insects and similar animal foods for a while after hatching, but within a week start to use some vegetable food. Their conversion to the use of more vegetable food is rapid, so that by late July their food balance is the same as that of the adults.

The need for drinking water has been discussed under "Habitat." The provision of this need is directly related to the weather, as is also the availability of many foods. Drouth is a critical matter to these desert birds, even though their tolerance of normally dry conditions is great. When the little rain the desert usually gets is not forthcoming, the water supply *and* food supply both suffer; the lack of greens is one of the first results of drouth.

The Gambel's quail feeding behavior is essentially the same as that of California quail. Coveys spread out and cover a wide swath while foraging in their morning and evening feeding periods; this enables the group to discover easily any good feeding spots.

The scaled quail eats more insect food than the other quails, according to Bailey (1928). Almost 30% of the total diet of the birds examined was made up of grasshoppers, ants, beetles, and other insects. Other evidence indicates that the insect food is primarily important from spring to fall. In southern Texas

the winter food of the chestnut-bellied scaled quail, based on 32 specimens examined by Lehmann and Ward (1941), was 97% vegetable. In this study, seeds from shrubs composed 68% of the food, greens only 7%, and seeds of herbs most of the rest; over 50% of the food in the Bailey study was weed seeds. Thus it appears that greens make up less of the diet of this quail than of the others.

Among the plants that furnish considerable amounts of seed food for the scaled quail are pigweed, wheat, sorghum, bindweed, elbow bush, round-flowered catclaw, Texas bluebonnet, wild bean, tansy mustard, snakeweed, deervetch, filaree, oats, mesquite, sotol, gulf croton, tropical neptunia, and capul. Fruits are used from desert hackberry, nopal prickly pear, brambles, Lindheimer globeberry and forestiera.

The information on scaled-quail food habits is very limited, and no doubt there is much variation in the plant foods used in different parts of the range and not included above.

Scaled quail require water either from their food or as free water. Their food provides less moisture in greens but more in insects than with most quails, but probably less in the total. For this reason these birds are more restricted much of the time than the others by the availability of drinking water.

Mountain quail use vegetable foods primarily, though insects are eaten in considerable amounts from spring to fall. In early fall they may consume insects in quantities up to 10% or more of the diet, but the yearly average of animal food is only about 3% to 5%. Vegetable foods are seeds, fruits, greens, flowers, buds, and some tubers. They eat much more food from woody plants than do the California quail. Greens are used mostly in winter and spring, and in those seasons may make up from 25% to 40% of their diet. Flowers and buds are eaten in spring and summer. The annual total of leaves, flowers, and buds is about a quarter of the diet. Seeds and fruits are eaten all year long but less in the spring, owing to their limited availability and the need for greens at that season.

Mast from pines and oaks is very important food in the early fall. Tubers and roots are scratched from the ground in the fall, and may amount to a tenth of the food at that time.

Some of the plants that provide fruits for mountain quail are smooth sumac (23% of fall food in southeastern Washington, according to Yocom and Harris [1953]); Douglas hackberry (5½% of fall food in Washington study noted above); western serviceberry; California grape; gooseberry; manzanitas; black nightshade; blueberry elder; Christmasberry, and snowberry. Seeds are taken from western yellow pine, Douglas fir, black locust, and various oaks as mast; from wild carrot, tarweed (*Madia*), fiddle-neck, gilia, mountain whitethorn, redroot pigweed, chickweed starwort, and alfileria, among the weeds; from the legumes, alfalfa, cassia, hairy vetch, lupine, deervetch, black medic, and hop clover; and from grasses and grains, wheat, corn, barley, oats, brome grass, and blue bunch wheatgrass. The grains and cultivated legumes are important only in limited areas of quail range that include farmland. Leaves of clovers are important food, and leaves of many other plants are also eaten when succulent. Flowers of manzanitas, blue-eyed grass, and some other plants are eaten in spring and early summer. The underground bulbs of oniongrass and a few other succulent bulbs and roots are scratched out of the ground (Judd, 1905).

Water is vital to the mountain quail, and is especially important in summer. During the brood season and at other dry times they must have free water available; at other periods they can get along on succulent greens, fruits, and insects for their moisture.

Winter snows are a factor in the food selection of this quail. When deep snows cover the low plant growth, they turn to the seeds and fruits of shrubs and trees; at such times most of their food may be taken from a single species of plant for days at a stretch. The birds rarely have difficulty in finding food in winter, and are not seriously limited in winter food, except in the northern limits of the range. Drouths are more likely than snow to cause serious food scarcity, and are most likely to occur in summer.

Grit is used in small quantities; their need for grit may be less than with some quails, owing to the amount of hard seeds in their diet.

The diet of the mountain quail is economically neutral; the seeds and leaves of grains and hay plants eaten by the birds are of no consequence to the harvest of those crops.

In the above discussions of the food habits of the Gambel's, scaled, and mountain quails, some sources of data were cited, but the information was pieced together from other sources too. All the sources used were: Bailey (1928); Gorsuch (1934); Judd (1905); Lehmann and Ward (1941); Martin, Zim, and Nelson (1951); McLean (1930); Yocom and Harris (1953); and *P-R Quarterlies* for January 1941 (Arizona), October 1942 (Arizona), January 1947 (California), July 1947 (California), July 1949 (California), April 1950 (Arizona, Utah), July 1952 (Nevada), and October 1952 (California).

THE EFFECTS OF WEATHER AND CLIMATE

FEW species are as clearly limited by climate in their geographic distribution as the Western quails. The close affinity of the vegetative types to rainfall pattern makes their habitat similarly limited; this is especially true of the desert species, the Gamble's and scaled quails, and also of the California quail. The mountain quail is restricted by the relations of climate to vegetation as regards both latitude and altitude, and also by the nature of the terrain itself. The density of forest and brush growth produced by certain combinations of rainfall, elevation, and locality excludes this quail, as well as combinations that produce sparse, arid vegetative cover.

Populations of all these quails are affected more by weather conditions than by any other factor; drouth is the great threat. When the small expected rainfall fails to come in winter, the normal annual bloom of the desert does not materialize. The green foods the birds need so much in late winter and early spring to condition them for reproduction do not appear, and as a result they have a poor breeding season; depending on the intensity and extent of the drouth, some, many, or most of the birds do not breed at all. Macgregor and Inlay (1951) examined several Gambel's quail during the drouth of 1950 in southeastern California, and found that, "Some of the male birds possessed slightly enlarged testes, but there was no sign of development of the female reproductive organs." There had been less than two inches of rain the previous season. The 1946 and 1947 seasons in Arizona were so dry that the age ratio of young to adults in the fall was below 0.4:1 each year (*P-R Quarterly,* January 1948). A similar result occurred in Nevada in 1950, an extension of the same situation already mentioned for California (*P-R Quarterly,* January 1951). The following year was dry in Utah, and it was observed that the Gambel's quail failed to breed except along the watercourses (*P-R Quarterly,* January 1952); but it was wet in California and nesting was normal again (*P-R Quarterly,* October 1951). Gorsuch (1934) summed up this relationship: " . . . roughly these populations are in direct proportion to the precipitation, increasing in wet years and decreasing during years of drouth."

Dry weather affects some Gambel's quail populations more than others. As Gordon Gullion of the Nevada Fish and Game Commission explains (letter), there are two distinct populations, "one is the 'valley' population, living in areas where underground water resources produce at least a certain amount of food each year more or less independently of that season's rainfall; the other is the 'hill' population whose food and water-through-succulence is directly dependent upon the rainfall during the preceding fall, winter and spring." The valley populations are relatively stable whereas those in the hill

range vary widely. Gullion suggests that the dry seasons with poor quail productivity may be the *normal* condition in the high land habitat.

The same relationship applies to the scaled and mountain quails. In the drouth years of 1942 and 1943 in Arizona, the fall age ratio of scaled quail was 1.0:1 and 0.3:1 respectively (*P-R Quarterly,* July 1944). In California during the 1949–50 drouth, the lack of green foods in winter and spring was so severe that only 10% of the mountain quail nested. A check of the condition of some of the birds showed that the females had no ovarian development and the males only 25% gonadal development (*P-R Quarterly,* October 1950).

Heavy downpours in the midsummer rainy period may occasionally cause the drowning of eggs and chicks of the Gambel's quail (Gorsuch, 1934), but this is rarely a high loss. More damaging is a lack of these rains, which reduces the development of fall seed crops and consequently the birds' food supply.

Low temperatures and winter snows do not ordinarily strike the Gambel's or scaled quails, but in the northern edges of their ranges and at higher altitudes they may occasionally endure heavy sudden losses from starvation, exposure, and predisposed predation. Heavy winters in Utah limit the Gambel's quail there (*P-R Quarterly,* January 1952), and also in Colorado and Idaho. The scaled quail in southeastern Colorado are sometimes decimated, as in a blizzard in November 1946, when 30 inches of snow fell (*P-R Quarterly,* April 1947).

Over most of their range mountain quail endure normally severe winter weather without any trouble. A note in a California study (*P-R Quarterly,* July 1949) stated that a survival of 80% through the 1948–49 severe winter of heavy snows and subzero temperatures indicated no abnormal losses. On the other hand in the northern marginal limits of its range mountain quail are definitely limited by the severity of winter weather. The populations in the lower mountains of southern Idaho sometimes rise to good levels when mild conditions permit good increases but do not remain high for long. (*P-R Quarterly,* January 1951.)

The day-to-day behavior of these quails is affected by weather just as with other similar birds. They seek shade in the heat of the day, remain under shelter during strong winds and stormy rains—even to the extent of shortening their feeding periods, and in other ways adjust their behavior to the whims of the elements. These influences are of little significance in affecting quail numbers, but extremes of drouth and of winter cold and snow are major factors in determining population levels.

PREDATION; DISEASES AND PARASITES; ACCIDENTS

PREDATION

A CONSIDERABLE proportion of the eggs, young, and adults of these quails are normally taken as food by predators each year. Rarely, however, are these depredations large enough to be a prime factor in determining the population level of a species, though this may occur locally. Where excessive predation does occur it is most commonly effected on the bird's eggs.

The more significant predators of these quails are essentially the same for all species; their destructiveness depends on the local condition of their own abundance and that of their staple foods. Nest predators of importance include small rodents like the cotton rat (except for mountain quail), and ground squirrels (several species, including round-tailed, Beechey's, antelope), skunks, domestic cat, and foxes. Others that may occasionally be locally important are snakes (*Coluber, Lampropeltis,* rarely others), coyote, jays, bobcat, ravens, and ants. Gorsuch (1934) relates a case of a scaled quail nest raided by ants. The hen quail ate them as they came until she died; then the rest consumed her, the eggs, and presumably their own brethren inside the quail. Gorsuch says of the Gambel's quail that "Contrary to general supposition coyotes, bobcats, and foxes do not account for most of the nesting losses. . . . It is to small rodents, snakes, and the domestic cat that most of the losses must be attributed. . . . Where at all abundant the skunk also proves detrimental. . . . "

The predators that kill adult and young quail most commonly are the accipitrine hawks. The Cooper's is destructive of both old and young quail, the sharp-shinned takes mostly chicks, and the goshawk catches mostly adult mountain quail. Domestic cats and foxes may be locally destructive. Western horned owls and western red-tailed hawks catch a few, but their net food habits are definitely beneficial. Ravens, coyotes, bobcats, and other predators are known to take a quail on occasion, but they have little influence on the welfare of the species.

DISEASES AND PARASITES

LITTLE is known about the prevalence and importance of disease organisms and parasites on these quails. The losses they induce are probably an unimportant factor in their total mortality.

The most comprehensive study made in this field is that by Gorsuch (1934) on the Gambel's quail. He examined 205 birds for ectoparasites, and found biting bird lice on 58, mites on 43 (none in winter or early spring), ticks on 42, louse flies (Hippoboscids) on 9 (all but one in late fall), and fleas on 2. There were two species of louse flies, one *Stilbometopa impressa* and the other unidentified. The bird lice were of two kinds, *Goniodes mammillatus* and *Lipeurus docophoroides.* Two species of fleas were found, *Hoplopsyllus* sp. and *Oropsylla* sp. The red mites were *Neoschongastia americana.* The ticks were of three kinds, *Argas persicus, Haemaphysalis leporis-palustris,* and *Haemaphysalis* sp. None of these parasites is known to cause any mortality. Most distressing to the birds are the mites, especially on chicks, and the ticks, which can cause temporary impairment of some funtions, such as sight.

Gorsuch checked endoparasites in 230

Gambel's quail. A caecal roundworm (*Sub-ulura strongylina*) was found in 96 birds, a proventriculus roundworm (*Habronema incerta*) in 64, and tapeworms (*Rhadbometra odiosa*) were found in the intestines of 92. No deaths could be attributed to these parasites, but enteritis, which is potentially serious, was noted in some birds with heavy tapeworm infestation.

A study of blood smears of the Gambel's and scaled quail in New Mexico has revealed a high incidence of the avian malaria protozoans, *Haemoproteus lophortyx* and *Plasmodium* sp. in the Gambel's quail, 42.8% of 1207 birds (Campbell and Lee, 1953). Of 689 scaled quail examined, only 1.6% showed positive. Despite this high incidence of a potentially serious blood parasite in the Gambel's quail, no serious losses have been known to occur from it. There was some evidence that Plasmodium infections might be severely pathogenic in young scaled quail.

Little is known of the parasites of mountain quail. Of 23 birds examined in California, 21 had mites and 11 had roundworms in the proventriculus (*P-R Quarterly,* July 1949). No significance could be attached to any of these cases.

ACCIDENTS

THESE quail encounter the same sort of accidents as the California quail and bobwhite, except that the losses from encounters with farm machinery are uncommon. Nests are disturbed by men cutting brush or wood, mending fence, riding range, and so on, with subsequent abandonment of the nest common. Livestock trample some nests; fire and floods destroy a few. Some young Gambel's quail are lost by falling into cracks in the ground during drouth, and into erosion gullies. Some birds are killed flying into wires and vehicles, and a few succumb from spine punctures in the body from collisions with cacti. Drownings in water tanks are fairly common. One unique type of accident sometimes happens to juvenile mountain quail while on their downward fall migration. The coveys frequently walk along lake shores en route, and if flushed while there some of the young birds may fly in the wrong direction out over the water and drown (*P-R Quarterly,* April 1947). The total significance of accidents as a mortality factor is not known, but it is probably rather high.

RELATIONS TO MAN

MAN exerts two primary influences on these quail. As a land operator he alters their habitat for better or worse, and in these activities may cause the birds some mortality. Ranching is the land management activity of greatest influence on the Gambel's and scaled quails, while lumbering is of most concern with mountain quail habitat. Farming, mostly irrigated, is locally important to all three species. Man's other influence is as a hunter. He has not yet affected these birds greatly as a conservationist, but the opportunities for developing this interest will be discussed below under "Management."

AS A HUNTER

THE Gambel's quail is the most important game bird in Arizona and in parts of southeastern California, southern Nevada, and southwestern New Mexico. It lives in many easily accessible areas, provides a fair target, and its flesh is tasty. In sporting qualities it is not the equal of the bobwhite or California quail, because it does not lie as well to dogs nor flush as easily; it lies better to dogs after being shot into a few times. Some hunters make a practice of shooting over or into flocks on the ground early in the season in order to scatter the birds; once scattered they lie better. They also lie better where cover is good. Many hunters, however, hesitate to use dogs in such cover because of the abundant cacti. But it can be readily hunted on foot without the aid of dogs. It has the aggravating habit of racing on the ground in a covey well ahead of hunters, while one bird after another splits off by itself into the brush; finally the hunter has only the last bird or two to pursue. They much prefer to use their legs to escape rather than to flush, and they do it very effectively. When they do flush it is often at an unexpected moment. If pursued far, they go uphill, seeking rough terrain and dense cover, which makes hunting them even more difficult.

As a game bird, the scaled quail has about the same qualities as the Gambel's quail, except that they are somewhat more shy, are distributed widely in thinner numbers, and their running habit is even stronger. Bird dogs are useless, and wing shots are few in early season. Shooting them on the ground is perfectly proper at this time. Late in the season, as the winter flocks begin to form, the hunting of scaled quail improves. They lie well to dogs after they have been shot into, and ground shooting is no longer called for.

The mountain quail is the least popular of these three species with the sportsman. In addition to its very strong ground-running behavior, the terrain itself is difficult for hunting; it is usually steep and rough. The birds' habit of living in small groups rather than flocking accentuates the problem of getting a good bag. A few California sportsmen, however, highly prize this quail for its sportiness, and say that a bag of these birds is worth a dozen of California quail. This largest of the quails is considered a specially fine table delicacy.

As a result of the inaccessibility of much of the range of these quails, and because only inveterate quail hunters pursue them to any extent, all are very much *under*hunted; this is in contrast to the situation of many of our farm game birds. Studies in Nevada based upon banded birds indicate that the hunter harvest of the Gambel's quail on one of the best desert ranges is only about 5% to 10% of the total fall population, and that kill represents hunting on not over 12% of the occupied range in the study area. Most of the other 88% of the occupied range of the species rarely ever sees a hunter (Gullion, letter). Swank (letter) says the Arizona game men believe that the hunting of the

Gambel's and scaled quail in that state, even at its most intensive periods, has little effect on the birds' populations; they are studying this matter now. In northern California the mountain quail is so little harvested that the state game men feel that more information is needed on how and where to hunt them, in order to make good use of the resource (*P-R Quarterly*, January 1951).

In farmed valleys and near roads the hunter has good success in gunning for these quail. An Arizona hunter check in 1949 showed a bag of 2.8 Gambel's and scaled quail per man, plus a crippling loss of about 14% of the bag. Near two water holes the kill per hunter was 3.1 and 3.4 birds. A special hunt for Gambel's quail in the Yuma Valley designed to reduce crop damage yielded 10,000 birds in two days on 200,000 acres (*P-R Quarterly*, April 1950). The average take on a controlled hunting area near Oracle, Arizona, was 2.0 per hunter for 1,594 hunters in 1951, and 3.9 for 1,099 hunters in 1952 (Swank and Gallizioli, 1953). In good years the toll of Gambel's quail in Arizona exceeds 200,000, and that of the scaled quail may be over 10,000.

The daily bag of Nevada Gambel's quail on one study area in 1950, '51, and '52 was 3.3, 2.7, and 4.6 respectively. In the first hunter check the crippling loss was 24% of the bag, or 0.8 bird per hunter. In 1950 the hunters fared best at higher altitudes, whereas in 1951 the best hunting was at the lower elevations. This illustrates the influence of weather on hunting, for it was difference in the weather that had caused the changes in the quail numbers in the two sections. On another Nevada area in 1952, 107 hunters got 4.8 birds each per day, plus an average of 1.1 cripples lost by each. The average daily bag during 4 years of study was 3.5 (Gullion, letter).

The mountain quail amounted to 15% of the total kill of all quail tabulated in 22 counties of California in 1946. This gives a fair indication of its relative importance in hunting as compared with the California quail (*P-R Quarterly*, April 1947).

AS A RANCHER, FARMER, AND LUMBERMAN

MAN'S use of the land has affected the habitat of these quails throughout their ranges. From irrigated farm fields to overgrazed desert and burned and cut forest slopes, the nature of the cover has been altered in greater or less degree. Where irrigation has made farming possible, the change has been complete; the new habitat on these lands is wholly unlike that that existed before. Whether it benefits or hurts these quail depends on its nature and extent. Grain and truck fields close to desert range are used by all species, and are often an improvment in the total habitat of the vicinity. But only the edges of these farm fields are tenable, for the birds must still have their desert or mountainside brush. Thus extensive areas of farmed land exclude quail from most of the area.

Probably the greatest influence man has wrought is by the grazing of livestock. Its effect on quail may be good or bad, depending on its intensity; severe overgrazing destroys both food and cover, but moderately heavy grazing helps induce annual food plants and prevent the growth of too dense brush.

The development of water for livestock has benefited the birds in many places where lack of water had been a limiting factor to their use of the range. Areas that would be otherwise unusable have been made tenable by the presence of dependable water. Another benefit that has helped the Gambel's quail has been the spread of its staple food plant, mesquite, by cattle.

Lumbering has made great changes in the habitat of the mountain quail; fires have compounded the effects. Generally speaking, the results of woodcutting have been a detriment to the birds, but here again there has been variation. When the changes resulted in moderately open brushy cover, the birds have benefited; where the cover became dense brush it excluded the quail from all except the edges. Logging operations have been in some places

the main cause of nest destruction. The cutting of mesquite on the desert for firewood has also affected the habitat, but mainly for the Gambel's quail. Its influence depends on whether the brush cover remained open and usable or dense and impenetrable.

PRODUCTIVITY AND POPULATIONS

PRODUCTIVITY

THE productivity characteristics of these quail follow rather closely those of the California quail. They have a high reproductive potential; mating behavior is typically monogamous; and they raise no more than one brood a year.

The sex ratio is practically even most of the time but occasionally a small excess of males prevails. Of 304 Gambel's quail winter-trapped by Gorsuch (1934) in two years, 50.7% were males. A California study of the Gambel's quail in the spring of 1950 revealed an even sex ratio where nesting did *not* occur due to drouth, but a 2:1 excess of males where nesting was normal; this indicated a heavy mortality of hens during the nesting season (*P-R Quarterly,* July 1951). A state-wide Arizona quail count in 1950 of 336 birds, mostly Gambel's, showed an even sex ratio (Lawson, 1950). A count of scaled quail in the summer of 1950 in Arizona showed 52% males among 48 birds (*P-R Quarterly,* July 1951). California studies of mountain quail showed a slight excess of cocks in the spring (*P-R Quarterly,* January 1951).

Nest mortality is normally high. Of 44 Gambel's quail nests observed by Gorsuch (1934), only 11 hatched. Of the 75% that failed to hatch, 41% were destroyed by predators, 20% were abandoned, mostly due to interference by man, and the fate of the rest was unknown. During serious drouths the nesting loss is excessively high, and few hens nest at all; a Colorado study of 26 scaled quail nests showed an 81% failure (*P-R Quarterly,* January 1947). The nest loss of mountain quail in California in the Sierra Nevadas in two different years was 43% (*P-R Quarterly*, January 1948 and January 1951); much of this loss was from logging operations, and the rest from predation. All evidence points to the almost perfect fertility and hatchability of the eggs of all three species.

Information on quail mortality is scanty. Recent studies indicate that the reduction of immature birds in summer is usually about 50%. Juvenile loss of the Gambel's quail on study areas in Arizona in 1942 was 42% to 51%; in 1946 it was 49%; and in 1949 it was 44% (*P-R Quarterly*, October 1942, January 1947, and April 1950). The fall covey size of mountain quail in California in September 1949 on three areas was 5, 7, and 11; these indicate brood losses of about 55%, 36%, and almost 0% respectively. The high loss was in a drouth area, and the low loss showed combined coveys (*P-R Quarterly*, April 1950).

Age ratios that reflect results of the production season have been recorded in recent years for all three species. In very dry years the age ratio of young to adult birds has been very low, a consequence of incomplete nesting and poor nesting results. For example, the age ratio of the Gambel's quail in Arizona in 1943 was 0.3:1; in 1946 it was 0.4:1; and in 1947 it was 0.36:1; all were bad drouth years. In contrast, in seasons of normal rainfall, like 1941, 1944, 1945, 1949, and 1950, the Arizona age ratios were 4.25:1, 2.9:1, 1.3:1, 2.2:1, and 1.1:1 respectively (*P-R Quarterly*, October 1942, April 1945, January 1947, January 1948, and January 1951). A striking contrast in the Gambel's quail productivity in a single year on nearby areas was reported in Nevada in 1950; in one area where a severe drouth prevailed the age ratio ranged from 0.1:1 to 0.3:1, while in the second area, which had normal rainfall, the ratio was 3.1:1 to 3.5:1 (*P-R Quarterly*, January 1951).

The same drouth relationship to productivity exhibited by the Gambel's quail is also true of scaled quail. In 1942 and 1943 in Arizona, both dry years, the age ratio of scaled quail was 1.0:1 and 0.3:1, closely paralleling the figures for the commoner species (*P-R Quarterly*, July 1944). This relationship also holds with the mountain quail, but drouth is less apt to strike them in their high-altitude breeding areas. Age ratios checked in California in 1948 and 1949 were 6.5:1 and 6.0:1, both exceptionally high for late summer or fall populations (*P-R Quarterly*, April 1949 and January 1950). In general, the age ratio must be above 2:1 in early fall if production is to do more than merely sustain the population level; when it falls below 1.5:1, a decline in numbers compared to the previous fall is almost certain.

The mortality of adult quail results from predation, gunning, accidents, and possibly now and then from disease, the proportion being high to low in the order given. Where hunting is not significant, as is true over much of the range of all these birds, the other decimating agents take up the slack. The periods of greatest regular loss are fall and spring, the first from hunting and the second due to high vulnerability in the breeding and nesting season, especially for hens. In some years of severe winters there may be a very high mortality, particularly at high altitudes and in the northern sections of the range. The high loss of hens in the nesting season is balanced somewhat by the greater vulnerability of the cocks to gunning, which results from their habit of guarding coveys and thus exposing themselves. According to an Arizona study on the Gambel's quail, the average monthly loss from November to March is about 7% (*P-R Quarterly*, January 1947). This is also about the average for scaled quail. Mountain quail may have less winter loss in ordinary years, as in 1948–49 in California, when it was only 20% (*P-R Quarterly*, July 1949). It may be much higher in very severe winters with any of these species, but specially with the mountain quail, as it was in some areas in 1949–50.

*POPULATION DENSITIES AND
FLUCTUATIONS*

EXCEPT for counting concentrations of quail at watering places, there have been few studies that have given accurate figures on population densities. Dozens and even hundreds of these quail may regularly use a single watering place during dry periods when succulent greens are not available. How many square miles of occupied range such groups come from is not accurately known.

An Arizona study of the Gambel's quail in the fall of 1941 found an average density of four birds per square mile (*P-R Quarterly,* October 1942). A later study near Oracle, Arizona, utilized two areas, one hunted and the other protected. The prehunting season population densities in 1951 and 1952 ranged from 36 to 88 birds per 100 acres; the postseason densities were from 55 to 61 birds per 100 acres (the lowest preseason population on the nonhunting area had *increased* during the fall). The average January population on both hunted and protected areas was about two acres per bird (Swank and Gallizioli, 1953). The spring breeding population on a small study area in Las Vegas Valley, Nevada, in 1951 was a bird for every two acres, an exceptionally high density (*P-R Quarterly,* October 1952).

California studies of mountain quail showed an early spring density of a bird per three acres in March 1949, after a winter of very high survival; the highest densities were two acres per bird near water. Nesting territories ranged from 5 to 50 acres, which indicated that the early spring concentrations spread out considerably during nesting (*P-R Quarterly,* July 1949, January 1950, and January 1951). These samples indicate that the population densities of these quails are of the same order of magnitude as those of the California quail, except that under very favorable circumstances the California quail can reach much greater concentrations.

Fluctuations in populations of these quail are frequent and often of extreme magnitude. Changes in seasonal weather from one year to another, particularly the advent of winter-spring drouths after one or more seasons of normal rains, often result by fall in low production and population declines. There was a general decline of the Gambel's quail from 1941 to 1947, and then a recovery for a few years. In 1950 the population declined again to about half that of the previous year (*P-R Quarterly,* January 1951). In northwestern Colorado a road count in 1950 and 1951 showed a drop from 34 birds per 100 miles the first year to only 14 the next year (*P-R Quarterly,* October 1951).

Quick declines of mountain quail sometimes accompany severe winter weather. Whether any of these fluctuations are cyclic is not known, but if they are it would be because the weather changes are themselves cyclic.

MANAGEMENT

MUCH of the range of these quails is public land; the management of the habitat is therefore predominantly a problem for public agencies. In general the practices recommended follow closely those described in the previous chapter for the California quail. These will not be repeated here in detail but will be discussed briefly, and such changes or additions as seem warranted will be covered.

LAND USE AND DEVELOPMENT

THERE is great opportunity for expanding and improving the range of these quails; especially that of the Gambel's quail, because of its greater significance in sport hunting. The expansion referred to is not a geographic extension of the range of the species, but an enlargement of the actually occupied habitat within its present geographic range. As Gorsuch (1934) said, "We can, by the adoption of correct game management policies, substantially increase the numbers of Gambel's quail. This can be done with comparatively small financial outlay, the sincere co-operation of interested parties, and the application of science. . . . " The parties concerned are the state wildlife agency, the landowning agency, the hunting public, and the private landowner, particularly the rancher.

The three needs of water, food, and shelter are the same as with the California quail, and the importance of improving them is in that order. Much range with adequate food and shelter for quail lacks water, and is thereby unusable except possibly in wet periods. By the development of guzzlers, as described on page 328, such areas can be made to support quail. The general pattern of such a development is the guzzler proper, which catches rain water and stores it through dry periods, together with a fenced area around it. This fenced area should be a minimum of half an acre, but preferably 10 to 15 acres. For scaled quail the fenced area should be predominantly a grassy cover, while for the Gambel's and mountain quails it should be open brush. Such developments are needed throughout the range of the Gambel's and scaled quails, but mainly in the low-altitude summer range of the mountain quail, and in other parts of its range in eastern and southern California. Where livestock or other watering facilities can be adjusted to provide water for quail (see page 328), a covey "headquarters" area should be fenced in above the watering place instead of around it. Wherever there is enough excess water from the facility to irrigate a small area of ground below by the construction of shallow channels on a slight grade, a seeding may be made to provide food.

Observations on the use of guzzlers by the Gambel's quail in Arizona indicate that a low ramp opening and lack of light are deterrents to the bird's willing entrance; if the guzzler has its opening facing east to the morning light this can be partly overcome. The height of the opening to the water should be ample for quail headroom, but not so large as to admit large predatory animals.

The location of guzzler developments should be in sheltered valley locations, where food and shelter conditions are good; a shaded spot is preferred, and one near good nesting cover. For the Gambel's quail they may be placed four miles apart or from other water sources, but for scaled and mountain quails they may be as close as a mile apart and still be adequately used.

The control of food and shelter vegetation for the Gambel's and scaled quails is largely a matter of having the right number of domestic livestock on the range. If overgrazing is avoided, the natural capacities of an area for making quail habitat will be achieved naturally. Artificial shelters such as described for California quail (see page 333) may also be used for the Gambel's quail in locations where adequate shelter cannot be got by some easier means.

The seeding of such legumes as alfalfa, clovers, and vetches, and such grains as sorghum, wheat, or oats may be made on irrigated areas below watering places, or on portions of valley farms. These seedings may be used as cover crops on farms growing truck or fruit crops, or as border seedings for headlands, or just for wildlife food patches. The legume and some of the grain seedings have farming utility as well as helping feed quail; on some truck farms they are worth their cost just to feed the quail and prevent the birds from raiding the valuable cash crops. This is especially true where the Gambel's quail is found.

The improvement of mountain quail habitat, apart from the water requirement, involves brush and woodland operations. The opening up of overdense brush on the summer range can be done in the same ways as described for California quail (see page 332), by the use of machinery, herbicides, controlled fire, and controlled grazing. The burning off of chaparral and similar brushy growth in the humid coastal mountains is more effective in improving quail habitat than the same process in the arid inland mountains (Gordon, 1950). The harvest of woodland products by sustained-yield methods that provide for a cutting rotation is beneficial under most conditions; a mixture of moderately open brush and young or old woodland tree growth on the mountainside provides the desired cover pattern. The cutting operations should strive to bring this about by any reasonable adjustments that can be made in the normal practices.

PREDATOR AND RODENT CONTROL

No *special* control of predators or rodents is recommended on behalf of these quail; ordinary rodent control that may be needed for agricultural reasons is all that can be justified. A fur harvest of some of the flesh-eating mammals is the only control of these species warranted, except that thorough suppression of feral cats is always in order.

REFUGES

In areas where hunting pressure is heavy, small refuges of a hundred acres or so around heavily used watering places may be needed; otherwise, refuges for the purpose of restricting hunting have no merit in the management of these birds.

RESTOCKING

No general recommendation for restocking any of these quail can be justified on the basis of economics or of the results obtained. The transplanting of wild-trapped birds from underhunted areas of abundance to vacant areas may sometimes be warranted, as recommended in California (*P-R Quarterly,* January 1951). This is an expensive process, and should not be done indiscriminately. When it is thought to be needed, the prospect of stocking the vacant range should be checked by competent biologists, and the operations of trapping and handling should be in similarly trained hands.

The transplanting of the Gambel's and mountain quails to new areas outside their natural ranges has been tried many times. The Gambel's quail transplants failed in Massachusetts, Pennsylvania, Kentucky, Oklahoma, Washington, eastern Colorado, northern California, and no doubt in other places as well. Very small successful introductions have been made in western Colorado and east-central Idaho (see Figure 25). Transplants of mountain quail have failed in Alabama, Nebraska, New Zealand, and other locations. The range has been successfully extended by transplants into western Washington, southeastern Washington, eastern Oregon, and southwestern and south-central Idaho (McLean, 1930). These populations do furnish some hunting.

It is doubtful if further effort to add new range for any of these quail by additional transplants is warranted.

CONTROL OF THE HARVEST

SINCE all three of these quail are underhunted over most of their ranges, the problem of harvest control is not as urgent as with some other species. The Gambel's quail is heavily hunted in parts of Arizona, but even there it does not require adjustments of hunting seasons and bag limits from year to year. Only marginal populations that concentrate at water holes need any special protection; this can be done with refuges. A standard, generous season of a month or more is proper for all these quails.

The populations of the Gambel's quail can be gauged with accuracy by means of summer counts. According to an Arizona study, a census by means of a roadside count taken in July will reveal year-to-year changes in population level needed for management purposes (*P-R Quarterly,* April 1945).

The need in connection with the harvest of mountain quail is for better information on how and where to hunt the bird more effectively. This information should be disseminated among sportsmen to encourage them to take up the sport of hunting these elusive mountain birds that make such a fine *pièce de résistance* for the table.

CHAPTER 10

The Chukar Partridge

ORIGIN AND CLASSIFICATION

THE chukar partridge is one of 22 subspecies of a species of rock partridge native to southern Asia. The original range of this rock partridge extended from southern Mongolia and China, through northern India and Iran, to Turkey; it has also long been successfully established in several parts of Europe. Its scientific name is *Alectoris graeca,* and the "chukar" subspecies is an Indian variety, *A. g. chukar,* whence came our name for it. There are three other rock partridges in the genus, including the red-legged partridge of southwestern Europe and the Barbary partridge of northern Africa. They belong to the family Perdicidae.

DESCRIPTION

THE chukar is a plump, chickenlike bird, somewhat larger than the Hungarian partridge, and a little smaller than the ruffed grouse. It is 15 or 16 inches long. The males weigh from 21 to 26 ounces, and the females from 16 to 19 ounces (Christensen, 1953).

The coloration of the bird is very striking, and is identical in the two sexes. The upper plumage is generally a light brownish gray. There is a prominent, rather wide black line that extends from the forehead through the eyes, down the sides of the neck, and across the upper breast like a bib. The throat is white, the belly and flanks are gray, and the sides are crossed with a series of vertical black and brown bars. The bill, feet, and legs are red.

The male may be distinguished from the female during the breeding season by its larger size and by the presence of spurs. When present, the female's spur is smaller and more pointed than that of the male (Galbreath, letter). Birds younger than one year are difficult to sex by the spur method; in fact, sexing is uncertain at all times when based only on external characters. The juveniles may be identified in early fall by their mottled secondary feathers and their light weight; after midautumn they are indistinguishable from the adults (Christensen, 1953).

INTRODUCTION INTO THE UNITED STATES

THE first chukars brought to the United States, as far as the records show, were liberated in Illinois in 1893; these birds came from the vicinity of Karachi, India (Phillips, 1928). The significance of the area of origin was evidently not then appreciated. As we know now, this bird in its many races is found in a great variety of climates, altitudes, and types of terrain, each race suited to its particular environment as a result of thousands of years of natural adaptation. A chukar to succeed in Illinois would have to come from an area like Illinois in climate and other basic environmental factors; these birds didn't, and they disappeared.

Since that first trial, nearly every state has liberated chukars in an effort to establish them, and several provinces of Canada also have received them. Most of these efforts have failed as completely as did the one in Illinois.

The state of California began raising chukars

357

PLATE 81. *The chukar partridge.*

in captivity in 1928, and released a total of 4,600 between 1932 and 1936 (Bade, 1937; True, 1937). They were stocked in Washington in 1931 and 1932 without success, but later releases beginning in 1938 were successful. The first releases in Nevada were made in 1933 by private citizens. More were distributed in 1934, and from 1939 to 1943 others were stocked. Between 1947 and 1952 additional birds were wild-trapped from areas where the early releases had succeeded and were redistributed. From 1950 to 1952 the state propagated and released 1,410 chukars from a game farm. Altogether, the stocking of chukars in Nevada involved fewer than 5,000 birds (Christensen and Wick, 1953). The success of the chukar here is one of the outstanding accomplishments with exotic game birds in this country. The chukar is already the most important upland game bird in Nevada.

Some success was achieved in establishing chukars in Idaho, Wyoming, and other western states in the late 1930's. By the early 1940's the fever was on, and great interest developed in the bird.

It is still not possible to appraise the final re-

sult of all these introductions. At this time it appears that the species is well established as a huntable game bird in two areas, one in Washington and the other in Nevada, and in some adjacent parts of California. There are small colonies that show definite promise in west-central Colorado, southern Idaho, and northern California. According to Sandfort (1952), " . . . the chukar now seems to be permanently established and at home in Colorado," though not yet in numbers adequate for public hunting. Some colonies have been started in southern and western Montana, east-central Utah, and eastern Arizona, but they are too small or too new and insecure to judge their success. It is very probable that other successful populations of chukars may be established in parts of the 11 western states. It is doubtful if this bird will ever achieve good populations in the country from the Dakotas to Texas and eastward.

GEOGRAPHICAL RANGE AND DISTRIBUTION

THE present range of well-established populations of chukars are in two areas: (1) in 10 counties of central Washington, mostly in the Columbia River Valley—Adams, Benton, Chelan, Douglas, Grant, Kittitas, Klickitat, Lincoln, Okanogan, and Yakima counties; in four counties of southeastern Washington—Whitman, Asotin, Garfield, and Franklin (Galbreath and Moreland, 1953); and (2) in four counties of eastern California—Mono, Plumas, Inyo, and San Bernadino; and in fourteen counties of Nevada, all of the state but Clark, Elko, and Lincoln counties (Christensen, 1954).

Promising colonies are established in northern California, north-central Wyoming, southern Idaho, and west-central Colorado (see Figure 26). Other locations where birds have held on a few years and where they may eventually succeed are shown on the map in parts of Montana, Colorado, Utah, and Arizona.

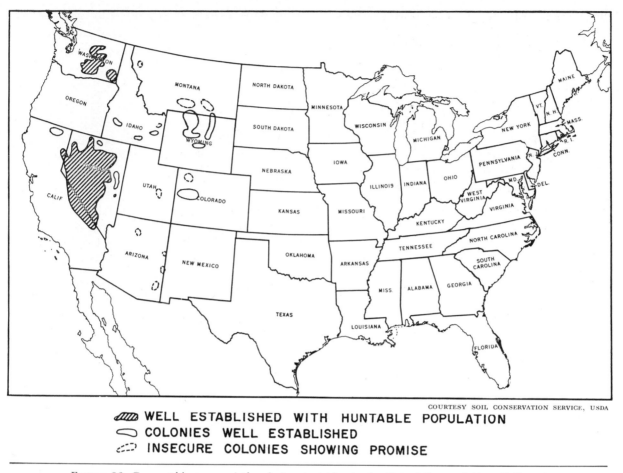

🔳 WELL ESTABLISHED WITH HUNTABLE POPULATION
◠ COLONIES WELL ESTABLISHED
⌒ INSECURE COLONIES SHOWING PROMISE

FIGURE 26. *Geographic range of the chukar partridge in the United States.* (*After Galbreath and Moreland, 1953; Christensen, letter; and others.*)

HABITS OF THE CHUKAR PARTRIDGE

WINTER flocks of chukars begin to break up in early February. The males do a good deal of fighting in the process of selecting mates, much like "huns" (Hungarian partridge). The pairs are made in the covey, but they do not actually leave until sometime in March or early April. When this happens the pairs disperse widely over the countryside in search of nesting territories. For several weeks they appear to be continually on the move (Galbreath and Moreland, 1953).

Mating begins in late March. The display of the male prior to mating was described by Galbreath and Moreland (1953) as follows: "During the feeding and resting period the cock suddenly runs at the hen with his head down and his neck extended; his wings are held in a drooping position and his neck feathers are ruffled. In such manner he runs around the hen several times . . . "

The nest is built on the ground beside a shrub, rock, or clump of grass. It is a shallow hollow, lined with dried grass and a few feathers. The clutch of 14 to 16 eggs (more or less) is begun in late April and completed early in May. The eggs are yellowish white, with brown speckles of variable size and number. Hatching begins in most years and localities in the last week of May, is at its peak in early June, and for late renests may extend into August. The hen does all the incubation; the cock bird usually deserts her some time before the eggs hatch. One or both parents may care for the brood for a while after the chicks hatch, but before long the male leaves them; he then joins other cocks, and they spend the summer in small groups of three to a dozen or more.

The summer is spent in lowland cover of valleys or foothills, or in canyons close to water and shade. The birds like to loaf in the shade of brush cover during hot summer days, while morning and early evening are devoted to foraging for food. During the hot, dry season they make daily trips to their watering place, often starting in early afternoon and loitering around the water for an hour or more. Toward evening they disperse again to the nearby foothills or canyon sides.

The chicks can fly some 30 to 60 feet when they are two weeks old. If disturbed the youngsters freeze while the mother feigns injury. After the young are about four weeks old, any danger encountered causes the whole brood to flush in flight to the nearest rocky terrain, preferably on a steep slope. The broods are somewhat gregarious, tending to join together for short periods; this takes place mostly around watering places. The chicks develop very rapidly, and are substantially full-grown at 12 weeks of age. Toward late summer the habit of families joining is stronger, and they stay together for days at a time. These groups may number from 30 to 50 or more birds; from 100 to 300 have been seen together on hot midsummer days in Washington (Galbreath and Moreland, 1953).

Chukar coveys converse among themselves almost constantly when active; all birds participate, hens as well as cocks. The birds' name is a description of their crowing call, *"cha! cha! cha-ker! cha-ker!"* which is given rhythmically. They also use a loud, repeated *"cheiou! cheiou! cheiou!"* note when flushing in alarm. Chucking notes, *"ka! ka! ka!"* are also used

by males when seeking a mate in the spring, and by members of a covey when scattered to regroup (Galbreath and Moreland, 1953).

In early autumn the flocks may be concentrated around water sources, sometimes in even larger numbers than in summer; at times there may be several hundred in a group. When the rains come in late fall the flocks disperse into smaller groups, and they are no longer held close to water holes. At this season they are able to use more of the available range and food supply.

Chukars generally prefer running as a means of escape, unless they are approached from above; then they flush in covey flight when disturbed. In autumn they fly up the nearest shale or rock slope when disturbed. The hunter that gets shots at a covey when they are on the wing finds a sporty target, much like the Hungarian partridge. There is difference of opinion as to how well chukar coveys lie for bird dogs; some say they lie well (Bade, 1937), and some say they don't (Moreland, 1950). Christensen (letter) says, "In my opinion a dog is essential in chukar hunting. Birds which have been shot at are extremely difficult to find without a dog. Also, after a covey has once been flushed, the birds appear to hold very well." It is generally agreed that they are difficult to reflush, for the scattered covey not only seeks rocky, steep, and rough terrain, but prefers to run rather than fly on further contact. But the tendency of a scattered covey to utter their regrouping call often gives the hunter advance information on their whereabouts. Galbreath (letter) says, "Perhaps the greatest value is its [the dog] ability to find dead and wounded birds once they are shot."

The chukar does not, as far as we know, conflict seriously with any of our other game birds, much to the relief of many who feared that it would cause trouble by displacing another species in the areas that it occupied. Despite the geographical overlapping of its present range with that of the ring-necked pheasant, California quail, Hungarian partridge,

PLATE 82. *The rugged, rocky habitat of the chukar partridge. This canyon with rock walls and talus slopes is in southeastern Washington.*

sage grouse, and mourning dove, the habitat it actually uses is little used by the others. At water sources and where its rocky slopes meet valley lands, the chukar may actually be found with other game birds. Even where they have been observed drinking from the same water hole with other birds, they have not caused any trouble. They have been known to use the same winter feeding stations as "huns" and valley quail, and the only unnatural occurrence was that the chukars waited before feeding until the quail left. On one 360-acre area in Washington, Moreland (1950) flushed 37 chukars, 160 pheasants, 40 valley quail, and 55 "huns," a remarkable compatibility.

The chukar is very easily grown in captivity on game farms, and thus can be made readily available in large numbers for such introductions as are needed.

HABITAT

SINCE the establishment of the chukar in the United States is still in progress, it may not be possible at this time to describe accurately all of its habitat. Conceivably it may yet achieve good populations on types of range not yet tried, or it may dwindle in numbers in some of the habitats that now seem to suit. All we can do is depict the type of cover that has so far supported the best populations.

It seems clear that the country must be arid. Certain kinds of range land and desert seem best. They are doing well in sections of Nevada where the annual rainfall is only *five* inches (Rutherford, 1949); this is even drier than the desert quail likes; most of their occupied range has from 5 to 20 inches of rainfall. They are well adapted to living at a variety of altitudes; most of the birds in this country are found at heights of from 1,000 to 8,000 feet, but some have been seen up to 10,000 feet, according to Rutherford. In their India homeland they are known to occur as high as 16,000 feet in summer (Baker, 1922).

One part of their habitat that is most distinctive is the steep, rocky, rugged slopes that they seek for roosting and escape. Here they choose the seemingly most inhospitable and unlikely cover possible—barren, windswept, and with very little vegetation. These areas may be rock outcrops, tallus slopes, or canyon walls. They combine this high ground, which is so devoid of other game birds, with rolling sage-cheat grass range land, creek bottoms, and the edges of valley farm lands.

According to Galbreath and Moreland (1953), the optimum range in Washington contains approximately 45% tallus slopes, rock outcroppings, cliffs, and bluffs, 5% brushy creek bottom, and 50% sagebrush and cheat grass association. Slopes associated with this growth should have a difference in elevation of more than 200 feet and be over 7% in grade. It is typical in Nevada to find the birds using slope grades of "30 to 40 degrees," according to Christensen (1953).

Nest locations are usually on open south slopes several hundred feet above creek bottoms. The cover is likely to be scattered grass and shrubs (Galbreath and Moreland, 1953).

They require free water in the summer and at other times when succulents are lacking. This water may be got from streams, springs, irrigated farms, impoundments, or other water facilities.

Creek bottoms, canyon floors, and farm edges are frequented mainly in the summer. Nesting cover is mainly barren slopes, with scattered vegetation. In winter when food is hard to find they live on wind-swept slopes and range lands most of the time, but occasionally may come to farm fields seeking food.

Bunch grass, cheat grass, and sagebrush are the prevalent plants in most of the chukar's habitat, but in the bottoms it is more likely to be willows and cottonwoods, along with shrubs and weeds.

FOOD HABITS

CHUKARS feed mostly on grass seeds and grass leaves, but winter annuals, grains, some fruits, and insects are also important at some times of the year. The most comprehensive food study so far made on the chukar is that of Galbreath and Moreland (1953), based on 216 samples. Cheat grass seeds made up 33% of the food in winter, 13% in spring, 14% in summer, and 28.9% in fall. Grass leaves amounted to 20.5% of the winter food, 19.6% of spring food, less than 2% in summer, and were not used in the fall. Wheat kernels ranked high, with 2.5%, zero, 7%, and 19.6% respectively of the foods eaten in winter, spring, summer, and fall. Other plant foods that composed 2% or more of the diet in any season were as follows: salsify leaves and seeds, 6.3% in spring; dandelion seeds and heads, 9.8%, and leaves 7.9% in spring; fringe cup bulblets, 9.8%, 1.9%, and 4.9% in spring, summer, and fall, respectively; shepherd's purse leaves and heads, 8.5% in spring; equisetum spikes and stems, 5.1% in spring; bunch grass crowns and seeds, 13.2% in summer, and 2.6% in fall; Western serviceberry (*A. florida*) fruits, 13.7% in summer; fiddle-neck, 8.6% in summer; Douglas hawthorn fruit, 11.9% in summer and 4.9% in fall; potatoes, 4.5% in summer; squaw currant seeds, 2.9% in summer; chokecherry, 7.1% in summer; oat kernels, 2.0% in summer; poison oak drupes, 2.6% in fall; apple, 4.3% in fall; desert parsley, 4.1% in fall; rye kernels, 2.9% in fall; redroot pigweed seeds, 20% in winter; smooth sumac drupes, 8.1% in winter; and wild rose fruits, 6.4% in winter.

The animal foods eaten ranged from about 15% of the diet in the fall, and 10% in spring and summer, down to about 3% in winter; they were chiefly grasshoppers, beetles, crickets, ants, yellow jackets, and squash bugs.

Several crops of Colorado chukars were examined by Sandfort (1952). He found seeds of cheat grass to be a prevalent food, " . . . along with seeds of foxtail, barnyard grass, pigweed, and bindweed." In the spring it was found that leaves of bluegrass and cheat grass and dandelion flowers and leaves were eaten.

According to Rutherford (1949), the chukars in some locations have taken such a liking to some farm crops that " . . . farmers are even beginning to growl about it." This is probably a very local situation, for their consumption of grain is almost wholly after harvest, their use of alfalfa and other greens could hardly make an appreciable dent in a crop, and such a bird could not likely do serious damage to fields of potatoes. Chukars have also been observed to concentrate in cattle-feeding yards in Washington to feed in midwinter (*P-R Quarterly,* July 1952), and to feed from weed seed piles left by threshing machines along the edges of grain fields in Montana (*P-R Quarterly,* January 1953). In Utah chukars use many greens in summer feeding, seeds in the fall, including seeds of Indian rice grass, and waste grain (*P-R Quarterly,* April 1953). They are adept at scratching in the ground litter to uncover seeds.

THE EFFECTS OF WEATHER AND CLIMATE

THE results of chukar introductions in this country show clearly that this bird is very much limited in its range by climate; in fact,

it is *probably* one of the most closely restricted of all our game birds. Aridity seems to be the dominant consideration; no chukars have been successfully established in humid areas, or even in the prairie zone of 20 to 30 inches of rainfall. Another climatic condition with which they are associated is the exposed, wind-swept slopes on which they roost. This habitat need may well be more a matter of the terrain than the atmosphere that goes with it, but the latter is a part of it.

There is evidence that some combinations of winter weather and habitat cause serious mortality of chukars through starvation. Heavy snows, with prolonged low temperatures that prevent any thawing, even on south slopes, cover all low plant growth and the birds' main foods. If there are no snowless lower elevations or farm areas nearby to which they can resort, severe malnutrition may result; this has been reported in Nevada (Christensen, 1952b). Moreland (1950) reports that winter losses in Washington in recent years have been negligible except in one period, January 1950; prolonged cold weather that went as low as 30° below zero without thaws on feeding slopes resulted in some starvation. Evidently the chukar is pretty tough when it comes to surviving extremely low winter temperatures. In controlled cold-box tests, results of which were summarized by Kendaigh (1945), the chukar survived longer (that is, was most resistant to low temperatures) than any other game bird except the wild turkey. Its vulnerable "Achilles heel" is evidently its stomach, for it is at times susceptible to winter starvation.

NATURAL DECIMATING AGENTS

TIME has not permitted gathering very much information on the natural mortality of chukars in this country. It may be presumed that the predators that take "huns," pheasants, and the like will also take chukars when they can. There does not appear to be anything about the chukar that makes it less vulnerable to predation than other birds of its type, unless there are fewer effective predators in some chukar habitat. This might conceivably be true of its roosting cover high on rocky slopes, but one can only conjecture on the matter until more detailed studies of the bird are made. In Idaho the accipitrine and rodent hawks, horned owl, eagles, coyote, and bobcat are named as chukar predators (*Upland Game Birds of Idaho*, published by Idaho Fish and Game Commission, no date but about 1952). Coyotes and horned owls are known to have killed both young and old birds in Washington, and in addition a few adults were taken by prairie falcons, golden eagles, and Cooper's, sharp-shinned, marsh, and red-tailed hawks. Many of these catches were conditioned by starvation, and no significance was attached to the predation (Galbreath and Moreland, 1953).

A ferruginous rough-legged hawk was observed killing a chukar in Montana (*P-R Quarterly,* January 1953), but little significance can be attached to predation on recently released game-farm birds. Such birds are so vulnerable that it must be normally expected that many will be taken by predators that could not catch a healthy wild bird.

Nothing is known about the disease of wild chukars; but Nagel (1945) notes that they are " . . . susceptible to common diseases of poultry and game birds" when in captivity. Moreland (1950) records an outbreak of avian malaria caused by a protozoan *Haemoproteus* sp. on a Washington state game farm that wiped out many birds. Galbreath and Moreland (1953) found no evidence of disease in wild chukars.

Little in particular is known of the chukars' propensity for accidents. It is unlikely that the bird encounters trouble with farm machinery, since it rarely nests where such machinery would be used. Galbreath and Moreland (1953) reported 54 chukars killed on highways in three years, and 7 dead from flying into wires. Range fires probably destroy some eggs and birds. It is reasonable to presume that a variety of accidents befall them, and that these are a source of considerable mortality.

RELATIONS WITH MAN

THE chukar is so new in this country that it is difficult now to evaluate adequately its relations with man. For the most part it chooses to inhabit country that is not farmed, but much of which is used very heavily for livestock range. Therefore man's range-management activities seem most likely to affect this game bird.

Some influences of man's land use can be pointed out. The overgrazing of the arid and semiarid range lands seems to enhance the ability of this land to grow chukars. Excessive foraging by domestic animals encourages some of the birds key food plants, such as cheat grass. Moderately heavy grazing permits most food plants to develop both leafy parts and seeds; also shelter plants, though of *relatively* little use to chukars, are not grazed down to uselessness. Water developed for stock is often available to chukars, and may be a vital requirement that enables the birds to live there. Thus the kind of care and development given the range by ranchers is fundamental to the welfare of the chukar.

Farmed land is of some use to chukars where it is situated close to their range land and rocky slopes. Its main value lies in providing such food as wheat, oats, weed seeds that go with grain farming, and succulent hay-crop greens like alfalfa, and potatoes. Most of this use of farm crops by chukars has no economic significance, though there have been some instances of local damage to potatoes, muskmelons, and watermelons (Galbreath, letter).

Chukar hunting is now—as of 1953—only six years old in this country. Nevada first placed the bird on the open hunting list in 1947; Washington followed in 1949. These are still the only states where one may hunt

PLATE 83. *Chukar partridges gathered at a guzzler water facility.*

chukars, though it is possible that one or more other states may be able to open the season on them soon. Its qualities as a game bird have already been described above under "Habits."

The hunter harvest in Nevada and Washington is now more than 100,000 birds in some years. In 1949 the kill in Washington was 44,860; it declined to 7,480 in 1950 after a severe winter loss, but rose to 16,740 in 1951, and 63,100 in 1952. In 1952 the daily bag limit was increased to five, and the season in some areas lengthened to 50 days. In 1953 the population was at its highest level ever, and the season in some counties was extended to 64 days (Galbreath, letter). The Nevada harvest increased from 36,184 in 1951 to 43,742 in 1952. In the 1952 season 6,899 hunters averaged 6.3 birds for the whole season and 2.2 per day of hunting—not bad for a new

sport (Nevada 1952 Game Harvest Report). The study of a sample area in Washington indicated that the kill was 24.5% of the population, but this was believed to be a higher take than general in the state. A field check on Nevada chukar hunting in 1952 and 1953 showed that the hunters got a daily average bag of from 0.5 to 2.1 birds on different areas, and that it took an average of from 2.2 to 10.5 hours of hunting to bag each bird (Christensen, 1954).

Nevada hunting is usually objectively aimed at bagging chukars, whereas in Washington the hunter may go afield with the intent of taking any one or more of several species. A check on the hunting on two Washington areas in 1952 revealed that only about one hunter in ten returned with a chukar in his bag, but that they had larger numbers of pheasants, and in addition a sprinkling of "huns," valley quail, and sage grouse (*P-R Quarterly,* April 1953). According to Galbreath (letter), "At the present time, our greatest problem in regard to chukars is harvesting the crop."

There appears to be no reason why the chukar should not remain with us as a huntable game bird, and very likely will some day be available in many more areas than at present.

PRODUCTIVITY AND POPULATIONS

THE known facts on the productivity of the chukar indicate that it is much like the Hungarian partridge. It is monogamous, breeds the year after birth, and raises no more than one brood a year. There is little data on the sex ratio; Christensen (letter) sexed 176 birds, and found 49% of them to be males. There is no reason to think that it is not similar to that of the "hun" at birth, that is even, but is less likely to have an excess of males among the adults like the "hun."

Little is known about chukar nest losses; in fact chukars nest in places so hard to find that few have been seen, much less studied enough in a single area to learn much about mortality. Some brood counts have been made, and they indicate that in *favorable* years the survival of young is high. In California in 1951 and 1952 the average hatch was 13 to 14 (*P-R Quarterly,* October 1952). In Nevada in 1952 July-August brood counts averaged 11.5, and in Washington the average brood size at 8 weeks was 14 in both 1950 and 1951 (Galbreath and Moreland, 1953). In 1953 the average size of 16 broods observed was 12.1 (Galbreath, letter). As with other gallinaceous birds in some years the survival may be low, as indicated by an age ratio of only 0.8:1 young to adults on a Colorado study area in 1951 (*P-R Quarterly,* July 1952).

Winter mortality may be high, and especially so when prolonged deep, unmelting snows pre-vent adequate feeding. According to a Washington study the general winter mortality in the rather severe winter of 1949–50 was 60% to 70%, but on one area in Kittitas County it was 90%, whereas on light snow areas along the Columbia River it was very low (*P-R Quarterly,* October 1950).

Cool, damp spring weather is conducive to good nesting and brood-rearing with the chukar, as it is with other arid-land species. Winter and spring drouths produce the opposite effect.

THE MANAGEMENT OF THE CHUKAR PARTRIDGE

THE management of the chukar is still in its elemental stage; only in parts of Nevada and Washington has it gone beyond the problem of obtaining successful introductions. Elsewhere the need is for continued and more careful attention to achieving the establishment of colonies in suitable habitats, which may then be able to self-propagate to populations big enough to provide sport hunting.

Most of the liberations of chukars (and other species as well) in the past have been rather haphazard, a sort of "shotgun" application made in the hope that somewhere the species would "take." It has been mostly luck that a few successes have come from this process. It is also very wasteful, in that most of the failures could have been predicted and thus avoided. Cahn (1938) predicted the failure of the efforts to establish the chukar in Tennessee, based on comparisons of the climate of the area from which the chukars came with that of Tennessee. His "climograph" technique (see page 379) showed them unlike in vital respects, and the chukars failed as he predicted they would.

It was pointed out early in this chapter that the species to which the chukar belongs has many varieties, which in the native range are adapted to many different combinations of climate and habitat. It seems reasonable therefore to expect that other subspecies of this rock partridge may be suited to parts of the United States and Canada different from those where the chukar has already succeeded. This matter can be tested scientifically, and stocking limited to areas where another game bird is needed, if we are smart enough to do so. This process is now being attempted for the first time. The United States Fish and Wildlife Service has undertaken a project, in co-operation with the states, to determine where in the United States another game bird is actually needed, and then to search the world for suitable ones to try (Bump, 1951). As an example of how this is working, it has been recommended that no more chukars be liberated in Arizona, where they have not shown much promise in the "trial and error" release of Indian chukars so far, until more suitable types can be obtained from the Near East instead of India (Lawson, 1951). The Near East is more comparable in climate and habitat to the parts of Arizona where it is desired to establish a game bird than is the section of India from which the chukar comes.

It is quite possible that the chukar that we now have may prove adaptable in more areas than are now solidly occupied. Parts of California, Colorado, Idaho, and Wyoming seem quite likely to develop substantial populations; other sections of our 11 westernmost states may also well prove suitable. Carefully planned trials and evaluations like those now in progress should continue there.

Chukars are easily produced on game farms, and the birds so grown are as satisfactory as game-farm birds can be for stocking (Bade, 1937). Wherever possible, new introductions should be made by transplanting wild-trapped birds from localities of abundance rather than using game-farm birds; this can now be done in several of the Western states. Releases should be made in suitable habitat by the "gentle" method of placing crates of birds in good protective cover, opening the door, and letting them go out in their own time. It is very important that enough birds be released at each location. Chukars have a habit of wandering from release points; hence a large number are needed to assure enough remaining together so that there will be breeding. A Utah study suggests 200 to 250 at a place (*P-R Quarterly*, January 1953). Two or more units of this size may well be released a few miles apart, where suitable water and cover exist, so that the wanderings of the different groups may overlap and give a greater chance of adequate groups remaining in the habitat they choose.

The species should of course be legally protected until populations are adequate for hunting. Special educational posters placed in the localities where the birds are released may be helpful in making hunters aware of the new birds, and help sportsmen to avoid accidental shooting. Publicity in newspapers and in state conservation magazines will also help to assure that the birds get every possible chance to survive. Where there are shootable populations in remote areas, the construction of access roads may be justified to encourage more hunting (Christensen, 1952a).

Little is known about the physical aids that may be given to chukars to increase their chances of survival in release areas. The provision of water may make some territories habitable for the birds that would otherwise be unsuitable (see page 328). Christensen (letter) says that "water development appears to have great possibilities for extending the range of the chukar in Nevada." Winter feeding by means of grain stations may at times be justified, especially with newly stocked birds. Except for the possibility of water developments as suggested above, the main habitat-management considerations are the sound but heavy use of the range lands for livestock grazing. Experience in years to come should give us other leads to help these birds thrive in their new lands. We are barely on the threshold of developing management techniques for the chukar in the United States. It holds the possibility of developing more sport in some areas that now lack a good upland game bird.

CHAPTER 11

The Hungarian Partridge

ORIGIN AND CLASSIFICATION

THE Hungarian partridge is a native of much of Europe and southwestern Asia, but is most common in central and southeastern Europe. It has been established successfully in several portions of the United States and Canada. It belongs to the order Galliformes and the family Perdicidae. The scientific name is *Perdix perdix perdix* (Linnaeus). Many races have been described in its native range, but these have no significance in this hemisphere.

Its proper common name is European gray partridge, but it is known throughout its American range as the Hungarian partridge, or just plain "hun."

DESCRIPTION

THE "hun" is a plump bird, with short, rounded wings and short tail; it is somewhat larger than the bobwhite, and smaller than the chukar partridge. It is 12 to 14 inches long, and weighs from 12 to 15 ounces.

The color of the male is variegated brown, chestnut, gray, and buff, finely set off with blackish lines. The back is brown to buff, with cross-barring of chestnut, gray, and black, these bars becoming wider on the rump and upper-tail coverts; the wings are dark brown on the primaries with buff markings, and the coverts are brown with a complex pattern of buff bars, tips, and shaft streaks; the tail is chestnut, with buff tips on the outer feathers, pale buff with black cross lines and chestnut shaft streaks on the middle feathers; the sides and flanks are widely and diagonally barred with chestnut and buff, and there is a horseshoe-shaped chestnut patch on the lower midbreast that is variably prominent in different individuals; gray surrounds the chestnut horseshoe, and extends below over the belly and above over the upper breast and neck; a light-chestnut area extends from the throat to the forehead and cheeks; the crown, back of neck, and ear region are dark brown with streaks of buff; there is a small reddish bare spot behind the eye that is brightest in late winter before breeding. The bill is short, blackish- or greenish-brown; the tarsus and toes are bare, and bluish-gray; the iris of the eye is brown.

The plumage of the female is similar to that of the male, but paler chestnut. The horseshoe breast patch is often very pale, and sometimes wanting. The wing coverts and scapular feathers have a broader buff shaft stripe, and two or three buff crossbars not on these feathers in the male.

Juveniles have yellow legs and feet, which change to yellowish-brown in the first winter and to bluish-gray by the next spring. The plumage of the juveniles most resembles the female, though it lacks the rich chestnut color of the adult and is a more somber mixture of brown, buff, whitish, and black. The downy young are pale- or yellowish-buff, with somewhat reddish-brown markings on the crown, back, rump, and base of wings; there is a wide black line down the center of the back of the neck; the face and throat are pale yellowish-buff with some blackish streaks.

368

PLATE 84. *The Hungarian partridge.*

GEOGRAPHICAL RANGE AND DISTRIBUTION

THE "hun" has been stocked profusely in many parts of the United States and Canada; most of these efforts resulted in failures, but a few were phenomenally successful. It spread rather widely from the points of successful introduction, and it is probable that it has now occupied most of the range to which it is adapted.

The present distribution of "huns" in North America consists of one large primary area of highest adaptability, two secondary areas of considerable size, and several spots where the birds hold on in small numbers (see Figure 27). The area of highest populations is the northern great plains region, extending from northwestern Iowa, western Minnesota, and southeastern Manitoba, through most of the Dakotas, southern Saskatchewan and Alberta, to west-central Montana and west-central Alberta. The two secondary areas are in the Southern lakes states region and the far Northwest. The one extends from northwestern Ohio

and southern Michigan, across northern Indiana and Illinois, into southern Wisconsin. The other covers most of Idaho, eastern Oregon and Washington, parts of west-central Oregon and Washington, and southern British Columbia.

These ranges edge over into several other states, as shown in Figure 27. In addition there are small areas where the "huns" are fairly well established in Colorado, Ontario, Pennsylvania, New York, and Nova Scotia. Though classed as legal game in some of these small areas, they are not of much significance in the total hunting picture.

HISTORY OF THE HUNGARIAN PARTRIDGE IN AMERICA

ACCORDING to Phillips (1928), the "hun" was first introduced into the United States in New Jersey in the late 18th century by Richard Bache, son-in-law of Benjamin Franklin. This effort failed, as did all others for more than a hundred years. Releases were later made in all the Eastern states from Maine to Florida, with the most widespread activity taking place between 1905 and 1915. Some of these birds survived a few years, but eventually died out. Liberations in the western states began in California in 1877, in Washington in 1897 (Yocom, 1943), in Oregon in 1900 (Oldys, 1909), and in the other Western states and Canadian provinces a few years later. Ultimately all but four states attempted to introduce the "hun."

The story of the introduction of the "huns" into Alberta is sensational. A sportsman's group imported some 200 pairs from Hungary and released them near Calgary in 1908 and 1909; within five years they had multiplied and spread throughout southern Alberta and into Saskatchewan. This remarkable result spurred a rash of "hun" introductions the length and breadth of the continent, for this was just what sportsmen dreamed would happen by introducing exotic game birds. This process continued until the

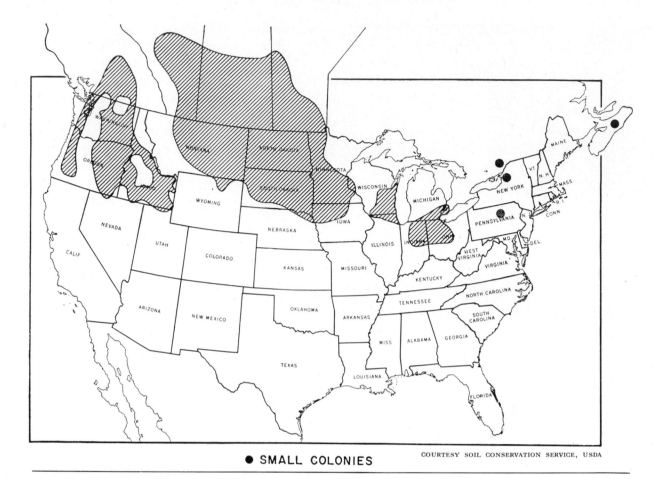

● SMALL COLONIES   COURTESY SOIL CONSERVATION SERVICE, USDA

FIGURE 27. *Geographic range of the Hungarian partridge in North America.* (*After Yocom, 1943; Cartwright, 1944; McCabe and Hawkins, 1946; and others.*)

early 1930's, by which time some 270,000 had been imported into the United States at a cost of over a million dollars (Gordon, 1935). Several states undertook to raise the birds in captivity on game farms in order to avoid the high cost of transporting them from Europe.

Most of these released birds disappeared, and the efforts to establish "huns" was abandoned in those places. The exceptions represent the second most significant success on this continent in providing game-bird hunting with exotic species; the greatest success was of course the pheasant.

In the areas where the "hun" did become established it spread widely and occupied all the suitable range. The rate of spread from the

Alberta planting was 28 miles per year, whereas another stocking of 6,470 "huns" in Wisconsin at the same time spread only five miles per year (McCabe and Hawkins, 1946). As a result several states and provinces discovered that they had colonies of "huns" without any effort on their part. Thus the birds drifted into Saskatchewan and Montana from Alberta, from Saskatchewan into North Dakota, from Washington into Idaho, from Manitoba and Iowa into Minnesota, and even got as far east as Ontario and Quebec.

After the great increase in numbers of "huns" in the prairie provinces, open hunting seasons were declared. Sportsmen quickly became enthusiastic about this crafty foreigner, for it lay fairly well to dogs and provided a fast target. Gordon (1935) quotes Colonel Mershon's observations on hunting huns in Saskatchewan in 1934: "In one day last October my companions and I saw over a thousand partridges. In the South years ago I flushed 34 coveys of quail in one day, and thought that was a big day, but it is not a match to the partridges here. Several days later we saw by actual count 69 coveys of partridges, some with twenty to thirty birds."

These phenomenal numbers have not held up through the years, for the "hun" is subject to the same environmental influences as are our native species; its populations increase and decrease much as do the populations of our grouse. Nevertheless in the last two decades it has consolidated its populations in the range where it is established, so that it is now a legal game bird in a dozen or more states and provinces, the exact number varying from year to year.

HABITS OF THE HUNGARIAN PARTRIDGE

COURTSHIP AND MATING

THE male partridge has no courtship performance as such, comparable to the drumming, hooting, or booming of the native grouse, the flight of the woodcock, or the "bobwhite" song of the quail. The selection of mates, or pairing, is done in the covey, and begins in midwinter, often as early as late January. The stimulus appears to be a period of warm weather, such as a succession of days above freezing. The males start calling in evening and morning, their "crow" or "cry" being variously described as *"kee-ah," "caer-wit," "kee-uck,"* and so on. They start chasing each other, pecking and skirmishing. The courtship seems to be a one-sided affair, the cocks vying with each other for the females, who appear unconcerned.

Fighting among cocks is a vigorous and sometimes protracted affair. When two cocks have

decided they each desire a certain hen, the approach of either of them to the hen precipitates a fight. They spar around and fly at each other with their wings, often jumping into the air a little for better effect. They keep it up for several minutes, and feathers may fly, but there is rarely any real damage done. The rivalry may continue for days, until one bird gives up and leaves and the other is victor. When he has the field to himself the cock may make his representations to his ladylove. This consists of short runs in front of the hen, with wings and tail fanned out, and accompanied by some vocal notes (McCabe and Hawkins, 1946). All the while the hen bird nonchalantly hangs around, seeming to pay no attention either to the furious contests being fought for her or the antics of the victor; she may not actually care how the battle comes out, since apparently she always accepts the winner. McCabe (letter) says, "I'm not sure it's that simple. I suspect (but I do not know) that once the pairing bond is made, the male may be defeated in a fight but is not abandoned by the female because of the loss."

After a pair have mated they keep together for several weeks in March and April. When the weather turns stormy, the pairs re-form the covey, but it is then a loose organization and very temporary; even when gathered in late winter coveys, the pairs are usually discernible. As spring advances the regathering of the covey gradually diminishes, and finally ceases altogether.

NESTING

NEST-BUILDING and egg-laying begin in late April. A shallow hollow about two inches deep is made in the ground by the hen, often in a slight depression. The nest is lined with a coarse outside layer of weed stems, shreds of woody material, dead grass, and the like, and a fine inner layer of soft leaves, grasses and feathers. The nest location is commonly in grassy cover of wild grass, hay- or grainfields, along fence rows or roadsides; field nests are usually close to the edge of the field. Yeatter (1934) found half of the field nests he observed within 24 feet of the margin, and 70% within 49 feet; more surprising, 30% of these nests were within 30 feet of a field *corner*. Thus the edge principle is a strong influence on Hungarian partridge nesting habits. The site chosen for nesting is usually in the same territory occupied by the covey in winter, or very close by.

Early-season nests are usually completed before any eggs are laid, but late nests may be built during the laying period, the first eggs being laid in a crude hollow. Eggs are laid at a rate of about 2 every 3 days, or 3 every 4 days, until the clutch is completed in mid-May. The average number laid is about 16, but this may vary from 5 to 25 or more, the larger ones usually being the product of two or more hens and the small ones incomplete. If the first nest is destroyed, the hen usually renests at least once; renests average about half as many eggs, the later the nest the smaller the clutch. Yeatter (1934) reported that June-hatching nests in Michigan averaged 19 eggs, July nests had a 15 average, and August nests 9. Broods from renests had less than half as many chicks as first-nest broods in a Washington study (Knott, Ball, and Yocom, 1943). In Wisconsin the second clutches averaged 10 eggs, as compared to 17 in first nests (McCabe and Hawkins, 1946). In areas where the "hun" and pheasant are both found it is common to find a few pheasant eggs in partridge nests.

During the nesting season and later in the summer the "huns" show little fear of operating farm machinery nearby; but if the hen is flushed from her nest early in the incubation period she may desert; later she is very persistent. McCabe and Hawkins (1946) tell of a hen that nested beside a road where a repair crew was operating. The workers flushed her repeatedly, and scraped the road ditch a foot from her; the cover around her was cut by a debrushing crew; and " . . . a farmer mowed, raked, and loaded his hay five feet from the nest. . . . " Yet she hatched 19 of her 21 eggs!

The eggs are olive color, varying in shade from almost white to a dark olive; occasionally the color will be more bluish than olive. The eggs average 1.4 inches by 1.0, and are pointed ovate.

The hen spends from a few minutes to an hour or more at her nest each day, even on days when no egg is laid. When she leaves the nest she covers the eggs with leaves or grass. As soon as the clutch is completed she arranges the eggs points down and begins incubation. The routine during incubation is to set almost continuously, except for a period in early morning and another in late afternoon; she then leaves the nest for a half hour or so to feed, dust, and exercise. Early in the setting period she may leave the nest at other times for a few minutes, but as hatching time approaches she sets almost continuously. Only the hen performs the incubation chore, though the cock remains in the immediate vicinity. The egg-development period is 24 days. The peak of hatching usually comes in early or mid-June in the southern part of the range, and about a week later farther north.

THE BROOD PERIOD

BOTH parents are at the nest when the chicks hatch, and lead them away as soon as they are dried off and the weather and time of day are favorable. The exodus usually starts as soon as the vegetation has dried off in the morning, or later in the day; the hen leads the procession and the cock brings up the rear. A soft clucking by the hen, and to a lesser extent by the cock, keeps the chicks under control, as they learn to catch insects, select other food, dust themselves, and cope with enemies. These conversational notes by the parents are accompanied by a constant twitching of the tail. The hen's primary job is training, while the cock acts as guard.

When the brood is attacked or disturbed the youngsters freeze in their tracks or scatter slightly, while the parents attempt to draw off the intruder with characteristic feigning of injury, accompanied by squealing calls. If the presence of the enemy is noticed before the attack, the male bird frequently flies off and tries to decoy it some distance from the brood. The adults may fly at a man or dog that comes close to the brood, in their effort to distract attention from the young; this attitude of reckless defense of the chicks continues for two or three weeks while the young ones are flightless; by that time the young "huns" are able to make short flights.

The brood spends most of its time in farm fields, and along the hedge rows, ditches, and roadsides that bound them; they use areas of rather substantial growth that afford good protection. As hayfields and grain crops are harvested, the birds shift around to cornfields, late hay, or other areas that still have good cover. Most of these fields provide all the summer needs of the birds—food, and roosting and dusting places. Dirt roads are favorite dusting places, and both broods and adults may frequently be seen there in the early morning. As the summer advances the brood becomes more mobile and less dependent on lush cover; they move about freely, though their cruising area rarely exceeds half a mile in diameter. When the brooding period is over the covey roosts in a close circle, much like quail; later they sleep in a larger circle, and tend to use open grain stubble or recently cut hay. The covey may be joined by one or two broodless adults some time in late summer as the youngsters reach full juvenile development. They become fully plumaged and grown in about ten weeks.

FALL AND WINTER ACTIVITIES

THE brood is the nucleus of the covey; they remain as a unit until the pairing time comes in late winter. Unattached adults may join a group at any time and increase the size of the covey, and two or more broods at times join together. Thus some fall coveys may number 20 to 30 birds.

"Huns" love open field cover; even in severe winter weather they prefer open grain stubble, corn- or hayfields to other places. When most game birds seek the shelter of high or rank vegetation, the "hun" continues to use the same cover as in the summer. They may seek the lee side of a hill, a windbreak, or a strawstack, but they remain in the open. When flushed the covey takes off with a single noisy burst of flight, the birds calling *"keep, keep"* as they get under way with whirring wings. Its flight is a short, oblique rise, and then a straight and rather low course over the ground for a couple of hundred yards or more, ending in a quick veering to one side before alighting. After the rapid wing beats of the initial rise they may coast for a ways, then alternate a series of quick wing beats with more coasting; this flight style is similar to that of the prairie chicken. They frequently fly to the nearest knoll or ridge, behind which they can drop out of sight. When they are reflushed they again rise as a covey—unlike the bobwhite, which scatters when alighting (Yocom, 1943).

The fall and winter feeding is done primarily in grain or corn stubble and other harvested crop fields—usually the most exposed part of the landscape. Bitter cold weather holds no terrors for the "hun," for it is among the hardiest of our important game birds. It prefers to roost in this exposed field cover even when the weather is at its worst. Sometimes a covey will allow itself to be covered by drifting snow, or may even purposely burrow in the snow when going to roost. Because of its ability to get along in its chosen cover come what may, it has surprisingly small covey-cruising radius; many coveys live through the fall and winter in an area only an eighth of a mile in diameter, and most of them travel over a span of less than half a mile. They do not migrate in the proper sense of the word, though under conditions of extreme food scarcity they may shift their home range considerably. Some adjustment in covey composition takes place in the fall, but there is less "shuffle" than with most gallinaceous species. During very severe winter weather and when food is scarce, coveys frequently combine temporarily into larger flocks.

RELATIONS WITH OTHER GAME BIRDS

THERE is always reason for concern about the possible effect of introduced exotic birds on our native species. The areas occupied by the "hun" are to some extent used by the ring-necked pheasant—also introduced—and to a less extent by the prairie chicken, sharp-tailed grouse, bobwhite quail, valley quail, and some others. The parasitism of "hun" nests by pheasants has been noted, but this is of no significance. There seems to be little other direct conflict caused by the "hun," as far as we know. It has been reputed to conflict with the sharp-tailed grouse and bobwhite quail, but specific evidence is lacking (Yocom, 1943). Even where it is found in good pheasant range, the portions of the habitat used by the two species are most of the time quite distinct; the "hun" sticks chiefly to the open, exposed fields, and the pheasant prefers the field edges where other and more protective cover is available. The time of the greatest overlapping of habitat use is the nesting season, but even then there is no evidence of serious competition. The possibility exists that each gallinaceous species affects all others in a range used by more than one species, and that the range carrying capacity is measured in terms of the numbers of *all* these species rather than of each one separately. This question was raised by Green and Hendrickson (1938) when they wrote: "It has been noticed that since the pheasant population [in Iowa] has been so decimated by hard winters and poor nesting seasons, the huns on the area have increased. Whether or not there is any correlation is not known."

ADAPTABILITY TO CHANGING ENVIRONMENT

THE "huns'" habitat requirements are specific, and it does not adapt easily to great changes in land use; still, since it has little need for woody or rank herbaceous cover, the trend toward clean farming that has so seriously affected the bobwhite and some other species is not a serious threat to the partridges' welfare. Should the agriculture of the northern great plains change from a grain to a grazing economy, the "hun" probably would not be able to adjust and thrive equally well under the new conditions. Such a change is unlikely to occur, and thus there is no environmental change that poses a major threat to this species in its best range.

ADAPTABILITY TO ARTIFICIAL PROPAGATION

THE Hungarian partridge is not easily raised in captivity and produced economically on game farms, compared with the pheasant and chukar partridge; but any legitimate needs for stocking can easily be met.

HABITAT OF THE HUNGARIAN PARTRIDGE

CLIMATE, soils, and topography are exceedingly important factors in habitat suitability for "huns"; a cool and moderately dry climate appears to be best. The highest populations in North America are found on the northern plains, where the annual rainfall is between 15 and 25 inches and the humidity is moderate. No substantial populations have developed in hot areas or in wet humid sections, though small colonies do persist in Nova Scotia, Ontario, New York, and Pennsylvania.

The best soils for "hun" habitat are highly fertile, of sandy loam, loamy, or clay-loam texture; very heavy soils appear to be less suitable, even if fertile; though some heavy soils that are well drained support fair numbers of these partridges (Dale, 1943). A gently rolling topography seems to suit them best; bare knolls and shallow depressions in the open farm landscape are preferred to either flat or hilly areas. "Huns" are found at altitudes up to at least 5,100 feet in Washington (Yocom,

PLATE 85. *Side canyons of the Snake River in southeastern Washington support many Hungarian partridges. The slopes are covered with bunchgrasses and the land above the canyon is in wheat.*

1943); at these high altitudes they are usually on open bunch grass ridges, and occasionally in ninebark-snowberry cover near conifers (Yocom, letter).

The two most important cover types are crop fields and grassland; no others are *essential*. Each may be used in many forms, but the optimum appear to be small grains and corn for the one, and native grass or hay for the other.

The major cover characteristic of the prairie habitat is the expanse of small grains, mainly wheat; the same is true of the Palouse region of eastern Washington. In recent years, however, the largest populations of "huns" in this area of Washington have been along the rough breaks of the 2,000-foot canyon of the Snake River (Yocom, letter). Wheat fields border the side canyons, which have brush in the bottoms and

PLATE 86. *The fabulous Palouse wheatlands of southeastern Washington are good range for both the Hungarian partridge and ring-necked pheasant. This vast expanse of wheat is all-year habitat for the hun. They nest in grass draws such as shown.*

bunch grasses on the slopes, as described by Yocom and Harris (1953). Grainfields furnish year-round cover, though the early nests are rarely in them. They are the source of much food, both grains and weed seeds. Corn, soybean, bean, oats, barley, and fallow fields serve the same purpose in parts of the range, especially from Michigan and Ohio to the Dakotas.

Grass cover is used for nesting, roosting, and to some extent for feeding. Hayfields are fine nesting cover, except for the great loss caused by the mowing machine. Pastures are used for general living, but are not acceptable for nesting if heavily grazed. Roadside grass strips are a common nesting place, and are also used by broods. In the irrigated lands of the Northwest

the watered farm fields are supplemented by the adjacent sagebrush range land, which is used some for nesting and roosting.

Woody cover is relatively unimportant to this bird. Fence rows furnish some nesting cover, but not ordinarily if there is much brush. Hedgerows also furnish shelter from the wind in winter, as do windbreaks, haystacks, ditches, and other obstacles. "Huns" often use the field cover on the lee side of such protective areas, rather than the shelters themselves. Woodlands in general have very little value for "huns," though a few nest in woody edges.

Nesting cover is selected on or close to the winter range; hayfields are used more than any other type, except native grass where that is

COURTESY SOIL CONSERVATION SERVICE

PLATE 87. *Some Palouse farms grow considerable hay as well as wheat, as on this one. Both huns and pheasants utilize this cover. The tree planting on the steep slope serves as shelter for pheasants and as a windbreak for huns.*

available. In checking 143 Michigan nests, Yeatter (1934) found 34% of them in hay, mostly close to the field edges. Knott, Ball, and Yocom (1943) reported that 49% of 113 Washington nests were in hay, mostly alfalfa. Wisconsin studies by McCabe and Hawkins (1946) revealed that 54% of 427 nests were in hayfields. Grainfields or grain stubble are the next most used cover for nesting, especially for late nests. The proportions of nests found in grainfields for each of the above areas were as follows: Michigan, 20%; Washington, 9%; Wisconsin, 11%. Roadside grass, fence rows of herbaceous or shrubby cover, pastures, and other grass cover make up most of the balance of cover used for nesting. Where the range is

composed of irrigated crop fields and semiarid range land, as in much of the Northwest, most of the nests are located in the dry range cover.

After hatching, the young broods spend much of their first few weeks in uncut hay, grain, or other fields of tall grass; here they feed on the plentiful insect fauna. In wet weather they are likely to move to the more open cover of corn or bean fields or grain stubble. After the chicks learn to fly they live more and more in the grain- and cornfields; considerable time is spent in dusting on dirt roads or in tilled fields. During hot weather they often seek shelter in gullies, draws, or drainage ditches, and beside hedges, windbreaks, and woods edges where such places are

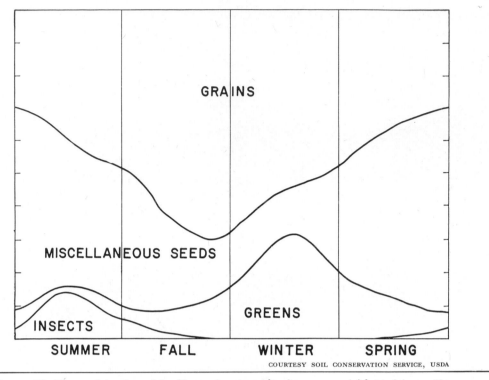

FIGURE 28. *Types of food used by Hungarian partridge by seasons. (Adapted from: Yocom, 1943; Hicks, 1936; Miller, Ball and Knott, 1948; Yeatter, 1934; Kelso, 1932; and others.)*

close to their usual field cover. Plum thickets are frequently used for protective shelter in Iowa (Green and Hendrickson, 1938), and in Washington rose and hawthorn thickets are utilized (Yocom, letter).

During the fall and winter seasons the partridges use the wide-open grain and corn stubble, standing corn, weed fields, and grasslands almost exclusively; they have less need for protective shelter than any other of our northern game birds. At times they seek out places behind hedges, windbreaks, or other shelter to escape wintry winds, but otherwise they seem to try to stay in open, exposed places.

FOOD HABITS

THE "hun" is mainly vegetarian except for the first few weeks of life, when it is insectivorous. The adults eat insects too, but animal food exceeds 10% of the diet only in summer; see Figure 28.

The vegetable food is waste grain, weed and miscellaneous seeds, and green leafy material; fall and winter is the season of the heaviest use of grains. In some localities waste grain may at times make up 90% or more of the food. Throughout the birds' range it is the primary type of food, and rarely drops below 30% of the diet at any time. Most of this grain is gleaned from the ground, from the harvest time of one year to the following summer. Wheat is the all-important, all-year grain in the Alberta-Saskatchewan-Montana-Washington area, with barley and oats also important. In the midwestern range, from Ohio to the Dakotas, corn and wheat are the primary grains eaten; other farm crop seeds, such as those of buckwheat, soybeans, garden peas, and the like may be of local significance.

From midspring to late summer, seeds other

than those from farm-crop plants make up the major source of food, the only season when any kind of food is taken more than grain; from 30% to 60% of the food at that time may be seeds from weeds and a few woody plants. Insects are eaten in significant amounts through the summer, and it is likely that more of them are consumed than indicated in the few records from this season. Among the plants that furnish seeds in largest quantity are the green and yellow foxtail, black bindweed, and ragweed. Other weeds of some value as a source of food include: lamb's-quarters, crab grass, smartweed (various species), prickly wild lettuce, spring beauty, ground cherry, nightshade, baby face, wild oats, and tarweed. A few grass seeds are eaten, such as brome grass, panic grass, and tall oat grass. Seeds or fruits from woody plants do not generally account for much of the "huns'" food, but around Pullman, Washington, Yocom (1943) and Miller, Ball, and Knott (1948) found them utilizing trailing raspberry and caragana seeds.

Green leafy material is eaten more in winter than at other seasons; for a time in midwinter, when one would expect them to be most difficult to find, greens may constitute as much as 30% of all food. Most of these greens come from hay and grain fields; the leaves of clovers, alfalfa, bluegrass, wheat, dandelion, mustard, and others are among the kinds regularly used.

The insects eaten are a miscellaneous lot, many of them in larval form; they are kinds that inhabit hay- and grain-fields and live on the ground. The larvae of butterflies, moths, and flies are eaten a great deal by chicks as well as by adults; grasshoppers, ants, ground beetles, bugs (Hemiptera), and some others are taken as available by both young and old birds.

The "huns" do not need free water, but do require dew to meet their water needs. They must have grit all year long; in winter they obtain their grit supply largely from gravel roads, a habit induced by necessity, that results in some losses from traffic accidents.

The "hun" has sometimes been accused of pulling sprouting grain, eating grain on the stalks, damaging ripening crops like tomatoes and apples, digging out newly planted seeds of such crops as melons, spreading seeds of noxious weeds, and other crimes against the farmer. Though specific instances of minor depredations have been verified (Yeatter, 1934; Yocom, 1943), they are very local, occasional, and of negligible significance. The economics of "hun" food habits is substantially neutral, and farmers reflect this by welcoming the birds.

THE EFFECTS OF WEATHER AND CLIMATE

THE impact of weather on a native game bird is by nature an influence effectuated within a climate suitable to the species; else the bird would not be there. With an introduced species like the Hungarian partridge there is a fundamental first question, "Is the *climate* suitable for the species?" This question is even more basic than "Is the habitat suitable?"

The "hun" was introduced widely over this continent without much regard to climate. Cahn (1938) uses six areas to illustrate the matter: "The Hungarian partridge was introduced into California, Missouri, New Jersey, southern and central Alberta, southern Wisconsin, and Montana. In the first three states it failed entirely; in the last three regions it established itself well, spreading in all directions . . . this notwithstanding the fact that all available data shows that these states [California, Missouri, New Jersey] have all that is required for the physical comfort of the bird— shelter, nesting sites, and abundant food. The *yearly* average for the temperature of each of these states is nearly identical with that of the native central European habitat of the birds; there is also very close correlation in respect to the yearly mean rainfall. But when the conditions of temperature and rainfall for *each month* individually has been established for the range of *Perdix* in central Europe, and this compared with . . . these areas of failure, very little correlation is to be found. . . . "

Cahn then proceeds to demonstrate that these failures could have been predicted by using a *climograph* analysis (Twomey, 1936) before the transplantings. "In constructing the climograph, the mean monthly rainfall and temperature over many years for a number of available localities which as nearly as possible outline the native distribution of the species in question, are used, and when all the locations have been plotted (using the mean rainfall in inches for each month as the abscissa and the mean monthly temperature in degrees F. as the ordinate for each point plotted), and an outline is drawn about the extremes of the points located on the graph, the result being an irregular figure which represents and includes within itself a graphic picture of the optimum conditions within the native habitat of the species. Then upon this same graph the same thing is done for the location into which the species is to be introduced. If the graph of the new locality falls well within the range limits indicated by the graph of the native environment —falls inside of the irregular figure—then it would seem that this new habitat might well be favorable in terms at least of two vital factors, without which correlation the species is predoomed to failure. If it falls outside of the native area figure, then failure may be prophesied."

Cahn goes on to apply the method to the six areas: "When the climograph of California was superimposed upon that of the native habitat, it was found that the months of breeding (May to September) fell beyond the conditions encountered in that native area; California was too hot and too dry. In a similar manner Missouri and New Jersey proved too hot and too wet. On the other hand, the climographs of the Alberta areas and of Wisconsin and Montana fell well within the tolerance range of the species in its native habitat, *at least during this critical period.*"

Though the climograph technique does not show all the complex relations of climate to a species, it does illustrate clearly the rather severe limits that climate places on the distribution of the "hun." Excessive moisture and heat during the production season make most of the United States and Canada unsuitable. Excessive dryness in the desert lands make them equally unsuitable.

There is no doubt a tolerance limit of winter severity of temperature and snow for the "hun," but this hardy bird does not ordinarily encounter these conditions. The extent of suitable habitat in the Canadian provinces sets a closer limit to its northern distribution.

Weather conditions influence the daily behavior of "huns" in several ways, but they are less affected by varying temperatures, wind, and precipitation than most game birds. During summer, especially when the chicks are young, they avoid thick cover when it is wet; even heavy dew will cause the broods to seek corn or bean fields, fallow places, or other open spots in preference to their usual hay and grain cover. They avoid strong winter winds by seeking the lee side of a hill, hedge row, windbreak, strawstack or any convenient obstacle; otherwise they seem to prefer to live completely exposed to the elements.

Weather may increase the rate of "hun" mortality, or reduce the success of reproduction, much as with other gallinaceous species. In portions of the occupied range, as in the East and the lakes states, where the climate is marginal, the nesting success is closely related to the rainfall; a series of dry years may result in an encouraging increase in numbers, as in southern Michigan during the early 1930's. Contrarily, a series of years with normal rainfall curtails production, and when a year or more of excessive breeding-season precipitation occurs, the population declines (Dale, 1941). The adverse influence of rainy weather is most pronounced in areas of heavy soils. In addition to the reduced hatching of eggs, the loss of young is heavy (Dale, 1942); this is partly due to the tendency of "hun" chicks to get their feet mud-balled on wet, clay ground (see also under "Accidents") (Yeatter, 1934). The same effects are found in the more optimum climate of the northern great plains, but they happen less frequently there. Cartwright (1944) described a spectacular "crash decline" of "huns" over most of the Canadian prairie provinces in 1942 and 1943, which was accompanied by low temperatures and high precipitation during the critical hatching periods. According to Yeatter (1934), high temperatures during nesting are more apt to cause spoilage of eggs in late hatches.

Extreme drouth during the nesting season may also reduce nest success. Errington and Hamerstrom (1938) studied the effects of the 1934 spring drouth in Iowa on "hun" reproduction, and concluded that it did not result in a drastic population change but was " . . . not without effect. The ecological picture seems to be essentially one of retardation and decreased productivity of the nesting season rather than one of ultimate failure." Gordon (1935), in reviewing the history of the "hun" in America, refers to a decline in Washington about 1926 " . . . due to a prolonged drought." Hawkins (1937) confirms for Wisconsin "Nolte's observation that in Germany there is a marked tendency for partridges to move from the uplands to the lowlands during drought periods. . . . "

There is still another relation between nesting season weather and nest success; the weather determines the growth of hay, and the time of cutting the first hay crop. If circumstances cause this operation to come before the majority of nests have hatched, the destruction of nests by mowing machines is very high. If, on the other hand, the season is delayed so that haying starts after most nests have hatched, the egg loss from mowing is slight.

Winter weather is not ordinarily a cause of exceptional mortality. The birds thrive in cold, snowy country, but there are circumstances when losses are increased because of the weather. Their custom of snow roosting may occasionally result in their being frozen in, but this is probably rare. Yocom (1943) says, however, "Deep, crusted snows, over a long period of time, in combination with freezing temperatures, is believed to be one of the main controlling factors of the partridge in [Washington]." Deep snows cause "huns" to seek gravel roads in search of grit. The mortality from auto traffic along such roads is sometimes high.

It is clear that climate and weather are the prime considerations that determine the population levels of the Hungarian partridge. Nolte (1934) simplified it to a formula, to the effect that the welfare of the species is directly proportional to warmth, sunshine, and dew, and inversely proportional to the rainfall during the breeding season. This may be an oversimplification, but it does illustrate a basic relationship.

PREDATION; DISEASES AND PARASITES; ACCIDENTS

PREDATION

PREDATION is a secondary mortality factor of Hungarian partridges. The proportion of losses resulting from this cause is small; many of these losses are conditioned by other factors, such as man's activities and the weather. Predation is most common on the eggs, less so on the chicks and adult birds.

Partridge eggs are eaten by a number of natural enemies. Among the ones that most commonly find "hun" nests are the skunk, red fox, crow, and the ground squirrels (Columbia, striped, and others); weasels, opossum, dogs, and other mammals do occasionally. Setting hens are sometimes killed by house cats or horned owls, and the eggs left to perish. Studies in Wisconsin showed these predation losses to be 10% of all nest losses, or 7% of all nests

(McCabe and Hawkins, 1946). Yeatter (1934) checked 68 Michigan nests that were destroyed, and found that 26% of them were by predation. Only 2.2% of 46 Washington nests that were broken up were destroyed by predation (Yocom, 1943).

There is a definite relationship between nest predation and cover type. In studying nests in southern Michigan, Yeatter (1934) found that only 8% of field nests were pilfered, while 23.5% of those along roadsides and 41% of those along narrow fence rows were destroyed by animals. This picture is somewhat complicated by the very large loss of hayfield nests from mowing machinery, but there is no doubt that some nest locations are more likely to be found by predators than others.

Young partridges are occasionally caught by such flesh-eaters as house cats, foxes, Cooper's, sharp-shinned, and marsh hawks, prairie falcons, and possibly others. The number succumbing this way is small, and of little significance in determining populations.

The adults are not as vulnerable to predation as most game birds; their covey-living habits and open field terrain give them good warning of danger. The predators that are most efficient in catching them are the horned owl, Cooper's hawk, prairie falcon, snowy owl, house cat, red fox and coyote. Errington and Hamerstrom (1938) found that from 1% to 10.5% of the animal remains in Iowa horned-owl pellets taken in partridge range were "huns"; the amount varied by seasons and years. They also found that the incidence of hun remains at red-fox dens and in fox fecal samples rose from about 1% to 2% from 1933 to 1934; the latter was a drouth year, and this factor possibly contributed to the change.

Golden eagles and snowy owls were believed to have taken a few partridges in winter in North Dakota (Hammond, 1941). Evidence of predation was very small, however; only 1 of 85 deaths noted had been caused by a predator. Yeatter (1934) examined 31 birds for which the cause of death could be ascertained;

of these, 8 or 26% were taken by predators, the house cat being the chief offender.

DISEASES AND PARASITES

"Huns" are relatively free of parasites, and rarely are infected with serious disease; of 26 specimens from Michigan and Ohio examined for parasites by Yeatter (1934), 14.5% had caecal worm (*Heterakis* sp.), and 31.6% had stomach worms (*Dispharynx spiralis*). The latter species is at times rather serious in the ruffed grouse, and may weaken "huns" also, since it impairs a vital part of the digestive system. The caecal worms are of no particular significance; Brugger (1941) examined 104 Washington birds, mostly from the Palouse area, and found three specimens with the caecal worm (*Heterakis gallinae*)—probably the same species as farther east. All others were parasite-free, and no significance was attached to the caecal worms in the three birds.

Yeatter noted three lethal cases of avian tuberculosis in female "huns," which indicated a serious potential threat in this disease. The disease organisms were probably obtained by the birds' feeding on the same ground used by domestic poultry. O'Roke (1932) also reported blackhead and gapeworms in Hungarian partridges. These three afflictions are rather common in game-farm birds, but fortunately are rare in the wild ones.

Our present limited knowledge of diseases and parasitism in this bird permits us to say merely that they are not known to be serious mortality agents, but could be.

ACCIDENTS

DEATH by the impact of inanimate things in a variety of kinds of accidents is a large source of "hun" mortality; most serious are the *nest* losses from farming activities. Mowing and harvesting machinery cause the most trouble, but plowing, molestation, and the trampling of domestic stock are also involved. Yocom (1943) found that about 85% of all nest losses were from these causes, mowing alone being responsible for 72%. Yeatter (1934) reported that 51% of nest destruction was caused by farming operations, including livestock trampling and poultry interference. Desertion caused by molestation is not included in the above figures, since some of it was due to activities of the study participants. Fire, and probably flooding also, account for a few nests.

Young partridges ranging on heavy soils have been known to die from gathering large balls of sticky mud on their feet during wet times. The mud cakes on, and they succumb from exhaustion, starvation, or exposure. Yeatter (1934) noted this odd trouble to be a possible high mortality cause when protracted late June rains fall on heavy-soil areas.

Mowers that killed young chicks were found by Hawkins (1937) to be an important source of mortality in Wisconsin.

Adult "huns" frequently fly into poles and wires, especially in winter. They frequent gravel roads in search of grit when snow is deep, and sometimes collide with fences, electric lines, and other obstacles. Automobiles also kill a good many birds along roads in winter; Hammond (1941) found that such losses in North Dakota amounted to about a bird per covey, and in some years may be higher. Yocom (1943) reports that a study of 46 miles of Palouse region roads in southeastern Washington revealed one "hun" killed per year on each 4.2 miles of road.

MAN'S RELATIONS WITH THE HUNGARIAN PARTRIDGE

MAN's first relationship to the Hungarian partridge in America was to import it from Europe and introduce it in many areas of this continent; thus its very existence here stems from man's interest in the species as a sporting bird. The interest in the "hun" for hunting has never ceased since its arrival, but it has waxed and waned in different localities. Where its numbers increased to huntable populations, its popularity grew; where it failed to take, most sportsmen have forgotten about it, except in magazine stories.

Apart from stocking and hunting the species, man's impact on the bird is mainly as a farmer. The kind of farming and the farming practices that are followed largely determine how suitable the habitat is.

AS A HUNTER

As a hunted species, the "hun" is highly prized by those who know him. In some respects he behaves like the bobwhite, laying fairly well to wide-ranging dogs, and often bursting into the air as a whole covey at once. Its flight is almost wholly in the open, and at top speed may reach 35 miles per hour; the covey usually alights together some 200 or more yards from the flushing point. The flesh is tasty, and is rated the equal of quail, grouse, and pheasant in eating quality.

Populations developed so rapidly in the Canadian prairie provinces and in Washington that legal hunting was opened just a few years after the initial introductions. In Alberta the first hunting began in 1913. Over 150,000 were harvested in Spokane County, Washington, alone in 1920 (Gordon, 1935), and it was not long before the kill in Alberta and Saskatchewan approached a million birds a year. Since then hunting harvest has varied greatly; it was generally high in the early 1930's, low in the late 1930's, high in the early 1940's, low in the middle 1940's, and high again toward the end of that decade. It is now hunted in about 10 states and in at least 4 provinces of Canada. The hunting region in this country is chiefly the northern tier of states from Wisconsin to Washington. As a general total, there are probably an average of 400,000 "huns" killed annually in the United States, and more than that in Canada. In the best years North Dakota alone has a harvest of about 400,000, with Washington the second highest state; in times of low numbers the United States total may drop below 200,000 a year.

In much of its range in the United States the "hun" is shot incidental to pheasant hunting; Yocom (1943) notes that on a study area in the Palouse region of Washington fewer "huns" were shot than pheasants, even though there were more "huns" present. He says, "The swift flight of partridges, the type of cover they utilize during the season, and the fact that they often flush out of range, makes them a very difficult bird for most hunters to get." On his study area 1,277 outside hunters killed 202 "huns" and 787 pheasants, while 148 landowners took 51 "huns" and 200 pheasants; thus one "hun" was killed for every 5.7 hunters, and one for every 132 acres. Two censuses made before and after the hunting season on two study plots indicated a hunting-season mortality of 9% and 14% in 1940, and 10% on one of the same plots in 1941. On two other Washington study areas in 1952, 1,762 hunters took 157 "huns" along with 1,004 pheasants and some valley quail, chukars, and sage hens (*P-R Quarterly,* April 1953). In Wisconsin the average kill was one bird per 259 acres of range for the whole state (McCabe and Hawkins, 1946). On three areas in Montana in 1952, 2,778 hunters bagged 86 "huns" and 4,435 cock pheasants (*P-R Quarterly,* April 1953), which clearly showed that the "huns" were taken as an "extra dividend" to pheasant shooting. In North Dakota the seasonal bag per hunter from 1938 to 1942 varied from 2.8 to 7.7 birds (*P-R Quarterly,* July 1943). This is the best success ratio in this country; in Alberta and Saskatchewan it is no doubt higher.

There has been little study of the crippling loss of "huns" as a result of hunting, but Einarsen (1943) estimates an incredible 60% of the bag as the number crippled in the Pacific coast states. Considering the nature of the bird and the terrain on which it is hunted, I doubt if anything like this prevails generally.

AS A FARMER

THE fact that farmers grow wheat, corn, and hay is the first matter of importance in the farmer's impact on the "hun." These crops compose most of its usable habitat; without them the bird could not thrive in large numbers.

The manner of handling these crops is the next consideration. In a general way we can say that hay harvest results in great nest destruction from the mowing operation, but much depends upon the kind of hay and the time of its harvest. Late-cut hay, such as timothy and red clover, is relatively safe for nesting as compared with alfalfa, for example, which is usually cut before hatching time.

Other grassland may be usable to the "hun" or not, depending on how it is managed; pastures and range land that are overgrazed are practically worthless. Where pasture rotation is practiced, the cover may be very useful to the birds. Grazing animals, and even ranging poultry, may cause some loss of nests from trampling or by just plain molestation.

Roadside grass and odd areas of grass not normally grazed or harvested are very valuable as habitat for "huns." But when road crews mow early in the year, or farmers graze livestock on such areas when pasture grass is poor because of drouth, "huns" nesting in them suffer heavy losses. Burning grass in the spring or fall is another practice that damages the habitat; cutting off cover in hedge rows and on ditch banks also has some bad effect.

PRODUCTIVITY AND POPULATIONS

PRODUCTIVITY

THE Hungarian partridge, together with some of the quails, has the highest potential productivity among our major upland game birds. "Huns" are monogamous, presumably on an annual basis; but since there is normally a slight excess of males, this should not appreciably lower the potential. They mature for breeding the year after they are hatched, and have but one brood a year.

There is not much data available on the sex ratio of the "hun" in this country, but what has been obtained is consistent. McCabe and

Hawkins (1946) gave the sex of 115 adult birds from Wisconsin, of which 58% were males; they also sexed 331 eggs before hatching (which gives the *secondary* sex ratio, that at hatching), and found them to be only 43% male. Yocom (1943) checked 137 "huns," of which an even 50% were male. Hickey and McCabe (1953) reported 55% of 69 adult Wisconsin "huns" and 52% of 227 juveniles were males, the total group being 53% male. The North Dakota State Game and Fish Department reported on the sex of "huns" in the fall of 1950, 1951, and 1952; the percentage of males was successively 60, 47, and 51 (*P-R Quarterly*, April 1951 and April 1952; *North Dakota Outdoors*, Vol. XV, No. 7, January 1953).

It thus seems clear that there is commonly a slight excess of males among adult "hun" populations, but that the sex ratio is about even among the young. This indicates a slight differential survival rate that favors males.

There is little definite information on the proportion of females that nest; in optimum range it is probable that all "huns" nest, but in marginal range this is probably not true. Renesting is frequent in the better range, and less likely in poor range. According to Knott, Ball, and Yocom (1943), about 70% of the hens eventually raise a brood in the Washington Palouse area.

MORTALITY

THE nesting loss is very high; Yeatter (1934) found an average nest loss of 68% over three years in southern Michigan, based on 143 cases. Errington and Hamerstrom (1938) checked 26 Iowa nests, of which 69% failed. Knott, Ball, and Yocom (1943) reported that 63% of 113 Washington nests observed over three years failed. Of 435 Wisconsin nests studied over a period of six years by McCabe and Hawkins (1946), 68% failed. In all areas the outstanding cause of destruction was farming operations; the mowing of hayfields was worst, but grain harvest, weed and brush cutting, plowing, and grazing all contributed.

More than half of the Michigan losses were from these causes; and at least 85% of those in Washington and 90% of those in Wisconsin. Predation is a secondary source of loss, from 4% in Washington to 10% in Wisconsin and 26% in Michigan. Other minor causes of nest destruction or loss are desertion, flooding, and roadside disturbance; the latter may be locally important.

The fertility and hatchability of the eggs is very high on good range, but may be low elsewhere. Yocom (1943) found approximately 1% of eggs sterile and 2% dead in the shell in nine clutches examined. Yeatter (1934) reported 92% hatchability for six June nests and 68% for 17 July-August hatches. McCabe and Hawkins (1946) checked 104 nests over six years, and found an average hatchability of 84.5%; it varied in those years from 93% to 74%. Most of the unhatched eggs were infertile, the amount of infertility ranging from 6.2% to 22.6%, with an average of 13.7%. Renests have a much higher proportion of infertile eggs than early nests.

Early broods start out with about 15 or 16 chicks, later ones with fewer; very late broods may have only 5 or 6. In normal years juvenile mortality is moderate, but in occasional years of bad weather after hatching the losses may be very high. Yeatter (1934) made 71 brood observations in a three-year period; the average brood size was 12 early in July, 8 by mid-September; and with little variation from year to year. The average number of chicks at hatching time in Washington was 17 (Yocom, 1943); this dropped to 9.5 after 8 weeks, most of the losses occurring in the first three weeks. Errington and Hamerstrom (1938) observed 11 Iowa broods in 1933 and 14 in 1934, the latter a drouth year; the brood size was 5.5 after nearly 8 weeks the first year, and only 4.9 after 5 weeks in 1934. Late summer brood sizes in North Dakota were 13.0 in 1938 (8 broods), and 11.75 in 1940 (79 broods) (Hammond, 1941). In a Pittman-Robertson study in North Dakota the average brood size in four years, 1941–44, was 12.4, 9.7, 8.9, and

8.8 respectively (*P-R Quarterly,* October 1944).

The major causes of chick deaths are exposure and accidents; predation is a secondary source of loss. The summer reduction in brood size probably runs about 50% generally, much higher in some years; and is likely to be higher in marginal range than in the northern great plains region.

The fall age ratios give a further measure of brood success and annual productivity. For example, the North Dakota records of brood size in 1941–44 noted above, of 12.4, 9.7, 8.9, and 8.8, correspond to juvenile-adult ratios of 4.2:1, 2.7:1, 1.5:1, and 2.2:1. In 1950 the age ratio was 3.3:1, in 1951 it was 2.3:1, and in 1952 it was 1.4:1 (*P-R Quarterly,* October 1944, April 1951, April 1952, and *North Dakota Outdoors,* Vol. XV, No. 1, Jan. 1953). A study of hunter-killed "huns" in Wisconsin in 1951 revealed a ratio of 3.3 young per adult (Hickey and McCabe, 1953). An age ratio exceeding about 2.2 juveniles per adult is usually indicative of equal or increasing populations, whereas a ratio below 2.2:1 reflects lower numbers in proportion to the lowness of the ratio.

The mortality of adults is a gradual process. Except during the hunting season (where hunting is permitted), there is not in most years a very great variation in the rate of loss at different times of the year. Along with the fall hunter toll, some birds are killed by accidents and predation. Though accurate data are lacking on the scope of the hunter kill, it is clear that it is not a major factor in affecting population levels; in all probability it is under 25% of the fall population, but this is mere opinion.

Winter losses may be somewhat accelerated in years of prolonged heavy snows; part of this results from the birds being killed by automobiles along gravel roads where they congregate to find grit. Predation is a constant source of loss, albeit a minor one at most times. Accidents like hitting fences, wires, and poles in flight cause some deaths. Snow confinement under crusting conditions may occasionally trap some birds. Yeatter (1934) counted a fall loss of 18% from September 1931 to January 1932, and 10% in the same period the following year, on Michigan areas having no hunting; the winter losses there were from 5% to 11% per month. Hammond (1941) found the autumn-to-March loss of North Dakota "huns" to be 20% in 1938–39, and 18% in 1940–41. Four-month losses from October through January on Yocom's (1943) study area in Washington were 14%. Fall-to-spring losses on a Wisconsin area for seven years from 1936 to 1943 varied from 19% to 67%, and averaged 40% (McCabe and Hawkins, 1946). In a Minnesota study the covey size declined 32% from November through February (*P-R Quarterly,* January 1952). Thus the fall and winter losses are about 5% to 10% per month.

Spring and early summer are a time of increased vulnerability for hen partridges; while they are incubating their eggs and watching over their young the hazard of farm machinery is great. McCabe and Hawkins (1946) found that 17 of the hens whose nests were destroyed by farm machinery were themselves also destroyed. This selective mortality may explain the slight excess of males among adults in the fall.

LIFE EQUATION

THE gains and losses of a sample population of 100 "huns" through a typical year is shown in Table 22. The year selected was one in which production exceeded consumption, and the net result of the changes is a gain in population; thus the "equation" in this instance is not a true one—as it rarely is. But such gains cannot continue many years in succession; a reversal comes when the new year's breeding population is only equal to the one before, or—more likely—is less. Once in a while the turnabout may be a drastic one and the decline precipitous; that happens when the population increase in item (3) of the table is very low, and is

TABLE 22

LIFE EQUATION OF 100 HUNGARIAN PARTRIDGES FOR A YEAR*

TIME	ACTIVITIES	NUMBER OF BIRDS	
		young	adult
SPRING	(1) 46 females mate with 54 males		100
	(2) All females nest, av. 17 eggs in first clutch, 10 in renests; total first eggs—782		
	(3) 35% first nests hatch, or 16 × 17 = 272; ⅚ of hens broken up renest, or 25 × 10 = 250; 60% of renests hatch, or 15 × 10 = 150; 5% of first clutches fail to hatch, or 14; 10% " 2nd " " " " " 15; Thus, 29 eggs of 422 in hatched nests are lost, and 393 hatch (av. 12.7)	393	
	(4) 15 adults die from accidents and predation, or 15%		85
SUMMER	(5) 8 " " " " " " " 9%		77
	(6) 197 chicks die from exposure, accidents, and predation, or 50%;		
FALL	Surviving chicks become adults		273
	(7) 55 are killed by hunters, or 20%		218
FALL & WINTER	(8) 87 " " " accidents and predation, or 40%		131
SPRING	(9) Breeding season arrives with 31 more birds than the year before		

* This population is assumed to live in good range, and the year chosen for the example is one of increasing numbers.

specially true if this happens two years in a row.

POPULATION DENSITIES

THE highest concentrations of "huns" in the United States that have been scientifically measured have been in North Dakota; Hammond (1941) counted prebreeding-season (February) population densities of from 3.5 to 5.3 acres per bird in 1939 on three plots on the Lower Souris Federal Refuge. Because of an average covey decline of about 20% since the previous fall, the maximum fall density was approximately 2.9 acres per bird, or 34 birds per 100 acres; this was a year of fairly high populations. Undoubtedly the more productive portions of the Canadian prairie provinces have greater concentrations than this in good years, as also do managed English estates; nevertheless the North Dakota figures represent high "hun" densities for this country.

Yocom (1943) gives prenesting and prehunting season densities for two Washington study areas. The spring population on one area near Pullman was 1 per 14 acres in 1940 and 1 per 12.7 acres in 1941; the early fall population was 4.3 acres per bird in 1940 and 4.1 in 1941. The second area had a bird per 29.4 acres in the spring of 1940, and only slightly more, 1 per 25.3 acres, the following fall; the next year it had 18.7 acres per bird in the fall. These were years of good populations. By 1953 the "huns" on the Pullman area had decreased to only 10% to 20% of their 1940–41 numbers; changes in land use are believed partly responsible for the change. The 1953 population on the second study area was about the same as it had been in the early 1940's (C. V. Swanson and C. F. Yocom, letter).

In Michigan Yeatter (1934) measured "hun" densities just before the species reached its peak population there. On three plots the density in late March 1933 was a bird per 4.4, 11.0, and 13.3 acres respectively; the previous September the population on these three and three other plots varied from 4.1 to 16.8 acres per bird, with an average of 6.5. These populations declined a few years afterward, and have never again regained these numbers. By 1940 the population density ran from about 20 to 30 acres per bird (*P-R Quarterly,* January 1941).

An area of some 2,400 acres around Faville Grove, Wisconsin, was censused for nine years from 1934 to 1943. The spring counts varied from 43 to 12 acres per bird, and the fall counts from 26 to 7.5 acres per bird. These figures cover years of both high and low populations, and probably represent typical "hun" densities on the secondary range in this country.

FLUCTUATIONS IN POPULATION

THE "hun" has not been observed carefully over a long enough period on this continent so that we can judge accurately its population-trend characteristics; but there is much indicative evidence. One characteristic, common to many introduced species, is that it seems to reach a peak population relatively soon after successful introduction that it does not again attain. This may apply particularly to marginal range, but it seems to have happened in the Ohio-Michigan range, and possibly in Wisconsin and Washington.

There is some evidence that "hun" populations may follow a ten-year cycle of abundance, with peaks and troughs, much as our native grouse do (Aldrich, 1947). The high populations in Washington in the early 1920's declined drastically in 1926 (Gordon, 1935). "Hun" numbers generally increased in the early 1930's,

and then declined about 1936. The same pattern was repeated in the next decade, with populations rising in the late 1930's and early 1940's, and then declining once more about 1946 or a little earlier. The years ending in 6 are not infallible years of decline, as evidenced by the great die-off in the Canadian prairie provinces in 1942–43 (Cartwright, 1944). Populations have been rising again in the late 1940's and early 1950's. For example, a P-R study in Washington reports that "hun" populations in the Columbia Basin in 1952 were the highest in ten years (*P-R Quarterly,* January 1953).

The increasing evidence that the introduced "hun" and pheasant both follow population trends about synchronous with those of our northern native game birds confirms the belief that the causes of these population changes lie in the environment and not in the species.

THE MANAGEMENT OF THE HUNGARIAN PARTRIDGE

THE fact that the "hun" is now an American game bird is some evidence that it is manageable; it became established through man's deliberate effort in its behalf: introduction, and protection. Yet the amount of management that can profitably be applied to an established population is limited. In the first place, major population changes result from weather and climatic factors about which we can do nothing. The primary decimating agency is a group of farming operations, particularly hay mowing. That can be altered slightly, but rather indirectly. There are a few habitat improvements that can be applied, and occasionally other measures; hunting can be regulated by appropriate conservation laws.

LAND USE AND DEVELOPMENT

SINCE the "hun" requires fertile farmland for its habitat, it is clear that it cannot and should not be aided by the purchase of public lands in its behalf; it is and should be an inhabitant of private lands, and primarily of cropland used for the production of commercial food crops. It will inhabit only such areas within its zones of climatic adaptation as have the right kinds of soils and the right land use. These crops will not be planted for the "hun," but rather it will be a by-product of the crops and the land they grow on.

The most profitable habitat development that can be accomplished is to improve nesting conditions. The objective here is (1) to provide good grass cover as widely intermixed as possible with grain fields; and (2) to arrange the greatest possible nesting safety in connection with the management of the grass. It should be recognized in this connection that native type grass stands are both more acceptable to "huns" and safer for them than heavy legume hay. It must further be understood that no adjustment in harvesting practices of high quality legume hay will (or should) be made in behalf of nesting game birds; the birds that nest in these hayfields are at the mercy of fortune—in other words, the luck of the weather in relation to the time of mowing. Our emphasis therefore should be on providing other kinds of grass as alternative nesting habitat.

Most farms and ranches offer opportunities to develop good grass that can make safe nesting cover; each property must be examined to find which kinds of grass developments suit it best. Most of these grass areas fit well with soil conservation needs, and thus are justified for more than mere game management. Some of the more common of these grass developments are:

(1) Arrange for all *roadsides* to be kept in grass. Farmers and local road commissions should co-operate in this matter. Maintenance mowing should be deferred as late in the season as possible, and none should be done until July. Newly graded cuts and fills on new and rebuilt roads, should be seeded to grass on as wide a strip as the right-of-way and local circumstances permit.

(2) *Headlands* and *fence rows* on crop-field edges and beside woodlands may be maintained in grass; the mowing of the borders can be delayed until midsummer or later.

(3) Many sloping crop fields that are subject to water erosion can profitably have *diversion terraces* constructed to control water run-off. Such terraces are kept in permanent grass, and include a filter strip of some 20 feet or more above the channel. This grass needs be mowed only once a year, and its mixture can be of a type suitable for nesting cover. It can just as well be mowed after the nesting season is over as before.

(4) Poorly drained crop fields can sometimes be improved by the construction of *open ditches* to carry off the excess water; such ditches should have wide, gently sloping banks. These banks and channels, and a narrow strip at the top of each side, are best managed in grass cover. Mowing is primarily for maintenance, and need not interfere with nesting.

(5) *Rights-of-way* over pipe lines and under pole lines are in many areas best managed in grass. Utilities companies are usually glad to handle the maintenance mowing in such a way as to promote good public relations.

(6) *Odd areas* exist on many farms that may best be devoted to grassy wildlife areas. These may be potholes, knolls of thin soil, rock outcrops, and the like.

All the above developments provide good nesting places that are relatively safe from the mower and other machinery. In addition, some hay, grain, and pasture management practices can properly be handled so as to favor nesting birds. The outer swath of both hay and grain fields can be cut *last* instead of first, harvesting from the center of the field out; this may give the many birds nesting in the field edge the extra day or two that might make the difference between hatching and destruction. Grain may be cut with high stubble—a good soil conservation practice—and thus avoid killing some hens and destroying their eggs. Pastures can be subdivided and rotated in use, and thus provide better grass cover in each part most of the time. Pastures should be stocked with only the number of animals that can be grazed without damaging the sod. Livestock should not be grazed outside of pastures (or range land) except in emergencies. Grasslands generally should not be burned.

Protective winter shelter is not a major problem for the "hun," but it does make good use of tall vegetation that cuts off strong winds. The planting of tree and shrub windbreaks or shelterbelts (the same as windbreaks, but extending long distances across the countryside) is a desirable practice that accomplishes this purpose. Some of the plants that are suitable for use in these plantings are: Siberian pea shrub, Russian olive, red cedar, wild plum, chokecherry, buckthorn, multiflora rose, Tatarian honeysuckle, cottonwood, and adaptable pines and spruces. Managed hedges are desirable around homesteads and some fields. The multiflora rose may be used as a living fence hedge on the southern, nonarid part of the "huns'" range and on irrigated land. Odd area plantings of trees and shrubs also provide much the same sort of protective shelter. Handpicked corn left standing makes good winter cover, and provides food as well.

The provision of special arrangements for winter food is not ordinarily needed, but those who wish to assure ample food supplies may adopt any of several means. Leaving an uncut swath of corn or durum wheat is an excellent and simple way of making a feeding area, if it can be afforded. The spreading of farm manure on fields on top of the snow is helpful, especially if it is planned for periods when feeding conditions are difficult. Where winter cover crops can be used on tilled fields they are helpful, particularly if planted early enough to make good fall growth; they furnish only green food, of course. Special food patches are seldom justified; the feeding of grain at stations is also not recommended.

Areas of suitable winter habitat that are not traversed by gravel or dirt roads may have a grit deficiency when the land is covered with snow. Having sand or gravel piles in sheltered spots next to grain fields, or on exposed knolls where the wind will keep them clean, will relieve this shortage.

MISCELLANEOUS MANAGEMENT PRACTICES

PREDATOR control is not needed as a rule in managing Hungarian partridges. An exception is the desirability of restraining farm cats and dogs during the nesting and early brood periods from May through July. At times, in some areas, snowy owls may be so plentiful as to justify some reduction (McCabe, letter).

Refuges have no value in the management of this game bird.

Restocking huns as a means of supplementing established populations is unnecessary. Where there are areas of suitable range that are unoccupied, the stocking of game-farm-reared birds may be desirable. It is no longer necessary to import these birds from Europe.

When stocking is done, the birds should be set out in groups of 20 to 30, and 4 to 6 such groups placed per square mile for an area of two or three square miles in a unit. This arrangement makes it possible for remnants of different groups to recombine and give the whole stocking a better chance of success. The birds should be at least eight weeks old when released—preferably ten or twelve weeks.

Some authorities recommend the use of a flushing bar on mowing machines to prevent nest destruction. The theory is that the operator will see the bird flush ahead of the machine as the drags scare it off the nest, raise the cutting bar, and leave an island of uncut hay around the nest. There are several doubts as to the wisdom of this recommendation, two of which have particular significance. The speed of modern power mowers is such that there is not adequate time to save flushed birds and their nests. Even if some are saved and a small island of cover is left around the nest, experience shows that most of them are found and destroyed by crows or other predators because of their exposure. For these reasons this practice is not advocated, though there is no reason why anyone should not do it if he wishes.

PROTECTION AND HARVEST

THE Hungarian partridge stands up well under hunting pressure, and does not require any exceptional protection. Hunting seasons of a month or two, with daily bags of 5 to 10 birds, are generally warranted in the good range; in the secondary range a more conservative arrangement of 2 to 4 weeks of hunting and a bag limit of from 3 to 5 birds per day is probably better. In years of low populations the usual practice is to close the season entirely, but it is doubtful if this is necessary. As with grouse, low populations are difficult to hunt, and the hunting pressure itself drops off automatically.

When populations are high, hunting seasons should be very liberal. Censuses may be made annually to determine population levels, so that proper hunting regulations may be set. Since the critical time in "hun" ecology is the nesting and early brood season, such censuses must be made in early summer to be accurate; this allows a minimum of time for arranging the legal requirements for the hunting rules. Responsibility for setting these rules should be vested in the state wildlife agency in order for this plan to work.

The census is based on brood counts made on sample areas used for this purpose year after year. Relatively little has been done to establish the requirements of such a census, but one standard method is available. Trained bird dogs can be worked in early mornings of cool days in July and early August. By comparing average brood size and the number of broods per square mile on the representative areas, year-to-year trends can be ascertained and the population level determined.

CHAPTER 12

The American Woodcock

CLASSIFICATION

THE woodcock is our only "shore bird" that is an upland game bird. It belongs to the order Charadriiformes, the shore birds, which includes the phalaropes, snipes, sandpipers, plovers, curlews, gulls, terns, and other related birds. Its family is Scolopacidae, the largest in the order, which includes the sandpipers and plovers as well as the more closely related snipes. The scientific name of the woodcock is *Philohela minor* (Gmelin). It is the only species of the genus and there is only the type form.

It is not surprising that so unusual a bird as the woodcock should have many colloquial names. Among its more common titles are timber doodle, bog borer, bog sucker, and brush snipe. In Louisiana it is known as "becasse."

DESCRIPTION

THE woodcock is a plump bird, with large head, short neck, short rounded wings, a very short pointed tail, moderately long legs, and a very long bill. Its large eyes are set high and aft on the head, giving it a frog-like or pop-eyed appearance that is probably its most distinguishing characteristic. Its average weight is about 6.2 ounces for males and 7.6 ounces for females, but there is considerable variation in weight among individuals; some males weigh as little as 4.3 ounces and some females as much as 9.2 ounces; the weight varies somewhat according to the season. The total length is from 10 to 12 inches.

The coloration of the sexes is identical. The general color is brown, with markings of black, gray, and rufous. The back is rufous or cinnamon, mixed with irregular spots of black and gray; the scapulars have similar coloration, but with four light gray stripes formed by the color of the outer vanes; the primaries are brown with some grayish color; the tail is brown or rufous above, with black markings and gray tip; the under parts are rufous or cinnamon with paler coloration on the throat and sides of the head, often grading into grayish; the tail is streaked blackish beneath and is light gray tipped. The top of the head is black, with three or four crossbars of pale rufous or gray. There is a blackish streak from the base of the bill to the eye, and another dark streak across the cheek.

The bill is very long, straight, and tapering toward the tip; its color is brownish-flesh. The ear is beneath the eye; the iris of the eye is brown. The legs are feathered on the tibia; the feet and toes are bare and flesh-colored.

The juvenile plumage is similar to that of the adult but softer; the bill is shorter. The downy young are pale brownish or buff with brown spots and stripes above, more rufous underneath than the adult, with a rather prominent patch on the front of the top of the head, and a dark bill-to-eye line.

The sexes cannot be differentiated by plumage coloration, but can be separated fairly well by certain measurements. The length of the bill varies significantly, with females having the longer ones. Measured in millimeters (100 mm. = 3.94 inches), birds with bills over 69 mm. are almost always females, while those

392

PLATE 88. *The American woodcock. The woodcock on her nest in an open woodland edge. She is so well camouflaged that it is very difficult to see her even when pointed out but a few feet away.*

with bills under 67 mm. are usually males; the average bill length of males is 64 mm., of females 71 mm. The weights of the sexes varies, as has been mentioned; birds weighing more than 210 grams (7.5 ounces) are almost all females, while those weighing under 170 grams (6.0 ounces) are almost all males (Mendall and Aldous, 1943). The width of the outer primary feather is greater on the females (average 3.9 mm.) than on the males (average 2.8 mm.). This measurement is made two centimeters from the tip, and there is very little overlap (Greeley, 1953). If all three of these measurements are used, the sex of any woodcock in hand can be determined with almost complete accuracy.

GEOGRAPHICAL RANGE AND DISTRIBUTION

THE woodcock is found in eastern North America from southern Newfoundland to southwestern Ontario and northern Minnesota, south to the Texas Gulf coast and central Florida. It breeds throughout this range except for portions in Texas and Oklahoma and the coastal area of Louisiana, Mississippi, Alabama,

and Florida. The wintering range is much more restricted; it extends from the Gulf region north to southern Missouri, northern Mississippi, Alabama and Georgia, and southern Virginia. Within this complete wintering area lies a zone of concentration in Louisiana and Mississippi that carries the greater part of the wintering population. These areas are shown in Figure 29.

The birds are much more widely scattered during the breeding season than in winter, but then also there are zones having greater numbers of breeders than others. The best breeding areas are in the zone from New Brunswick, Nova Scotia, and Prince Edward Island westward and southward through eastern and southern Maine. Good breeding populations are found scattered through the rest of New England, southern Quebec, New York, Pennsylvania, Ohio, northern Indiana, northeastern Illinois, Michigan, northern Wisconsin, and northeastern Minnesota. The occurrence of breeding woodcock through the rest of the known breeding range is occasional to rare.

HISTORY OF THE WOODCOCK

THE great changes that have taken place in the American landscape in the last 200 years seem to have adversely affected the woodcock as little as any of our native game birds. The general extent of its breeding and wintering ranges remains as always. The land changes brought about by agriculture have benefited the woodcock in some ways, but have also destroyed some of its habitat. The total change was probably beneficial in the period before World War I, particularly in the range south and west of the choice northern breeding grounds. The later intensive development of agriculture has damaged much of the woodcock habitat.

During the era of commercial hunting the woodcock was marketed in the large Eastern cities along with the ruffed grouse; Pettingill (1936) quotes an editorial from *Forest and*

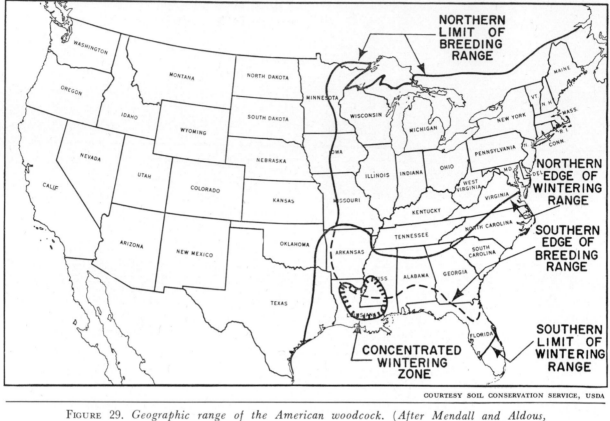

COURTESY SOIL CONSERVATION SERVICE, USDA

FIGURE 29. *Geographic range of the American woodcock.* (*After Mendall and Aldous, 1943.*)

Stream in 1874 that gave the weekly receipts of woodcock in New York City markets as about 1,800 birds, and the price as $1.50 per pair. In Louisiana the practice of "fire hunting" was once followed, with blazing pine knots as torches to spotlight the birds at night; great numbers of birds were killed in this manner. Modern-day law violators use electric flashlights to shine the birds in similar manner.

Present-day populations of woodcock are considerably lower than they have been at times in the past. Bent (1927) quotes Audubon's description of the height of the spring flight along the Mississippi and Ohio Rivers in the mid-19th century " . . . when almost every instant there whizzes past him a woodcock . . . " He then quotes Forbush's account of a more recent heavy spring flight through

New England in 1923, when "At evening one could find them almost anywhere." It is doubtful if these notes represent typical conditions in those times, for it is clear from hunter-kill records that woodcock numbers have varied greatly over the past half century. New York State license reports for 30 years from 1918 through 1948 show two periods when the kill dropped to below 10,000 a year, in the late 1920's and again in the middle and late 1940's. The periods of highest harvest were in the years 1919 and 1920 and again in the late 1930's, when the kill exceeded 25,000 birds annually (these are unadjusted license reports). Pennsylvania license reports show that the kill in that state has varied from about 13,000 to 73,000 since 1915, and is no lower in recent years than it was in 1915 and 1923. Wing

(1937) records the average daily kill of a Rhode Island hunter each year from 1895 to 1930; his lowest success was in 1895 and 1896. Other poor hunting years after the first ones were from 1903 to 1908, 1912, 1914, and 1930. His highest kills were in 1922 and 1925.

From this evidence it seems clear that the woodcock has been relatively abundant in some years of the last half century, probably comparable to earlier years of plenty. It is also probable that the species dropped to rather low numbers at times in the 19th century, comparable with the low populations of the late 1940's. We may conclude that it is a species that varies erratically in numbers, and that it may still reach relatively high populations again in some years ahead.

IMPORTANCE AS A GAME BIRD

WOODCOCK hunting is a select sport, and is very highly prized by those who participate. The bird lies well to dogs, and offers a peculiarly difficult target. It rises vertically to clear the brushy cover in which it is usually found in the fall, and then levels off in an erratic flight that is most disconcerting to the gunner. The whistling noise made by the wings is often startling when the bird rises close by. Its flight is not nearly as fast as that of the ruffed grouse, but the jerky manner of its travel makes it equally difficult to hit.

It is hunted each fall from Nova Scotia to Minnesota and Texas; populations are always adequate for some hunting, but in some years are better than others. Being migratory, the birds from the northern breeding range are subjected to hunting for three months or more in all the provinces and states that they visit. It is lawfully hunted in 27 states as well as in the eastern provinces of Canada, though the migration route of any single flight of birds would cover only a third to a half of these areas. Not all these states have open seasons every year. Despite this long period of gunning that the

woodcock faces, it stands the ordeal well. The hunting is seldom concentrated as it is with some of the farm-game birds, and the total number of woodcock hunters is comparatively small. What they lack in numbers they make up for in their enthusiasm for this fine bird. Some of the more skilful among them may harvest their full season's bag limit with fair regularity.

The flesh of the woodcock is edible, but is not as highly relished as that of most other game birds. It has a taste something like liver.

WOODCOCK HABITS

COURTSHIP

THE scene of the courtship of the male woodcock is known as a *singing ground*. It is usually an open grassy area in a field, woodland clearing, or along a road. The actual area used is small, about 10 to 70 feet across. One or more such spots are used by an individual bird, so that the whole area of activity may cover an acre or two. Part of the activity is on the ground and part in the air; the aerial performance may take place over several acres.

The woodcock is crepuscular in its courtship habits, and performs in the twilight of morning and evening. The evening is a more active period than the morning, though both are used regularly at the height of the breeding and nesting season. The duration of the activity is from 20 to 50 minutes, beginning in the evening at the time of a certain light intensity after sunset; according to Mendall and Aldous (1943), the starting time is when the light is two candles a square foot measured by a Weston phototronic light meter pointed at zenith; this is 5 to 25 minutes after sunset, depending on sky condition. The morning performance begins in almost total darkness, and ends when the light reaches the intensity noted above. On moonlight nights they sometimes perform in full darkness. The performances begin each spring as soon as the birds have returned from the South to their breeding areas, and they continue through the nesting period. In the deep South, courtship activity starts in February or early March; in Maine and New Brunswick it begins in early April and reaches its peak late in April. Most old males return to the same breeding area they have previously used, and frequently use the same singing grounds; at least some year-old males return to their covert of origin (Sheldon, 1953, and letter).

The male flies quietly on to his singing ground from his nearby shrubby diurnal coverts. His first action is to utter a nasal sound described as *"peent"*; he may have made some of these calls from his daytime cover before arriving. He repeats this call at one to two second intervals while he stands still or struts about stiffly. The "peent" can be heard for a considerable distance, but another sound that precedes it is audible for only a few feet; it is described as *"took-oo."* Thus each utterance is a quiet "took-oo" followed by a loud "peent." After a little of this he suddenly flies up into the air in spiral fashion, until he is 200 to 300 feet high. Then he comes down again in a series of fast swoops, first one way and then another, going at top speed. Throughout the flight the wings make a whistling sound, and with each surge he utters a liquid song of warbling and twittering notes until he nears the ground. He completes the flight by fluttering in to the spot he left slightly less than a minute earlier. This performance is repeated several times each morning and evening period, at intervals of from two to five minutes.

Males may use one or more of these singing grounds each spring. They defend them against the intrusion of other males, often to the accompaniment of cackling noises. The performances attract females to the singing ground, but the act goes on whether or not a hen is present. Mating takes place on the singing ground. Mendall and Aldous (1943) concluded that the males were monogamous, but substantial evidence points to polygamy as the normal behavior (Sheldon, 1953).

Another breeding-season activity that may occur anywhere in the male's territory is a strutting performance. I once observed this piece of histrionics from a distance of about 15 feet. The bird was in the center of a country road, and remained undisturbed as I approached in a car. I stopped close to him and watched for the 15 minutes it took him to strut a few feet into the roadside cover. He stood stiffly with his head thrown back, tail spread upward, and wings slightly drooped. Every few seconds he would take a slow, deliberate step forward, or two or three. This act is sometimes done before a female while she is incubating her eggs (Pettingill, 1936), but in the case I observed I could find no other woodcock in the vicinity.

The woodcock prefers pleasant weather in which to court; strong winds, snow, rain, heavy fog, or low temperatures in any combination reduce or entirely curtail activity for a day or more. They are very active in light mist on warm nights.

NESTING

NESTING begins in February or March in the South, April in the northern states, and late April or early May in the eastern Canadian provinces. The nest is a rough hollow in the ground lined with leaves, conifer needles, or grasses, depending on what is convenient. It is usually on well-drained ground, and may be fully exposed, or sheltered by branches of overhanging trees or shrubs. The cover type selected for nesting may be second-growth hardwoods, mixed conifers and hardwoods, brushland, or open grassy fields. The nests I have seen in New York were in abandoned farm fields of grasses and weeds, with some brush, or in open second-growth hardwoods. Of 128 nests observed by Mendall and Aldous (1943), 44% were in mixed growth of aspen, birch, spruce, and fir; 26% were in young stands of alders, or willows and alders; and 21% were in hardwood stands of birch and aspen, or birch, aspen, and maple. A few were in brushland and cleared land. Few nests are found in the common beech-birch-maple stands of the Northern states, or in coniferous forest. The nests are usually 200 to 500 yards from a singing ground.

The hen woodcock almost always lays four eggs in her first clutch; very rarely five are laid. There are occasional renests after the destruction of the first clutch; these commonly have three eggs. Incubation takes about 21 days; only hens incubate, as far as is known. The eggs are exceptionally large for the size of the bird; they are ovate, and measure 1.5 by 1.1 inches in length and width on an average. The color is buff to light brown, sometimes with a pinkish cast; sometimes there are spots or blotches of darker brownish color, often concentrated on the larger end.

Incubating woodcocks blend so perfectly into their surroundings that they are exceptionally well protected; they depend heavily on this camouflage for avoiding enemies, and they flush from the nest only at the last instant before probable capture. Late in incubation some hens remain on the nest even when stroked by a man's hand.

Because of their early nesting and the small clutch of eggs, which requires less than a week to lay, incubating woodcocks are commonly surrounded by snow. Hatching time starts in March in the South, and ends in late May or early June in the northernmost range. I have seen half-grown young in central New York by May 10th, long before the first grouse egg has hatched. Despite this early development, only one brood a year is raised. Late broods are sometimes seen, but they are from renests.

THE BROOD PERIOD

THE four young woodcocks are out of their shells within one or two days after pipping starts, and within a few hours of one another. They emerge in a manner that leaves the egg shells characteristically split lengthwise and infolded. The chicks are led away from the nest as soon as they are dry, which is just a few hours after hatching. They are brooded much of the time for a few days, and they do not travel far. The mother feeds the chicks at first with earthworms that she has probed from the ground, but after a few days they begin to forage in soft ground for their own food.

When disturbed, the young chicks freeze in whatever position they are, while the mother engages in a strenuous injury-feigning act to draw away the intruder; she drags her wings, flutters, and stumbles over the ground to attract attention away from her young ones. I have occasionally seen young woodcocks lying motionless upside down with feet in the air, just as they landed when the mother flushed and upset them; not until they are actually touched will they move or make a sound.

The youngsters grow rapidly, and can fly when they are two weeks old; by three weeks they are well feathered. During this time they usually remain within 100 to 200 yards of the place where they were hatched. The mother keeps the chicks close to her, and exercises close supervision over their activities for about four weeks; by that time they are nearly fully developed physically, and are well able to care for themselves. For the rest of the summer they may be found alone or in small family groups in their chosen coverts.

Cover used in the summer is substantially the same as in the spring, except that in dry periods the birds are found more frequently in damp swales. During very hot weather they frequently seek the shade of young conifers.

FALL AND WINTER ACTIVITIES

WOODCOCK are satisfied to remain in their summer haunts until the first freezes of the autumn; in the northern breeding area this usually comes in September. Then they move from their regular cover to soft springy ground, where probing for worms can still be done. Some birds from the northernmost areas start southward at once, but most wait until the solid freeze-up is imminent. The time of the flight varies according to the season, but it reaches northern New England late in September or early in October in most years. These northern-flight birds pass through New York and Pennsylvania from mid-October to early November, and arrive in the Gulf coast wintering area in December. By the time these flight-birds reach each section on their southward journey, many of the "native" birds that bred there have already departed for the South. The common belief that all locally-bred birds depart before the northern birds arrive is erroneous; some remain until well into November (Sheldon, letter). Nevertheless in many localities there are in some years two hunting periods, an early one for the natives and a later one for the flight-birds from the North. How well these two opportunities fit the legal hunting season is partly a matter of chance.

Migration is always at night, and at low altitude. The birds travel about 50 feet above the ground, and as a result meet with numerous accidents by flying into wires and other obstacles. They travel singly, though the procession of birds gives the semblance of loose flocking. This congregating is accentuated by the limited areas of suitable diurnal feeding and roosting areas the birds must use. A hunter may cover a favorite woodcock haunt on one morning and find no birds, and repeat the hunt the next day and find the place full of woodcocks. It is natural to assume that they came as a flock, because they arrived at one place at the same time; actually these same birds may travel to entirely different localities as they progress southward.

One of the most unusual features of woodcock habits is the distribution on the wintering grounds. Much evidence indicates that a majority of all woodcocks from the entire breeding range spend the winter in a relatively small area consisting of about two-thirds of Louisiana and a part of southwestern Mississippi; the rest of the birds are spread over a wide area from Texas to Virginia (see Figure 29).

The birds sometimes "pile up" in some sec-

tions of the wintering range when exceptionally cold weather freezes their usual habitat. Lynch (in Aldrich, 1952) describes how woodcock concentrated in southern Louisiana in the winter of 1951 after a freeze-up; 64 were flushed from one place not 150 feet across. In five days the observers averaged 32 birds per hour, mostly from narrow strips of wooded cover along bayou banks and stream bottoms. Mortality from freezing or from having their food supply frozen may be high in such periods. Except for these occasional trying periods, they are able to use all the habitat available all winter.

The woodcock seems very anxious to return to its northern summer range, for it starts the migration early. The first birds in the procession reach Pennsylvania, New York, and southern New England by March 1. Since they progress only about 50 miles a day, many must leave their wintering area early in February. The individuals going to the Maritime Provinces reach their destination by mid-April. Courtship, which may have started in migration, begins in earnest as soon as they reach the breeding area.

ADAPTABILITY TO CHANGING ENVIRONMENT

THE woodcock has not altered its habitat adaptabilities appreciably as the environment has been changed by man; it has taken advantage of habitat accidentally made to its liking by farming or lumbering; when its habitat was destroyed it has retreated.

Since it is a bird of early plant successional stages, it is normal for its habitat to change; openings created by land clearing and lumbering often made new habitat, just as natural forest fires had done for ages. Loss of habitat from the growth of the forest to maturity was a natural process, even though it occurred on more area in recent times than long ago. Some drainage of wet lands has resulted in a permanent loss of habitat that is a distinct detriment to the woodcock. This practice has been most destructive where alder runs in pasture have been cleared and drained to provide more and better livestock forage. The woodcock cannot adjust to such changes except to move to another area of habitat it likes—if such can be found. So far the land use changes have not been disastrously destructive to woodcock cover, but the trend is in that direction. We can be reasonably sure that the woodcock will not adjust to living in different habitat than it has always lived in.

TOLERANCE OF OTHER GAME BIRDS

THE common use of their habitat by other species of game birds has no effect on the woodcock. Ruffed grouse are frequently found in the same cover with them; to a lesser extent pheasants, bobwhite quail, mourning doves, and wild turkeys use the same habitat. In no instance is there any appreciable competition between these birds and the woodcock for either food or living space.

HABITAT OF THE WOODCOCK

THE cover needs of the woodcock fall into four classes according to seasons. In spring the need is for breeding and nesting cover. The summer cover is determined mostly by the needs of the broods. For a few weeks in the spring and fall, the birds need feeding and roosting cover during migrations. The fourth requirement is for wintering grounds in the South.

The spring habitat requirements are primarily of two types. Open grassy areas are needed for courtship and breeding. These "singing grounds" do not need to be large; a tenth of an acre or less in a woodland clearing, along a country road or in a grassy field, will do. It must be herbaceous cover, though a few scattered shrubs are tolerable; the use made of these spots during courtship has already been described. The second cover type needed in the spring is either brushy cover or second-growth woodland. The brush need not be solid cover;

a good scattering of shrubs in an old field will do. Very dense brushy cover is generally avoided. Moderately open young woodlands of hardwoods, or mixed conifers and hardwoods, may serve the same purposes. The hens use these cover types for nesting; the cock birds use them for roosting and loafing. Both sexes feed in sections of these cover types where the ground is soft enough for them to probe for worms. Any coverts will be used more or less in any season, depending on rainfall; dry areas may be used only in wet years.

The plant composition of these spring habitat types varies considerably in different areas. Alder patches beside streams, or on seepy lowlands or slopes, are favorite coverts. Brushy pasture fields with patches of hawthorn, spirea, plum, or crab apple are used in the Northern states; in the Carolinas, Virginia, and Maryland the plant cover is frequently made up of sweet gum, red maple, and Virginia pine brush (Stewart in Aldrich, 1952); in parts of central Pennsylvania and elsewhere the scrub oak and pitch pine "barrens" are good woodcock habitat. Breeding season cover in Maine and the maritime provinces is made up of combinations of birch, aspen, willow, alder, maple, spruce, and fir, plus the plants that grow with them. Stands of the fast-growing trees like aspen and birch appear to be preferred to those of slower growing species. Birds in the lake states are commonly found in cover of aspen, alder, willow, blueberry, serviceberry, and associated plants (Dangler and Marshall, 1950). All these shrubby plant associations are better for woodcock when interspersed with patches of grasses, sedges, goldenrod, and other herbs. All these types of habitat except the alder thickets are early plant succession stages that are very transitory; thus much of the woodcock's upland habitat is naturally in a rapid state of change.

Variety is important in habitat for woodcock, as with most game birds. Alder runs are enhanced by nearby aspen groves, hawthorn thickets, and stands of young conifers; in the same way any cover type used by the birds is better if other usable types are close by.

An abundance of earthworms is essential to any feeding cover. Soil types, moisture content of the soil, and surface litter may have more to do with earthworm abundance than vegetative type; some plants, however, provide a better leaf litter for earthworms than others; aspen appears to be one of these. Where woodcock use one portion of a uniform cover and avoid others, the reason is usually the distribution of earthworms.

Summer cover chosen by woodcock mothers for their broods is essentially the same as the spring nesting habitat; open shubby cover and open young hardwood woodland are the chosen types. The adult males loaf, feed, and roost in the same cover types, but do not ordinarily associate with the broods. The dry periods of midsummer often require some adjustment in cover use. When the soil of well-drained sites becomes dry and hard the birds move to low areas of springy or marshy ground, along streams or pond margins, or to seepy hillsides. Here they are able to feed with ease despite the generally dry conditions.

During the hot days of July and August woodcock often seek cool, shady places in moist woodlands or along streams. When moulting times comes they become inactive, and retire to thicker cover than used at other times. These changes in cover do not mean extensive travels, for they should exist within a very few hundred yards of the general spring and summer habitat.

When the birds set out on their long migration to the wintering grounds, they become more exacting in their choice of cover. They are on the move many nights, and must find food and resting shelter in strange country each following morning; it appears that they do this by sticking close to water. It is then that the alder thicket becomes the dominant cover type used, though some upland cover is chosen. That is why most hunters think of the woodcock as closely associated with alder runs and stream bottoms. When they cannot find a convenient patch of alders in their southward travels, they seek other low-ground cover of mixed hardwoods, or young conifers and hardwoods. As they approach the winter range the plant species change, though the cover type remains much the same. Instead of alders the woody plants are likely to be sweet gum, black gum, elm, willow, baldcypress, wet ground oaks and maples, and loblolly pine. When the return flight is made northward in the spring, the same kind of cover is used; not until they reach the breeding grounds do they once again use upland cover.

The winter range habitat is associated with the streams, bayous, swamps, and marshes of the Southern states, and espeçially of Louisiana and Mississippi. These lowland waters are bordered by or covered by swamp hardwood trees, pine knolls, grass and sedge prairies, rice fields, and grassy roadsides. The woodlands used are mostly open stands of longleaf, loblolly and slash pines, gums, cypress, overcup oak, and other Southern hardwoods. The ground cover is generally open, and composed of grasses and herbs. When exceptionally cold weather freezes the ground in the usual habitat, they may seek emergency cover along the bayou banks and stream bottoms closer to the Gulf coast than their usual inland range. They have been known under such circumstances to frequent farm manure piles in evenings in search of food (Lynch in Aldrich, 1952).

FOOD OF THE WOODCOCK

FEW birds have as simple and uniform a diet as the woodcock; no other upland game bird gets along on as few kinds of food as does the timber doodle. But while its diet lacks great variety and change, it is not obtainable in all areas or under all conditions; in fact, the specialized feeding adaptations of the woodcock limit its habitat adaptabilities, and are one of the reasons for its annual migration.

The long bill is adapted to probing in soft

ground and in the ground litter for animal life. The tips of the bill are flexible and sensitive, so that organisms can be located and grabbed easily. Dry ground and frozen ground are not suitable for woodcock feeding; the soil must be moist and soft to enable them to penetrate it in search of food. It is for this reason that these birds are so much of the time found in damp locations.

From 90% to 94% of all of the food eaten by woodcocks is animal life. Most of this animal food is earthworms; the rest is insects, plus a few small animals. The plant food is almost all seeds from a few kinds of plants.

Two studies have been made and reported that quantitatively analyze woodcock food habits. Sperry (1940) examined 261 stomachs of birds taken from March through December in 16 states and three Canadian provinces; this summary included the specimens discussed by Pettingill (1936 and 1939) and Aldous (1939). Mendall and Aldous (1943) examined the stomach contents of 20 Maine woodcocks taken from April through July.

The volume of earthworms in the stomachs of Sperry's widely collected birds was only 68% of the total food, whereas in the Maine birds examined by Mendall and Aldous it was 86%. These authors note, however, that the birds in Sperry's collection from the northeastern states and the maritime provinces had eaten more earthworms than the general average. Both the groups of birds collected by Pettingill (1939) from Nova Scotia and by Aldous (1939) from Maine and New Brunswick (total of 133) had 86% of their food made up of earthworms. Earthworms are the major woodcock food throughout the year, but are taken in somewhat less amount in winter than at other seasons.

Insects composed 18% of the food eaten by the birds examined by Sperry, and 7% of those examined by Mendall and Aldous. Beetles and flies (including larvae) and larvae of moths and butterflies were eaten most commonly, and about in that order of abundance. Most of these insects were larvae of aquatic and damp-ground species. Some of the other kinds of animals occasionally eaten include small crustaceans, millipedes, centipedes, and spiders. A woodcock may rarely eat a small frog or salamander.

The vegetable food eaten by woodcocks is even less important than the small volume taken would indicate. Some of this material is eaten because it sticks to the animal food or is in the digestive tract of earthworms; some seeds are eaten deliberately. Those most commonly consumed, according to available records, include seeds of alder, raspberry, blackberry, sedges, violet, elder, smartweeds, foxtail, ragweed, cinquefoil, panicum, and bedstraw; miscellaneous plant fragments make up the balance. Altogether the plant foods are 6% to 10% of total food used, and are eaten more in winter than at other times.

The woodcock has a prodigious appetite; most of its feeding is done at night or at twilight, but in a single 24 hours it may eat more than its own weight in food (Bent, 1927). Bent quotes an observer who watched a captive woodcock use trickery in locating earthworms. The woodcock would " . . . walk over the ground, slowly and deliberately, pausing every instant or two as if listening intently. Then he would stamp with one foot, giving several sharp, quick blows, after which he would bow his head near the ground and again listen. Then suddenly he would turn either to the right or left or take a step or two forward, plunge his bill into the earth, and draw out a worm. . . . "

The food of the young is the same as that of the adults, as far as is known; they consume huge quantities of earthworms, as do the adults. Sheldon (letter) raised a woodcock that ate 50 night crawlers in twenty-four hours when three months old.

When sudden freezes limit their feeding opportunity, the birds concentrate in the feeding areas that remain available. In such times of stress they may resort to emergency measures, including feeding on manure piles, in decayed wood, on town lawns, and in woodland ground litter. Despite their rapid digestive process, short periods of such emergency feeding seldom cause them serious trouble, though they may lose some weight. When they are caught in prolonged freezing periods from which they cannot escape they may suffer considerable mortality from starvation.

THE EFFECTS OF WEATHER ON WOODCOCK

EVERY-DAY weather conditions have considerable influence on woodcock activities, but little effect on their welfare. Some extremes of weather have been known to cause loss of eggs and birds, but only in the most exceptional circumstances has weather been a primary mortality factor.

The start of migration in the fall is stimulated by the change of seasons, and to a certain extent the oncoming cold weather "chases" the birds most of the way down to the South. The time of nesting depends on whether the spring is early or late. Courtship behavior is tuned to the weather of the moment; any adverse conditions result in less activity or temporary cessation of singing ground performances. The location of feeding is affected by drouth and by freezing. In prolonged dry weather the birds must seek out the wet grounds around springs, marshes, ponds, or along streams where the ground is still soft. Woodcock are occasionally caught by quick freezes in the North that make probe feeding temporarily impossible in coverts that are normally satisfactory for the season; such occasions spur the southward migration. Freezing weather is uncommon on their wintering range, but when it does occur the birds are often forced to seek new feeding locations. The places that provide dependable feeding conditions when the ground is frozen are the same locations sought in dry weather—springs, marshes, bayous, and stream bottoms.

All these weather influences are normal expectations, and are experienced by woodcock more or less regularly. Occasionally these conditions may induce some mortality by causing the birds to expose themselves to predation, as when moving to and feeding in a strange place. Under most circumstances such adverse weather is taken as a matter of course, and is unimportant as a mortality factor.

Certain extremes of weather can cause losses of woodcocks, as is true with all game birds. These losses may occur at several times during the year, and may affect eggs, young, or adults. Eggs have been known to freeze despite the adaptability of the woodcock for nesting very early in the spring. Mendall and Aldous (1943) listed four nests lost from freezing among the 52 nest losses they observed in Maine. They also reported two others among this group that failed to hatch after pipping because, as they believed, of excessive drouth. Thus six of 52, or about 11% of the nest loss resulted directly from weather conditions.

The four frozen nests were among 21 found on their study area in a single season. They report that only one of all these nests in existence during the cold stormy period was known to have hatched; as a result there were many renests and late hatchings that year.

There is little specific information available on the effect of adverse weather on newly-hatched woodcock chicks. It is probable that some losses occur to broods caught in cold wet weather during the first few days after hatching The circumstantial evidence of brood sizes indicates that such losses are exceptionally low; they do not appear to be the critical sort of losses that many game birds suffer in this period.

Fall weather often affects the hunting harvest. The kill is higher when the weather is dry, presumably because the birds are then forced into more restricted habitat than in wet seasons (Sheldon, letter).

Winter weather carries a potential threat to woodcock, since freezing *can* occur in their

Southern range. Some records exist to indicate the seriousness of prolonged or very severe freezing weather at this season and the different degrees of mortality that may occur as a result of different storms. A bad storm in South Carolina in February 1899 that caused great losses of woodcock was described by Wayne (1899): "The cold wave . . . was the severest recorded for 200 years . . . snow from four to five inches deep . . . 6° above zero. . . .

"The woodcock arrived in countless thousands . . . Tens of thousands were killed by would-be sportsmen, and thousands were frozen to death. The great majority were so emaciated that they were practically feathers, and of course were unable to withstand the cold."

The winter of 1940 in Louisana had about three weeks of subfreezing weather in one stretch; a large part of the woodcock population of the continent was in that area at the time. The cold was accompanied by snow and sleet, and the woodcocks had great difficulty in finding food. They concentrated in the very restricted localities where water and ground conditions remained at all suitable for feeding. Mendall and Aldous (1943) quote a number of the reports of observers who saw large numbers of distressed birds and found many dead. Still there is considerable difference of opinion as to just how big a catastrophe that winter loss of woodcocks was. At the time it appeared as though it might be a major disaster; but breeding season counts in the North a few months later indicated only about a 40% reduction from the previous year—bad but not disastrous.

The same Louisiana area had another bad freeze in early 1951; but this one lasted only six days as compared with the 19-day spell of 1940. The birds moved considerably in search of feeding areas and gathered in concentrations, but there was no evidence of mortality or even serious emaciation (Lynch, and Goodrum, and Reid, in Aldrich, 1952).

Mendall and Aldous (1943) reported one occasion of midwinter weather in early April, 1939 in Maine that caused some woodcock losses. Heavy snows and low temperatures occurred throughout the best woodcock breeding grounds just as the birds arrived from the South. They concluded that " . . . while the birds suffered losses over an extensive area, there were no instances of heavy, local mortality. However, the widely scattered occurrences of dead birds being found . . . must have been considerable when taken as a whole."

From these instances we can get a pretty good picture of the place weather plays in affecting woodcock populations. Under the worst conditions, which fortunately happen rarely, the losses may be tremendous, and subsequent recovery probably slow. Yet, considering the specialized nature of the bird, especially regarding its feeding habits, it stands adverse weather remarkably well. Weather is not ordinarily an appreciable mortality factor, and rarely is it a limiting factor.

PREDATION; DISEASES AND PARASITES; ACCIDENTS

PREDATION

THE seclusive life and protective coloring of the woodcock makes it fairly safe from attack by natural enemies; few species of game birds suffer as little loss from predation as does the woodcock; this is true for the young birds in the summer as well as for the adults all year long. This rather exceptional situation is not due to any reticence on the part of predators to eat woodcock; in fact, we can be reasonably sure that all predatory animals in the range of the woodcock and physically able to take the eggs, young, or adults, do so as they have opportunity when they are hungry.

The specific evidence of woodcocks being consumed by flesh-eaters is scattered among the records of many independent observers. It is inadequate to enable one to make an accurate quantitative appraisal of the importance of predation in woodcock ecology. But there is enough knowledge of woodcock populations and of predator relations to make a fair estimate of the factor.

Incubating woodcock hens are almost impossible to locate by sight, so well their colors harmonize into the background. Their reluctance to flush from the nest, and the little scent given off when they are on the nest, make it all the more difficult for predators to find them; even the very skilful fox rarely finds one. I have seen many woodcock nests in central New York over several years, and have not known of a single one being destroyed by egg-eating animals. The most comprehensive evaluation of nesting success was made by Mendall and Aldous (1943) in Maine. They checked the fate of 136 nests in six years and found that 38% of them failed; but 11 of the 52 nests lost were the result of their own study activities, hence 41 nests of 125 natural cases were lost. Predation was responsible for 19 of them, or 15% of all nests and 47% of all the nests that failed. The ruffed grouse, which nests in similar locations in much the same habitat, regularly loses from two to three times this proportion of its nests from predation.

The animals responsible for destroying 10 of the 19 nests eaten by predators in the above records were identified: 4 nests were taken by red squirrels, two by birds of unknown species, and one each by fox, cat, weasel, and skunk. The authors also record that the black snake has been known to eat woodcock eggs. It is altogether probable that crows, blue jays, raccoons, and others also eat woodcock eggs occasionally, and that many other predators rarely may destroy a nest by capturing the hen.

Predation on juvenile woodcocks is normally very low; in fact, the total mortality of the young birds is low. This matter is relatively easy to check with this species, since the starting brood is almost invariably four birds. Most broods are raised to full maturity without loss. Mendall and Aldous (1943) list two cases of chicks known to have been eaten by black snakes. The accipitrine hawks no doubt take a few young woodcocks.

Many kinds of predators are known to have killed adult woodcock, but none have given evidence of taking very many, with the possible exception of the house cat. Both Pettingill (1936) and Mendall and Aldous expressed the opinion that the cat is the cause of more nest destruction than other predators, and is the primary woodcock destroyer. They cite many cases of cats bringing in dead woodcock—instances found in literature and from their own observations. The cat is most destructive in habitats in well-settled farming country, less so where dwellings are widely separated.

Among the other animals known to kill woodcock occasionally, and which may sometimes be of some significance as a mortality factor, are the great horned owl, Cooper's hawk, sharp-shinned hawk, goshawk, fox, and dog. Sheldon (in Aldrich, 1952) tells of several predators that attacked the dummy woodcock he used in trapping the birds for banding studies. Most persistent was the crow, but also included were the Cooper's hawk, sharp-shinned hawk, weasel, and bobcat. There are records of several of the lesser predators having killed woodcock, but they are not believed to be of any significance.

DISEASES AND PARASITES

RELATIVELY little is known about the significance of parasitic and disease organisms in the ecology of the woodcock. Birds captured in weakened condition were suffering from the complications of gunshot wounds or other physical accidents; no cases of infectious disease have been found.

The woodcock is a remarkably "tough" fellow. Sheldon (letter) noted that birds injured in live-trapping work recovered quickly. One bird caught on April 13 was "bleeding badly at the mouth and nostrils; he was recaptured May 26 the same year, completely recovered."

The most information we have on internal

parasites came from the studies by Mendall and Aldous (1943) of 258 intestinal tracts of birds from Maine and New Brunswick. Ninety-three or 36% of these birds harbored helminth parasites in numbers from one to 20 each; none had done any evident damage to the host. These worms were tapeworms (*Hymenolepis* sp.), roundworms of the family Acuariidae, and flukes (*Pseudapatemon aldousi*).

ACCIDENTS

MORTALITY from various types of accidents is a major cause of the losses of woodcock; probably more woodcock succumb from this cause, in proportion to their numbers, than any other game bird. This matter has been commented on and discussed by most authors who have studied the species.

Most of these accidents occur during migration, and result from flying into obstacles. Electric wires seem to be the worst hazard; lighthouses, other lights, buildings, and similar barriers also take some toll. One may conjecture as to the reason for this high loss; it stems in part from the low altitude the woodcock uses in migration. Its reckless flights in the courtship performance also occasionally have tragic endings. But there must be more to it than this; the bird may have poor vision for spotting such things as wires quickly enough to dodge them effectively. Their difficulty with lights no doubt is caused by the same attraction that lures many migrating songbirds to their doom each year.

In addition to the mortality from flight obstructions, there are some other losses from accidents. Some nests are destroyed by fire, and a few are trampled by domestic livestock. The loss of eggs from burning is not generally high in most years, but may be very high locally at times. The practice of deliberately burning blueberry land in Maine has been known to cause the loss of many nests (Mendall and Aldous, 1943). In addition to these set fires, the nests are sometimes caught in wild forest fires. The woodcock nesting season is a time of high forest-fire hazard throughout much of the bird's best breeding range.

Automobiles take a small toll of woodcocks by hitting them at night, when the birds seem to be blinded and confused by the headlights. Woodcocks are also occasionally killed in muskrat traps.

Adding up the accident factor, we have one of the most exceptional mortality sources in game-bird ecology. Since most of the causes of the fatal accidents are man-made or are otherwise induced by man's activities, we may conclude that this change in the bird's ecology is a result of modern conditions, and may well be a significant reason for the generally reduced populations of today.

MAN'S RELATIONS WITH THE WOODCOCK

THE net effect on woodcock populations of man's various activities is difficult to judge. As a hunter he is thought by some to be the primary limiting factor, but there is some doubt about this under our present hunting arrangements. Farming and lumbering have direct effects on the habitat, some of which are harmful and some beneficial.

AS A HUNTER

THE woodcock is a very popular game bird with a rather small but select group of sportsmen. Once the bird was hunted over long seasons, including spring and summer, but between 1900 and 1920 all the states and provinces limited legal hunting to the autumn months. Hunting seasons are now set by Federal law for all the states, since the woodcock is a migratory bird.

There are frequently two opportune periods for woodcock hunting through much of the range in the Northern states. The native birds are still in their summer territories during the early part of the season, unless there has been a specially early fall freeze-up or drouth. After

PLATE 89. *Woodcock lie well to trained hunting dogs and provide a fine type of hunting.*

the first freeze many of these birds have gone southward. Then follows a short period, which is quite variable as to dates and length, when most of the flight birds from the North come through. This is the time of best hunting, since these birds are more restricted in the habitat they use in migration than the native birds. These flight-birds are more likely to be found in good numbers in these select coverts because they are so concentrated.

Fairly reliable records are available on the volume of the legal hunting harvest. Mendall and Aldous (1943) compiled a list of the annual kill from 1935 to 1939 in 18 states and 5 provinces. The areas of greatest harvest were Michigan (average 52,000). Pennsylvania (42,-000), New York (41,000), and Maine (37,-000). The total kill was estimated to be about 296,000 in these 18 states and 5 provinces. The 1942 woodcock harvest in the northeastern states alone was estimated by Pearce (1943) to be 201,900. Using these figures as a guide, and taking into account the areas where woodcock are commonly hunted that were not included in these estimates, and considering general trends in woodcock populations, it seems probable that the total annual harvest in the

late 1940's was not much over 200,000. In periods of high abundance the kill may be close to half a million birds.

The crippling loss and the illegal kill must be added to the legal hunting totals to get the total reduction of birds from hunting; neither is obtainable accurately. The illegal kill may have been heavy at times, but it is not generally so today. When the birds are concentrated in very limited areas by freezing weather, there is likely to be more of this slaughter than usual. Lynch (in Aldrich, 1952) summarized this situation after a bad freeze-up: "While the illegal kill of woodcock in South Louisiana certainly was greater than it would have been had the birds remained in their normal range, we feel that it was not so great as to make serious inroads into the population as a whole." The crippling loss is probably rather large considering the difficult target, and the ease of losing dead birds camouflaged in the thick cover where they often drop; it is much less where trained dogs are used. These two sources of loss probably add 20% to the reported harvest. This would make the annual toll of woodcocks from hunting range from about 240,000 to 600,000 annually.

It is not known how many sportsmen hunt woodcock. Possibly more birds are killed incidental to general hunting for rabbits, grouse, squirrels, quail, and other game than in woodcock hunting as such. But the individual game bag is far higher with the real woodcock hunter; this is specially true if he uses a well-trained bird dog. Though the large bags reported 60 to 80 years ago are a thing of the past for legal reasons as well as others, many good woodcock hunters still get their daily limit one or more times a season. Recently the daily bag limit in most years has been four birds. Where guides and hunting parties are used, the camp records are sometimes surprising; Mendall and Aldous (1943) cite a number of such instances from Maine and the Maritime Provinces. The highest of these records was from a guide in Nova Scotia, who in 1939 had 600 woodcock shot over his dog, with an average of three hunters a day participating.

What effect does this reduction in numbers have on the woodcock populations? We cannot answer this question with accuracy, since we do not know the size of the total woodcock population. The fact that the species is migratory, and is hunted successively in one state after another from Canada to the Gulf, makes local kill records of little use. We can only estimate the significance of the hunting factor by observing trends in woodcock populations and by appraising them in comparison with other factors. Hunting is no doubt one of the largest sources of woodcock mortality; yet under present conditions it probably is not the primary reason for woodcock populations increasing or decreasing.

AS A FARMER AND LUMBERMAN

LUMBERING makes some improvements in woodcock habitat by opening the canopy of the forest and providing herbaceous and brushy cover. Where this occurs on damp ground or close to natural streams, swales, or marshes, woodcocks may breed and raise their young, or winter in areas otherwise unusable. It is probable that the first full lumber harvest in the East in the 19th century greatly increased the extent of woodcock cover. The fires that followed lumbering extended the useful time of some of this habitat. This condition has deteriorated in the past half century, as these forests have grown back to closed canopy condition. The abandonment of submarginal farm land in parts of the northern woodcock range in recent decades improved some habitat as cropland converted to grass and brush. This land too is rapidly growing into forest, and therefore the benefit is temporary. Forest cuttings continue to benefit woodcock cover wherever they are made on suitable soils.

Farming both benefits and destroys woodcock habitat under different circumstances. Pastures that include alder runs are often fine cover for the timber doodles; the grazing prevents the area from returning to forest, and prevents the alders from becoming too dense. On the other hand, if the farmer clears off the brush along the brook, or if he overgrazes the pasture, most of its value as woodcock habitat is lost. Sometimes such areas of wet pasture are drained with tile or ditches, and destroyed for woodcock use.

As a generality we can say that farming generally benefited woodcock habitat until the modern period of intensive, mechanized, commercial agriculture. Brush clearing and drainage for pasture improvement are now so widely practiced in good agricultural areas that farming in these areas does more damage than improvement to woodcock habitat. This trend is offset to some degree in modern conservation farming, where practices of pond building and the planting of conifers and shrubs often improve woodcock cover.

AS A CONSERVATIONIST

THE improvement of habitat mentioned above is man's highest achievement as a conservationist; but it is a fortuitous circumstance if woodcock are benefited, for little if any of such work is done objectively to improve habitat for this species.

The one positive conservation effort to benefit woodcock has been the enactment and enforcement of laws to give the species adequate protection from hunting.

PRODUCTIVITY AND POPULATIONS

PRODUCTIVITY AND MORTALITY

THE woodcock have a low potential productivity as game birds go. They are apparently polygamous, breed the year after birth, and have one brood a year.

The sex ratio is about even. There is some difficulty in being certain on this point, because the data are almost all from birds shot in the fall. Since many of them were on migration, there is a possibility that a variation in the migration habits of the sexes could throw off the accuracy of the data; this is not known to be, but is a possibility. Then too we must presume that the sex ratio in the fall is the same as in the spring breeding season; this might not be true. Mendall and Aldous (1943) found the sex ratio of 669 birds from Maine, New Brunswick, and Nova Scotia to be 43% males. Thirty-seven winter-collected Louisiana birds were 49% male (Goodrum and Reid in Aldrich, 1952). Greeley (1953) examined 209 fall Wisconsin birds and found 44% of them to be males. This consistency of records indicates a slight preponderance of females.

Breeding is probably perfect, or nearly so, but information is not adequate on the occurrence of unbred hens. The clutch is four eggs in the first set, and three for renests. The fertility and hatchability of the eggs is very high; Mendall and Aldous (1943) reported that over 98% of 529 eggs they checked were fertile. Dead embryos are almost unknown. Nest losses are low; these same authors found one-third of the nests they examined were destroyed (not counting those disturbed by their own actions). Nest losses are mostly from predation, but some are burned in fires, trampled by livestock, disturbed by man, and deserted for unknown reasons. Renesting is frequent, but probably is practiced by less than half the birds that lose their first nests.

The survival of the young is normally very high. Mendall and Aldous estimate " . . . that the rate of juvenile mortality does not exceed 10 percent." This loss is from exposure to bad weather at hatching time, and from predation.

Thus, while the potential productivity of the woodcock is low because of the small number of eggs laid, this deficiency is overcome by the exceptional adaptation and skill of the birds in bringing off their nests and in raising their young with few losses. Such are the ways of nature in assuring each species its means of replacing itself.

The fall age ratio is the measure of the year's productivity. With most game birds a good year is measured by a juvenile-adult fall age ratio of 2:1 or more; with the woodcock a 2:1 ratio is close to the theoretical maximum. With an even sex ratio, if all birds breed successfully, hatch all nests, and raise all the young, the fall age ratio would be 2:1; actually it will always be somewhat lower than this. For the woodcock we may consider that a 1.3:1 fall age ratio reflects a normally succesful breeding season. Examination of 209 Wisconsin birds by Greeley (1953) from 1946 to 1951 showed that the age ratio was 1.4:1.

The major losses that the woodcock sustains are of adults. This begins with the hunting season, which, incidentally, lasts about three months from North to South. What proportion of the birds succumb to the hunter is not known, and one can only express a professional opinion based on the available evidence. There is little doubt that the kill is very uneven as to locality. Migration coverts convenient to hunters may be heavily hunted, while those remote from roads are hunted hardly at all. By the time the last open season is over in the Gulf region, the birds will have run the gauntlet of many hunters. It seems to me that the total

CHAPTER 13

The Band-tailed Pigeon

CLASSIFICATION AND DESCRIPTION

THE order Columbiformes includes all dove- and pigeonlike birds, and has representatives of only one family in the United States; it is Columbidae, the "true Pigeons or doves," and has three subfamilies. The first of these is Columbinae, the arboreal pigeons, to which the band-tailed pigeon belongs. Its scientific name is *Columba fasciata* Say. Other arboreal pigeons that occur in the United States but that will not be covered in this book are the red-billed pigeon (*Columba flavirostris*), white-crowned pigeon (*Columba leucocephala*), and the feral rock dove or domestic pigeon (*Columba livia*). The extinct passenger pigeon (*Ectopistes migratorius*) also belonged to this group.

The second subfamily is Zenaidinae, the ground doves. We shall discuss the mourning dove and the white-winged dove in the next two chapters. The other ground doves that are found in the United States are the white-fronted dove (*Engyptila fulviventris*), ground dove (*Columbigallina passerina*) and Inca dove (*Scardafella inca*). The last three will not be included here.

The third subfamily, Starnoenadinae, the quail doves, has but one West Indian species; we shall not cover it, since it does not occur regularly in the United States.

The type form of the band-tailed pigeon (*C. f. fasciata* Say) is the only one that occurs in the United States. A second subspecies known as Viosca's pigeon (*C. f. vioscae*) is considered a resident form in southern Lower California,

Mexico. Other subspecies occur in Central America. Additional common names of the band-tailed pigeon include blue pigeon, blue rock, white-collared pigeon, and band-tail.

The band-tail more nearly resembles the domestic pigeon in size and form than it does the mourning or white-winged doves. It is large and stockily built, weighing an average of 11 to 12 ounces but occasionally up to a pound. It is from 13 to 16 inches long. It has a broad rounded tail that easily distinguishes it from the mourning dove, while a lack of white on the wings and tail distinguishes it from the white-winged dove. Its legs are yellow.

The head, neck, and under parts of the male are purplish brown or vignaceous, fading to whitish on the lower belly. A narrow white crescent makes a half collar on the nape of the neck. Below the white collar is a patch of iridescent, scaly, bronze-green feathers. The back is dark green-brown, which grades into bluish gray on the rump and tail. A wide blackish band crosses the midtail, and the tip of the tail is pale bluish gray. The wing quill feathers are brownish black, paler on the outer webs, while the wing coverts are dark grayish blue with light gray edgings. The bill is yellow with a black tip; and the eyelids are red and naked.

The female is similar to the male but slightly smaller. The green-bronze lustre on the neck is less pronounced, and the white collar is less prominent. The coloration is generally duller than on the male. Juveniles resemble the female, but lack the white collar and have indistinct pale edgings on many of the feathers.

415

COURTESY R. J. NIEDRACH

PLATE 90. *The band-tailed pigeon.*

GEOGRAPHICAL RANGE AND DISTRIBUTION

THE primary breeding range of the band-tail is in the far western mountain ranges, from southwestern British Columbia southward through western Washington, Oregon, and California, into Lower California and mainland Mexico. The birds live primarily in the coast range and on the western slopes of the Cascades and Sierra Nevadas, being most abundant near the coast. The second breeding area lies farther east in southeastern Utah, southern and western Colorado, eastern Arizona, all of New Mexico except the eastern edge, southwestern Texas, and southward far into Mexico and Central America. In this vast region the birds are largely confined to scattered mountain forest areas and are mostly small populations (see Figure 30). These breeding areas are mostly in the transition and upper Sonoran life zones in forested localities at fairly high altitudes.

The winter range extends from east-central and southeastern California, southeastern Arizona, southern New Mexico, southwestern Texas far south to the tip of Lower California, and through Mexico to Guatemala, Central America. In the zone where the breeding and winter ranges overlap in Mexico and Central America, it is believed that many of the birds are nonmigratory except for moving to high altitudes to nest and to lower levels in the winter. A few birds occasionally winter in sheltered locations as far north as Puget Sound in Washington and near Albuquerque, New Mexico.

There are infrequent occurrences of band-tails far outside the usual range. Circles on the map (Figure 30) indicate where some of these have been recorded by Neff (1947) and others.

HABITS

NORTHWARD migration begins in January and February from the southern wintering areas. Some of these birds reach southern and central California by mid-February; farther inland they arrive in Arizona and New Mexico in early April. They travel northward in small flocks at a very erratic pace. Where feeding is easy or when weather conditions are rough they tarry, but at other times they move along by fits and starts. The few birds that wintered in the United States may merely move up the mountain sides to a higher elevation for their summer range. These birds may be nesting in this southern zone from March to August, or occasionally a little later. The birds that go farther north reach Colorado, Utah, and northern California in April or early May; those that go on to Washington and British Columbia arrive in May or June, occasionally earlier.

The courtship is typical of birds of this type; it is described by Swarth (quoted in Bent, 1932): "The male chooses a prominent perch high in a treetop from which he makes his owl-like "coo" note. He then flies upward with wings and tail stiffly spread, makes a circle and returns to starting position . . . uttering meanwhile a peculiar wheezing noise impossible of description . . . " Another type of courtship activity is given by Neff (1947) from a description by Pearse: "Short flights in a hesitant, quivering manner, during which the bird seems almost to float, form the basis of

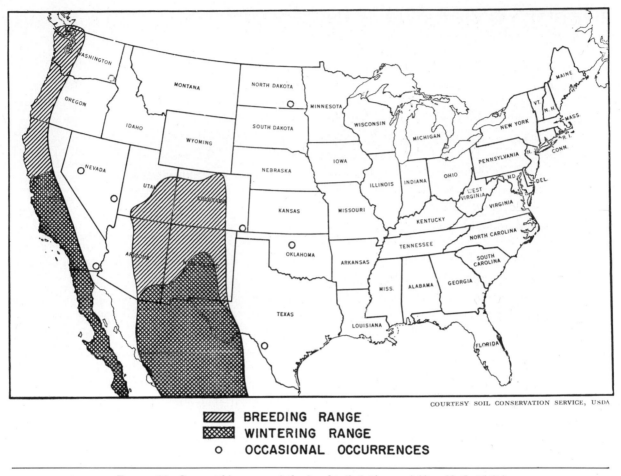

COURTESY SOIL CONSERVATION SERVICE, USDA

▨ **BREEDING RANGE**
▩ **WINTERING RANGE**
○ **OCCASIONAL OCCURRENCES**

FIGURE 30. *Geographic range of the band-tailed pigeon. (After Neff, 1947.)*

this display. The tail is fully spread and Pearse says that the tips of the wings appear to be held down. The display is accompanied by two separate very low calls, one of which he describes as being very like the modified chirping of a cricket."

The cooing note may be either one or two syllables. The male stretches his neck out and bends it down, the bill opens slightly, and he gathers in air to fill the neck skin to three times its usual size and in so doing makes a faint "oo," then expels the air from the lungs, keeping the neck inflated while calling "whoo-oo." He repeats this note seven or more times, then brings the neck back to normal position and lets the air escape from the neck area (Bent, 1932). Before incubation his calling is done

mostly in the early morning and late afternoon; it may be done at any time of day from perches in nest trees.

In addition to the resonant cooing call, the adult pigeons use low conversational notes while around the nest. These sound much like the familiar gurglings of the domestic pigeon.

After pigeons pair off they may or may not nest at once. Even during the breeding season many of them will be found living in small groups, either awaiting their desire to nest or after the completion of nesting. Nesting is normally singly in widely scattered spots, but they sometimes nest close enough together to make loose rookeries; at least there appears to be some social significance to these relatively close nests. Neff (1947) quotes an observation in Arizona by Fowler of some 35 pairs nesting so that they averaged 3 to 4 acres per nest. Glover (1953) reported nesting territories in northwestern California to be from one-tenth to one-half mile in radius, averaging one-fourth mile.

Nesting is chiefly in forest cover, often in remote locations, and usually close to a water course. Many kinds of trees are selected for nest sites, including Douglas fir, red and white alders, Sitka spruce, black, live, and golden oaks, tanoak, lowland white fir, piñon and lodgepole pines, blue blossom ceanothus, and others. Steep slopes in rugged terrain are often chosen for nesting locations. In Arizona, however, they commonly nest in the oaks and alders of canyon or ravine bottoms (Neff, letter). The nest is placed on a horizontal limb, usually close to the trunk; it may be a few feet above ground or as high as 60 or 70 feet; most are about 15 to 20 feet above ground; nests are occasionally placed on a stump or even on the ground. The female does most of the nest-building, and takes her time doing it; as much as a week may pass, while she piles up a large loose stack of sticks that passes for a nest. It is an extremely flimsy structure; many an observer has marvelled at the way they manage to keep their eggs from rolling to destruction. Pairs often return to nest in the same tree year after year, and sometimes on the same limb, adding a few twigs on top of the old nest at each nesting.

They lay a single egg, or rarely two. The egg is pure white, elliptical-ovate and pointed, and measures about 1.6 inches by 1.1. Incubation takes 18 to 20 days, varying with the weather; both birds participate. It seems likely that the weather affects the development of the embryo more with this species than most, because of the ease with which air penetrates the loosely built nest.

When the young one hatches it has some yellowish orange down but is quite naked. Its food is regurgitated pigeon's "milk" from the glands in the walls of the crops of both parents.

Both male and female help in brooding and caring for the squab. Brooding is performed conscientiously for nearly three weeks, after which the young one is exposed more and more. It is usually fed three times a day at first, later twice daily, the first feeding being early in the morning. After about a week the regurgitated material contains some vegetable food as well as the milk. The squab grows slowly at first, but by two weeks of age it is fairly well covered with down and has a scattering of ugly looking quills developing. Its food by this time is about half-and-half milk and vegetable material. At three weeks its feather coat is well developed except for the head region. The regurgitation of milk has ceased by this time, and the food of the squab is made up mostly of fruits and seeds; according to the local food supply, the food may be all seeds, even at times including whole barley (Neff, letter).

The parents brood the squab less and less as conditions warrant; during the late nestling stage, when they are not feeding or brooding it, they pay it little attention. One or both birds may fly close to the nest once in a while to look over the situation, but quickly leave again. As its feathers develop completely, the squab spends a good deal of time preening. It climbs about on the nest limb, and flaps its wings and exercises its legs and neck in preparation for its exodus. This it takes on the 28th to 30th day after hatching.

In the northern portions of the breeding range the pigeons have but a single nesting a year; in parts of California and in Arizona, New Mexico, Texas, and Mexico they may have two and rarely three nesting periods. Marked pairs have brought off two successive broods in the same nest (Wallace Macgregor, letter). This is a rather skimpy effort when one considers the length of time available for breeding—three months or more in the northern areas, and longer in the southern sections. Breeding in the Monterey area of California has been observed from February through October (Macgregor, letter). Neff (1947) gives

COURTESY J. A. NEFF

PLATE 91. *Location near Larkspur, Colorado, where band-tails come down from the mountain forest to feed in farm fields.*

PLATE 92. *Band-tailed pigeon squab in its flimsy nest.*

COURTESY J. A. NEFF

dates in September and early October in most of the breeding range, including Washington, when birds collected had well-developed milk pads in the crop-lobe walls. Thus it would seem that they are biologically able to breed and feed their young for a long enough period to have at least two layings. The lack of adequate summer food probably limits nesting in many areas.

When the young have left the nest and the breeding season is over, the band-tails once more gather in small flocks; they are gregarious in habit at all times; even when nesting the bird "off duty" often joins others similarly free (Neff, letter). These small groups that gather in early fall start wandering in search of good feeding areas, and combine into larger and larger groups. If they find good feeding spots in the forests they remain for a time; if they do not, they may drop into the valleys and seek grainfields. As the pressure mounts from cold weather and scarcer food, they move south-

ward on their long, erratic migration. This may start in late August or early September in the north, and occasionally in areas south of Washington, Oregon, Utah, and Colorado; in mild seasons some birds may not start south until October or November.

Most of the migrating flocks have from 10 to 40 birds, but occasionally they number hundreds and even thousands. The larger concentrations occur in the coastal zone; large numbers have been seen congregated at mineral and salt springs in Oregon and elsewhere, and at times birds along the coast drink salt water from the ocean. This urge for salt seems to be felt chiefly during the fall.

Their daily habits while not actually migrating are divided between feeding and roosting activities, with some loafing in between. Roosts are generally in heavy forest cover at high altitudes. At daybreak a large roosting flock breaks up into smaller groups as each plummets down the mountainside in swift flight, wings held close to the body, beating infrequently, veering a little from side to side, and making a swishing sound as they go. They may wind up in an oak grove in a canyon, on a hillside where the madrone berries are plentiful, in a farmer's harvested grainfield, or in other spots where food is to be found. When feeding on nuts and fruits in trees, they go through many acrobatic antics to reach each morsel. After stretching to pick a piece of food just out of reach, the bird may fall over and pick the item on the way as it swings down to the next lower limb. A flock foraging in a grainfield have an odd habit that may be described as a sort of "rolling" across the field. The birds in the rear of the group, on discovering their end position, fly forward over their companions and drop down in front and then keep on walking and eating. As each few in the back do this in rapid succession, it gives a rolling motion to the group in addition to their walking.

The morning feeding period is over by 8 or 9 o'clock if food is plentiful; the birds then loaf around, or make some headway to the south. They love to find perches in the tops of high trees, and sit motionless for long periods. The late feeding time begins around four o'clock and continues until nearly dark. As they finish feeding, each flock flies upward in a spiral motion, joins with other flocks, and then takes off for the roost. This flight may be several miles long, and may go up a thousand feet or more.

When food is scarce the migration is more erratic and rapid, as the search for food becomes more urgent; at such times the migrating population makes up into larger flocks than normal. When they do find good feeding areas they descend on them with a vengeance. When these feeding areas are farms and the food is a farm crop, the birds may do great damage.

On a few occasions the pigeon concentration has been so complete as to bring most of the birds from the coastal flights into one small area. This happened in the winter of 1911-12, when some half million more or less were gathered in the area from Paso Robles to Nordhoff, California (Bent, 1932).

Pigeons from the northern breeding range may take up to three months to reach southern California in the fall flight. They may take either of two routes, through the coast range or the western slope of the Sierra Nevadas. Then they spend the winter in wandering, restless flocks, moving about with changing conditions of food supply and weather.

FOOD AND SHELTER

THE band-tailed pigeon is essentially a bird of the natural forest, and prefers high altitudes and rugged terrain. In the spring it seeks the mountain slopes covered with forest of conifers and hardwoods, usually above 4,000 feet. In Washington and Oregon the cover is likely to be Douglas fir, with red and white alder in the gulches and other associated plants. In California it is commonly made up of Douglas fir and Sitka spruce, spruce and redwood, ponderosa pine, California black oak, madrone, and others that grow with them; in Colorado and New Mexico the nesting cover may be lodgepole pine forest; in Arizona it may be oaks of various kinds, and piñon pine at elevations of 5,000 to 8,000 feet or more. Spruce groves, alder thickets, and redwood snags were most used by pigeons in summer in northwestern California (Glover, 1953). When nesting duties are done the pigeons go farther afield in their foraging and use more cover types than in early summer. It is common for them to fly down a mountainside to a valley bottom or to lower foothills of blue oak and digger pine (in California) to feed, and to return to the high-elevation forest in the evening. The low-altitude forests become their regular habitat in the winter range, and the composition of these forests varies greatly. In the coastal range they use the redwood type to some extent, but the various combinations of oaks are more used than most forest types.

PLATE 93. *Band-tailed pigeon summer range in the Colorado Rockies. The altitude here is from 8,000 to 9,000 feet.*

Another part of their modern habitat is farm land; it makes little difference what kind of farm land it is, as long as it has an edible crop and is located close to their mountain forests. Barley, wheat, oats, cherries, grapes, walnuts, and peas are some of the crops favored by the pigeons. Naturally those fields located *within* a forested region are most commonly used.

These pigeons are seed- and fruit-eaters for the most part; they consume very little animal food, though they do eat some grasshoppers and other large insects. Acorns are their preferred food in fall, winter, and spring in the coastal states, and in the fall in the interior mountains. Neff's (1947) analysis of 639 pigeon crops showed that 50.1% of the total food was mast— mostly acorns but some pine seeds. If there are plenty of acorns the birds subsist largely on them, but if the acorn crop is spotty they move about in search for mast or a substitute for it. The acorns of blue and California live oaks are chosen in preference to those of California black oak when there is a choice; acorns of all the oaks found in the birds' range are eaten to some extent. Oak blossoms are also eaten some in the spring. Pine seeds, especially those of piñon pine, are important fall and winter foods, particularly in the interior range and in

Mexico. Cultivated fruits, notably cherries, prunes, and grapes, are eaten in large quantities in some years; Neff's records revealed that 11% of the diet came from this source.

The fruits of Pacific dogwood, madrone, cascara, and blueberry elder are used in the fall through the coast range; the madrone berries are also taken in winter and spring, and the cascara and elder in summer. Other fruits commonly eaten in summer and fall include those of salal, thick-leaved hackberry, grapes, olive, junipers, white mulberry, blueberries, bearberry, manzanitas, western serviceberry, twinberry honeysuckle, salmonberry, and Douglas hawthorn. Fruits of Christmasberry and manzanitas are common winter foods; wild strawberries and the fruits of various brambles are eaten in spring and early summer.

The grains represent the other major source of pigeon foods besides fruits and nuts; their liking for grains is an acquired taste, developed since man invaded their domain with his agriculture. Most of the grain used is eaten in summer and fall, but some is gleaned through winter and spring. The birds examined by Neff (1947) had obtained 12.8% of their food from grains. They are also accused of pulling sprouting grains in the spring, but this charge seems to be exaggerated. Barley, wheat, and oats kernels are the grain seeds eaten most, but those of rice are also used some. Garden peas are another food added to the band-tails' diet within the past 30 years. Five percent of the food of the birds checked by Neff was peas.

The vegetative parts of a number of plants are eaten at times. Their use of oak flowers was noted above. Madrone blossoms and the early shoots of native and cultivated grasses are taken during the spring migration (Glover, 1953); they are also known to eat sycamore balls, and buds of spruce, almond, and walnut.

They generally eat one food at a time, and concentrate on it to the exclusion of others at that meal. [Note: the above information on food habits was obtained from Neff (1947 and 1952), Kinghorn and Neff (1948), Martin, Zim, and Nelson (1951), Bent (1932), Glover (1953), and others.]

The habits and welfare of these birds are affected more by food supplies than by any other consideration. When food is widely plentiful, especially acorns, pigeons are widely scattered, and not especially inclined to wander about; under these circumstances they do little raiding of farm crops, and hunting does not seriously reduce their numbers, even locally. But when the acorn crop is very short or is very spottily distributed, the birds keep on the move in search of better food supplies. They gather in large flocks, especially where a good food source is discovered; then they are easy prey to hunters in some localities. They invade cultivated areas and get in trouble with farmers. Bad food years are often followed by reduced pigeon populations.

Band-tails have a strong need for salt; they drink at mineral and salt springs, and at the seashore, gather at "salt lick" sandbanks, and even peck at the drippings from cattle salt blocks. This has been observed mostly in the fall (Neff, 1947, and letter; *P-R Quarterly,* April 1951 for California). Except in interior arid range they have no great need for free water for drinking at most times, and their distribution in humid areas is little affected by water availability. They are, however, commonly seen drinking at water holes along with other game birds.

These birds require gravel in their stomachs to aid in grinding their food; Neff (1947) found that the volume of grit in the stomach varied from 7.5% of the total contents in July to 31.4% in December. When such foods as dogwoods or cherries are eaten, the hard pits in them make gravel unnecessary for breaking up the food.

The economics of band-tail food habits is complicated. In years of good oak mast crops they feed almost entirely on wild foods, and the effect on man's interests is almost completely neutral. But when acorns are scarce, the pigeons commonly invade farm fields in large or small flocks, and often do considerable damage to crop plants or cause a material reduction in the amount of crop harvested. It should be noted, however, that much of the alleged damage is less real than imagined, or is sometimes conjured for the purpose of obtaining special permits to shoot them. This is not to belittle the real damage that the birds do, but rather to recognize that some of the contentions have ulterior motives.

Small fruits are the crops commonly damaged to a serious degree; cherries and grapes are most affected; prunes are also sometimes damaged. Neff (1947) gives a comprehensive account of many instances of such damages; these may be illustrated by such quotes as: " . . . a loss of 20 to 30 percent of the cherry crop"; " . . . had to hire a guard for four weeks, at that I lost over 1,500 pounds of cherries"; " . . . about 20 growers who estimate their [cherry] losses at from one-fifth to three-fourths of the crop"; " . . . they came in here by the hundreds and fed on green prunes, stripping the trees . . . in six miles along the foothills they did damage amounting to from $2,000 to $2,500 to the prune orchards"; " . . . estimated that 200,000 pigeons were involved . . . enormous flocks of band-tails would alight on the trellised grape vines, then drop to the ground to feed on the waste raisins; in doing this they broke off the tender new growth carrying the current season's crop. In the nearby deciduous fruit trees they alighted at times in such numbers as to break branches and to knock off the blossoms. . . . They estimated a total loss of $5,000 for the grapes and $1,000 for the peaches and plums. In addition, it was said the owners of the ranch and the State Division of Fish and Game together expended about $2,000 in attempting to drive the pigeons from the vineyards."

Damage to grain is less marked than to fruits, and often is less than the farmer thinks; other kinds of birds also take grain, and the band-tail sometimes takes the discredit for all. Most of the legitimate loss is from raids on harvested grain left in the fields in shocks. The claims of spring sprout-pulling are not well substantiated.

Though the above are selected examples, they are unfortunately not too uncommon; it is clear that one of the major problems in managing this species is to do all that is reasonably possible to prevent and reduce such agricultural damages.

THE EFFECTS OF WEATHER

THERE is little evidence that weather is an important decimating agent of band-tails; they are so mobile that it is easy for them to move away from areas of cold and snow that might cause trouble. They can survive harsh winter weather as long as they are well fed. The literature does not show any serious loss of eggs or young from high winds, such as affect the nesting success of mourning and white-winged doves; but some occurs. Hard-driving summer hailstorms in the Rockies may cause some injury to squabs.

Despite the relative freedom from mortality caused by adverse weather, the band-tail population status is very positively affected by the weather, though indirectly; it acts mainly through its effects on the birds' food supply. The foods affected are mainly the fall and winter mast crops, but the weather that does the job comes in the spring. An example of how this takes place was reported by Kinghorn and Neff (1948) in summarizing the status of band-tails in Colorado in 1947: "Late spring freezes again raised havoc with wild foods favored by the pigeons in parts of Colorado. While the southerly third of the mountains of the state contained a fair, though spotty, mast crop, the central and northerly thirds of the pigeon habitat were hard hit. The only acorn crop in these districts was at altitudes somewhat below normal pigeon range. Heavy damage to the oak blossoms and near-total destruction of the acorn crop at higher elevations was noted . . . " The oaks that constitute the pigeons' major source of food are normally notoriously erratic in their acorn yields. When bad spring weather eliminates the acorn crop over large areas of the birds' range, it may also freeze the cherries and other fruits; this causes them to move about constantly in search of food, to gather in large flocks, and often to get in trouble by invading farm crop fields. As a result they suffer excessive mortality from starvation, from man's killing them to reduce depredations, and from concentrated hunting kill in accessible areas where the birds congregate.

PREDATION; DISEASES AND PARASITES; ACCIDENTS

THERE is not a great deal of information available on the natural mortality of band-tails. They appear to be remarkably free from predation, though more thorough study will almost surely reveal greater losses from this source than are now known. Bent (1932) quotes Kitchin to the effect that a gray squirrel may occasionally appropriate a pigeon nest for its own use. Though not a matter of record, owing to the rather few observations of band-tail nests, it would be surprising indeed if there were not rather frequent losses of eggs and young from their being eaten by tree-living species like jays, crows, ravens, squirrels, and horned owls. Neff (1947) summarizes the known instances of predation on adult pigeons as follows: prairie falcons and Cooper's hawks reported by Willard as taking " . . . considerable toll from the flocks" in Arizona; a sharp-shinned hawk that took a bird from a flock in Utah, reported by Cottam; and a western goshawk " . . . pursued band-tails in Yosemite National Park," observed by McLean. At the very least, the horned owl could be added to this list as a probable predator. Neff (letter) says the goshawk is potentially the worst pigeon predator in Colorado. Even though the information on the subject is scanty, it does seem that the size of the bird, its mode of life, especially its flocking habits, and its habitat all help to keep predation low.

There is little information on pigeon disease. Neff (1947) collected one Colorado specimen that had 12 flatworms in the abdominal cavity. Of 109 band-tails trapped near Colorado Springs in 1948–49, 21 were revealed by microscopic analysis to react positively to trichomoniasis; the strain evidently was a light one (Stabler, 1951). A small outbreak of sickness on Whidby Island in Washington in September 1939 affected birds around waterholes; 6 specimens were collected and analyzed, but no cause could be determined.

There is no information on the significance of accidents in band-tailed pigeon ecology. Judging by the nature of the bird and its habitat, collisions with wires and vehicles and encounters with farm machinery are probably uncommon. Some mortality from collision with obstacles probably takes place, and there is some loss of young squabs and eggs from their falling out of the flimsy nests in high winds. Often 6 to 8 squabs that have fallen from nests are turned in to pet shops in the Carmel, California, area (Macgregor, letter).

MAN'S RELATIONS WITH THE BAND-TAILED PIGEON

THE interest in hunting hand-tailed pigeons began during the latter part of the 19th century; it was very much localized because of the rather inaccessible habitat of the birds and the poor transportation available to reach hunting areas. The erratic size and distribution of the populations also discouraged general interest in hunting them; they might be plentiful in an area one week but gone the next; or they would migrate through a given area one year but would hardly be seen the next. Some market hunters now and then shipped band-tails to the cities along with other game, but they did not often pay particular attention to them. No great interest in the band-tail, either for sport or commercial hunting, developed; nor did hunting seriously affect the pigeon populations, until an unusual situation developed in the fall and winter of 1911–12 in California. There was a tremendous flight of pigeons down the California coast, one of the greatest ever observed by white men, and the birds settled in the area from Paso Robles to Nordhoff (Neff, 1947); possibly most of the whole west coast population was in this area at the time. It may be presumed that food supplies were good there and poor generally, else there would not have been such a concentration. The news of the great flocks of pigeons spread, and large numbers of hunters came from far and wide to take advantage of the unusual opportunity. Many were shipped to market. According to Dawson as quoted by Bent (1932), "what followed on this occasion was a humiliating example of what human cupidity, callousness, and ignorance, when unrestrained, will accomplish toward the destruction of birds. . . . The country was aroar with gunfire. . . . The stupid birds, knowing nothing of their offense, flew miserably from one part of the valley to another, but would not, or could not, forsake their food. How great the destruction of that winter really was is a matter of merest conjecture, but it must have been a very sensible proportion, possibly more than half the entire species."

The terrible destruction of band-tails in California that year had one good result: it aroused the interest of people to do something for the species. As a result the bird was given protection from hunting by the Biological Survey of the United States Department of Agriculture (now the Fish and Wildlife Service of the Department of the Interior), beginning in 1913. Originally designated for five years, the period of protection was actually extended until 1932. In the meantime the pigeon population gradually increased, and by 1924 the complaints of crop damage were so insistent that permits were issued for killing pigeons where they were doing damage. Then in 1932 a public hunting season was again allowed in California, Oregon, Washington, Arizona, and New Mexico. Limited hunting has been continued since then in the coastal states. In 1944 and 1945 a portion of Colorado was opened to band-tail hunting. Hunting was again prohibited in Arizona and New Mexico in 1951 because of low pigeon populations, and remained closed through 1953.

Any year that large concentrations occur in accessible areas when the hunting season is open, there is likely to be abusive shooting; Neff (1947) described how this happened in a locality in California in 1932 and again in 1934. Two canyons separated by a narrow saddle where a road crossed provided the situation within the area of pigeon concentration; the pigeons flew back and forth between the canyons. Hunters came in great numbers on hearing of the flocks of band-tails. As Neff said, " . . . the picture was not pleasant, as ten men shot where one would have been enough. Sportsmanship was virtually absent. In the continued fusillade of long-range shots, many wounded pigeons plunged to earth. . . . Owing to the steepness of the slopes and their dense vegetation, the loss of birds was very high, possibly as many as five pigeons being lost or mortally wounded for every bird picked up by a hunter."

The band-tail is not an ideal game bird. It is a fairly difficult target; though not very hard to hit, it is very hard to kill. It is susceptible to overshooting where it congregates to feed or roost; but most of the birds are in inaccessible localities and cannot be harvested at all. The type of hunting they offer often induces wasteful crippling; large numbers of downed birds become unretrieved kills. Because of their low reproductive potential, they cannot thrive under heavy hunting pressure (see next topic). Pigeon populations in any given locality are undependable as to numbers and availability, more so than most game birds. And their flesh is often rather bitter from the tannin content of their food.

On the other side of the ledger it may be said that the band-tail is a very distinctive bird that can create real interest in good sportsmen; it takes the hunter into lovely mountain country, where he may find inspiring recreation while hunting; with care in shooting, the good sportsman need not cause excessive crippling, or drop birds where he cannot retrieve them; and, with care in its preparation the flesh is tasty even when the birds have been feeding on acorns. Thus the band-tail certainly should have a modest though important place in our hunting.

Present-day pigeon hunting may be allowed in either a single or double period in the fall; California has had a split season in some years to take advantage of "native" birds before they depart southward, and later the migrants from the North. But the late season provides about 90% of the kill (*P-R Quarterly*, April 1953). Both California and Oregon have made hunter-bag checks in recent years to evaluate the effect of hunting on the band-tail. In Oregon, in the five years from 1949 to 1953, the hunters averaged 1.7 pigeons each per day's hunt in 1952 (the poorest score), to 2.4 in 1950 (the best). It required about 2 hours of hunting for each bird bagged (letter, P. W.

Schneider). The proportion of the local population at Dutch Canyon taken in 1950 was only about 25%, but in 1951, with many more hunters, it was over half (*P-R Quarterly,* January 1952). A check of 174 hunters in Monterey County, California, in 1951 showed that they took an average of 3.9 pigeons each; in Kern, Ventura, and Los Angeles Counties in 1952, 2,814 hunters in one section averaged 1.4 birds each, and 1,014 hunters in another averaged 2.7 (*P-R Quarterly,* July 1952, April 1953). It was estimated that the total hunter kill on one study area in California exceeded 50% of the available population in accessible areas, and that about half of that was retrieved (*P-R Quarterly,* December 1950).

It is fortunate that the habits and distribution of the band-tail make only a part of its population available for hunting; else it could not long remain a legal game bird.

The relations of the band-tailed pigeon to man's farming have already been discussed under "Food and Shelter Needs"; but it may bear repeating that, because of the pigeon's liking for certain crops, notably small fruits, and its inclination to forsake its natural forest haunts at times for farm fields, it becomes a management problem. The species should not be encouraged to reach very great populations, even if we knew how to do that. When in the natural course of events large concentrations of band-tails do occur on farm lands, steps have to be taken to keep the birds from causing excessive damage to crops.

Man's lumbering operations undoubtedly have considerable influence on band-tails, since they alter the habitat so markedly. Little is known about the specific effects of lumbering on the distribution and numbers of the birds, but it undoubtedly varies with the type of operation. *Extensive* clear-cutting probably makes the forest relatively useless for pigeons for many years. Where the cutting is patchy, and large trees are left along with second-growth and brushy areas, the effect on the pigeon's use of the area may be beneficial.

PRODUCTIVITY AND POPULATIONS

THE potential productivity of the band-tail is the lowest of any of our American game birds. It is probably monogamous, and breeds the year after birth. It has but one nesting period in the northern portions of the breeding range, and possibly two in the southern sections. A single egg is the usual "clutch."

Little is known about the sex ratio of the species. Neff and Culbreath (1947) state that visual sexing in spring in Colorado in 1946 indicated there were 60% to 80% males. Of 88 hunter-shot birds checked in Shasta County, California, in 1952, 68% were females (*P-R Quarterly,* January 1953). The species may typically have an excess of males, but no conclusion can be reached on the matter until more studies have been made.

With such a low potential for breeding, it is not surprising that fall populations are predominantly composed of adult birds. The species cannot even approach a doubling of its numbers annually, since to do so would require an average of two successful nestings per year; this doesn't happen. Hence fall age ratios are well below 1:1, juveniles to adults. The age ratio of hunter-killed birds checked at Dutch Canyon, Oregon was 0.33:1 in 1949, 1950, and 1951. It then dropped to 0.29:1 in 1952 and to 0.26:1 in 1953 (letter, Schneider). A California study of 77 hunter kills in Shasta County in 1952 revealed an age ratio of 0.3:1; 161 birds checked in another area had a ratio of 2.0:1, a high exception to the general rule; while 171 from a third area were 0.8:1, juveniles to adults (*P-R Quarterly,* January, April 1953). Age was determined by the presence of the bursa Fabricius in juveniles as well as by plumage differences. Adding the story together—a single nesting, a single egg, an unbalanced sex ratio—it is little wonder the band-tail has a hard time holding its own.

Information on the natural mortality rates of eggs and young is scanty, but it appears that they are low; this would almost be a necessity, to offset the low-productivity potential if the species is to thrive at all. The only quantitative information on adult mortality is that from hunting. Where the birds are accessible and regularly hunted, the kill is often high, sometimes as much as 50% or more; but this applies in only a few areas. In remote places, where the birds are hardly hunted at all—which constitute about 90% of the California range, according to Glading (letter)—predation and other natural mortality agents must take some toll, but how much is conjectural. The prime limiting factor appears to be the food supply in the winter season.

Mention has been made of the erratic nature of pigeon populations. When food is plentiful and widely available, fall and winter survival is high and populations may increase. When food is scarce, losses from hunting, starvation, and allied factors are likely to be very high; pigeon numbers then decline, even though they seem very plentiful in some areas because of concentrations. Food scarcity forces them to gather in great flocks, where they do find food. Thus in December 1952 there were some 30,000 seen in Kern County, California, in the Mt. Pinos area (*P-R Quarterly,* April 1953). There may be great numbers of birds in a few square miles, yet none at all in thousands of square miles.

THE MANAGEMENT OF THE BAND-TAILED PIGEON

WHEN so little is known about the ecology of a species as of the band-tailed pigeon, the first need of management is for more facts—that is, research. The state game departments of Oregon and Washington have begun studies to learn more about the band-tail's needs, but much more attention is needed.

The things that can be done for and with this species primarily concern two types of the regulation of human activity: the hunting laws and the protection of farm crops.

Shooting regulations must be moderate, since the bird cannot stand heavy hunting where it concentrates in large numbers; seasons have to be short, and bag limits low. Two to four weeks are now generally allowed, and the daily bag is usually from 5 to 10. Locations known to be conducive to overshooting may properly be made into refuges where they occur on public land, or on private land where the landowner will co-operate. This may be done in many cases by the United States Forest Service or the state wildlife agency. The latter will involve the California Department of Fish and Game more than any other, since that state has by far the largest fall populations. It should not be inferred, however, that hunting is endangering the species; it is amply protected by its predominantly inaccessible habitat.

The setting of hunting seasons properly to conserve pigeon populations needs an annual inventory to appraise the situation. This is a difficult matter, and present techniques are far from adequate; counts at salt springs in the postnesting period are used in Oregon for this purpose. Neff (1952) suggested a large number of small samplings, using some 150 to 200 men who work in the bird's range and are familiar with it and its habitat. This plan would cover the three-state interior range, and would utilize game technicians, forest and park rangers, game wardens, selected ranchers, bird students, and others interested in the bird and qualified to make dependable observations. The data would be obtained incidental to the men's regular work.

Just as it is important to protect the band-tail by carefully restricted hunting regulations, so is it equally important that provisions be made to allow enough hunting to harvest the surplus birds, and prevent excessive populations and the associated damages to farm crops. Beyond ordinary hunting, special means may be required in specific situations to prevent local pigeon populations from causing crop losses. Discouraging them by gunfire is the best known method, though it is far from adequate; this may involve killing them by permit, or merely noisemaking. Either way it is most effective when applied quickly, as soon as there is evidence of pigeon invasion and damage. As Neff (1947) says, "It is far easier to discourage the birds at the beginning of an attack than after the flight has developed to large proportions."

Shotguns with black-powder shells is the most satisfactory equipment for scaring them. An adequate number of men to patrol the crop fields at the right time and for a short time is better than using just a few men who would have to stay on the job for a long period. A method that uses automatic acetylene flash guns, combined with a smaller amount of shotgun patrol, is also described by Neff.

The management of the habitat must of necessity be of the most general sort; it consists mainly of practices for forestry purposes that also benefit game. The prevention of forest fire is of prime importance, though small burns become excellent feeding areas for a time. Sustained-yield harvest cuttings in a system that retains a good distribution of mature trees, with second-growth and small clear-cuts, is desirable for making good pigeon habitat. Of particular importance is the retention of adequate spruce groves and stands of mast-producing oaks and pines. Glover (1953) recommends the leaving of strips of uncut forest along water courses, and clear-cutting in small blocks as measures that lumbermen may properly use that will benefit pigeons. Margins of such cuttings and of farms are sources of food from fruit-producing trees and shrubs. The reforestation of some areas that lack seed trees of desired species that would provide natural regeneration is desirable for long-term cover improvement; Neff (1947) suggests that the planting of some food trees like mulberry in "high mountain park areas" may be desirable. This may also be practical near commercial fruit farms that may be raided by pigeons, to help dissuade the birds from using cultivated fruit.

The provision of salt may be a practical management measure in areas where pigeon food supplies are ample; recently the Oregon game men have been experimenting with devices for this purpose (Neff, letter). Guzzlers may be built in arid regions to make water available to band-tails along with other game birds (see page 328).

The preservation of the wilderness character of the high-mountain habitat of the band-tail is very desirable, where it can be harmonized with other more important land-use problems; this means primarily the avoidance of lumbering and road construction in such areas; this objective is fortunately desirable for other reasons than preserving pigeon habitat. Civilized man needs to retain segments of all kinds of wilderness, so that he may use them for their biological and cultural values. It is also true that many high-mountain areas have a higher value for water production and watershed conservation than for their wood products, and may best be kept in their primitive state rather than harvested.

CHAPTER 14

The Mourning Dove

CLASSIFICATION

THE mourning dove belongs to the family Columbidae; its scientific name is *Zenaidura macroura* (Linnaeus). There is but one species in the genus, and it has five subspecies. The eastern mourning dove is *Z. m. carolinensis* (Linnaeus), and the western mourning dove is *Z. m. marginella* (Woodhouse); these are the only two that occur in the United States. The type form occurs only in Central America and the Greater Antilles; the other two subspecies occur on islands off the west coast of Mexico.

It is also known by such colloquial names as turtledove, wild pigeon, and wild dove.

DESCRIPTION

THE eastern mourning dove is a sleek, streamlined bird somewhat similar to the domestic pigeon but much smaller. Its length varies from 11 to 13 inches; its weight is but 3½ to 5 ounces—slightly higher in winter than at other seasons. It has long, pointed wings that spread 17 to 19 inches. The tail, narrow and pointed, is 5½ to 7 inches long. The neck is long, and the head rather small.

The coloration of the male is delicately beautiful. It is a grayish olive-brown above on the back, rump, and middle tail feathers; the lateral tail feathers are bluish-gray, with a black crossbar and a white tip; the outer tail feathers have the outer web white also; the neck and head are fawn-brown on the forehead and sides and bluish-gray on the crown; the bare skin around the eye is bluish; the lower sides of the neck are iridescent, with metallic purplish bronze and gold; there is a small glossy bluish-black spot beneath the ear coverts; the wings are similar to the back in color, but are more bluish-gray on the flight feathers; there are a number of black spots on the scapulars and wing coverts.

The under parts are purplish buff, darkest on the breast, paler on the throat, chin, and under-tail coverts. The flanks and under-wing linings are bluish-gray.

The bill is slender, small, and black, and somewhat glaucous on the tumid nasal portion; the legs and feet are red; and the iris of the eye is dark brown.

The female is similar to the male, but with somewhat duller colors. She is slightly smaller, and has a somewhat shorter tail.

The juvenile bird has much duller plumage than the adult male, is smaller, and has a shorter tail. The dark spots and iridescent coloring are lacking until after the autumn molt.

The Western subspecies is slightly paler and slightly larger than the Eastern bird; its upper parts are more grayish.

GEOGRAPHICAL RANGE AND DISTRIBUTION

THE mourning dove has the largest range of any of our game birds, and is the only one to breed in all 48 states. Its breeding range extends from British Columbia to Ontario and Maine, and south to central Mexico, Cuba, and Haiti. The wintering range is from California, Nebraska, and New Jersey, south to

COURTESY A. A. ALLEN

PLATE 94. *The mourning dove at nest in crotch of tree, a typical location.*

Panama. Most of the eastern birds winter in our southeastern states; stray birds sometimes winter in the northern states, and in summer may occasionally be found as far north as Alaska and Greenland.

The eastern subspecies is found from the great plains to the Atlantic, and the western form from the great plains to the Pacific.

HISTORY OF THE MOURNING DOVE

THE mourning dove has resided on this continent for a long time; remains of the species have been found in the La Brea tar pits in California, and in Pleistocene cave deposits in Arizona. It was probably a contemporary of the giant sloths and sabre-toothed tigers. It was well known by the Indians; to the Shoshoni it was known as *Ha-wo;* to the Selish, *Wa-u-ia-uk;* to the Pima, *Haw-he;* to the Chippewa, *Wa-ba-mi-mi;* all probably phonetic names that imitated the bird's call (McClure, letter).

The dove was not particularly prominent in the affairs of the early settlers; it was not uncommon around the forest edges, but neither was it abundant. Its small size, rather drab colors, and quiet habits obscured it in comparison with the larger, more noisy turkey, grouse, and waterfowl. In its own group, the pigeons and doves, the vastly more abundant passenger pigeon drew attention away from its smaller relative.

The settlers encountered the mourning dove wherever they went—even to the Far West, Mexico, and much of southern Canada. But it was not a bird of the forest, nor of the open plain, but rather of the open woodland edges. As the forests were opened up for agriculture the amount of suitable habitat was increased; the dove moved into these new areas, but not in large numbers. The ever-present passenger pigeon probably exercised competitive restraint on the increase of doves; not until the pigeons disappeared in one of the tragic biologic mysteries of history did the doves begin to build up large populations. In time they became common to abundant over much of their geographical range, and remain so today.

The dove has for a long time been a popular game bird in the southern states. How much effect hunting has had on its populations is difficult to say, but it probably was not a limiting factor on the bird's increase until recent years; the dove was not specially sought by market hunters during the era of game commercialization. Modern sport hunting exacts a large harvest, and in many areas in some years it may be a major mortality factor. But the mourning dove should continue to be an important game bird.

IMPORTANCE AS A GAME BIRD

DOVE-SHOOTING is a distinctive sport. It does not receive the acclaim that is accorded bobwhite, ruffed grouse, wild turkey, or even ring-necked-pheasant hunting. It may not have such enthusiastic devotees as those that extol the virtues of hunting woodcock or waterfowl. Yet dove-shooting is prime sport for hundreds of thousands of hunters in 28 states of the

United States, as well as for others in Mexico and Cuba. The dove offers a swift aerial target that challenges the best shots, provided they do not take too great advantage of birds coming to water holes or heavily baited spots. It is open-field shooting, and lacks the thrill of the flush of ground-roosting species; neither does it offer shooting over trained dogs.

Mourning doves are legally hunted in all our southern states, where it competes with the bobwhite for popularity as a farm-game bird. It is popular in the Southwest, in California, and is hunted as far north as Washington, Idaho, Illinois, and Pennsylvania. More doves are bagged annually than any other upland game bird except the bobwhite and ringnecked pheasant.

The flesh is considered very tasty when cooked with care; since it is small, a good many birds are needed for a family meal.

HABITS OF THE MOURNING DOVE

COURTSHIP

THE time in the spring when courtship starts is related to the development of the gonads (probably in turn related to the amount of daylight per day), and possibly to the time of arrival in the breeding territory. There is evidence, however, that some pairs arrive at the breeding grounds with mates already chosen (McClure, letter). For mourning doves breeding in the southern states this may be very early, for they are essentially sedentary. In the Gulf states cooing may occur throughout the year, and mating starts for some birds in January or February. Northern birds arrive at their breeding areas in March and April and at once begin (or continue) courting.

The male bird selects a nesting territory, and defends it against other males; frequently the first male in a given locality at once attempts to control a rather large area. As other males arrive the first bird often "gives" under the pressure, and ultimately is satisfied with a relatively small area. This he defends with

greater vigor, by cooing and by flying at and pecking intruders.

A female is attracted by the cooing of the male, which he does from dawn to dark when the weather is suitable. Prominent perches, like electric wires, poles, dead tree limbs, television aerials, and house ridges are used as cooing places; later he may coo from the nest site.

Cooing is the activity well known to all observers, and is the prevailing form of courtship and attention to the female bird. It is a mournful sound, and gives the bird its reputation as a sad, doleful creature. Each coo is composed of a series of notes, the first one followed by a second at a higher pitch, and then from three to five longer notes at the same lower pitch as the first one. They have a ventriloquistic quality, and seem to come from various directions and often from a greater distance than they actually do. Cooing is most intense in early morning, beginning before dawn; each male may coo several times a minute for an hour or more. It diminishes from midmorning until late afternoon, and then increases in frequency, but not nearly to the degree of the early morning activity. The female may coo in response, but her calls are weak and scarcely audible. The peak season of cooing is in late May and June; it ceases when temperatures fall below freezing, and during the heat of very hot days. Rain and strong winds reduce the cooing activity in proportion to their intensity (McClure, 1939).

The cooing notes are accompanied by varying degrees of body movement; typically the tail is bobbed at each note, the body is held rigid, the neck arched, and the throat puffed out.

When a female has accepted him and a nesting site has been selected, the male bird performs a nuptial flight; McClure (1939) describes it thus: " . . . he coos several times in succession, leaps from his perch, flies in a steep, whistling climb for 50 to 100 yards, often attaining heights of 150 feet or more, then banks to the right or left, and with wings rigid and tail spread, sails in a great arc back to the same perch, or to the female." These flights occur before and all during nesting. They may even be involved in the establishment of territories, and again may be performed for the sheer joy of flying (McClure, letter).

Mourning doves make other sounds besides the ordinary coo; the whistling sound in flight is familiar to all, yet is still somewhat of a mystery. It sounds like the wing noise of some of the waterfowl, but doves do not always make it; some believed it came from the throat rather than the wings. McClure (letter) says, "It now appears to me to be a wing sound controllable by feather pitch." There are also variations of the cooing note used by both sexes, probably for warnings. The male also sometimes struts, stamps, and postures, much like the domestic pigeon.

NESTING

By the time the male bird has attracted a mate, he has selected a spot for nest-building. If the female concurs in his choice, he brings sticks to her, which she forms into a loose platform that serves as a nest; this process takes several days. By the time the nest is completed, the female is usually ready to lay the first egg; the second and last egg usually comes two days later, and incubation then begins at once. On rare occasions a third egg is laid (possibly by an impostor), and occasionally only one is laid.

The eggs are elliptical-oval, and pure white. They measure 28 by 21 mm. as an average, but there is considerable variation; McClure (1943) reported a maximum size of 32 by 22, and a minimum of 18 by 15 mm. The two eggs of a single clutch are usually different in size.

The first nesting begins in February and early March in the deep South, and is under way by mid-April in the northern parts of the breeding range. Only a part of the birds nest early, but the percentage that are nesting increases until about June, when a very high proportion of the birds have nests; the in-cidence of nesting then declines gradually in July and August. Most birds are through by early September, but a few are still nesting through this month; a very few nests are still active in early October. The proportion of adult birds still breeding in September is generally less than 10%, and in October it is less than 1%; Georgia records (Dan Nelson, letter) 3.5% of birds nesting in September, and a "trace" of October nesting activity as typical. During this long breeding season there are usually from two to five or more periods for each pair, depending on where they are and how many are shortened by losses; the farther south they nest, the more nesting periods they have each year. But there is relatively little nesting in the early and late parts of the season, even in the South, for few of the females are then in breeding condition (J. H. Jenkins, letter).

If a nest is destroyed the pair immediately make another nest, or on rare occasions proceed to lay another clutch in the same nest.

Most nests are made in trees; a few are made in vines, in fallen trees, on stumps, or on the ground; occasionally they nest in an isolated tree, or on a broken tree, entirely surrounded by water. Of 592 nests observed in Alabama by Pearson and Moore (1939), only six were not in trees; Quay (1951) reported on 771 North Carolina nests, of which 30 were not in live trees, bushes, or vines. Most of the tree nests are placed 5 to 25 feet above the ground, but some are as high as 75 feet. The average height of Mid-west country nests was 15 feet, while town nests averaged 23 feet above the ground (McClure, letter); the average height of California nests on a study area was 11 feet (Cowan, 1952). Certain trees are chosen in preference to others in a given locality. The same sites are used year after year, possibly by the same birds; 4% of the nests seen by McClure (letter) were placed in the same locations for three consecutive years; some trees are so favored that nesting colonies result. McClure says that 1.1% of the nest trees he checked contained 10 or more

PLATE 95. *Two mourning dove squabs, the usual number.*

nests each year; most of these were red pines and Norway spruces. The greatest number supported by any one tree was 21; the average of all nest trees was 1.6 nests per year.

The crotch in the tree where the nest is placed is usually on the leeward side if there are prevailing winds; the prevalent aspect may change from spring through summer as seasonal winds change (McClure, letter).

Doves frequently appropriate other birds' nests on which to build their own; these may be old abandoned nests or ones occupied or newly built. The robin is the species most commonly imposed on, but several others may be, including the blue jay, bronzed grackle, and English sparrow.

Incubation takes 14 or 15 days; both birds participate. McClure (1943) observed that the birds follow a regular routine of turns; of the pair he watched, the female covered the eggs from 5 P.M. to 8 A.M. and the male from 8 A.M. to 5 P.M. each day. This is rather typical of the incubation pattern, but it is not rigidly followed by all birds; generally the male sets 8 to 9 hours a day, and usually during daylight. When they change in morning and afternoon they frequently fly off together

for a while; the eggs may be left exposed for as long as an hour on some occasions.

THE BROOD PERIODS

THE mourning dove, like all doves and pigeons, is altricial. Unlike the gallinaceous birds, whose youngsters leave the nest a few hours after hatching, doves care for their squabs in the nest for about 14 days. There is considerable variation in their rate of development, and in the time before they leave the nest; Quay (1951) reports a single instance of nestlings flying at nine days, and another that required 17 days.

The total time for a brood to be raised is about a month; this includes egg-laying, incubation, and the care of the squabs until they leave the nest. From two to five nestings are attempted in a season, which may result in a maximum of the same number of broods. The farther south the birds breed the more time they have to produce young. Within a week after the youngsters leave the nest the parents forget them, and either start to lay another clutch or begin to flock for autumn travels. The juveniles grow and complete their feather development for another two weeks after leaving the nest; then they gather in small flocks and live a gregarious life. Those that are raised north of the wintering area begin their southward migration in July or August, ahead of their elders.

Parental care is thorough; the squabs are brooded almost continuously. Both parents share in the task, though the female is on the nest each day longer than the male. The youngsters may be left unbrooded for a few minutes at a time when they are very young, and for longer periods as they develop. At hatching they are practically naked, with only a scattering of short down feathers through which the yellow skin shows. As the quill feathers start to develop, the squab has an ugly, spiny appearance.

All feeding of the squabs is done by regurgitation; both parents participate. For the first couple of days the food given the squabs is almost entirely "pigeon milk," a glandular secretion from the crop of the adult bird; some tiny seeds may be mixed in. After that a variety of seeds is provided; some as large as corn may be fed after the squabs are five days old. The feedings occur several times each day, and the youngsters are perpetually hungry.

The bird of a pair that is not incubating or brooding spends some of its time near the nest; there is frequent cooing. The balance of the time is spent in feeding, roosting, loafing, and watering.

The doves make little effort at sanitation, as is done by most birds; at first the adults eat the feces of the young, but after about a week the fecal deposits accumulate around the edge of the nest.

Doves with few exceptions complete their family activities in August or September; some may still be in breeding condition when the fall flocking and migration has begun. McClure (letter) found almost all local doves on a California study area still nesting or with barely fledged young on September 1. Birds from the northernmost breeding areas are on their way south by mid-September; for this reason most of the northern states and the Canadian provinces do not have hunting seasons for the mourning dove.

FALL AND WINTER ACTIVITIES

THE peak population of doves generally comes in August in the North; by September some of the young of the year have gone south. Farther south the peak population of the year comes in September or possibly in October in the Gulf states. Some birds are still breeding or completing the care of their last pair of squabs at this time, but most have finished their family affairs and have gathered in loose flocks; these flocks are made up of both the adults and the juveniles from summer broods.

The migration southward is a leisurely process. Small groups of from a few to 20 birds or more travel together; at times these groups are so closely associated that there is the appearance of much larger flocks. This is accentuated by their habit of resting on electric wires, and gathering in restricted feeding or roosting areas. I recall one occasion in early October, when I was traveling some 30 miles by slow train from Lancaster to York, Pennsylvania, a continuous flock of doves arose from the railroad right-of-way as the train approached; the birds were resting on the cinder embankment and on the paralleling electric pole lines. Possibly the warmth of the cinders had influenced their gathering. At any rate, the flock was practically continuous for most of the 30 miles, and totaled many thousands of birds.

They do most of the actual flying of migration in the morning and late afternoon; at night they roost, and during the middle of the day they rest. There is some evidence of night migration obtained by moon-watching in Georgia (Jenkins, letter). While travelling they stop frequently to feed and to drink. The hours devoted to this erratic stop-and-go migration net them but a few miles a day, probably averaging about 15 miles (McClure, 1943).

Most of the eastern birds travel down through the states along the Atlantic coast; some complete their travels in the latitude of the Carolinas, but most continue to the Gulf states; a few go on to Texas. Another major flight lane is the Mississippi valley. Some of these birds stop in the south-central states, but most continue to the Gulf states, some moving toward Florida and some toward Texas. The doves from west of the great plains move into the southwestern states and Mexico for the winter; a few go on to Central America. The migration is completed by early December.

The birds still in the northern states in October encounter their first gunshots in Pennsylvania, Illinois, Idaho, and Washington; the toll from hunting is not great in most of these states, Illinois being an exception. But from that time on they and the doves already farther south are subjected to a barrage of gunfire all the way to the wintering areas. Hunting cuts down the fall populations considerably, especially in the area from the Carolinas, Kentucky, southern Illinois, Arkansas, Oklahoma, and southward, and in California and Arizona.

During the winter the birds live in small flocks where food is plentiful and good roosting cover is easily accessible. Feeding is mostly in farm fields or open woods, where waste corn, soybeans, peanuts, sorghum, rice and weed seeds are plentiful. They roost in the trees of woodland edges, along streams, in orchards, and other rather open situations. There is much shifting of the flocks in late fall and winter; sometimes there will be gatherings of several hundred birds, especially where food is plentiful. These flocks are partly an expediency, and not a strong social organization such as occurs with some birds; they are more common in the northern portions of the wintering range. When the weather is stormy these northern doves stay by themselves and are rather inactive; then they roost in sheltered southern exposures, such as along streambanks.

Some birds begin to coo and court and pair off as early as January in the deep South; a few will actually nest and have eggs laid by early February. For the transients the northward migration begins early; some doves spend a mere month or two at their southernmost wintering place. Then they begin the slow northward movement, often as early as January. The birds going farthest north may take two or three months to reach their breeding area; thus the winter is partly spent in a slow northward migration. Progress is gauged to a considerable degree by the weather; stormy weather keeps them inactive, whereas in pleasant periods they move northward a few miles a day between their times of resting and of feeding.

As the doves reach their breeding localities the small flocks disintegrate and pairing begins.

ADAPTABILITY TO CHANGING ENVIRONMENT

DESPITE the mourning dove's seemingly shy and retiring nature, it has shown remarkable ability to adapt itself to changing conditions in the land cover. More than that, it has learned to live in close association with man, not only on farms but in towns and city suburbs as well; it is our only game bird that is commonly a backyard dweller. One morning while I was waiting for a bus on a street corner in Lansdowne, Pennsylvania, I saw a mourning dove fly into a small spruce tree on a lawn; I watched as she settled on her nest not over 10 feet from the sidewalk and 15 feet from where auto traffic passes almost constantly!

This dove has found much of our man-made environment to its liking; it nests in orchards, ornamental trees, windbreaks, and hedge rows, in addition to the woodland edges that were its original habitat. It feeds in harvested crop fields from midsummer to spring. It chooses electric wires, house tops, television aerials, and such exposed artificial locations for its favorite perches.

This adaptation has taken place throughout its country-wide range in various ways, depending on the nature of the habitat changes. M. M. Dodson in the *P-R Quarterly* for January 1953 expressed it thus: "The salvation of the mourning dove in central and western Oklahoma has apparently been its ability to become adapted to an ever-changing environment. Fifteen years ago the dove population in this area was very high. A sudden change-over to summer fallowing of wheat land reflected a rapid population decline. Most doves formerly nested on the ground in these fields, but summer fallowing disrupted such activity throughout the summer months. Now a sizable population nests in trees and shrubs."

The good dove populations of the present day would not be possible if it were not for the bird's great ability to alter its ways as conditions change; it has taken advantage of habitat changes in one of the most complete adjustments of any of our upland game birds.

TOLERANCE OF OTHER BIRDS

THERE is no territorial conflict between the mourning dove and other game birds, with the possible exception of the white-winged dove in parts of the Southwest. It nests in the same kind of situations as the white-wing, and may therefore compete for space with this similar species. It does occasionally have some strife with other tree-nesting birds; the dove frequently builds its own nest on top of another bird's nest; the other species may be using its nest at the time. There have been instances reported of the eggs of robins, blue jays, cowbirds, and others in the same nest with those of the mourning dove; the dove is usually the aggressor in these cases—strange as that seems. In some instances the cowbird may lay its eggs in a dove's nest. Other instances have been noted of doves nesting within a few feet of other actively nesting birds with no evidence of any conflict between them. McClure (letter) says that there is definite conflict between the mourning dove and the Chinese spotted-neck dove (*Streptopelia chinensis*) in parts of California; in the Bakersfield area, wherever the one species is nesting, the other will not be found.

The winter food of the mourning dove is somewhat the same as that of the bobwhite quail; throughout much of the southeastern and Gulf states wintering area, they may feed in the same fields. The dove is more mobile, and utilizes open feeding areas more widely than the bobwhite; the quail uses field edges and heavier feeding cover. The dove thus has some advantage, but there is no evidence that the bobwhite suffers from this competition.

ADAPTABILITY TO ARTIFICIAL PROPAGATION AND TRANSPLANTING

THE altricial nature and migrating habits of the mourning dove make it wholly unsuitable to game-farming and to programs of live-trapping and transplanting.

HABITAT OF THE MOURNING DOVE

THE mourning dove lives in many kinds of habitat; it is equally at home in arid, semi-desert mesquite brushland, irrigated citrus groves, plains windbreaks, farm fields and hedge rows, and open woodlands. The plant associations in these various habitats may be wholly different from each other, yet have similarities that give clues to the basic requirements of the bird.

It may help to define dove habitat if we first discard some kinds of cover they do not use. It is not a forest bird. It is not a plains bird, or one of vast open fields, marshes, or prairies. Woody plants are vital in its habitat, but more as individual plants than as extensive cover. This dove is an inhabitant of farm land with scattered trees and shrub areas, and of other types of open country with scattered woody plants.

The primary breeding season requirements center in the nesting site; this need sets the pattern of the cover used for half the year or more. The nesting cover used most commonly is a tree mostly surrounded by open land. It may be a tree in a cut-over woodland, or in a woodland edge where the surrounding vegetation is low brush and herbs; or a tree in a fence row, or one standing alone in a field and surrounded by crops and pasture; or an ornamental tree in a farm or town yard with lawn and buildings around it; or a fruit tree in an orchard with grass beneath and other fruit trees nearby; or a tree in a prairie windbreak with other trees on two sides and open fields on the other two; or a tree or shrub in an open area of scattered trees and shrubs, with intervening herbaceous cover or bare ground such as abandoned farmland or desert scrub. The common element in all these very different situations is the home base, a tree for a nest site, surrounded by open cover. A shrub or a vine or a stump may occasionally be used, rather than a tree; once in a while a house eave or a chimney corner may be substituted. And sometimes they may nest on the ground in grass or other herbaceous cover, especially in the plains country. But always they choose the mixture of isolated woody plants in a generally open setting.

The birds are somewhat selective of the kind of tree used for the nest site, though they are also very adaptable in this respect. In North Dakota shelterbelts the favorite nesting trees were found to be Chinese elm, American elm, and Russianolive (Boldt and Hendrickson, 1952). In Iowa, the red pine and Norway spruce seemed to have early season preference, according to McClure (1943), while American and slippery elms were used more in summer; apple, soft maple, box elder, plum, red mulberry, and Scotch pine were also used. Pearson and Moore (1939) found that in Alabama the shortleaf pine, longleaf pine, pecan, and oaks were preferred, in that order. Oaks and black willow were most commonly used in an area in Louisiana (Gresham, 1950). In North Carolina Quay (1951) found that the loblolly pine was preferred for nesting sites, with shortleaf pine, red cedar, and Japanese honeysuckle

used considerably, and 51 other kinds of trees, shrubs, and vines selected occasionally. Willow is commonly used in California (Cowan, 1952). Other species frequently used for nest sites include osage orange, black locust, hackberry, honey locust, mesquite, hickory, thorn apple, and white pine.

The species is less important than the character of the tree selected for nesting. Broad surfaces provided by dense branches or crotches of sloping limbs are needed to hold the nest; protection from wind makes conifers preferable in early spring when hardwoods are leafless. The size of the tree is important, large trees being more desirable. The average trunk diameter of nesting trees in the Midwest was 19 inches, and larger in the case of nest trees in towns than those in the country, the largest available trees being selected (McClure, letter).

There are other breeding season habitat requirements besides the nesting site. Exposed perches of dead tree limbs, wires, poles, and house tops are much desired, and some are needed close to the nest. Feeding cover is essential, but generally easily found; it may be farm crop or grass fields, or almost any other kind of open herbaceous cover where plant seeds are plentiful.

Once the breeding season is over, the habitat needs are no longer tied to a particular tree. Trees suitable for resting or roosting are part of the fall and winter habitat needs; places sheltered from strong winds are then important. Good feeding areas must be conveniently close, but there is a range of several miles. Feeding locations in fall and winter are mainly fields of farm crops such as corn, sorghum, rice, peas, soybeans, peanuts, wheat, oats, and millet. Fields where the crop has been harvested by mechanical pickers, or is being "hogged off," are especially suitable as dove feeding areas; fields of hay, pasture or grassy range areas also provide considerable food in fall and winter, as at other seasons. These habitat requirements are found widely distributed throughout the United States.

TABLE 24

IMPORTANT FOOD PLANTS FOR THE MOURNING DOVE*

Figures opposite plant group titles represent the average range of the percentage of total food in areas where important.

Areas where food plants are important:

NE—Northeastern and mid-western states.
SE—Southeastern and eastern Gulf coast states.
PL—Plains states between Mississippi River and Rocky Mts.
MT—Rocky Mountains and adjacent arid states.
PA—Pacific coast states.

Within each group, the species are listed in the approximate order of their use.

TYPE AND KIND OF PLANT FROM WHICH SEEDS ARE EATEN	SEASON AND AREA OF USE			
	spring	summer	fall	winter
Grains	20–50	10–30	5–15	10–25
Corn	NE, SE, PL	NE, SE, PL	NE, SE, PL	SE, PL
Wheat	NE, SE, MT	NE, SE, PL, MT, PA	NE, MT, PA	SE, PL
Sorghum	SE, PL		SE, PL	SE, PL
Oats	NE, SE	NE, SE	NE, SE	SE
Rice			SE, PL	
Barley	NE, SE	NE, SE, MT	NE, SE, MT	SE
Rye	NE, SE	NE, SE	NE, SE	SE
Buckwheat	NE	NE	NE	
Millet			SE	SE
Legumes	0–15	5–15	10–30	5–15
Soybean	SE		NE, SE, PL	SE, PL
Peanut	SE		SE	SE
Cowpea, garden pea	SE	SE	SE, PL	SE
Common lespedeza	SE		SE, PL	SE, PL
Vetch	SE	SE		
Milk pea	SE			SE
Trailing wild bean				SE
Grasses and sedges	5–15	30–50	20–40	30–60
Bull grass	SE	SE	SE, PL	SE
Green and yellow foxtail	NE, PL	NE, SE, PL, MT	NE, SE, PL, MT	SE
Panic grasses	SE	NE, SE, PL	NE, SE	
Crab grass	SE	NE, SE	NE, SE	SE
Goose grass	SE		SE	SE
Annual bluegrass	SE		NE, SE	
Barnyard grass			NE, SE	SE
Flat sedge	SE			SE
Egyptian grass	SE		SE	SE
Johnson grass				SE

* Derived from: Martin, Zim, and Nelson, 1951; McClure, 1943; Gresham, 1950; Knappen, 1938; Pearson and Webb, 1942; and other sources.

TYPE AND KIND OF PLANT FROM WHICH SEEDS ARE EATEN	SEASON AND AREA OF USE			
	spring	*summer*	*fall*	*winter*
Trees and shrubs	0–5	0	0–10	0–15
Pines (loblolly, slash, longleaf)	SE		SE	SE
Hollies (American, inkberry)				SE
Spurges	0–5	5–20	0–10	0–5
Croton doveweeds (woolly, glandular)	SE	SE, PL, MT	SE, PL, MT	SE
Euphorbia (painted, spotted)	PL	PL	PL	
Weeds and misc. herbs	20–50	5–25	15–25	5–15
Pokeberry	NE, SE		NE, SE	SE
Amaranth (prostrate, redroot)	PL, MT	PL, MT, PA	PL, MT, PA	PL, MT
Common sunflower		PL, MT, PA	PL, MT, PA	PL
Chickweed	SE	SE, PA	PA	
Wood sorrel	NE, SE	NE, SE, PL		
Carolina crane's-bill	SE	SE		
Knotweed, smartweed		NE, PL, MT	NE, MT	
Hemp	PL	PL	PL	
Cocklebur	SE			
Lesser ragweed	NE, PL	NE, PL	NE, SE	SE
Evening primrose	SE			
Buttercup	SE			
California poppy		PA		
Mustard		PA	PA	
Turkey mullein			PA	
Fiddle-neck		PA	PA	
Tarweed		PA	PA	
Woolly verbena			SE	SE

Table title: TABLE 24 (Continued)

FOODS OF THE MOURNING DOVE

MOURNING doves are almost wholly seed-eaters. The fraction of 1% of their diet that is animal is composed of insects probably taken by accident, and snails that may be mistaken for seeds, taken as grit or to satisfy a need for lime. Seeds compose over 98% of the diet. Few game birds have a diet so closely limited to one form of food as this dove.

Almost any small seed may be eaten by these birds; the kinds of seeds that provide the bulk of the diet at any particular time are mainly those that happen to be in plentiful supply. As the doves change localities in migration, or as the availability of any seed foods change, they alter their eating habits accordingly. Though they partake of a great many kinds of seeds they do have preferences, and a rather limited number of species of plants may provide most of their food.

The size of the seed has much to do with its choice or avoidance; few seeds are too small, but many are too large. Few woody-plant seeds are eaten, the main exception being certain kinds of pine seeds. Like the bobwhite, they have a great fondness for a number of kinds of legume seeds; for example, it is said that peanut fields attract and hold doves as strongly as any food source when there are plenty of the "nuts" available.

Since doves eat many kinds of very small seeds it would be expected they would need to pick a large number to make a substantial meal; even so, it is surprising how many seeds are sometimes found in the crop of a single bird. The physical work of picking up several thousand seeds in a few hours must be tremendous, especially as each seed is tested by pressure of the bill and touch of the tongue before it is swallowed (McClure, letter). Yet this is not an uncommon occurrence; Bent (1932) quotes records of birds having 7,500 seeds of wood sorrel and 6,400 seeds of foxtail grass in their crops.

The major foods of the mourning dove as presently known are summarized above in Table 24; their seasonal use is shown, and also the section of the country in which they are known to be used regularly. Since the young bird is fed entirely by regurgitation, its food is similar to that of the adult after the first few days. The groupings of the plants from which the seeds are taken is somewhat according to the preferences of the bird, somewhat according to taxonomic and economic relations, and partly arbitrary.

It will be seen from this summary that grasses and grains (mostly grasses) furnish a large share of mourning dove food. These plants are found on farm crop fields, pastures, range lands, and waste places that are covered with herbaceous vegetation. Their presence and abundance in most areas is largely a result of farming. The legumes that are important in the dove food supply are also grown on farms, particularly in the southern states. A large number of miscellaneous weeds and other plants also provide considerable dove food. Two of these are worthy of special note, doveweed and poke-berry; both have a special attraction for the doves, one getting its name for this reason; and pokeberry is sometimes called "pigeonberry."

Though the doves consume a number of agricultural crop plant seeds, especially grains and legumes, these are mostly waste, after the harvest is completed; there is little crop loss from dove feeding. They have been known to eat newly planted seeds of some crops, like cantaloupe and peas, and pine seeds from nursery beds; from such depredations there is occasionally some local crop loss. Otherwise their food habits are neutral or slightly beneficial—the latter owing to the quantities of weed seeds they eat.

The need for grit to aid in grinding their seed food affects the dove's habitat selection at times. McClure (1943) noted that doves were frequently found in cover along gravel roads, but that similar cover without the gravel road was not used. Grit may be taken as gravel, quartz, cinders, glass, or any other small hard material.

Doves need water daily. Ordinarily they fly to a source of water in morning and evening as a regular routine; they often drink at other times too. In arid country, water sources are frequently the key element in determining areas habitable for them.

Food is not ordinarily a limiting factor with this species; they are mobile enough to go to places where food is adequate, and there usually are such places. Seasons of severe drouth may cause severe food shortage, and if prevalent over large areas can cause serious trouble. The location of good food supplies definitely determines the distribution of doves in fall and winter.

THE EFFECTS OF WEATHER AND CLIMATE

CLIMATE limits the geographical distribution of the mourning dove more in winter than at other seasons; one may conjecture that dove migration to the South in winter (those that are not already there) began in order to find food more easily and to be comfortable; at present it is an instinctive habit. Food is easier to obtain below the snow belt, but winter food is present in the northern range. Thus the dove would not have to migrate just to obtain food, though it could not get it from beneath the snow since it cannot scratch as a pheasant does.

The northern limit of summer distribution may not be set by climate, but rather by the distance from its southern wintering grounds, and the time required for two migrations a year and an intervening breeding season. This is only an opinion, but it is indicated by the extent of suitable habitat to the north of that actually occupied in summer.

High humidity and aridity are both tolerable to this dove as long as its ingestive water requirement is met. Thus there is no climatic limitation in so far as air moisture is concerned; all in all, the mourning dove is a very widely adapted bird.

Throughout its winter and summer ranges the dove's activities are greatly influenced and affected by weather conditions. The changes of the seasons bring on its semiannual migrations. Its time of beginning nesting in spring is partly a consequence of the weather. Its feeding habits are greatly affected by different weather conditions; in stormy periods it is inactive. Seasons of excessive drouth cause poor seed crops of many food plants. Summers that are very wet result in much sprouting of waste grain, and its consequent loss as dove food. These conditions make the search for food harder, and require more traveling. The birds are more vulnerable to predation, and there is more chance for accidents when they have to work hard to eat. Snow and ice storms make feeding difficult. When snow is accompanied by very low temperatures on the wintering range, heavy dove mortality may occur. This is partly due to chilling and starvation, and partly the result of increased vulnerability to

attack by natural enemies. During the severe winter of 1940 in the Gulf states, doves " . . . starved to death by the thousands, and they were so reduced in numbers that drastic regulatory action was required to give them a chance to recover" (Lincoln, 1945).

Summer storms cause a considerable loss of eggs and nestlings; the worst storms are those accompanied by high winds, which may blow the flimsy nests off their supports. During such storms one or both adults set on the nest facing into the wind; this helps to hold the nest in place. In seasons when such storms are common they may be the largest cause of egg and squab mortality, displacing predation, which is normally the greatest decimator. These destructive windstorms are more prevalent in the midwestern and south-central portions of the breeding range than elsewhere. For example, McClure (1943) noted that in 1938 in Iowa, where he did his studies, there were 18 storms severe enough to destroy dove nests, in 1939 there were 25 such storms, and in mild 1940 only 11. Hailstorms may kill adults as well as young; one storm in 1939, which was severe enough to snap many trees and limbs, resulted in the loss of about a third of all dove nests active at the time. In the three years of his Iowa study McClure found that about half of all dove nests lost, and for which the cause was known, were destroyed by bad weather; this constituted 22% of all nesting attempts.

Weather is in most years a major factor in the determining of the population level of doves. In occasional years of very severe weather that strikes when the birds are susceptible it is clearly the limiting factor.

PREDATION; DISEASES AND PARASITES; ACCIDENTS

PREDATION

No single predator is particularly notable as a destroyer of the mourning dove; yet despite this lack of outstanding culprits a large share of dove eggs and adult doves are eaten by natural enemies. This is done through gradual attrition by a number of kinds of birds, mammals, and reptiles. The nest predators in particular are an odd lot, most of them being generally considered as prey themselves rather than predators.

Among the known mourning dove egg-eaters are the blue jay, bronzed grackle, English sparrow, starling, raven, shrikes (probably), crows, fox squirrel, flying squirrel, Beechey ground squirrel, house cat, and snakes. There are no doubt many more that would be revealed if adequate studies of this subject were made; taken all together they manage to exert a very depressing effect on dove production. Since dove production is accomplished by from two to five successive small units per season, their destruction is also in small units. When a blue jay eats a clutch of two dove eggs it takes only a fraction of the year's production effort, as compared, for example, to the usual total season loss of a rifled ruffed grouse nest. Nevertheless each small clutch lost is a loss that can never be made up, since the productive season is limited and fully used.

Predation is the greatest cause of egg loss in most years; only when seasons of many bad storms occur does that source of egg destruction exceed predation. Pearson and Moore (1939) studied 592 nests in Alabama, where storms are less severe than in the Midwest, and found 48% of them destroyed, mostly by predators. Grackles, shrikes, and other predators were believed to have caused most of the loss of 22 of 48 nests observed in Mississippi (*P-R Quarterly*, October 1949). Of nearly 4,000 nests observed by McClure (1943) in Iowa, about 45% were destroyed; only about a quarter of those lost from known causes were by predation. Locally predation was very high; McClure wrote: "In one blue jay territory of 25 dove nests only four were successful, although the jays probably were not to blame for all of these losses. During 1940 a large elm bore nests of six doves, two robins, one English sparrow, and a kingbird, of which none was suc-

cessful. Squirrels, and possibly it was only one squirrel, systematically worked the tree at least once a week."

Both squabs and adult doves are occasionally killed in the nest. A high rate of predation occurs in ground nests that terrestrial mammals like foxes, dogs and skunks can reach. Tree nests may be plundered by birds, squirrels, house cats, and other tree-climbing flesh-eaters. McClure (1943) notes that grackles sometimes throw squabs from their nests. Screech owls and Cooper's hawks are known to kill squabs occasionally, and no doubt sharp-shins and other avian predators do too.

Predation on adult doves during fall and winter follows the usual pattern of game bird-predator relations, except that the avian predators play a more important role than the terrestrial species. A variety of hawks and owls are known to take doves; probably the most destructive are the Cooper's, sharp-shinned, and duck hawks, and the great horned owl; other hawks and owls occasionally eat doves. Foxes are the most important of the mammals that take doves; they are most destructive of birds feeding in farm fields or roosting in sheltered ground locations. More doves succumb to predation in ordinary times than to any other decimating agent; though in some areas and some years losses from hunting or from bad weather may be higher than those from predation.

DISEASES AND PARASITES

THE mourning dove is very susceptible to one disease that at times causes considerable mortality; it is called trichomoniasis, canker disease, frounce, or dove disease. A number of other birds are known to be susceptible to it; these include most kinds of domesticated pigeons and doves, the band-tailed pigeon, some hawks, and domestic chickens and turkeys (Stabler and Herman, 1951). The causative organism is a protozoan flagellate, *Trichomonas gallinae*, found most prevalently in the mouth, throat, and head passages, but at times found also in the crop and liver. There are different strains of the organism, some much more virulent than others. Doves may have the disease chronically, or have a light case and recover. When a virulent strain is present, however, an infected bird develops an acute condition very rapidly; symptoms begin to appear after five or six days, and by the end of ten days the victim is usually dead.

Symptoms of acute cases include emaciation and sometimes diarrhea. Clear identity of the disease is indicated by yellow, necrotic, cheesy growths in the mouth and throat; they usually appear first as pimples in the back of the mouth, but then grow into large masses that fill the throat and head passages until food is no longer ingestible. The crop and esophagus may also be covered with lesions, and even the outside of the throat may have some; the pressure of these growths may cause the eyes to bulge and close. The material has a foul, characteristic odor.

The disease is transmitted directly from parent to offspring in the feeding process; it may also be carried from one adult to another by contaminated food material. Carriers that hold the organisms but are immune to their effects transmit the protozoans to new areas and to other birds that may be more susceptible. It may also be spread by contaminated drinking pools, and through other birds like domestic pigeons (Stabler and Herman, 1951).

This disease was discovered in mourning doves in the early 1930's, but it was not until the late 1940's that it received much notice. An epizootic in Alabama in 1950 revealed its lethal potentialities (Haugen and Keeler, 1952). These authors estimated losses in 1950 in Alabama alone as between 25 and 50 thousand, and not as bad as the previous year; 5,000 of these were from one county; one farmer saw at least 50 dead doves in one farmyard. The result in Alabama was poor hunting in the affected areas the following year.

Since greater attention has been given to this matter by dove workers in the last few years, it has been found to be common in many areas. Pittman-Robertson Project workers have reported it from Kentucky, Florida, North Carolina, and Missouri; in Missouri 7% of the birds shot in September 1951 had symptoms of the disease (P-R Quarterly, April 1952). It is very seasonal in its effectiveness; for example, Florida workers found few symptoms in birds trapped in August of 1951, but 20% of them retrapped in September had the disease; then by mid-October the incidence was reduced to less than 1% (P-R Quarterly, April 1952). The disease has also been recognized in mourning doves in New York, Colorado, Wisconsin, Nebraska, Arkansas, Illinois, California, Indiana, Ohio, Georgia, Massachusetts, Connecticut, Pennsylvania, Maryland, and Virginia.

Canker disease is a serious threat to mourning doves throughout the breeding range. It is ordinarily of only local significance as a mortality factor, but occasionally epizootics are widespread enough to affect populations over fairly wide areas. There is no known control.

Relatively little is known about parasitic infestations of mourning doves. McClure (1943) summarized the scattered records that indicate a low incidence of parasitism. A tapeworm was the only internal parasite noted—truly an exceptional situation, even considering that there has been little study in this field.

Several kinds of ectoparasites have been found on the mourning dove. Two species of hippoboscid flies, Microlynchia pusilla, and Stilbometopa podopostyla, the former more common, have been found on nestlings. Three kinds of lice have been recorded from this dove, all of them evidently uncommon: Physconelloides zenaidurae, Mecacanthus sp., and Columbicula columba. The most common external parasites on Iowa doves, according to McClure, were feather mites, Fonsecaonyssus sylviarum; sometimes these are abundant in nests, but are not known to have seriously affected the birds. Another mite of the genus Falciger has also been found on the mourning dove. Young doves are sometimes infested with larvae of the fly

Protocalliphora. None of these parasites is known to be significant in dove mortality.

ACCIDENTS

Many motorists have noted that doves on the highway remain unmoved until the last instant before being run down; yet few are run over, so agile are they in taking quick flight. Most of those that are hit are young birds. Juveniles also occasionally fly into wires and other obstacles.

Losses of nestling doves from a variety of types of accidents are common. They may be knocked from the nest by wind, by human or other molesters, or by the parents. Molestation by children and other humans is mostly in town nesting areas. Cowbirds sometimes cause trouble by laying their eggs in dove nests.

The use of strychnine in rodent control work has caused the death of many doves, which are susceptible to this poison (Bent, 1932).

MAN'S RELATIONS WITH THE MOURNING DOVE

Man's major direct influence on doves is in hunting. As a matter of history, the changes in the landscape wrought by the white man have greatly altered its value as dove habitat, but those effects are not as notable today as with many other game birds. As a conservationist man can improve some habitat for the dove and regulate the hunting harvest.

AS A HUNTER

According to McClure (1944), 11 million doves were harvested in the United States in 1942; in all probability this figure represents about the maximum annual harvest in years of high populations. The harvest in most years ranges from three to nine million birds. Some of the states that have the largest harvest are California, Texas, Oklahoma, Tennessee, Kentucky, Georgia, and Alabama. The California and Georgia harvests alone are each estimated

to be two million a year (Cowan, 1952; Nelson, letter).

Most of the state wildlife agencies in the southeastern and south-central states have been studying dove hunting since about 1948 under Pittman-Robertson projects. They have found that hunters who go hunting specifically for doves commonly bag one to three per hour; the daily bag for a hunting day ran from three to six doves per man. Sometimes the hunting is very much concentrated, as for example in an area in Tennessee where 100 hunters took 800 doves from one 75-acre millet field on the opening day (*P-R Quarterly*, April 1951).

The degree of skill required for dove shooting is indicated by the average of four shells shot for each dove retrieved in most areas checked in several states.

The total season bag in Oklahoma for the years 1948 through 1952 was 20, 18, 23, 21, and 17 doves per dove hunter (*P-R Quarterly*, January 1951, January 1953); these figures are exceptionally high. The average daily bag per hunter in North Carolina was 3.2 in 1948–49 and 5.3 in 1949–50 (*P-R Quarterly*, April 1950); these figures are more representative of general conditions.

More hunting is done in late afternoon, when the birds come in to feeding and watering areas, than at other times. In the Southeast much of the hunting is in grainfields; in the West it is around both feeding and watering places. In Georgia during the 1951 fall season 12% of the dove hunters checked had obtained their legal limit of eight birds for the day (*P-R Quarterly*, April 1952).

Since the dove is migratory and very mobile, it is very difficult to determine the population in a given area at any specific time; thus it is hard to find what proportion of the dove population is killed by hunters. In North Carolina, it was estimated that 35% of the fall population present on 14 hunts in 1949 was bagged (*P-R Quarterly*, April 1950). In 1951, 24% of the population on 27 fields was killed (*P-R Quarterly*, April 1952). These figures are probably from heavily shot areas, and presumably include the cripples, which were 28% of the net bag the first year and 16% the last. In Alabama the hunting loss is estimated as 21% of the population, of which about one-quarter is the crippling loss. Since part of the dove population of the Southern states receives some of its hunting pressure north of the wintering area, the Alabama estimate may be lower than the actual reduction in the whole population that hunting makes. It is likely that the harvest ranges from 10% to 35% of the fall dove population, and may average about 25%. Cripples account for an additional part of the toll from hunting; the crippling loss is variable, but is generally high; Jenkins (letter) believes it is higher than records show. It averages at least 30% of the bag, or about 8% of the population, but may in some areas run as high as half the retrieved birds. Thus the total reduction of doves from man's hunting may be from 15% to 35% of the fall population in various localities of the eastern part of the country.

AS A FARMER OR TOWN DWELLER

WITH most of our upland game birds we speak of man and his use of the land as affecting them in his role of farmer or lumberman. The mourning dove is also affected by the actions of suburban and town dwellers; it is little affected by lumbering except on farms.

The clearing of the forests for farming extended the area of dove habitat, and continued farming maintains it. The production of grain and grass crops provides staple foods for doves. Such harvest methods as mechanical picking and shocking have much to do with the quantity of grain available to the birds. Open-grown trees on the farm in hedge rows, orchards, windbreaks, landscaping, or in fields, provide nesting sites, and their number and distribution set limits on the population of breeding doves that may live there. All these trees exist because of the attitudes of the farmer, the type of farming, and the farming methods used. In towns the kind and amount of tree landscaping on home lots exerts the same kind of influence, but generally to a less degree. Thus during the breeding season the dove is a farm and town bird; at other times it is predominantly a farm-game bird, and is influenced to a great extent by farming methods.

PRODUCTIVITY AND POPULATIONS

PRODUCTIVITY

THE productivity pattern of the mourning dove is very different from that of the gallinaceous birds. Its potential productivity is high, despite the fact that its clutch size is one of the smallest of all game species. This shortcoming is surmounted by its excellent care for the young until they can care for themselves, and by its having several clutches each year.

The dove is presumed to be monogamous on an annual basis, but there is little reliable evidence on this point; more observations of marked birds are needed before we can determine their mating habits. All doves breed early in the spring after their year of birth. Up to five broods a year are raised—occasionally more, depending on where they nest and how many nests are lost. Birds in the northernmost breeding areas generally have but two nestings if both are successful, or three if one or more are lost; the birds breeding in the zone of southern New England, Pennsylvania, and Iowa generally have at least three nestings; and those in the South have four or more. On a California study area the pairs averaged 5.1 nestings a year (Cowan 1952). In some years the number of nestings is lower than indicated above, possibly because of adverse conditions that we cannot easily recognize.

The sex ratio is very difficult to ascertain, because of the problem of differentiating the sexes; with juveniles an autopsy of the sex organs is the only dependable way. The plumage may be used to check the sex of adults-in-hand with fair accuracy. There is some evidence that among adult birds a preponderance of males may be normal. Quay (1951) checked the sex of 812 adults trapped in North Carolina at all times of the year over a three-year period, and found 58% of them males. Another 605 adult doves examined, most of them shot from September to January in three years, were 56% males; but of 386 juveniles taken in the same period only 53% were males. Studies in Alabama revealed that only 52% of all doves checked were males (Pearson and Moore, 1941). Thus it seems probable that the sex ratio of young birds is about even, but that males may at times predominate among adults.

The fall age ratio reflects the degree of the year's productivity, as it does with other game birds, but there are some complications. Some of the juveniles from the first spring broods may by late September or October be classed as adults; this fact tends to reduce the evident age ratio, and to belittle the year's production. The early migration of juveniles from the northern breeding areas, which leaves the adults with only a part of their offspring in early fall and adds to the juveniles in the South, further complicates the problem. Some of the adults are still breeding in September; an age ratio taken at that time, with some offspring still to fly and others in migration, is difficult to appraise.

There has been much work done checking breeding results in the southeastern states, but little in the northern or western parts of the range. To give the best measure of productivity, the age ratio as of late September is best; this covers almost all the young raised, and includes few young that would appear as adults. Thompson (1951) summarized hunting-bag counts made in five southeastern states during September and October of 1949 and 1950; in 1950 the percentage of juveniles ranged from 57 in Tennessee to 89 in Florida. Expressed in other terms, these age ratios were 1.3:1 and 8.1:1, the former reflecting rather poor production and the latter indicating exceptionally high production. In five of the ten instances the age ratio was 2.0:1 or higher, which is indicative of a good year's production.

Among the September birds in four of these states, from 2% to 15% of the adults were in breeding condition, as evidenced by the glandular crop. In contrast, Hopkins and Odum (1953) studied the doves on a 700-acre tract in Georgia and found the number of young per pair only slightly above two. This low production rate was not due to exceptionally high mortality, but rather to low natality, fewer than three nests per pair, a surprising situation. They are continuing this study to find the cause (Odum, letter).

MORTALITY

NEST destruction is generally about the same as with ground-nesting species; it is higher on early season nests than on later ones. McClure (1950) reported on the fate of 4,598 nests observed in 12 years in Iowa, Nebraska, and California; in Iowa and Nebraska the losses were 52%, and in California 45%; in all, 49% of the eggs produced young that flew from the nests. Pearson and Moore (1939) checked 529 Alabama nests, of which 48% were destroyed. Quay (1951) found 45.5% of 771 North Carolina nests were destroyed. Lawson (1950) observed 150 nests in Arizona in three years, among which the loss was 41%, 45%, and 35% in successive years. Progress reports of Pittman-Robertson projects in recent years have reported on this problem from several states. Some of the rates of nest loss were: 46% in 1948 in Mississippi and 38% in 1949; 45% in Tennessee in 1949; 33% in Arkansas in 1949; 35% in Louisiana in 1950; 44% in Kentucky in 1951, and 50% in 1952 (*P-R Quarterly* reports). In general, the nesting loss approximates half of the nesting attempts.

Predation and bad weather are the two main causes of nest destruction; in most years predation is the major source of loss, but in seasons of many bad windstorms weather may take first place. Human molestation is another common reason for nest loss. Some nests are deserted without an evident reason.

Mourning doves have a short period of about

two weeks when the young are squabs in the nest, and specially vulnerable to predation and accident; during this time there may be losses of one or both nestlings. Occasionally a nest will contain an infertile egg, and only one squab will hatch from the pair of eggs; of 347 North Carolina nests that fledged nestlings, 94% had two squabs and 6% had a single squab (Quay, 1951). McClure (1950) reported an 18% loss of nestlings in Iowa, Nebraska, and California. Most other studies have revealed a rather consistent survival of nestlings of about 90%; thus some 1.6 to 1.8 fledgelings on an average will leave the nests. This low mortality of the young birds cannot properly be compared to the juvenile losses of most other game birds; there are further losses of fledgelings after leaving the nest that have not been carefully appraised, because of the difficulties of studying the birds after they leave the nest. They are on their own and very mobile, quite unlike the gallinaceous species, which remain in broods for two to three months or more. Thus we can say only that a loss of some 10% more or less of immature doves takes place in the first two weeks; after that we must count the rest of the juvenile loss in the general balance of all dove losses.

The production of young varies with the locality and the number of nesting attempts; four nesting tries is about a general average, though there may be fewer in the North and more in the deep South. Of the potential eight fledgelings from four nests, almost half are likely to be lost before hatching. Of the four nestlings that may hatch, one or two in some nests may die, which on an average would be about half of one of the three birds; thus 3½ fledgelings per pair of adults per season would result. This would give about a 2:1 fall age ratio, since some adult loss would also occur during the breeding season.

The mortality of adult and juvenile doves is heavy. Owing to the difficulty of censusing this species because of its migratory and mobile nature, it is impossible to draw an accurate pic-ture of when and how the losses occur. Some losses from predation, accidents, and weather take place throughout the spring and summer breeding season. Toward the end of summer there may be high losses locally in some years from the canker disease. The fall season brings the period of most rapid loss—from hunting; this factor is the one most accurately appraised among all the mortality causes; it may take 30% to 35% of the fall dove population.

During the fall hunting season and after it in late fall and winter there is a continuous attrition of doves from predation and accident. At times there may be winter losses from very bad weather, and occasionally from starvation.

Adding it all up, the year's mortality of adult and juvenile doves is 50% to 70% in most years. Austin (1951) figured that the general mortality of adults and juveniles raised on Cape Cod, Massachusetts, was about 69% a year. A news report in the Birmingham (Alabama) *Post-Herald* in 1952 on the dove study in that state quoted James Keeler to the effect that "more than 60 percent" of doves are lost in a year; this is probably about the normal situation. When the mortality is as low as 50%, the next year's breeding population is higher than the year before; when the losses reach 70% or more a decline occurs.

LIFE EQUATION

THE annual round of population changes of the mourning dove follows a very different pattern than with most other game birds. Though much remains to be learned about dove mortality factors, the general picture can be traced. The increases of numbers in the production season take place in increments rather than in a single brood. The early mortality of young doves is low. Hunting often plays a larger part in the reduction of numbers than with many game birds.

An illustration of the changes in a theoretical population of 100 breeding doves in a year is shown in Table 25.

The particular year illustrated resulted in no

TABLE 25

LIFE EQUATION OF 100 MOURNING DOVES FOR A YEAR

TIME	ACTIVITIES	NUMBER OF BIRDS		
		squabs	juvenile	adult
SPRING	(1) 48 females mate with 52 males			100
	(2) All hens nest, lay 2 eggs each, or 96 eggs			
	(3) 50% of nests hatch, in which 2 eggs are infertile, 46 become squabs	46		
	(4) 10 adults die from predation, etc.			90
SUMMER	(5) 43 hens nest again and continue throughout summer, averaging 3 more nesting attempts, from which an average of 41 squabs hatch	123		
	5 of first hatch die in nest and 41 squabs become juveniles		41	
	(6) 21 of 123 squabs die in nest, 36 of 41 juveniles become adult, and 9 adults die from predation, disease		102	117
FALL	(7) 90 of juveniles become adult			207
	(8) 73 (35%) are taken or crippled by hunters			134
FALL AND WINTER	(9) 34 die from predation, accidents, weather, etc. (25%)			100
SPRING	(10) Breeding season returns with same number of breeders as before			

net change in the breeding population. In years when the production is higher than shown and the mortality less, there will be an increase in doves the next year; contrarily, if the production is lower and/or the mortality higher, the result may be a smaller number of breeders the following spring.

POPULATION DENSITIES

THE concept of population density is not as applicable to migratory birds as it is to sedentary species. During fall and winter the birds spend much time in migration, live in flocks, and move freely from area to area. It has its greatest significance during the breeding season; the distribution of breeding birds is itself likely to be very uneven, because of the way suitable tree-nesting sites are located. Quay (1951) censused the nests on four areas in North Carolina that totaled 9,746 acres; there was a dove nest per 33 acres on these areas in each

of two years, 1940 and 1941; the highest nest density was one per 18 acres on some 3,000 acres, and the lowest was 59 acres per nest on approximately the same amount of land. The nesting density on 1,000 acres in Georgia in 1950 and 1951 was one nest per 30 acres (Hopkins and Odum 1953). Boldt and Hendrickson (1952) counted four pairs of nesting doves per mile of windbreaks in North Dakota, or about a pair to three acres of this nesting cover, not counting the rest of their habitat. The production of young was 15 per mile of windbreak or one per acre of nesting cover.

McClure (1943) reported on the nesting density in selected Iowa farmyards. In one yard of 1.5 acres there were 47 nests per acre in 1938 and 19 per acre in 1940, the extremes for three farmyards studied in a single locality. The average for 5,950 acres of farmyards was 9.5 nests per acre in 1938, only 6.7 in 1940. On 20,480 acres in nine towns, there were

4.3 nests per acre in 1938, 6.8 in 1940. These select nesting areas are a contrast to farm fields, where on 342,000 acres the nesting density was one nest to every 8 to 10 acres. "Towns with 6 percent of the area [of the county] produced about 65 percent of the birds. Farm lots with 1.6 percent of the total area produced 20 percent of the birds. The remaining 92.4 percent of the area produced only 15 percent of the bird population."

Nesting sites used by doves in the eastern states indicate they are less selective than in the midwestern and western states; this is no doubt because suitable trees for nesting sites are more widely available on many kinds of land. Even in the East most of the doves are produced on a small share of the total land.

FLUCTUATIONS IN POPULATION

THERE is little dependable information on the changes in dove population levels through the years; there is no doubt that great changes take place, but only in the last few years have there been facilities to gauge these trends. The censuses made have not continued long enough in any area to do more than indicate the degree of population changes for a very few years. The census data are usually given in terms of doves counted per 100 miles of standardized road-driving, or in 20 miles of call counting; these may be compared by months, or a yearly average may be derived. McClure (1950) gives April road counts for Nebraska of .05, 4.8, 21.5, and 6.6 for the years 1941 through 1944; this indicates a rapid upward trend in the second and third years of the period and a sharp drop in the fourth. His seven-month average (April through October) for the years 1941–43 was 18.0, 46.0, and 58.6, which generally followed the April trend for the same years. His work later shifted to California, and he gives annual average counts for 1946, '47, and '48 in that state as 38.6, 20.4, and 21.1, which showed a considerable decline there in that time. Quay (1951) gives similar data for several North Carolina counties for the years

1939 through 1942, though the counts were not complete for all areas in all years. September counts for the first three years in Rowan and Buncombe Counties were: 88, 43, 24; and 13, 10, 123 respectively. The obviously different trends indicate the need for adequate quantitative data, statistically accurate, and obtained consistently in procedure and continuity, all of which the author points out. (See comments on census techniques under next heading, "Management.")

There is no evidence of regularity in the population trends of the mourning dove; ordinary production and mortality factors combine to bring about the changes. When these operate in one direction for several years a long trend results; when they change every year or two the population shifts up and down without any "curve" effect.

THE MANAGEMENT OF THE MOURNING DOVE

THE management of the mourning dove is primarily the control of the hunting harvest. The opportunity for objective land management for doves is limited mainly to the provision of fall food supplies, designed to "bait" in the birds for shooting purposes. Improvements for nesting cover can be made in towns and farmyards and on farms, and water can be provided in arid areas.

LAND USE AND DEVELOPMENT

SINCE the dove is adaptable to a variety of habitat conditions, and since there is no local control over dove populations because of its mobile habits and migration, there is little incentive to adapt land conditions and practices to its needs; this is especially true in the northern breeding range, where there is no dove hunting.

The dove is an attractive bird to have around one's home; this aesthetic consideration alone may justify some measures in its behalf. Some

PLATE 96. *Shelterbelts and windbreaks provide nesting cover for mourning doves in the prairie states. A set of evergreen farmstead windbreaks is shown above.*

practices suitable for improving dove habitat fit well into the landscaping of the home grounds, and thus need not be an extra effort or a cost chargeable to game management. The planting of certain kinds of shade trees, and the provision of bird baths for drinking water, are examples. Some of the trees suitable for nest sites are the American elm, Chinese elm, red pine, loblolly pine, shortleaf pine, longleaf pine, and Norway spruce. Most kinds of shade trees are acceptable to the doves if none of these species are adapted or wanted.

Home orchards are attractive nesting cover; apple and citrus trees seem to have special appeal to doves. Though one would not ordinarily plant fruit trees just to favor doves, this may be an added reason for having an orchard.

Windbreak plantings around homesteads and shelterbelts across prairie farm lands may be set out for erosion control, wind damage reduction, and to improve the habitat for doves and other kinds of farm wildlife.

In the southern states hunting may be concentrated at convenient locations by the provision of food that attracts doves; corn, soybeans, peanuts, cowpeas and sorghum are some of the crops suitable for this purpose. Moore and Pearson (1941) suggest making such plantings somewhere in large open fields to give the birds open access, and they recommend seeding lightly so that the vegetation does not grow too dense. The plots can be planted and left unharvested, or they can be "hogged off" by livestock. Leaving some of a grainfield in shocks through the hunting season is another suitable technique for making fall food areas.

PLATE 97. *A field shelterbelt planted with conifers and hardwoods, viewed from one end.*

Doves must have water every day; in arid country the lack of water may be the one factor preventing the presence of doves. It can be provided by the construction of open earthen tanks (ponds), wells, "gallinaceous guzzlers" (see chapter on California quail), or other means. The land is then improved for domestic livestock and for game, including mourning doves.

MISCELLANEOUS MANAGEMENT PRACTICES

THE reduction of English sparrow populations in small towns and around farmyards is suggested by McClure (1943) as beneficial for doves. Since this recommendation is also desirable in order to encourage other kinds of native songbirds displaced by the sparrow, it should be done wherever they are abundant. More than common control of house-cat numbers is also warranted as a means of protecting doves and other birds.

Refuges, restocking, and artificial feeding (except for baiting) have no place in mourning-dove management.

CONTROL OF THE HARVEST

HUNTING by man is an important mortality agent of the mourning dove; adequate control of the shooting harvest is an essential part of the job of managing this species. Since it is migratory, the responsibility for setting the maximum open seasons and bag limits rests with the U. S. Fish and Wildlife Service. Within the limits set by the Federal statutes, any state may prescribe stricter rules, but may not liberalize them.

Dove hunting is impractical in the northern part of the bird's breeding range, because the migration from there takes place too early. By modern custom in the North, no hunting begins before October; by then the doves have gone. The northernmost states that permit dove hunting are Pennsylvania in the East, Illinois in the Central area, and Idaho and Washington in the Far West. In most of these states the harvest is very small; real dove shooting begins below the Mason-Dixon line.

No dove shooting should be allowed anywhere before September 15; in early September in the southern and midwestern states a part of the adult population is still breeding, though only a small portion of the season's production is fledged then; it would be wrong to permit hunting while many squabs are still present. The schedule of open seasons may properly begin in mid-September and early October in the northern and "upper South" (piedmont and mountain zones) hunting areas, and at later dates in the coastal plain South; in the Gulf states the season should not open until late in November or early in December.

A fairly liberal bag limit may be allowed when hunting is justified at all; a daily limit of eight or ten should be permitted. Ten doves gross only about 2½ pounds—less than a single cock pheasant.

The determination of whether an open hunting season is warranted and how long it should be depends on the population level; this can be worked out by annual censuses. Since the shooting over much of the open hunting area involves birds from many states, no single state censusing is adequate, even for its own needs; a standard system of censusing throughout the important breeding range is needed, carried on by all the state wildlife agencies concerned. The correlation of the information gathered is logically the job of the Federal Fish and Wildlife Service. Such a system has been developing in recent years, but it is not yet complete or adequate; there is little participation by Northern states, largely because they have no direct concern in the hunting. Probably the Fish and Wildlife Service will have to do this part of the job, and they have already done a little of it (Foote *et al*, 1952). Not all the southern states have participated either, but most have made a start. Part of the reason for delay is that the census techniques have not

even now been standardized satisfactorily; this phase of the technology should be finished after a few more years of experience with the present procedures.

In order to be useful in management, a census has to be completed in time to use the information in setting fall hunting seasons; with a migratory bird that requires Federal proclamation for the entire country, this census must be completed by midsummer at the latest; for the mourning dove the best census time is from late April to early July, depending on the latitude. In most areas May and June are the peak production months.

The census is based on roadside counts, made either by the recording of doves heard cooing or of doves sighted. Most of the men who have worked on dove censuses feel that the call-count is the better way, but they concede that there is great variation in the audio-accuracy of observers as well as in the visual; thus it is important for personnel of equal training and ability to carry on this work. Two-man teams are more effective than single individuals.

In any area the intensity of dove cooing reaches a high peak early in the season, then levels off on a "plateau" of moderate rate for a month or more, and finally declines. This plateau period is the best time for census work, since the data will be of greater uniformity at that time. This period must be known in each area where the work is to be done.

Routes along roads that cover a good cross-section of dove habitat are laid out for census work; each may be 20 miles long. The more routes used, and the more times they are covered, the more accurate will be the data. According to Duvall and Robbins (in Foote, *et al*, 1952), with three routes in an area at least 12 trips per route are needed in order to detect significant population changes from year to year.

The technique found most suitable in the work done so far is about as follows: a 20-mile route is followed by a single observer in a car; be begins 30 minutes before official sunrise, *or* two hours before official sunset—whichever daily period is used must be used consistently for the whole area. He stops each mile, and waits three minutes away from the car and with the motor off; at each waiting station (and between stations) all doves heard calling or seen are counted and recorded.

The data so gathered are only an index of population status; they do not reveal the dove population at the time. They are useful only in comparison with similar data for previous years; thus they reveal trends in the level of population. They become really valuable after several years' data have been gathered. Their accuracy depends on the uniformity of censusing technique, on the consistency of observation of the technicians, and on the care with which the routes are selected. Such factors as the number of farmyards on the route, the extent of electric wires, the amount of gravel road, the traffic conditions, and the cover types along the route, must be taken into account. Censuses should not be made during stormy weather (wind not over Beaufort-3, and no rain) (Odum, letter).

The census data from representative areas in all important parts of the breeding range must be gathered together promptly in a single place and analyzed; from all this information the population level of the year may be gauged, and the hunting regulations set accordingly.

CHAPTER 15

The White-winged Dove

CLASSIFICATION AND DESCRIPTION

THE white-winged dove is closely related to the more widespread mourning dove. There are two subspecies in the United States, the eastern white-winged dove, *Zenaida asiatica asiatica,* being the type form; the western white-winged dove is *Z. a. mearnsi.* Two additional subspecies are found in Central and South America. Along with the mourning dove, the whitewing belongs to the subfamily Zenaidinae of the family Columbidae, the ground doves, in contrast with the arboreal pigeons and doves like the band-tailed pigeon and the extinct passenger pigeon.

The whitewing is generally similar to the mourning dove in form. It weighs from 4½ to 7 ounces, averaging about 6 (Saunders, letter); this is somewhat more than the mourning dove. It is from 11¼ to 12¼ inches long, slightly less than the mourning dove; this results from its rounded instead of graduated tail feathers. The spread is 19 to 20 inches, the wings being longer than the tail, whereas in the mourning dove they are equal.

The coloration of the sexes is almost identical, the female being slightly duller. The back, inner portions of the wings, and middle tail feathers are olive brown, with some lustre; the rump, middle wing coverts, wing lining and under parts are slate gray; the outer tail feathers vary from dark blue to black, and are tipped with white; the primaries are blackish, edged with white, and there is a prominent white patch on the middle coverts of the wing. In the male the crown and back of the neck are purplish, and the sides of the neck iridescent green-gold; these parts on the female are grayish brown, and only slightly iridescent. There is a blue-black spot below the ear and a large bluish bare space around the eye. The bill is slender, black, and long, equaling four-fifths of the tarsus in length. The iris is coral red.

The western whitewing is somewhat larger than the eastern, and averages paler and grayer in its coloration (Bent, 1932).

The juveniles are similar to adults, but have scantier and grayer plumage. The greater primary coverts are light tipped, a useful means of field distinction of young from adults in the fall. The white wing and tail bars are prominent on the nestlings at two weeks of age.

GEOGRAPHICAL RANGE AND DISTRIBUTION

WHITEWINGS occur in our four Southwestern states and southward into Mexico, Central and South America, and the West Indies. The northern part of the breeding range in the United States extends from southeastern California, over 50,000 square miles of southern Arizona, across the southern edge of New Mexico into the Rio Grande valley, and south-eastward in Texas to the Gulf coast. They breed in Arizona at altitudes of 150 feet near Yuma, and as high as 5,000 feet or more in the canyons and foothills of the higher mountains (Arnold, 1943). The highest populations in this country occur in the lower Rio Grande valley of Texas, and in sections of south-central and southwestern Arizona along certain river bottoms; elsewhere they are sparsely distributed or rare.

The wintering range of our subspecies is from central Mexico south through much of Central America.

The eastern subspecies occupies the range in the Texas Rio Grande valley, eastern Mexico, Central America, and the West Indies, while the western form is found in California, Arizona, and New Mexico, southward into Lower California, and in Central America.

The range is essentially the same today as it was when the Southwest was first settled by white men.

HABITS

WHITEWINGS return to their breeding ground in south Texas each spring in early April; the Arizona birds arrive in middle to late April. The height of the nesting period is in May and June, when most of the birds have their first nest.

Courtship is somewhat similar to that of the mourning dove but more showy; Wetmore (1920) describes it thus: "In displaying before females males had a curious habit or pose in which they raised the tail high and tilted the body forward. At the same time the tail was spread widely and then closed with a quick flash . . . males at intervals flow out with quick full strokes of the spread wings, rising until they were 30 or 40 feet in the air. The wings were then set stiffly with the tips decurved, while the birds scaled around . . . in a great circle that often brought them to their original perches." The song of the whitewing is an owl-like coo or hoot, and is given only by the males. They call persistently, and the effect of many birds' hooting is both eerie and monotonous.

The nest is loosely built of twigs and small sticks in a tree, usually 10 to 12 feet above the ground. The normal clutch is two eggs, which require 14 days of incubation (Saunders, 1940)

possibly somewhat longer at high elevations (Neff, 1940b). The eggs are dull buffy-white, and average 22 × 31 mm. Both sexes share the incubation duties, the male usually spending the middaytime period on the nest and the female the longer night shift.

Nesting is commonly in colonies, especially where suitable nesting cover is limited. These colonies may be from a few nests per acre up to a dozen, or, rarely, 100 or more; the latter indicates abnormal crowding.

When a nest is destroyed or the eggs taken the bird may renest. In favorable seasons it is normal that two broods be raised, but in many years unfavorable factors such as drouth, human disturbance, or food shortages so upset the birds that only a single nesting period is used. Second nesting periods, when they do occur, are at their height in July, and may extend to mid-August.

The squabs remain in the nest about two weeks before flying away; they may leave a little earlier if disturbed, but if life is easy they may remain a few days longer. They are fed by regurgitation by both parents. After leaving the nest, they usually stay in the immediate vicinity for another week or more. For a time some parental care is given the fledgelings away from the nest, including some feeding.

The adults leave the nesting area singly, morning and evening, to feed and drink; the evening trip may require a rather long flight, since then they seek water as well as food.

The southward migration begins in mid-August in Arizona, and in September in Texas; about the time hunting starts, the Arizona doves tend to move out rapidly. This may have no connection with the hunting itself (W. Swank, letter); nevertheless the hunting opportunity there is short-lived; about 75% of the birds have left by September 1, and by mid-September few birds are left. Texas doves remain until weather changes stimulate migration; all but a few stragglers leave Texas before the end of October.

PLATE 98. *Nest and eggs of white-winged dove.*

COURTESY J. A. NEFF

FOOD AND SHELTER NEEDS

THE breeding season habitat requirements are of three kinds, namely: (1) nesting cover; (2) feeding areas; (3) water. Nesting cover is woodland, or brushland that includes trees of fair size; it is frequently dense, though this is not essential. In Arizona it is typically mesquite "forest," tamarisk, or other bottom-land thickets, or water-course scrub in canyons or mountain foothills (Arnold, 1943). Preferred nesting sites are in mesquite, screw bean, quail brush, lotebush, paloverde, desert ironwood, catclaw, tamarisk, cottonwood, willow, oak, citrus, giant cactus, cholla cactus, and other plants of similar stature (Neff, 1940b). Some doves nest in orchards, in town shade trees, and in ranch groves.

Typical Texas nesting cover is the south Texas delta woodland. Important plants in this type may include Texas ebony, mesquite, western hackberry, live oak, catclaw, and huisache. Large hackberry trees, especially the thorny western hackberry, make especially good nesting sites, and afford better than ordinary protection against predation; the same plants in towns or in ranch groves may also be used as nesting sites. Citrus groves recently became very important nesting cover in the southern Rio Grande valley. Nesting cover in the counties north of the optimum delta area are the mesquite-grassland and live oak-grassland types, chiefly on ranch land.

Feeding areas should be within a few miles of the nesting cover, in order that daily foraging be convenient. While some feeding is done in the nesting cover, it is frequently in a different vegetation type. In Arizona, the early summer feeding cover is the saguaro-paloverde plant association; the fruits of the giant cactus or saguaro are the main food. They also eat the fruits of the lotebush or wild jujube as long as it is available, in late spring and early summer. Other summer foods include fruits of western hackberry, seeds of catclaw, chicalote, and California croton. Later in the summer the doves resort to grainfield feeding where kernels of oats, sorghum, barley, or wheat are available. Sunflower seeds are taken freely; and they sometimes frequent fields of cantaloupe to get the seeds of the decaying fruits (Neff, 1940a). The late-fruiting organ-pipe cactus provide desert food after the saguaro has finished fruiting (Arnold, 1943).

Summer foods used by doves in Texas are the fruits and seeds of a large variety of trees, shrubs, and herbaceous plants, plus waste grain and other agricultural crops. In the early part of the season wild sunflower seeds and wild fruits are their mainstay, but toward the end of summer they resort more to grain kernels and wild seeds like those of croton.

Free water is an absolute requirement in the breeding range habitat; it may come from streams, springs, impoundments, tanks, wells, or irrigation canals, as long as it is exposed and accessible. Despite this rigid requirement, the doves do not necessarily nest very close to water; in Arizona they seem to prefer to fly some distance to drink, and can use any suitable cover for nesting within ten miles of water. Thus, according to Arnold (1943), " . . . one water-hole will make available at least 314 square miles of potential breeding areas." The birds do not mind sharing the water even at small water sources, as is evidenced by the fact that hundreds and even thousands of them will use a single such watering place daily. The flights between feeding or watering areas and roosting cover furnish the opportunity for most dove hunting; in Texas much of the hunting is at feeding areas, as well as on flight routes to or from feeding grounds.

The whitewing has shown some aptitude for using man's artificial land cover, especially in Texas. Feeding in grainfields has long been the common practice of these doves, but only in recent years have they begun to use citrus orchards for nesting sites; they have nested longer in ranch groves and town trees. Since much of their natural nesting cover has been and is being destroyed in connection with agricultural development, this adaptability to change their nesting and feeding habits may well be essential to their survival in good numbers. So far, this dove has not shown the degree of adaptiveness of the mourning dove, but it has at least made a good start; the prospects seem fair that the whitewing will make the conversion successfully.

THE EFFECTS OF WEATHER

DROUTH is the great weather threat to whitewings, especially in Arizona; even in their desert habitat the requirements of food and water depend on the summer rains. When these rains fail to come, water sources dry up and food plants produce little or no fruit. Winter rains are also important in developing saguaro fruits, a good nesting season food. Drouth in the desert, beyond its normal dryness, is as critical as in humid areas.

Extremes of winter drouth seem to be closely related to whitewing population declines. Neff (1940a) described conditions in Arizona in 1939, a drouth year. The doves returned in the spring in normal numbers, but "Food and water conditions grew rapidly worse after mid-May. Many desert water holes and tanks were dry by June 1 and others were rapidly drying up. Numerous wild foods were in very poor condition. Giant cactus blossomed normally but . . . the fruit soon ceased to develop. . . . " In some Arizona areas the summer whitewing populations were only 5% to 10% of the populations a year before; some of the nestlings from early nests were fledged, but none later. The birds scattered widely in search of food and water. By 1940 the dove population had declined to a low ebb, but recovered in subsequent years of normal weather. These effects of drouth are frequently accentuated by the overgrazing of the vegetation by domestic livestock.

Texas whitewing populations also declined in the late 1930's, and for several years it was feared that the species was doomed; yet it recovered by the late 1940's to such an extent that the Texas and northeastern Mexico population once again exceeded a million birds by the end of the decade. Then a great decline occurred, which reduced the September 1951 population to less than 20% of what it had been the year before; this was probably caused by drouth combined with a winter freeze (*P-R Quarterly*, January 1952), which reduced the citrus nesting cover. There was a slight recovery in 1952, but the prospects in 1953, as this is written, are poor indeed. In early May the Rio Grande was at an all-time low level, due to the protracted drouth.

Winter freezes do not ordinarily affect the doves directly, since they winter in the tropics; but the indirect effects of cold winters on the birds are sometimes serious through damage to breeding-grounds cover. This is increasingly true in south Texas, when the birds' native brush is removed and they resort to nesting in citrus groves. A freeze in the 1950–51 winter killed some 7 million citrus trees, so that "When the whitewings, which had been so plentiful the previous fall, began returning to the Valley in April of 1951, there was no adequate place to nest" (Arnold, 1952).

PREDATION; DISEASES AND PARASITES; ACCIDENTS

THE most important loss by predation on whitewings is the destruction of eggs and squabs in the nests. From studies made it appears that nest predation is heavier in the Texas breeding area than in Arizona; P-R project progress reports for work in Texas from 1943 to 1949 indicate that an average of 30% to 50% of eggs and 10% to 25% of squabs are eaten by natural enemies. The great-tailed grackle is the worst offender; in some nesting grounds this bird lives in the same tree cover with the whitewings, and causes most of the predation. Other predators of eggs and young include the green jay, and occasionally the indigo and bull snakes (*P-R Quarterly*, April 1943). Young doves are occasionally taken by Cooper's and sharp-shinned hawks, domestic cats, bobcats, possibly rats of various kinds, and other small mammals; the mammals catch mostly squabs fallen to the ground. In Arizona even such birds as the Gila woodpecker, cactus wren (Arnold, 1943), and mockingbird are suspected of occasional molestation that results in egg losses.

The total effect of predation on whitewings is generally moderate, and not severe enough seriously to limit populations; but egg losses in some localities may be so excessive in some years as severely to curtail production.

Little is known about the place of disease organisms and parasites in whitewing ecology. Saunders (1940) has found infestation of hippoboscid flies common, and intestinal worms fairly common; he also noted a few cases of bird pox. But during the years the Fish and Wildlife Service and the state of Texas were making studies, no local epidemics of any contagious disease were found. Since no evidence of mortality from disease has appeared, it may be presumed to be of minor importance.

Accidents are a common cause of the loss of dove eggs and young, especially in areas of human activity. Whitewings are shy birds, and easily disturbed; people travelling close to their nests in pursuit of livestock, cutting wood, or on other missions often cause the birds to leave the nest with such a sudden burst of flight that some eggs and squabs are tumbled to the ground; domestic or wild animals occasionally have the same effect. Arnold (1943) concluded that "Human interference during nesting season is probably the greatest controllable factor causing direct and indirect loss of eggs and young among the western white-winged doves in Arizona." Much of the nesting territory there is isolated, however, and human interference insignificant (Swank, letter). Doves nesting in citrus orchards may sometimes suffer losses of eggs from the effects of irrigation by high-pressure rotating sprayers; the mowing and disking of ground cover in the orchards may also disturb them and result in accidents (*P-R Quarterly*, April 1951).

MAN'S RELATIONS WITH THE WHITE-WINGED DOVE

HUNTING whitewings is one of the most concentrated forms of upland-game sport. It is mostly limited to a few counties in the southern portions of Texas and Arizona; there is rela-

PLATE 99. *White-winged dove range in southeastern Arizona.*

tively little hunting of whitewings in Mexico. Modern hunting seasons in the United States are restricted to a few days, and in Texas hunting is further limited to a few hours in late afternoon.

Hunters spot flight-lines of doves where the flocks pass from feeding to watering or from watering to roosting places; there they gather awaiting the morning or afternoon passing of the whitewings. The birds hold to their flight course regardless of consequences, and the shooting is like a barrage while it lasts. Though they seem reckless in their straight flight over the hunters, many of those that survive do not repeat the performance many times, for the time of migration has arrived.

The hunting toll may be heavy, even with the very limited time allowed for the sport; Neff (1940a) gives Arizona warden estimates

of the kill in various areas in 1938, the first year of Federal regulation, ranging from 35% to 85% of the available population. But with 75% of the birds migrated before the present September 1 season opening, Swank (letter) believes that the hunting harvest is only 5% to 8% of the breeding population. Estimates of the annual harvest in Texas have been made since 1939 (Arnold, 1952; *P-R Quarterly* reports). When the population of doves is high, as in 1949 and 1950, a kill of around a quarter million represents only a 25% to 30% harvest. When the population declines, as in 1951, the kill may drop proportionally, as it did then, to 58,000. But if flight timing and weather favor the hunter, even a small population may suffer a heavy kill, as in 1952, when hunters killed about 59% of the total number of birds, with a harvest of 152,000.

Arnold (1952) says " . . . the waste in [Texas] whitewing shooting, involving the wounded and nonretrieved birds, exceeds that in any other sport." This unfortunate situation results from the nature and time of the shooting; hunters have but a few hours of legal shooting; they shoot fast as the flocks streak by overhead, and there is little inclination to search carefully for downed birds not easily retrieved. The crippling loss is at least 20% as high as the harvest, and probably much higher. In Arizona, where the season is longer, there is not the same tendency to ignore crippled birds.

The popularity of whitewing shooting is evidenced by the number of participants, and the fact that they come to Texas and Arizona for the event from far and wide. The dove's flesh is considered exceptionally tasty, " . . . especially a sliver of white meat along each side of the breast bone" (Arnold, 1952). It can fly up to 55 miles an hour, and makes a speedy target. Yet the open type of shooting makes possible a good bag; Lawson (1950) reports that 616 Arizona hunters in 1950 bagged an average of 1.1 whitewings on a hunt, plus more than four mourning doves. In 1951 and 1952 the average individual bag of doves was 5.0, of which 26.5% were whitewings and the rest mourning doves (Gallizioli, 1953). The average seasonal (three-day) bag in Texas varies from between one and two in poor years to six, seven or more per man in good years.

Land-use changes and practices associated with farming and ranching have had great influence on dove habits and numbers. Probably most significant has been the clearing of wood- and brushland for crop and range use, thus eliminating dove nesting cover; this has accelerated in the past two decades, so that well over a million acres of nesting habitat have been destroyed in south Texas alone. Offsetting this to some degree was the establishment of citrus groves on some of this land; but unfortunately the disastrous freeze of 1951 greatly reduced this newly-accepted nesting cover. Crop fields

of grains and fruits have become favorite late-summer feeding areas for the birds, possibly holding them in the United States longer than they would otherwise stay, thus making them more available for sport hunting. The building of water impoundments, irrigation canals, tanks, and wells on range land, especially in Arizona, has helped improve their summer habitat by making more of it usable.

Thus man's changes in the land cover have both damaged and improved dove habitat; so far, however, the net effect on the Texas habitat is predominantly on the loss side. The changes in the Arizona habitat have been less marked, and there are about as many whitewings there today as ever (Swank, letter). The general decline in Texas dove populations in the past 30 years is primarily associated with man's influence on the bird, particularly the changes he has wrought on the land.

The mortality of eggs and squabs that result from molestation by man and domestic livestock has already been noted.

PRODUCTIVITY AND POPULATIONS

PRODUCTIVITY

THE whitewing has a relatively low potential productivity compared to most other game birds. It is monogamous on an annual basis, as far as known. The sex ratio is approximately equal, as revealed by bag checks and the sexing of nestlings (Saunders, 1940). They breed the year after birth, and have either one or two broods in a season, averaging about 1½ broods or somewhat less. The clutch is two eggs in most cases, occasionally one or three.

Egg and squab mortality is variable. About 2% of the eggs are likely to be infertile, according to Texas studies (P-R Quarterly, Oct. 1947). Arizona observations on several hundred nests by Neff (1940b) in 1938 and 1939 revealed a loss of about 33% each year. Lee Arnold (1943) studied nest success on two Arizona areas in 1941 and 1942; the losses were 47% and 48% the first year and 25% and

40% the second. Lawson (1950) checked 371 nests in Arizona in 1948–50 with an average mortality of 31%, which varied little from year to year. Studies in south Texas from 1940 to 1952 (*P-R Quarterly* reports) report egg losses ranging from 26% to 96% in different years in various study areas, with the average loss between 50% and 60%. The 96% loss was in an overpopulated woodland haveing an abundance of grackles (Saunders, letter). The losses of squabs that never fledged was 8% to 23%, averaging about 15%. Thus the total nest loss in south Texas appears to be about 60%, more or less. From this it seems that losses are higher in the Texas range than in Arizona, evidently due to higher predation, attracted by larger dove populations.

The success of a season's production of young birds can be gauged in part by the age ratio of the population during the hunting season, that is, in late August or early September. Neff (1940a) reported a 2:1 juvenile-adult proportion among 700 Arizona birds in 1939. Lawson (1950) found the age ratio of Arizona doves in 1948 and 1949 to be 2.2:1; the same age ratio was found in 1948 hunter bags in south Texas, based on 12,000 birds checked (*P-R Quarterly*, Jan. 1949), and was only slightly less in 1949. But in 1950 the ratio in Texas dropped to 1.1:1 (*P-R Quarterly*, April 1951). In 1951 it declined to 0.6:1, a sure sign of a population decline, and in 1952 rose to 1.1:1 again (*P-R Quarterly*, Jan. 1952, Jan. 1953). Thus in five years in Texas, there were two seasons of good dove production, two of bare replacement and one very poor. This is probably about a typical balance, though it might not occur that way in any other particular five-year period.

Information on the mortality of the adult doves is very limited; the hunter toll in the United States is believed to be 30% or more of the birds available there, but is probably less that that for birds produced south of the border and those that migrate early from the United States. There are no doubt considerable losses from predation, and possibly some from accidents, disease, and weather, but their amount and significance can only be conjectured.

POPULATIONS

Since the whitewing is gregarious in both nesting and flocking habits, population densities may be very high for limited areas but not representative of the range in general; this results in part from the distribution of nesting cover, feeding places, and water sources. It is probably true that the degree of colonial nesting reflects the inadequacy of well-distributed nesting cover.

These are typical examples of nesting densities in Arizona: seven nests in a ten-acre thicket (Arnold, 1943); 500 pairs nesting in a 300-acre thicket (Neff, 1940b); and about 3 nests per acre in 32 acres of citrus trees (Gallizioli, 1953). In contrast, Texas nesting densities in some small areas of woodland are often phenomenal; concentrations exceeding 100 nests per acre in native woodland have been reported. Citrus groves in some instances have had 5 to 8 nests per acre (*P-R Quarterly*, Oct. 1948). When good habitat is adequately available the nesting density is much lower than these figures.

By midsummer the first juveniles start flocking; by the hunting season in August or September most of the adults have finished nesting and have joined the flocks. They travel in daily routine from roost to feeding fields to watering place and back to roost. In Arizona the concentrations are often greatest at the watering places, for water is likely to be available in but a few spots; in Texas the greatest concentrations are at feeding grounds and roosts. Sometimes these flocks number thousands of birds, and contain all the doves extant in a considerable area.

Populations of whitewings have declined greatly in some of the range they occupy in the United States. The late summer population in southern Texas is thought to have been from two to four million birds in the early 1920's, but in the past few decades it has ranged from about one million to 200,000, a drop of 75% or more. The Arizona population declined generally through the 1930's, but evidently dropped sharply from 1937 to 1938; Neff (1940a) reports that in some areas there was not more than 5% of the population in 1938 compared with the year before. Populations generally improved through the 1940's, and were high in 1949 and 1950, but declined again in 1951. These fluctuations seem to be related to habitat changes in the long trend, and to weather, predation, and hunting factors in the year-to-year adjustments.

THE MANAGEMENT OF THE WHITE-WINGED DOVE

LAND AND WATER DEVELOPMENT

HABITAT deficiencies are critical matters with the whitewing. To some extent these can be remedied by man, as he has been responsible for causing them; but very little land and water improvement can be economically justified exclusively for the benefit of the dove. Fortunately most that is feasible has other benefits than improved wildlife habitat; in fact, such land and water developments as will be done will improve agriculture, and the improvements to dove habitat will in some instances be a by-product.

When agricultural improvements are contemplated in dove range, the needs of the birds should be kept in mind. Land clearing should be planned with care, so that it is limited to land well suited to farming. Woodland or brush cover on land with low agricultural use capability should be left alone. Since, however, most of the remaining whitewing nesting grounds in the Rio Grande valley are on good agricultural land, eventually (and probably soon) the entire delta will be cleared; this will leave little nesting cover available, except in citrus groves and on parts of the two National Wildlife Refuges there. Wood cutting

should be avoided in dove-nesting areas during the late spring and summer.

Range land that is cleared but unsuited to farming and grazing can be revegetated by fencing it out of grazing; sometimes it may help to plant suitable trees and shrubs on such areas. The planting of clumps of trees around ranch houses and in towns in the bird's arid range can combine landscaping with the creation of nesting sites. To limit grazing herds to the number that the grass can carry without damage to the range is a sound practice, which helps preserve the woody cover in good condition. The development of grain farming in arid areas by means of irrigation provides late summer food for doves, provided the stubble is not plowed under in summer. Those who wish to plant for late summer feeding areas may use hegari or other adaptable sorghums to good advantage.

The development of free water in arid locations is probably the most useful single habitat improvement practice that can be made for doves. Where nesting and feeding cover areas are adequate but unusable because of the lack of water, the building of tanks or wells may be justified by the wildlife benefits alone; a number of the western state game agencies are doing this sort of work (see chapter on the California quail). A single water area will serve nesting doves for an area ten miles around, and in late summer may water hundreds or even thousands of birds. Where water areas are built so that the water is not easily available to the birds, the placing of ramps or floats will correct the trouble, and prevent the drowning of wildlife.

MISCELLANEOUS MANAGEMENT PRACTICES

THE establishment of public game lands and refuges may be desirable in some situations. Except in the Rio Grande valley, where land prices are prohibitive, select breeding areas threatened with elimination by agricultural development may be considered for acquisition by state wildlife agencies. Such areas may, in most instances, be used as public hunting grounds, since the reason for purchase is to protect the habitat rather than to protect the birds from hunting. Refuges may be needed around some watering places and roosts to prevent overshooting; these need not be publicly acquired, but merely set up by arrangement between the state wildlife agency and landowners, if they are on private land.

The control of predators to aid doves is rarely feasible; a possible exception is where grackles are so abundant as seriously to reduce dove production. The Texas state game men tried grackle control experimentally, and found that they could reduce the loss of doves somewhat; but despite their best efforts the grackles still destroyed 40% of the eggs and squabs. They concluded that the control effort was too expensive for the results obtained (*P-R Quarterly,* Jan. 1944). Unless better methods of grackle control are developed, it cannot be recommended for general application.

HUNTING CONTROL

THE setting of the hunting seasons for whitewings is a vital part of managing this species; it must be done with great care in order to assure a reasonable hunting opportunity, and yet not endanger the population with overshooting.

The season must necessarily be short; the birds migrate early, and thus terminate their stay in this country. Their vulnerability to hunting would require a short shooting period even if the birds remained available. Experience in Texas has shown that hunting, if limited to about three hours in the late afternoon on three days spaced alternately, is good management practice; but it has the disadvantage of encouraging the neglect of crippled birds by hunters who have but a couple of hours in which to shoot. In Arizona the season should come no earlier than the last ten days of August, whereas in Texas it should be deferred until mid-September. These dates come before the usual time of migration, and yet late enough to avoid the shooting of breeding birds.

The use of no-hunting refuges at points of concentration where the birds water or roost in order to avoid excessive shooting has already been mentioned. Another phase of management needed in connection with proper hunting regulations is an annual production census. The first of these surveys in Arizona, made in the late 1930's, was a co-operative project between the state and the United States Fish and Wildlife Service. The Texas surveys began in 1940, also on a co-operative basis. These counts are now made by the Arizona and Texas game men to keep track of the population trends, and aid the Fish and Wildlife Service in setting the regulations.

Chapter 1. THE RING-NECKED PHEASANT

BASKETT, THOMAS S., 1941. "Production of Pheasants in North-central Iowa in 1939," *Journ. Wildlife Mgt.,* Vol. 5, No. 2, Apr. 1941.

BENNITT, R., and H. V. TERRILL, 1940. "Possible Temperature Factors in North Central Pheasant Distribution," *Trans. 5th No. Am. Wildlife Conf.*

BUSS, IRVEN O. "Wisconsin Pheasant Populations," *Pub. 326, A-46, Wisc. Cons. Dep't.,* Madison, Wisc., 184 pp.

COWAN, I. McT., 1942. "Economic Status of the Pheasant on the Cultivated Lands of the Okanagan Valley, British Columbia," *Rep. Prov. Game Comm.,* 1942.

ERICKSON, A. B., D. B. VESALL, C. E. CARLSON, and C. T. ROLLINGS, 1951. "Minnesota's Most Important Game Bird, the Pheasant," *The Flicker,* Vol. 23, No. 3, Sept. 1951.

ERRINGTON, PAUL L., and F. N. HAMMERSTROM, 1937. "The Evaluation of Nesting Losses and Juvenile Mortality of the Ring-necked Pheasant," *Journ. Wildlife Mgt.,* Vol. 1, No. 1–2, July 1937.

FERRELL, C. M., H. TWINING, and N. B. HERKENHAM, 1949. "Food Habits of the Ring-necked Pheasant in the Sacramento Valley, California," *Cal. Fish and Game,* Vol. 35, No. 1, Jan. 1949.

FOOTE, L. E., 1942. "Vermont Pheasant Investigation," *State Bull.,* No. 8, Dec. 1, 1942.

FRIED, LOUIS A., 1940. "The Food Habits of the Ring-necked Pheasant in Minnesota," *Journ. Wildlife Mgt.,* Vol. 4, No. 1, Jan. 1940.

GOULD, ERNEST W., 1940. "A Study of the Pheasant in New Hampshire during the Spring and Early Summer," *N. H. Fish and Game Dep't.* (mimeo.).

GREEN, W. E., 1938. "The Food and Cover Relationship in the Winter Survival of the Ring-necked Pheasant, *Phasianus colchicus torquatus* Gmelin, in Northern Iowa," *Iowa State College Journ. Science,* Vol. XII, No. 3, Apr. 1938.

HIATT, R. W., 1947. "The Relation of Pheasants to Agriculture in the Yellowstone and Bighorn River Valleys of Montana," *Montana State Fish and Game Comm.,* 72 pp., 1947.

HJERSMAN, H. A., 1947. "A History of the Establishment of the Ring-necked Pheasant in California," *Cal. Fish and Game,* Vol. 33, No. 1, Jan. 1947.

KIMBALL, J. W., 1948. "Pheasant Population Characteristics and Trends in the Dakotas," *Trans. 13th No. Am. Wildlife Conf.,* 1948.

McATEE, W. L., ed. (17 authors), 1945. "The Ring-necked Pheasant," *Am. Wildlife Inst.,* Wash., D. C., 320 pp., 1945.

MOHLER, L. L., 1948. "Nebraska's Pheasant Inventory," *Wildlife Management Notes,* Vol. 1, No. 2, *Neb. Game, Forest and Parks Comm.,* Dec. 1948.

PERRY, R. F., 1946. "An Appraisal of Pheasant Abundance in New York State during 1945 and some of the Factors Responsible for the Recent Decline," *Trans. 11th No. Am. Wildlife Conf.,* 1946.

RANDALL, PIERCE E., 1939. "Nesting Habits and Causes of Nest Mortality of the Ringneck Pheasant," *Pa. Game News,* Vol. 10, No. 9, 1939.

——, 1940. "The Life Equation of the Ringneck Pheasant in Pennsylvania," *Trans. 5th No. Am. Wildlife Conf.,* 1940.

——, 1940a. "Causes of Juvenile Mortality of the Ringneck Pheasant," *Pa. Game News,* Vol. 11, No. 3, 1940.

SEVERIN, H. C., 1933. "An Economic Study of the Food of the Ring-necked Pheasant in South Dakota," *So. Dak. Dep't. Game and Fish,* 252 pp. mimeo., 1933.

SHICK, C., 1952. "A Study of Pheasants on the 9,000-acre Prairie Farm, Saginaw County, Michigan," *Mich. Dep't. of Cons.,* 134 pp., June 1952.

STOKES, A. W., 1952. "Pheasant Survival Studies on Pelee Island, Ontario, 1946–1950," *Trans. 17th No. Am. Wildlife Conf.,* 1952.

THORNTHWAITE, C. W., 1931. "The Climates of North America according to a New Classification," *Geogr. Rev. 21,* 1931.

TRAUTMAN, C. G., 1952. "Pheasant Food Habits in South Dakota," *Tech. Bull. No. 1, So. Dak. Dep't. Game, Fish and Parks,* Pierre, So. Dak., 89 pp., 1952.

WRIGHT, T., JR., 1941. "A Study of the Fall Food Supply of the Ring-necked Pheasant and the Bobwhite Quail in Washington County, Rhode Island," *Journ. Wildlife Mgt.,* Vol. 5, No. 3, July 1941.

YEATTER, R. E., 1950. "Effects of Different Pre-incubation Temperatures on the Hatchability of Pheasant Eggs," *Science,* Vol. 112, No. 2914, Nov. 3, 1950.

ANON., 1942. "The Ringneck Pheasant in Pennsylvania," *Educ. Pamph. No. 5, Pa. Game Comm.,* Harrisburg, Pa., 1942.

Chapter 2. THE WILD TURKEY

BENT, A. C., 1932. "Life Histories of North American Gallinaceous Birds," *U. S. Nat. Mus. Bull. 162,* Wash. D. C.

——, 1938. "Life Histories of North American Birds of Prey," Part 2, *U. S. Nat. Mus. Bull. 170,* Wash. D. C.

BICK, G. H., 1947. "The Wild Turkey in Louisiana," *Journ. Wildlife Mgt.,* Vol. 11, No. 2, April 1947.

BLAKEY, HAROLD L., 1937. "Wild Turkey Management on the Missouri Ozark Range," *Trans. 2nd No. Am. Wildlife Conf.,* 1937.

——, 1941. "Status and Management of the Eastern Wild Turkey," *Am. Wildlife,* Vol. 30, No. 3.

——, 1947. "The Role of Brush Control in Habitat Improvement on the Aransas National Wildlife Refuge," *Trans. 12th No. Am. Wildlife Conf.,* 1947.

COPE, E. B., 1932. "The Wild Turkey, Its Hunting and Future in Louisiana," *La. Cons. Rev.,* July 1932.

DALKE, PAUL D., 1943. "Recent Developments in Census Techniques Applied to Upland Game in Missouri," *Trans. 8th No. Am. Wildlife Conf.,* 1943.

——, W. K. CLARK, JR., and L. J. KIRSCHGEN, 1942. "Food Habit Trends of the Wild Turkey in Missouri as Determined by Dropping Analysis," *Journ. Wildlife Mgt.,* Vol. 6, No. 3, July 1942.

——, A. STARKER LEOPOLD, and DAVID L. SPENCER, 1946. "The Ecology and Management of the Wild Turkey in Missouri," *Tech. Bull. No. 1, Mo. Cons. Comm.,* 1946, 86 pp.

DOERZBACHER, RAYMOND E., 1947. "The Eastern Wild Turkey, " *Pa. Game News,* Vol. XVIII, No. 7, Oct. 1947.

GLOVER, FRED A., 1948. "Winter Activities of Wild Turkey in West Virginia," *Journ. Wildlife Mgt.,* Vol. 12, No. 4, Oct. 1948.

——, and R. WAYNE BAILEY, 1947. "Wild Turkey Investigation—Final Report and Management Plan," *West Virginia P-R Project No. 12-R-3,* mimeo., June 30, 1947.

GOOD, HENRY G., and LLOYD G. WEBB, 1940. "Spring Foods of the Wild Turkey in Alabama," *Am. Wildlife,* Vol. 29, No. 6, Nov.–Dec. 1940.

JUDD, SYLVESTER D., 1905. "The Grouse and Wild Turkeys of the United States and Their Economic Value," *U. S. D. A. Biol. Surv. Bull. No. 24,* 1905.

KOZICKY, EDWARD L., 1942. "Pennsylvania Wild Turkey Food Habits Based on Dropping Analysis," *Pa. Game News,* Vol. XIII, No. 8, Nov. 1942.

——, 1948. "Some Protozoan Parasites of the Eastern Wild Turkey in Pennsylvania," *Journ. Wildlife Mgt.,* Vol. 12, No. 3, July 1948.

——, and ROSS METZ, 1948. "The Management of the Wild Turkey in Pennsylvania," *Pa. Game News,* Vol. XIX, No. 4 and Vol. XIX, No. 6.

LATHAM, ROGER M., 1939. "Pennsylvania's Wild Turkey Range," *Pa. Game News,* Vol. X, No. 4, July 1939.

LIGON, J. STOKLEY, 1946. "History and Management of Merriam's Wild Turkey," *New Mexico Game and Fish Comm.,* x + 84 pp., 1946.

——, 1946a. "Upland Game Bird Restoration through Trapping and Transplanting," *New Mexico Game and Fish Comm.,* x + 77 pp., 1946.

MARTIN, A. C., FRANKLIN H. MAY, and TALBOTT E. CLARKE, 1939. "Early Winter Food Preferences of the Wild Turkey on the George Washington National Forest," *Trans. 4th No. Am. Wildlife Conf.,* 1939.

MCILHENNY, EDWARD A., 1914. "The Wild Turkey and Its Hunting," *Doubleday, Page and Co.,* N. Y., 245 pp.

MORTON, THOMAS, 1632. New English Canaan.

MOSBY, HENRY S., and CHARLES O. HANDLEY, 1943. "The Wild Turkey in Virginia," *Comm. of Game and Inland Fisheries,* Richmond, Virginia, xx + 281 pp., 1943.

MURIE, ADOLPH, 1946. "The Merriam Turkey on the San Carlos Indian Reservation," *Journ. Wildlife Mgt.,* Vol. 10, No. 4, Oct. 1946.

NEWMAN, COLEMAN C., 1945. "Turkey Restocking Efforts in East Texas," *Journ. Wildlife Mgt.,* Vol. 9, No. 4, Oct. 1945.

PETRIDES, GEORGE A., 1942. "Age Determination in American Gallinaceous Game Birds," *Trans. 7th No. Am. Wildlife Conf.,* 1942.

SHILLINGER, J. E., and L. C. MORLEY, 1937. "Diseases of Upland Game Birds," *U. S. Dep't. Agr., Bull. 1781,* 33 pp., 1937.

STODDARD, HERBERT L., 1935. "Wild Turkey Management," *Trans. 21st Am. Game Conf.,* 1935.

——, 1936. "Management of Wild Turkey," *Trans. 1st No. Am. Wildlife Conf.,* 1936.

SYLVESTER, W. R., and P. W. LANE, 1946. "Trapping Wild Turkeys on the Kentucky Woodlands Refuge," *Journ. Wildlife Mgt.,* Vol. 10, No. 4, Oct. 1946.

WEHR, EVERETT E., and DON R. COBURN, 1943. "Some Economically Important Parasites of the Wild Turkey and Hungarian Partridge of Pennsylvania," *Pa. Game News,* Vol. XIII, No. 11, Feb. 1943.

WRIGHT, A. H., 1914–1915. "Early Records of the Wild Turkey," *Auk.,* Vol. XXXI, pp. 334–358, 462–473; Vol. XXXII, pp. 61–81, 206–224.

ANON. (Wilson, K.), 1947. "Wild Turkey of Green Ridge," *Md. Conservationist,* Vol. XXIV, No. 3, Summer-Fall, 1947.

Chapter 3. THE SAGE GROUSE

BATTERSON, W. M., and W. B. MORSE, 1948. "Oregon Sage Grouse," *Ore. Game Comm. Fauna Series 1,* 1948.

GIRARD, G. L., 1937. "Life History, Habits, and Food of the Sage Grouse," *Univ. of Wyo. Public.,* Vol. 3, No. 1, April 1937.

GRINER, L. A., 1939. "A Study of the Sage Grouse, with Special Reference to Life History, Habitat Requirements, and Numbers and Distribution," unpub. Master's thesis, Utah State Agr. Coll. Library, Logan, Utah, 1939.

HONESS, R. F., and W. J. ALLRED, 1942. "Sage Grouse Studies," *Wyo. Game and Fish Dept. Bull. No. 2,* 1942.

MARTIN, A. C., H. S. ZIM, and A. L. NELSON, 1951. "American Wildlife and Plants," *McGraw-Hill Book Co.,* N. Y., 1951, 500 pp.

PATTERSON, R. L., 1952. "The Sage Grouse in Wyo-

ming," *Wyo. Game and Fish Comm., Sage Books Inc.,* Denver, 1952, 341 pp.

POST, G., 1951a. "The Effects of Aldrin Insecticide on Birds," Rep. Wyo. Fed. Aid Proj. 28-R-5, *Wyo. Game and Fish Comm.,* 1951.

——, 1951b. "Effects of Toxaphene and Chlordane on Certain Game Birds," *Journ. Wildlife Mgt.,* Vol. 15, No. 4, Oct. 1951.

PRESNALL, C. C., and A. WOOD, 1953. "Coyote Predation on Sage Grouse," *Journ. Mammalogy,* Feb. 1953.

RASMUSSEN, D. I., and L. A. GRINER, 1938. "Life History and Management Studies of the Sage Grouse in Utah," *Trans. 3rd No. Am. Wildlife Conf.,* 1938.

SCOTT, J. W., 1940. "The Role of Coccidia as Parasites of Wildlife," *Journ. Colo.-Wyo. Acad. Sci.,* Vol. 2, No. 6, 1940.

SIMON, F., 1940. "The Parasites of the Sage Grouse," *Univ. of Wyo. Public.,* Vol. 7, No. 5, 1940.

Chapter 4. THE SHARP-TAILED GROUSE

ALDOUS, S. E., 1943. "Sharp-tailed Grouse in the Sand Dune Country of North-central North Dakota," *Journ. Wildlife Mgt.,* Vol. 7, No. 1, January 1943.

AMMANN, G. A., 1952. "What is Ideal Sharptail Habitat?" *Info. Circ. No. 72, Mich. Dept. Cons., Game Div.,* 4 pp. mimeo., March 3, 1952.

BAUMGARTNER, F. M., 1939. "Studies on the Distribution and Habits of the Sharptail Grouse in Michigan," *Trans. 4th No. Am. Wildlife Conf.,* 1939.

BOUGHTON, R. V., 1937. "Endoparasitic Infestations in Grouse, Their Pathogenicity and Correlation with Meteoro-Topographical Conditions," *Tech. Bull. 121, Univ. Minn. Agr. Exp. Sta.,* August 1937.

GRANGE, W. B., 1948. "Wisconsin Grouse Problems," *Wisc. Cons. Dep't.,* Madison, Wisc., 1948, 318 pp.

GROSS, A. O., 1930. "Progress Report of the Wisconsin Prairie Chicken Investigation," *Wisc. Cons. Comm.,* Madison, Wisc., 1930, 112 pp.

HAMERSTROM, F. N., Jr., 1939. "A Study of Wisconsin Prairie Chicken and Sharp-tailed Grouse," *Wilson Bull.,* Vol. 51, No. 2, June 1939.

——, 1941. "A Study of Wisconsin Prairie Grouse, Breeding Habits, Winter Foods, Endoparasites, and Movements," *unpub. thesis, Univ. of Wisc.,* 140 pp., 1941.

——, and F. HAMERSTROM, 1951a. "Mobility of the Sharp-tailed Grouse in Relation to Its Ecology and Distribution," *Am. Midl. Nat.,* Vol. 46, No. 1, July 1951.

——, 1951b. "Grouse of the Brushlands," *Wisc. Cons. Bull.,* Vol. 16, No. 10, Oct. 1951.

——, and O. E. MATTSON, 1952. "Sharptails into the Shadows?" *Wisc. Wildlife No. 1, Wisc. Cons. Dept.,* 1952.

HART, C. M., O. S. LEE, and J. B. Low, 1950. "The Sharp-tailed Grouse in Utah," *Pub. No. 3, Utah St. Dept. Fish and Game,* 1950.

JENKINS, B. C., 1948. "The Role of Fire in Wildlife Management," *Mich. Conservation,* April 1948.

MARSHALL, W. H., and M. S. JENSEN, 1937. "Winter and Spring Studies of the Sharp-tailed Grouse in Utah," *Journ. Wildlife Mgt.,* Vol. 1, Nos. 3–4, October 1937.

MORGAN, B. B., and F. N. HAMERSTROM, JR., 1941. "Notes on the Endoparasites of Wisconsin Pinnated and Sharp-tailed Grouse," *Journ. Wildlife Mgt.,* Vol. 5, No. 2, April 1941.

SAUNDERS, G. B., 1935. "Michigan's Studies of Sharp-tailed Grouse," *Trans. 21st Am. Game Conf.,* 1935.

SCHMIDT, F. J. W., 1936. "Winter Food of the Sharp-tailed Grouse and Pinnated Grouse in Wisconsin," *Wilson Bull.,* XLVIII, Sept. 1936.

SCHORGER, A. W., 1943. "The Prairie Chicken and Sharp-tailed Grouse in Early Wisconsin," *Trans. Wisc. Acad. Sci., Arts and Letters,* Vol. 35, 1943.

SCOTT, W. E., 1947. "The Prairie Sharp-tailed Grouse," *Wisc. Cons. Bull.,* Vol. XII, No. 2, February 1947.

SNYDER, L. L., 1935. "A Study of the Sharp-tailed Grouse," *Univ. of Toronto Studies, Biol. Series, No. 40,* 1935.

SWENK, M. H., and L. F. SELKO, 1938. "Late Autumn Food of the Sharp-tailed Grouse in Western Nebraska," *Journ. Wildlife Mgt.,* Vol. 2, No. 4, Oct. 1938.

YOCOM, C. F., 1952. "Columbian Sharp-tailed Grouse in the State of Washington," *Am. Midl. Nat.,* Vol. 48, No. 1, July 1952.

Chapter 5. THE PRAIRIE CHICKEN

AMMANN, G. A., 1944. "Determining the Age of Pinnated and Sharp-tailed Grouse," *Journ. Wildlife Mgt.,* Vol. 8, No. 2, April 1944.

BAKER, M. F., 1952. "Population Changes of the Greater Prairie Chicken in Kansas," *Trans. 17th No. Am. Wildlife Conf.,* 1952.

——, 1953. "Prairie Chickens of Kansas," *Univ. Kans. Misc. Publ. No. 5,* 68 pp., March 10, 1953.

BENNITT, R., 1939. "Some Agricultural Characteristics of the Missouri Prairie Chicken Range," *Trans. 4th No. Am. Wildlife Conf.,* 1939.

BENT, A. C., 1932. "Life Histories of North American Gallinaceous Birds," *U. S. Nat. Mus. Bull. 162,* Wash., D. C., 1932.

DALKE, P. D., 1943. "Recent Developments in Census Techniques Applied to Upland Game in Missouri," *Trans. 8th No. Am. Wildlife Conf.,* 1943.

DAVISON, V. E., 1940. "An 8-Year Census of Lesser Prairie Chickens," *Journ. Wildlife Mgt.,* Vol. 4, No. 1, Jan. 1940.

EDMINSTER, F. C., 1947. "The Ruffed Grouse, Its Life Story, Ecology and Management," *The Macmillan Co.,* N. Y., 1947, 385 pp.

GRANGE, W. B., 1948. "Wisconsin Grouse Problems," *Wisc. Cons. Dep't.*, Madison, Wisc., 1948, 318 pp.

GROSS, A. O., 1928. "The Heath Hen," *Mem. Boston Soc. Nat. Hist.*, Vol. 6, No. 4, May 1928.

——, 1930. "Progress Report of the Wisconsin Prairie Chicken Investigation," *Wisc. Cons. Comm.*, Madison, Wisc., 1930, 112 pp.

HAMERSTROM, F. N., JR., 1939. "A Study of Wisconsin Prairie Chicken and Sharp-tailed Grouse," *Wilson Bull.*, Vol. 51, No. 2, June 1939.

JANSON, R. G., 1952. "South Dakota Prairie Grouse Population Trends," *So. Dak. Cons. Digest,* Vol. XIX, No. 6, June 1952.

LEHMANN, V. W., 1939. "The Heath Hen of the South," *Bull. No. 16, Tex. Game, Fish and Oyster Comm.,* Austin, Tex., July 1929, 11 pp.

——, 1941. "Attwater's Prairie Chicken, Its Life History and Management," *No. Am. Fauna No. 57, U. S. Fish and Wildlife Serv.,* Wash., D. C., 1941, 65 pp.

LEIGH, W. H., 1940. "Preliminary Studies on Para-

sites of Upland Game Birds and Fur-bearing Mammals in Illinois," *Ill. Nat. Hist. Surv. Bull.,* Vol. 21, Art. 5, 1940.

MOHLER, L. L., 1952. "Fall and Winter Habits of Prairie Chickens in Southwest Nebraska," *Journ. Wildlife Mgt.,* Vol. 16, No. 1, Jan. 1952.

MORGAN, B. B., and F. N. HAMERSTROM, JR., 1941. "Notes on the Endoparasites of Wisconsin Pinnated and Sharp-tailed Grouse," *Journ. Wildlife Mgt.,* Vol. 5, No. 2, April 1941.

SCHORGER, A. W., 1943. "The Prairie Chicken and Sharp-tailed Grouse in Early Wisconsin," *Trans. Wisc. Acad. Sci., Arts and Letters,* Vol. 35, 1943.

SCHWARTZ, C. W., 1945. "The Ecology of the Prairie Chicken in Missouri," *Mo. Univ. Studies,* Vol. 20, No. 1, 1945.

SCOTT, W. E., 1947. "The Greater Prairie Chicken," *Wisc. Cons. Bull.,* Vol. XII, No. 1, Jan. 1947.

YEATTER, R. E., 1943. "The Prairie Chicken in Illinois," *Bull. Ill. Nat. Hist. Surv.,* Vol. 22, Art. 4, 1943.

Chapter 6. THE RUFFED GROUSE

ALDRICH, J. W., and H. FRIEDMANN, 1943. "A Revision of the Ruffed Grouse," *Condor,* Vol. 45, No. 3, May–June, 1943.

ALLEN, A. A., 1929. "Ten Years' Experiments in the Rearing of the Ruffed Grouse in Captivity," *Trans. 16th Am. Game Conf.,* 1929.

——, 1934. "Sex Rhythm in the Ruffed Grouse and Other Birds," *Auk,* Vol. LI, No. 2, April 1934.

ALLEN, A. A., and A. O. GROSS, 1926. "Report of the Ruffed Grouse Investigation, Season of 1925–26," *Am. Game,* Oct. 1926.

BASS, C. C., 1941. "Specific Cause and Nature of Ulcerative Enteritis of Quail," *Proc. Soc. Exp. Biol. and Med.,* Vol. 46, No. 2, Feb. 1941.

BOUGHTON, R. V., 1937. "Endoparasitic Infestations in Grouse, Their Pathogenicity and Correlation with Meteoro-Topographical Conditions," *Tech. Bull. 121, Univ. Minn. Agr. Exp. Sta.,* Aug. 1937.

BUMP, G., R. DARROW, F. EDMINSTER, and W. CRISSEY, 1947. "The Ruffed Grouse, Life History, Propagation and Management," *N. Y. State Conservation Dep't.,* 1947, 915 pp.

CLARKE, C. H. D., 1936. "Fluctuations in Numbers of Ruffed Grouse," *Univ. of Toronto Studies, Biol. Series No. 41,* Univ. of Toronto Press, 1936.

EDMINSTER, F. C., 1937. "An Analysis of the Value of Refuges for Cyclic Game Species," *Journ. Wildlife Mgt.,* Vol. 1, No. 1–2, July 1937.

——, 1947. "The Ruffed Grouse, Its Life Story, Ecology and Management," *The Macmillan Co.,* N. Y., 1947, 385 pp.

FISHER, L. W., 1939. "Studies of the Eastern Ruffed Grouse in Michigan," *Tech. Bull. 166, Mich. State College,* 1939.

GRANGE, W. B., 1948. "Wisconsin Grouse Problems," *Wisc. Cons. Dep't.,* 1948, 318 pp.

——, 1949. "The Way to Game Abundance, with an Explanation of Game Cycles," *Chas. Scribner's Sons,* N. Y., 1949, 365 pp.

GREENE, R. G., and J. E. SHILLINGER, 1934. "Wildlife Cycles and What They Mean to the Grouse Supply," *Trans. 20th Am. Game Conf.,* 1934.

KING, R. T., 1937. "Ruffed Grouse Management," *Journ. Forestry,* Vol. XXXV, No. 6, June 1937.

MARSHALL, W. H., 1946. "Cover Preferences, Seasonal Movements, and Food Habits of Richardson's Grouse and Ruffed Grouse in Southern Idaho," *Wilson Bull.,* Vol. 58, No. 1, March 1946.

MORLEY, L. C., and P. W. WETMORE, 1936. "Dis-

covery of the Organism of Ulcerative Enteritis," *Trans. 1st No. Am. Wildlife Conf.,* 1936.

STODDART, A. M., 1918. "Ruffed Grouse in New York State," Albany, N. Y., 1918.

WOODRUFF, E. S., 1908. "The Ruffed Grouse, A Study of the Causes of Its Scarcity in 1907," Albany, N. Y., 1908.

Chapter 7. THE BOBWHITE QUAIL

BALDWIN, W. P., JR., and C. O. HANDLEY, 1946. "Winter Food of Bobwhite Quail in Virginia," *Journ. Wildlife Mgt.,* Vol. 10, No. 2, Apr. 1946.

BAUMGARTNER, F. M., 1944. "Bobwhite Quail Populations on Hunted vs. Protected Areas," *Journ. Wildlife Mgt.,* Vol. 8, No. 3, July 1944.

BEADEL, H. L., 1939. "Hawks vs. Quail on Quail Preserves," *Journ. Wildlife Mgt.,* Vol. 3, No. 1, Jan. 1939.

BENNETT, L. J., and G. D. HENDRICKSON, 1938. "Censusing Quail in Early Fall," *Journ. Wildlife Mgt.,* Vol. 2, No. 4, Oct. 1938.

BENNITT, R., 1945. "Some Social Factors Influencing Quail Hunting in Missouri, 1938–44," *Journ. Wildlife Mgt.,* Vol. 9, No. 3, July 1945.

——, 1951. "Some Aspects of Missouri Quail and Quail Hunting, 1938–48," *Tech. Bull. No. 2, Mo. Cons. Comm.,* 51 pp., 1951.

BENT, A. C., 1932. "Life Histories of North American Gallinaceous Birds," *U. S. Nat. Mus. Bull. No. 162,* 1932.

BUECHNER, H. K., 1950. "An Evaluation of Restocking with Pen-Reared Bobwhite," *Journ. Wildlife Mgt.,* Vol. 14, No. 4, Oct. 1950.

BUSS, I. O., H. MATTISON, and F. M. KOZLIK, 1947. "The Bobwhite Quail in Dunn County, Wisconsin," *Wisc. Cons. Bull.,* Vol XII, No. 7, 8 pp., July 1947.

CRIDER, F. J., 1952. "Natob—A New Bush Lespedeza for Soil Conservation," *U. S. D. A. Circ. No. 900,* 10 pp., 1952.

DALKE, P. D., 1943. "Recent Developments in Census Techniques Applied to Upland Game in Missouri," *Trans. 8th No. Am. Wildlife Conf.,* 1943.

DAMON, D., 1949. "Winter Foods of Quail in Nebraska," *Wildlife Mgt. Notes,* Vol. 1, No. 6; *Neb. Game, Forestation and Parks Comm.,* July 1949.

DAVISON, V. E., 1942. "Bobwhite Foods and Conservation Farming," *Journ. Wildlife Mgt.,* Vol. 6, No. 2, Apr. 1942.

——, 1949. "Bobwhites on the Rise," *Charles Scribner's Sons,* N. Y., 150 pp., 1949.

DUCK, L. G., 1943. "Seasonal Movements of Bobwhite Quail in Northwestern Oklahoma," *Journ. Wildlife Mgt.,* Vol. 7, No. 4, Oct. 1943.

ERRINGTON, P. L., 1935. "The 1934 Drought and Southern Iowa Bobwhite," *Iowa Bird Life,* Vol. V, No. 2, June 1935.

——, 1939. "The Comparative Ability of the Bobwhite and the Ring-necked Pheasant to Withstand Cold and Hunger," *Wilson Bull.,* Vol. 51, No. 1, March 1939.

——, 1939a. "Foods of Bobwhite in Wisconsin," *Auk,* Vol. 56, Apr. 1939.

——, and F. N. HAMERSTROM, JR., "The Northern Bobwhite's Winter Territory," *Res. Bull. No. 201, Iowa Agr. Exp. Sta.,* June 1936.

GALE, L. R., 1950. "Effects of Quail Refuges in Kentucky," mimeo. FA Report on Project 19R, *Ky. Div. of Game and Fish,* 20 pp., May 1950.

GERSTELL, R., 1939. "Certain Mechanics of Winter Quail Losses Revealed by Laboratory Experimentation," *Pa. Game News,* Vol. 10, No. 2, 1939.

GOODRUM, P., 1949. "Status of Bobwhite Quail in the United States," *Trans. 14th No. Am. Wildlife Conf.,* 1949.

GRAY, A. M., 1938. "Winter Foods of the Bobwhite Quail in the Black Belt Soil Province of Alabama," *Bull. Ala. Dept. Cons.,* 23 pp., Dec. 1938.

GREENE, S. W., 1935. "Effect of Annual Grass Fires on Organic Matter . . . of Virgin Longleaf Pine Soils," *U. S. Gov't. Print. Off.,* 1935.

GREENWELL, G. A., 1948. "Wildlife Values of Missouri Farm Ponds," *Trans. 13th No. Am. Wildlife Conf.,* 1948.

JACKSON, A. S., 1947. "A Bobwhite Quail Irruption in Northwest Texas Lower Plains Terminated by Predation," *Trans. 12th No. Am. Wildlife Conf.,* 1947.

——, 1951. "The Bobwhite Quail in Relation to Land Management in the Western Cross Timbers," FA Report Series No. 7, *Tex. Game, Fish and Oyster Comm.,* 47 pp., Feb. 1951.

JOHNSON, J. A., 1941. "A Study of Bobwhite Foods in Relation to Farm Problems in Northern Mississippi," *Trans. 5th No. Am. Wildlife Conf.,* 1941.

KORSCHGEN, L. J., 1948. "Late-Fall and Early-Winter Food Habits of Bobwhite Quail in Missouri," *Journ. Wildlife Mgt.,* Vol. 12, No. 1, Jan. 1948.

——, 1952. "Food Habits of the Bobwhite Quail in Missouri," *Mo. Cons. Comm.,* 59 pp., March 1952.

LATHAM, R. M., and C. R. STUDHOLME, 1952. "The Bobwhite Quail in Pennsylvania," *Pa. Game News,* Spec. Issue No. 4, 95 pp., March 1952.

LAY, D. W., 1940. "Bobwhite Populations as Affected by Woodland Management in Eastern Texas," *Bull. No. 592, Tex. Agr. Exp. Sta.,* 37 pp., Aug. 1940.

LEE, L., 1948. "The Fall and Winter Food of the Bobwhite in Oklahoma," *Bull. of Okla. Game and Fish Dep't.,* 23 pp., 1948.

LEHMANN, V. W., and H. WARD, 1941. "Some Plants Valuable to Quail in Southwestern Texas," *Journ. Wildlife Mgt.,* Vol. 5, No. 2, Apr. 1941.

MARTIN, A. C., 1935. "Quail Food Plants of the Southeastern States," *U. S. D. A. Circ. No. 348,* 16 pp., Apr. 1935.

MURPHY, D. A., and T. S. BASKETT, 1952. "Bobwhite Mobility in Central Missouri," *Journ. Wildlife Mgt.,* Vol. 16, No. 4, Oct. 1952.

MURRAY, R. W., 1948. "Wintering Bobwhite in Boone County, Missouri," *Journ. Wildlife Mgt.,* Vol. 12, No. 1, Jan. 1948.

STEEN, M. O., 1950. "Road to Restoration," *Trans. 15th No. Am. Wildlife Conf.,* 1950.

STODDARD, H. L., 1932. "The Bobwhite Quail," *Charles Scribners' Sons,* N. Y., 559 pp., 1932.

——, 1940. "Eighth Annual Report," *Cooperative Quail Study Association,* Thomasville, Ga., 27 pp., Aug. 1940.

——, 1942. "Ninth and Tenth Annual Reports," *Cooperative Quail Study Association,* Thomasville, Ga., 39 pp., July 1942.

STUDHOLME, C. R., 1945. "Bob's Private Life," *Pa. Game News,* Vol. XV, No. 12, March 1945.

WILSON, K. A., 1938. "Quail Management in Maryland," *Trans. 3rd No. Am. Wildlife Conf.,* 1938.

WRIGHT, T., JR., 1941. "A Study of the Fall Food Supply of the Ring-necked Pheasant and the Bobwhite Quail in Washington County, Rhode Island," *Journ. Wildlife Mgt.,* Vol. 5, No. 3, July 1941.

Chapter 8. THE CALIFORNIA QUAIL

BEER, J., and W. TIDYMAN, 1942. "The Substitution of Hard Seeds for Grit," *Journ. Wildlife Mgt.,* Vol. 6, No. 1, Jan. 1942.

DAWSON, W. L., and J. H. BOWLES, 1909. "The Birds of Washington," 2 Vols., Seattle, 1909.

DILL, H. H., 1939. "Winter Feeding and Shelters for the California Valley Quail," *Trans. 4th No. Am. Wildlife Conf.,* 1939.

EMLEN, J. T., JR., 1939. "Seasonal Movements of a Low-Density Valley Quail Population," *Journ. Wildlife Mgt.,* Vol. 3, No. 2, April 1939.

——, 1940. "Sex and Age Ratios in Survival of the California Quail," *Journ. Wildlife Mgt.,* Vol. 4, No. 1, Jan. 1940.

——, and B. GLADING, 1945. "Increasing Valley Quail in California," *Bull. 695, Univ. Cal. Agr. Exp. Sta.,* 56 pp., Nov. 1945.

GLADING, B., 1938. "Studies on the Nesting Cycle of the California Valley Quail in 1937," *Cal. Fish and Game,* Vol. 24, No. 4, Oct. 1938.

——, 1941. "Valley Quail Census Methods and Populations at the San Joaquin Experimental Range," *Cal. Fish and Game,* Vol. 27, No. 2, April 1941.

——, 1946. "Upland Game Birds in Relation to California Agriculture," *Trans. 11th No. Am. Wildlife Conf.,* 1946.

EMLEN, J. T., JR., 1947. Game Watering Devices for the Arid Southwest," *Trans. 12th No. Am. Wildlife Conf.,* 1947.

——, H. H. BISWELL, and C. F. SMITH, 1940. "Studies on the Food of the California Quail in 1937," *Journ. Wildlife Mgt.,* Vol. 4, No. 2, April 1940.

——, and R. W. ENDERLIN, and H. A. HJERSMAN, 1945. "The Kettleman Hills Quail Project," *Cal. Fish and Game,* Vol. 31, No. 3, July 1945.

——, and R. W. SAARNI, 1944. "Effect of Hunting on a Valley Quail Population," *Cal. Fish and Game,* Vol. 30, No. 2, Apr. 1944.

——, D. M. SELLECK, and F. T. Ross, 1945. "Valley Quail under Private Management at the Dune Lakes Club," *Cal. Fish and Game,* Vol. 31, No. 4, Oct. 1945.

GRINNELL, J., H. C. BRYANT, and T. I. STORER, 1918. "The Game Birds of California," *Univ. Cal. Press,* Berkeley, 642 pp., 1918.

HERMAN, C. M., and B. GLADING, 1942. "The Protozoan Blood Parasite *Haemoproteus lophortyx* O'Roke in Quail at the San Joaquin Experimental Range, California," *Cal. Fish and Game,* Vol. 28, No. 3, July 1942.

——, and A. I. BISCHOFF, 1949. "The Duration of *Haemoproteus* Infection in California Quail," *Cal. Fish and Game,* Vol. 35, No. 4, Oct. 1949.

——, and J. E. CHATTIN, 1943. "Epidemiological Studies on Coccidiosis of California Quail," *Cal. Fish and Game,* Vol. 29, No. 4, Oct. 1943.

HORN, E. E., 1938a. "Factors in Nesting Losses of the California Valley Quail," *Trans. 3rd No. Am. Wildlife Conf.,* 1938.

——, 1938b. "Some Relationships of Quail and Ground Squirrels in California," *Journ. Wildlife Mgt.,* Vol. 2, No. 2, April 1938.

LEOPOLD, A. S., 1939. "Age Determination in Quail," *Journ. Wildlife Mgt.,* Vol. 3, No. 3, July 1939.

MACGREGOR, W. G., 1950. "The Artificial Roost—A New Management Tool for California Quail," *Cal. Fish and Game,* Vol. 36, No. 3, July 1950.

McLEAN, D. D., 1930. "The Quail of California," *Game Bull. No. 2, Cal. Div. Fish and Game,* 47 pp., 1930.

RICHARDSON, F., 1941. "Results of the Southern California Quail Banding Program," *Cal. Fish and Game,* Vol. 27, No. 4, Oct. 1941.

SUMNER, E. L., JR., 1935. "A Life History Study of the California Quail, with Recommendations for Conservation and Management," reprint from *Cal. Fish and Game,* Vol. 21, Nos. 3 and 4, July and Oct. 1935.

TWINING, H., 1939. "Some Opinions of Early California Quail Hunters," *Cal. Fish and Game,* Vol. 25, No. 1, Jan. 1939.

ANON., 1950. "California's Fish and Game Program," *Report to the Cal. Wildlife Cons. Board,* May 15, 1950.

Chapter 9. THE GAMBEL'S, SCALED, AND MOUNTAIN QUAILS

BAILEY, F. M., 1928. "Birds of New Mexico," 807 pp., Santa Fe, 1928.

BENT, A. C., 1932. "Life Histories of North American Gallinaceous Birds," *U. S. Nat. Museum Bull. 162,* Washington, D. C., 1932.

CAMPBELL, H., and L. LEE, 1953. "Studies on Quail Malaria in New Mexico and Notes on Other Aspects of Quail Populations," *Bull. New Mexico Dep't. of Game and Fish,* 79 pp., 1953.

GORDON, S., 1950. "California's Fish and Game Program," *Report to the Cal. Wildlife Cons. Board,* May 1950.

GORSUCH, D. M., 1934. "Life History of the Gambel Quail in Arizona," *Univ. Arizona Bull.,* Vol. V, No. 4; *Biol. Sci. Bull. No. 2,* Tucson, May 1934.

JUDD, S. D., 1905. "The Bobwhite and Other Quails of the United States in Their Economic Relations," *U. S. Dep't. Agr. Biol. Surv. Bull. 21,* 1905.

LAWSON, L. L., 1950. "Quail Research and Investigation in Southern Arizona," Multilith Completion Report Project 40-R-2, *Ariz. Game and Fish Comm.,* Nov. 1950.

LEHMANN, V. W., and H. WARD, 1941. "Some Plants Valuable to Quail in Southwestern Texas," *Journ. Wildlife Mgt.,* Vol. 5, No. 2, April 1941.

MACGREGOR, W., JR., and M. Inlay, 1951. "Observations on Failure of Gambel Quail to Breed," *Cal. Fish and Game,* Vol. 37, No. 2, April 1951.

MARTIN, A. C., H. S. ZIM, and A. L. NELSON, 1951. "American Wildlife and Plants," 500 pp., *McGraw-Hill Book Co.,* N. Y., 1951.

McLEAN, D. D., 1930. "The Quail of California," *Game Bull. No. 2, Cal. Div. Fish and Game,* Sacramento, 1930.

SWANK, W. G., and S. GALLIZIOLI, 1953. "The Effect of Hunting upon a Gambel's Quail Population," *Proc. 19th Ann. Meet. Western Ass'n. of Game Commissioners,* March 1953.

YOCOM, C. F., and S. W. HARRIS, 1952. "Food Habits of Mountain Quail (*Oreortyx picta*) in Eastern Washington," *Journ. Wildlife Mgt.,* Vol. 17, No. 2, April 1953.

Chapter 10. THE CHUKAR PARTRIDGE

ALDRICH, J. W., 1947. "The Hungarian and Chukar Partridges in America," *Wildlife Leaflet 292* (mimeo.), *U. S. Fish and Wildlife Service,* February 1947.

BADE, A., 1937. "The Chukar Partridge in California," *Cal. Fish and Game,* Vol. 23, No. 3, July 1937.

BAKER, E. C. S., 1922. "The Game Birds of India, Burma and Ceylon," *Journ. Bombay Nat. Hist. Soc.,* Vol. 28, No. 2, 1922.

BUMP, G., 1951. "Game Introductions—When, Where and How," *Trans. 16th No. Am. Wildlife Conf.,* 1951.

CAHN, A. R., 1938. "A Climographic Analysis of the Problem of Introducing Three Exotic Game Birds into the Tennessee Valley and Vicinity," *Trans. 3rd No. Am. Wildlife Conf.,* 1938.

CHRISTENSEN, G. C., 1952a. "The Status of the Chukar Partridge in Nevada," 11 pp. mimeo., *Nev. Fish and Game Comm.,* Nov. 1, 1952.

——, 1952b. "Overwintering of the Chukar Partridge in Nevada, U. S. A.," *Journ. Bombay Nat. Hist. Soc.,* Dec. 1952.

——, 1954. "The Chukar Partridge in Nevada," *Biol. Bull. No. 1, Nev. Fish and Game Comm.,* 77 pp., April 1954.

——, and W. Q. WICK, 1953. "Phantoms of the Rimrock," *Nev. Fish and Game News,* June 1953.

GALBREATH, D. S., and R. MORELAND, 1953. "The Chukar Partridge in Washington," *Biol. Bull. No. 11, Wash. State Game Dep't.,* 55 pp., Feb. 1953.

KENDEIGH, S. C., 1945. "Resistance to Hunger in Birds," *Journ. Wildlife Mgt.,* Vol. 9, No. 3, July 1945.

LAWSON, L. L., 1951. "Special Investigations on the Status of Pheasant and Chukar Partridge in Arizona," Multilith Completion Report Project 40-R-2, *Ariz. Game and Fish Comm.,* March 1951.

MORELAND, R., 1950. "Success of Chukar Partridge in the State of Washington," *Trans. 15th No. Am. Wildlife Conf.,* 1950.

NAGEL, W. O., 1945. "Adaptability of the Chukar Partridge to Missouri Conditions," *Journ. Wildlife Mgt.,* Vol. 9, No. 3, July 1945.

PETRIDES, G. A., 1942. "Age Determination in American Gallinaceous Game Birds," *Trans. 7th No. Am. Wildlife Conf.,* 1942.

PHILLIPS, J. C., 1928. "Wild Birds Introduced or Transplanted in North America," *U. S. Dep't. Agr. Tech. Bull. 61,* 63 pp., 1928.

RUTHERFORD, R. M., 1949. "The Chukar Makes Good," *Outdoors,* March 1949.

SANDFORT, W. W., 1952. "Chukar Partridge," *Colorado Conservation,* March–April, 1952.

TRUE, G. H., JR., 1937. "The Chukar Partridge of Asia," *Cal. Fish and Game,* Vol. 23, No. 3, July 1937.

Chapter 11. THE HUNGARIAN PARTRIDGE

ALDRICH, J. W., 1947. "The Hungarian and Chukar Partridges in America," *Wildlife Leaflet 292, U. S. Fish and Wildlife Service,* Washington, D. C., 10 pp. mimeo., February 1947.

BRUGGER, L., 1941. "A Survey of the Endoparasites of the Digestive and Respiratory Tracts of the Hungarian Partridge (*Perdix perdix perdix* Linn.) in Whitman County, Washington," *unpublished Master's thesis, Washington State College,* Pullman, Wash., 1941.

CAHN, A. R., 1938. "A Climographic Analysis of the Problem of Introducing Three Exotic Game Birds into the Tennessee Valley and Vicinity," *Trans. 3rd No. Am. Wildlife Conf.,* 1938.

CARTWRIGHT, B. W., 1944. "The Crash Decline in Sharp-tailed Grouse and Hungarian Partridge in Western Canada and the Role of the Predator," *Trans. 9th No. Am. Wildlife Conf.,* 1944.

DALE, F. H., 1941. "Hungarian Partridge in Michigan," *Michigan Conservation,* Vol. X, No. 10, Sept. 1941.

——, 1942. "Influence of Rainfall and Soil on Hungarian Partridges and Pheasants in Southeastern Michigan," *Journ. Wildlife Mgt.,* Vol. 6, No. 1, Jan. 1942.

——, 1943. "History and Status of the Hungarian Partridge in Michigan," *Journ. Wildlife Mgt.,* Vol. 7, No. 4, Oct. 1943.

EINARSEN, A. S., 1943. "Methods of Utilizing Small Game Crops during Wartime on the West Coast," *Trans. 8th No. Am. Wildlife Conf.,* 1943.

ERRINGTON, P. L., and F. N. Hamerstrom, Jr., 1938. "Observations on the Effect of a Spring Drought on Reproduction in the Hungarian Partridge," *Condor,* Vol. XL, March–April 1938.

GORDON, S., 1935. "The Hungarian Partridge, a Complete Record of This Great Game Bird in America," *Field and Stream,* May 1935.

GREEN, W. E., and G. O. HENDRICKSON, 1938. "The European Partridge in North-Central Iowa," *Iowa Bird Life,* Vol. VIII, June 1938.

HAMMOND, M. C., 1941. "Fall and Winter Mortality Among Hungarian Partridges in Bottineau and Mc-Henry Counties, North Dakota," *Journ. Wildlife Mgt.,* Vol. 5, No. 4, Oct. 1941.

HAWKINS, A. S., 1937. "Hungarian Partridge Nesting Studies at Faville Grove," *Trans. 2nd No. Am. Wildlife Conf.,* 1937.

HICKEY, J. J., and R. A. McCABE, 1953. "Sex and Age Classes in the Hungarian Partridge," *Journ. Wildlife Mgt.,* Vol. 17, No. 1, Jan. 1953.

HICKS, L. E., 1936. "Food Habits of the Hungarian Partridge in Ohio," *Bull. 104, Ohio Div. Cons.,* 7 pp. mimeo., 1936.

KELSO, L., 1932. "A Note on the Food of the Hungarian Partridge," *Auk,* Vol. 49, pp. 204–207, 1932.

KNOTT, N. P., C. C. BALL, and C. F. YOCOM, 1943. "Nesting of the Hungarian Partridge and Ring-necked Pheasant in Whitman County, Washington," *Journ. Wildlife Mgt.,* Vol. 7, No. 3, July 1943.

McCABE, R. A., and A. S. HAWKINS, 1946. "The Hungarian Partridge in Wisconsin," *Am. Midl. Nat.,* Vol. 36, No. 1, July 1946.

MILLER, H. W., C. C. BALL, and N. P. KNOTT, 1948. "The Comparative Value of Woody Plants as Food for Upland Game Birds," *Biol. Bull. No. 8, Washington State Game Dep't.,* 39 pp., April 1948.

NOLTE, W., 1934. "Biology of the Hungarian Partridge (in German)," pub. by *J. Neumann,* Berlin, 105 pp., 1934. (Note: See review by Aldo Leopold in *Wilson Bull.,* Vol. XLVII, Dec. 1935.)

OLDYS, H., 1909. "Introduction of the Hungarian Partridge in the United States," *U. S. Dep't. Agr. Yearbook,* 1909.

PHILLIPS, J. C., 1928. "Wild Birds Introduced or Transplanted in North America," *U. S. Dep't. Agr. Tech. Bull. 61,* 64 pp., 1928.

TWOMEY, A. C., 1936. "Climographic Studies of Certain Introduced and Migratory Birds," *Ecology,* Vol. 17, pp. 122–132, 1936.

YEATTER, R. E., 1934. "The Hungarian Partridge in the Great Lakes Region," *Bull. No. 5, Univ. Michigan School Forestry and Conservation,* 92 pp., Ann Arbor, Mich., Dec. 1934.

YOCOM, C. F., 1943. "The Hungarian Partridge in the Palouse Region, Washington," *Ecol. Monographs,* Vol. 13, pp. 167–202, 1943,

——, and S. W. HARRIS, 1953. "Food Habits of the Mountain Quail in Eastern Washington," *Journ. Wildlife Mgt.,* Vol. 17, No. 2, April 1953.

Chapter 12. THE AMERICAN WOODCOCK

ALDOUS, C. M., 1939. "Studies on Woodcock Management in Maine, 1938," *Trans. 4th No. Am. Wildlife Conf.,* 1939.

ALDRICH, J. W., and OTHERS, 1952. "Investigations of Woodcock, Snipe and Rails in 1951," *Special Scientific Report—Wildlife No. 14, U. S. Fish and Wildlife Service and Canadian Wildlife Service,* January 1952.

BENNETT, L. J., and P. F. ENGLISH, 1947. "The 1946 Fall Woodcock Population," *Pa. Game News,* Vol. 18, No. 11, February 1947.

BENT, A. C., 1927. "Life Histories of North American Shore Birds," Part 1, *U. S. Nat. Mus. Bull. 142,* 1927.

BRADLEY, B. O., and A. H. COOK, 1951. "Small Marsh Development in New York," *Trans. 16th No. Am. Wildlife Conf.,* 1951.

DANGLER, E. W., and W. H. MARSHALL, 1950. "Woodcock Studies at Cloquet Forest Experiment Station, Minnesota," *The Flicker,* Vol. 22, No. 1, March 1950.

GREELEY, F., 1953. "Sex and Age Studies in Fall-Shot Woodcock from Southern Wisconsin," *Journ. Wildlife Mgt.,* Vol. 17, No. 1, Jan. 1953.

MENDALL, H. L., and C. M. ALDOUS, 1943. "The Ecology and Management of the American Woodcock," *Maine Cooperative Wildlife Research Unit,* Orono, Maine, 1943.

PEARCE, J., 1943. "Methods of Utilizing Small Game Crops During Wartime in the Northeast," *Trans. 8th No. Am. Wildlife Conf.,* 1943.

PETTINGILL, O. S., JR., 1936. "The American Woodcock," *Mem. Boston Soc. Nat. Hist.,* Vol. 9, No. 2, 1936, 391 pp.

——, 1939. "Additional Information on the Food of the American Woodcock," *Wilson Bull.,* Vol. 58, pp. 78–82.

SHELDON, W. G., 1953. "Woodcock Studies in Massachusetts," *Trans. 18th No. Am. Wildlife Conf.,* 1953.

SPERRY, C. C., 1940 "Food Habits of a Group of Shorebirds: Woodcock, Snipe, Knot, and Dowitcher," *Wildlife Research Bull. No. 1, U. S. Bureau Biological Survey,* 1940.

STUDHOLME, A. S., J. D. BEULE, and R. T. NORRIS, 1940. "A Study of Pennsylvania Woodcocks," *Pa. Game News,* Vol. 11, No. 11, Feb. 1940.

WAYNE, A. T., 1899. "Destruction of Birds by the Great Cold Wave of February 13 and 14, 1899," *Auk,* Vol. 16, pp. 197–198.

WING, L. W., 1937. "Further Studies of Wildlife Cycles," *Trans. 2nd No. Am. Wildlife Conf.,* 1937.

Chapter 13. THE BAND-TAILED PIGEON

BENT, A. C., 1932. "Life Histories of North American Gallinaceous Birds," *U. S. Nat. Mus. Bull. 162,* Washington, D. C., 1932.

GLOVER, F. A., 1953. "A Nesting Study of the Band-tailed Pigeon in Northwestern California," *Cal. Fish and Game,* Vol. 39, No. 3, July 1953.

KINGHORN, R. G., and J. A. NEFF, 1948. "Status of the Band-tailed Pigeon in Colorado, Season of 1947," 13 pp. multigraph, *Colo. Game and Fish Dep't.,* Denver, Colo., July 15, 1948.

MARTIN, A. C., H. S. ZIM, and A. L. NELSON, 1951. "American Wildlife and Plants," *McGraw-Hill Book Co.,* N. Y., 1951.

NEFF, J. A., 1947. "Habits, Food and Economic Status of the Band-tailed Pigeon," *North American Fauna*

58, *U. S. Fish and Wildlife Service,* Washington, D. C., 76 pp., 1947.

——, 1952. "Inventory of Band-tailed Pigeon Populations in Arizona, Colorado and New Mexico, 1952," 26 pp. mimeo., *Denver Wildlife Research Lab., U. S. Fish and Wildlife Service,* Denver, Colo., December 1, 1952.

——, and J. C. CULBREATH, 1947. "Status of the Band-tailed Pigeon in Colorado, Season of 1946," *Colo. Game and Fish Dep't.,* 24 pp., 1947.

STABLER, R. M., 1951. "A Survey of Colorado Band-tailed Pigeons, Mourning Doves and Wild Common Pigeons for *Trichomonas gallinae,*" *Journ. Parasitology,* Vol. 37, No. 5, Oct. 1951.

Chapter 14. THE MOURNING DOVE

AUSTIN, O. L., JR., 1951. "The Mourning Dove on Cape Cod," *Bird-Banding,* Vol. 22, pp. 149–174.

BENT, A. C., 1932. "Life Histories of North American Gallinaceous Birds," *U. S. Nat. Mus. Bull. 162,* Washington, D. C., 1932.

BOLDT, W., and G. O. HENDRICKSON, 1952. "Mourning

Dove Production in North Dakota Shelterbelts, 1950," *Journ. Wildlife Mgt.,* Vol. 16, No. 2, April 1952.

COWAN, J. B., 1952. "Life History and Productivity of a Population of Western Mourning Doves in California," *Cal. Fish and Game,* Vol. 38, No. 4, Oct. 1952.

FOOTE, L. E., and OTHERS, 1952. "Investigations of Methods of Appraising the Abundance of Mourning Doves," *Special Scientific Report: Wildlife No. 17, U. S. Fish and Wildlife Service,* Washington, D. C., September 1952.

GRESHAM, C. H., JR., 1950. "The Mourning Dove in East Baton Rouge Parish, Louisiana and Vicinity," *M.S. thesis, Louisiana State Univ.,* May 1950.

HAUGEN, A. O., and J. KEELER, 1952. "Mortality of Mourning Doves from Trichomoniasis in Alabama During 1951," *Trans. 17th No. Am. Wildlife Conf.,* 1952.

HOPKINS, M. N., and E. P. ODUM, 1953. "Some Aspects of the Population Ecology of Breeding Mourning Doves in Georgia," *Journ. Wildlife Mgt.,* Vol. 17, No. 2, April 1953.

KNAPPEN, P., 1938. "Preliminary Report on some of the Important Foods of the Mourning Dove in the Southeastern United States," *Trans. 3rd No. Am. Wildlife Conf.,* 1938.

LAWSON, L. L., 1950. "White-winged and Mourning Dove Investigation," Multilith Completion Report, Project 40-R-2, *Ariz. Game and Fish Comm.,* October 1950.

LINCOLN, F. C., 1945. "The Mourning Dove as a Game Bird," Circular 10, *U. S. Fish and Wildlife Service,* Washington, D. C., 1945, 8 pp.

McCLURE, H. E., 1939. "Cooing Activity and Censusing of the Mourning Dove," *Journ. Wildlife Mgt.,* Vol. 3, No. 4, Oct. 1939.

——, 1943. "Ecology and Management of the Mourning Dove, *Zenaidura macroura* (Linn.), in Cass County, Iowa," *Res. Bull. 310, Iowa State College of Agr. and Mech. Arts,* Feb. 1943.

——, 1944. "Mourning Dove Management," *Journ. Wildlife Mgt.,* Vol. 8, No. 2, Apr. 1944.

——, 1950. "An Eleven-Year Summary of Mourning Dove Observations in the West," *Trans. 15th No. Am. Wildlife Conf.,* 1950.

MOORE, G. C., and A. M. PEARSON, 1941. "The Mourning Dove in Alabama," *Ala. Coop. Wildlife Res. Unit,* Auburn, Ala., July 1941, 37 pp.

PEARSON, A. M., and G. C. MOORE, 1939. "Nesting Habits of the Mourning Dove in Alabama," *Trans. 4th No. Am. Wildlife Conf.,* 1939.

——, 1941. "Dove Sex Ratio Found Almost Evenly Divided," *Ala. Conservation,* May 1941.

PEARSON, A. M., and L. G. WEBB, 1942. "Mourning Dove a Strict Vegetarian," *Ala. Conservation,* July 1942.

QUAY, T. L., 1951. "Mourning Dove Studies in North Carolina," *No. Carolina Wildlife Resources Comm.,* 1951, 90 pp.

STABLER, R. M., and C. M. HERMAN, 1951. "Upper Digestive Tract Trichomoniasis in Mourning Doves and Other Birds," *Trans. 16th No. Am. Wildlife Conf.,* 1951.

THOMPSON, St. C., 1951. "The Southeastern Cooperative Dove Study," *Trans. 16th No. Am. Wildlife Conf.,* 1951.

Chapter 15. THE WHITE-WINGED DOVE

ARNOLD, L. W., 1943. "The Western White-winged Dove in Arizona," *Ariz. Game and Fish Comm.,* 103 pp, Doc. 1010.

ARNOLD, J., 1952. "Whitewing Dilemma," *Tex. Game and Fish,* Sept. 1952.

BENT, A. C., 1932. "Life Histories of North American Gallinaceous Birds," *U. S. Nat. Mus. Bull. 162,* Washington, D. C., 1932.

GALLIZIOLI, S., 1953. "Dove Investigation," Completion Report Project W-53-R-3, *Ariz. Game and Fish Comm.,* 35 pp. mimeo., Apr. 1953.

LAWSON, L. L., 1950. "White-winged and Mourning Dove Investigation," Multilith Completion Report, Project 40-R-2, *Ariz. Game and Fish Comm.,* October 1950.

NEFF, J. A., 1940a. "Range, Population, and Game Status of the Western White-winged Dove in Arizona," *Journ. Wildlife Mgt.,* Vol. 4, No. 2, April 1940.

——, 1940b. "Notes on Nesting and Other Habits of the Western White-winged Dove in Arizona," *Journ. Wildlife Mgt.,* Vol. 4, No. 3, July 1940.

SAUNDERS, G. B., 1940. "The Eastern White-winged Dove in Southeastern Texas," unpub. manuscript in files of *U. S. Fish and Wildlife Service,* 135 pp., 1940.

WETMORE, A., 1920. "Observations on the Habits of the White-winged Dove," *Condor,* Vol. 22, No. 4, July–Aug. 1920.

LIST OF PLANT NAMES

⤜⤜⟨⤛⟩⟩⟩

The names listed in this index are all of those mentioned in the text. For an explanation of the usage followed, see page xviii.

A

Acacia, feather — *Acacia decurrens*
  sweet (huisache) — *farnesiana*
Agoseris — *Agoseris sp.*
Alder — *Alnus sp.*
  red — *rubra*
  white — *rhombifolia*
Alfalfa — *Medicago sativa*
Alfilcria — *Erodium botrys*
Almond — *Prunus amygdalus*
Amaranth, prostrate — *Amaranthus blitoides*
  redroot — *retroflexus*
Apple — *Malus sp.*
  custard (may apple) — *Aronaceae*
  may (custard apple) — *Aronaceae*
Arborvitae — *Thuja occidentalis*
Arrowwood — *Viburnum dentatum*
Arum — *Araceae*
Ash — *Fraxinus sp.*
  white — *americana*
Asparagus — *Asparagus officinalis*
Aspen — *Populus sp.*
  largetooth — *grandidentata*
  quaking — *tremuloides*
Aster — *Aster sp.*
  golden — *Chrysopsis mariana*

B

Babyface (fringe cup) — *Lithophragma bulbifera*
Baldcypress (cypress) — *Taxodium distichum*
Balsam (balsam fir) — *Abies balsamea*
  cut-leaf — *Balsamorhiza macrophylla*
Balsamroot — *sagittata*
Barberry — *Berberis sp.*
  thunberg — *thunbergi*
Barley — *Hordeum vulgare*
  wild — *murinum; H. pusillum*
Barnyardgrass (wild millet) — *Echinochloa crus-galli*
Bassia — *Bassia sp.*
Bayberry — *Myrica pensylvanica*
Beachgrass, European — *Ammophila arenaria*
Beakrush — *Rhynchospora sp.*
Bean, wild — *Phaseolus sp.*
Bearberry — *Arctostaphylos uva-ursi*
Beardgrass — *Andropogon sp.*
Beargrass — *Xerophyllum sp.*
Beech — *Fagus grandifolia*
Bedstraw — *Galium sp.*
  catchweed — *aparine*
Beeplant, Rocky Mountain — *Cleome serrulata*
Beet, sugar — *Beta saccharifera*
Beggartick — *Bidens sp.*
Beggarweed, Florida — *Desmodium tortuosum*
Bentgrass — *Agrostis sp.*
Bindweed — *Polygonum sp.*
  black (dullseed cornbind) — *convolvulus*
Birch — *Betula sp.*
  black (sweet birch) — *lenta*
Birch, bog — *Betula glandulosa*
  paper (white birch) — *papyrifera*
  yellow — *lutea*
Birthwort — *Aristochlia clematitis*
Bittersweet — *Celastrus scandens*
Blackberry — *Rubus sp.*
  alleghany — *alleghaniensis*
  California — *ursinus vitifolius*
Blackbrush — *Flourensia cernua*
Blackhaw — *Viburnum prunifolium*
Blueberry — *Vaccinium sp.*
Blue-eyedgrass — *Sisyrinchium sp.*
Bluegrass — *Poa sp.*
  annual — *annua*
  sandberg — *secunda*
Bluejointgrass — *Calamagrostis canadensis*
Bluestem, big — *Andropogon furcatus*
  little — *scoparius*
Boneset (white snakeroot) — *Eupatorium rugosum*
Boxelder — *Acer negundo*
Brambles — *Rubus sp.*
Bristlegrass (foxtail) — *Setaria sp.*
  green (green foxtail) — *viridis*
  yellow (yellow foxtail) — *lutescens*
Bromegrass — *Bromus sp.*
Broom, Scotch — *Cytisus scoparius*
Broomsedge — *Andropogon virginicus*
Buckeye, California — *Aesculus californica*
Buckthorn — *Rhamnus cathartica*
  California — *californica*
Buckwheat — *Fagopyrum esculentum*
  bush — *Eriogonum giganteum*
  California — *fasciculatum*
  climbing false — *Polygonum dumetorum; P. scandens*
  wild — *Eriogonum sp.*
Bullgrass (bull paspalum) — *Paspalum boscianum*
Bumelia — *Bumelia spp.*
Bunchberry — *Cornus canadensis*
Bunchgrass (bluebunch wheatgrass) — *Agropyron spicatum*
Burclover — *Medicago sp.*
  California — *hispida*
Burdock — *Arctium tomentosum*
Buttercup — *Ranunculus sp.*
  California — *californicus*
Buttonweed — *Diodia sp.*

C

Cactus, cholla (prickly pear) — *Opuntia sp.*
  giant (sahuaro) — *Cereus giganteus*
  organ-pipe — *Pachycereus marginatus*
Cancer-root — *Conopholis americana*
Capul — *Schaefferia cuneifolia*
Caragana — *Caragana arborescens*
Carrot, wild (queen-Anne's lace) — *Daucus carota*
Cascara — *Rhamnus purshiana*
Cassia (senna) — *Cassia sp.*
Catbrier — *Smilax rotundifolia*
Catchfly, sleepy — *Silene antirrhina*

Catclaw, long-flowered	*Acacia greggi*		**D**
round-flowered	*roemeriana*		
Cattail	*Typha sp.*	Daisy (European daisy)	*Bellis perennis*
Ceanothus, blueblossom	*Ceanothus thyrsiflorus*	Dandelion	*Taraxacum officinale*
wedgeleaf	*cuneatus*	Deervetch	*Lotus sp.*
Cedar, incense	*Libocedrus decurrens*	American (Spanish	
northern white	*Thuja occidentalis*	clover)	*americanus*
(arborvitae)		broom (deerweed)	*scoparius*
Port Orford	*Chamaecyparis lawsoniana*	Chilean	*subpinnatus*
southern white	*thyoides*	foothill	*humistratus*
western red	*Thuja plicata*	Deerweed	*scoparius*
Chamise	*Adenostoma fasciculatum*	Dewberry	*Rubus sp.*
Cheatgrass	*Bromus tectorum*	Dock (sorrel)	*Rumex sp.*
Cherry	*Prunus sp.*	mule ears	*Wyethia amplexicaulis*
Bessey (sand cherry)	*besseyi*	Dogwood	*Cornus sp.*
black	*serotina*	flowering	*florida*
pin	*pensylvanica*	gray	*paniculata*
Chicalote	*Argemone platyceras*	Pacific	*nuttalli*
Chickweed	*Cerastium sp.*	silky	*amomum*
Chinquapin	*Castanea pumila*	stiffcornel	*foemina*
Chokeberry	*Aronia sp.*	Doveweed (croton)	*Croton sp.*
Chokecherry	*Prunus virginiana*	Dropseed, hairy (pine	*Blepharoneuron tricholepis*
western	*demissa*	dropseed)	
Christmasberry	*Photinia arbutifolia*	sand	*Sporobolus cryptandrus*
Chufa (nutgrass)	*Cyperus esculentus*	sixweeks	*microspermus*
Cinquefoil	*Potentilla sp.*		
Clover	*Trifolium sp.*		**E**
hop	*agrarium*		
pinole	*bifidum*	Ebony, Texas	*Pithecollobium flexicaule*
puff (sour clover)	*fucatum*	Egyptiangrass (durban	*Dactyloctenium aegyptium*
red	*pratense*	crowfootgrass)	
Spanish	*Lotus americanus*	Elder	*Sambucus sp.*
tomcat	*Trifolium tridentatum*	blueberry	*caerulea*
white	*repens*	Elm	*Ulmus sp.*
Clubmoss	*Lycopodium sp.*	American	*americana*
Cocklebur	*Xanthium sp.*	Chinese	*parvifolia*
Coralberry	*Symphoricarpos orbiculatus*	slippery	*fulva*
Cordgrass	*Spartina sp.*	Equisetum	*Equisetum sp.*
Corn	*Zea mays*	Eriogonum, wirestem	*Eriogonum pharnaceoides*
Cornbind, dullseed	*Polygonum convolvulus*	Euphorbia	*Euphorbia sp.*
Cornsalad	*Valerianella sp.*	painted	*heterophylla*
Cotton	*Gossypium sp.*	spotted	*maculata*
Cottonwood	*Populus sp.*	Evolvulus, Arizona	*Evolvulus arizonicus*
Cowpea	*Vigna sinensis*		
Crabapple	*Malus sp.*		**F**
Crabgrass	*Digitaria sp.*		
Cranberry	*Vaccinium sp.*	Fern, christmas	*Polystichum*
Cranberry, highbush	*Viburnum trilobum*		*achrostichoides*
Cranesbill (Carolina	*Geranium carolinianum*	polypody	*Polypodium vulgare*
geranium)		shield	*Dryopteris sp.*
Creeper, Virginia	*Parthenocissus quinquefolia*	marginal shield	*marginalis*
Creosotebush	*Larrea sp.*	spiny-toothed shield	*spinulosum*
Croton (doveweed)	*Croton sp.*	Fescue	*Festuca sp.*
California	*californicus*	foxtail	*megalura*
glandular	*glandulosis*	Fiddleneck	*Amsinckia sp.*
gulf	*punctatus*	tassel	*tesselata*
Texas	*texensis*	Filaree (heron bill)	*Erodium sp.*
wooly	*capitatus*	red-stem	*cicutarium*
Crowfootgrass, durban	*Dactyloctenium aegyptium*	Filbert, hybrid	*Corylus americana x*
(Egyptiangrass)			*avellana*
Crownbeard, golden	*Verbesina encelioides*	Fir, balsam (balsam)	*Abies balsamea*
Cucumber, wild	*Melothria pendula*	Douglas	*Pseudotsuga taxifolia*
Cuphea	*Cuphea sp.*	white	*Abies concolor*
Currant, squaw	*Ribes cereum*	Flax	*Linum usitatissimum*
Cutgrass	*Leersia sp.*	Flatsedge (see chufa, also)	*Cyperus sp.*
rice	*oryzoides*	Forestiera	*Forestiera angustifolia*
Cypress (baldcypress)	*Taxodium distichum*		

Foxtail (bristlegrass)	*Setaria sp.*
green	*viridis*
yellow	*lutescens*
Fringe cup (baby face)	*Lithophragma bulbifera*

G

Gallberry (inkberry)	*Ilex glabra*
Geranium	*Geranium sp.*
Carolina	*carolinianum*
Gilia	*Gilia sp.*
Globeberry, Lindheimer	*Ibervillea lindheimeri*
Goldenbush	*Aplopappus sp.*
Goldeneye	*Viguiera sp.*
Goldenrod	*Solidago sp.*
Goldstargrass (stargrass)	*Hypoxis sp.*
Gooseberry	*Ribes sp.*
Goosefoot	*Chenopodium sp.*
Goosegrass	*Eleusine indica*
Grama, blue	*Bouteloua gracilis*
Gramagrass	*sp.*
Grape	*Vitis sp.*
California	*californica*
Greasewood	*Sarcobatus sp.*
Greenbrier	*Smilax sp.*
bristly	*hispida*
Groundcherry	*Physalis sp.*
prairie	*lanceolata*
Gum, black	*Nyssa sylvatica*
sweet	*Liquidambar styraciflua*

H

Hackberry	*Celtis occidentalis*
desert (western)	*pallida*
Douglas	*douglasi*
thick-leaved	*reticulata*
Hawkweed	*Hieracium sp.*
orange (devil's paintbrush)	*aurantiacum*
Hawthorn (thornapple)	*Crataegus sp.*
Douglas	*douglasi*
red	*chrysocarpa*
river	*rivularis*
Hazelnut	*Corylus americana*
Hemlock	*Tsuga canadensis*
Hemp	*Cannabis sativa*
Hepatica	*Hepatica sp.*
Heron bill (filaree)	*Erodium sp.*
Hickory	*Carya sp.*
Holly, American	*Ilex opaca*
deciduous (winterberry)	*verticillata*
mountain	*montana*
Honeylocust	*Gleditsia triacanthos*
Honeysuckle, amur	*Lonicera maacki*
Hall's	*japonica halliana*
tatarian	*tatarica*
twinberry	*involucrata*
Hophornbeam	*Ostrya virginiana*
Huckleberry	*Gaylussacia sp.*
Huisache (sweet acacia)	*Acacia farnesiana*

I

Indiangrass	*Sorghastrum sp.*
Indigo, wild	*Baptisia tinctoria*
Inkberry (gallberry)	*Ilex glabra*
Ironwood, desert	*Olneya tesota*

J

Jewelweed (touch-me-not)	*Impatiens sp.*
Johnsongrass	*Sorphum halepense*
Jujube, wild (lotebush)	*Condalia lycioides*
Junegrass	*Koeleria cristata*
Juniper	*Juniperus sp.*
alligator	*pachyphloea*
California	*californica*
cherrystone	*monosperma*

K

Knotweed	*Polygonum sp.*, including *P. careyi, P. cilinode, P. douglasi, P. lapathifolium*

L

Labrador-tea	*Ledum groenlandicum*
Lace, queen Anne's	*Daucus carota*
Lady's thumb	*Polygonum persicaria*
Lambsquarters	*Chenopodium album*
Larch (tamarack)	*Larix laracina*
Japanese	*leptolepis*
Laurel, California	*Umbellularia californica*
Leatherleaf	*Chamaedaphnae calyculata*
Lespedeza	*Lespedeza sp.*
bicolor	*bicolor*
common	*striata*
cyrto	*cyrtobotrya*
Japan	*japonica*
Korean	*stipulacea*
natob	*bicolor natob*
sericea (sericea)	*cuneata*
Lily	*Lilium sp.*
Locust, black	*Robinia pseudoacacia*
Loosestrife	*Lysimachia sp.*
Lotebush (wild jujube)	*Condalia lycioides*
Lovegrass, spreading	*Eragrostis diffusa*
weeping	*curvula*
Lupine	*Lupinus sp.*
arroyo	*succulentus*
bicolor	*bicolor*
lunara	*formosus*
partcolor	*variicolor*
silver	*albifrons*
tree	*arboreus*

M

Madrone	*Arbutus menziesi*
Magnolia	*Magnolia sp.*
Mahogany, mountain	*Cercocarpus montanus*
Mannagrass	*Glyceria sp.*
Manzanita	*Arctostaphylos sp.*
mariposa	*mariposa*
pointleaf	*pungens*
whiteleaf	*viscida*
Maple	*Acer sp.*
bigtooth	*grandidentatum*
Douglas	*glabrum douglasi*
hard (sugar maple)	*saccharum*
red (soft maple)	*rubrum*
striped	*pensylvanicum*
Mayflower, Canada	*Maianthemum canadense*
Medic, black	*Medicago lupulina*
Mesquite	*Prosopis chilensis*
Milkvetch	*Astragalus sp.*

Millet, foxtail (German millet)	*Setaria italica var.*
proso	*Panicum miliaceum*
wild (barnyardgrass)	*Echinochloa crus-galli*
Miterwort	*Mitella diphylla*
false	*Tiarella sp.*
Mortonia	*Mortonia scabrella*
Mountainash	*Sorbus americana*
Greene's	*scopulina*
Mountainlaurel	*Kalmia latifolia*
Mountain misery	*Chamaebatia foliolosa*
Muhlenbergia (muhly)	*Muhlenbergia sp.*
Texas	*texana*
Muhly (muhlenbergia)	*sp.*
Mulberry	*Morus sp.*
red	*rubra*
white	*alba*
Mustard, wild	*Brassica sp.*
Myrtle, wax	*Myrica cerifera*

N

Nannyberry (nannyberry viburnum)	*Viburnum lentago*
Needle-and-thread-grass	*Stipa comata*
Neptunia, tropical	*Neptunia pubescens*
Nightshade	*Solanum sp.*
black	*nigrum*
Nimblewill	*Muhlenbergia screberi*
Ninebark	*Physocarpus sp.*
Nutgrass (chufa)	*Cyperus esculentus*
Nutrush (razorsedge)	*Scleria sp.*

O

Oak	*Quercus sp.*
bear (scrub oak)	*ilicifolia*
black	*velutina*
blackjack	*marilandica*
blue	*douglasi*
bur	*macrocarpa*
California black	*kelloggi*
California live	*agrifolia*
California scrub	*dumosa*
canyon live (golden oak)	*chrysolepis*
chestnut	*montana*
Emory	*emoryi*
fendler	*fendleri*
gambel	*gambeli*
golden (canyon live oak)	*chrysolepis*
interior live	*wislizeni*
laurel	*laurifolia*
live	*virginiana*
Mexican blue	*oblongifolia*
New Mexican (New Mexican shinnery oak)	*novamexicana*
northern red	*borealis*
overcup	*lyrata*
pin	*palustris*
post	*stellata*
Rocky Mountain shin (wavyleaf oak)	*undulata*
Rocky Mountain white (socorro oak)	*leptophylla*
scarlet	*coccinea*
scrub (bear oak)	*ilicifolia*
shinnery	*havardi*
socorro	*leptophylla*

Oak, southern red	*Quercus rubra (falcata)*
swamp chestnut	*prinus*
swamp white	*bicolor*
turkey	*laevis*
Utah white	*utahensis*
water	*nigra*
wavyleaf	*undulata*
white	*alba*
willow	*phellos*
Oatgrass (povertygrass)	*Danthonia spicata*
tall	*Arrhenatherum elatius*
Oats	*Avena sativa*
wild	*fatua*
Olive	*Olea europaea*
autumn	*Elaeagnus umbellata*
Russian	*angustifolia*
Oniongrass	*Melica bulbosa*
Oregongrape	*Mahonia aquifolium*
Osageorange	*Maclura pomifera*
Oxalis (wood sorrel)	*Oxalis sp.*

P

Paintbrush, devils (orange hawkweed)	*Hieracium aurantiacum*
Paloverde	*Cercidium floridum*
Pampasgrass	*Cortaderia selloana*
Panicgrass	*Panicum sp.*
Panicum, blue	*antidotale*
beaked	*anceps*
Hall's	*halli*
redtop	*agrostoides*
roundseed	*sphaerocarpon*
Texas	*texanum*
Parsley, desert	*Lomatium gormani*
Partridgeberry	*Mitchella repens*
Partridgepea	*Chamaechrista fasciculata*
small	*aspera*
Paspalum, barestem (small-seeded paspalum; sloughgrass)	*Paspalum longepedunculatum*
bull (bullgrass)	*boscianum*
Florida	*floridanum*
Pawpaw	*Asimina triloba*
Pea, butterfly	*Centrosema virginiana*
garden	*Pisum sativum*
milk	*Galactia sp.*
Peach	*Prunus persica*
Peanut	*Arachis hypogeae*
hog	*Amphicarpa bracteata*
Pear	*Pyrus communis*
prickly (cholla cactus)	*Opuntia sp.*
Peavine, Arizona	*Lathyrus arizonicus*
Pecan	*Carya sp.*
Pepper, water	*Polygonum hydropiper*
Pepperweed	*Lepidium sp.*
Persimmon	*Diospyros virginiana*
Pigweed	*Amaranthus sp; Chenopodium sp.*
prostrate	*Amaranthus blitoides*
redroot	*retroflexus*
Pimpernel	*Anagallis arvensis*
Pine	*Pinus sp.*
Austrian	*nigra*
Banks (jack pine)	*banksiana*
Colorado pinon	*cembroides edulis*

Pine, digger	*Pinus sabiniana*
jack (Banks pine)	*banksiana*
loblolly	*taeda*
lodgepole	*murrayana*
longleaf	*palustris*
Mexican piñon	*cembroides*
piñon (piñon)	*edulis*
pitch	*rigida*
ponderosa	*ponderosa*
red	*resinosa*
Rocky Mountain yellow	*brachyptera*
Scotch	*sylvestris*
shortleaf	*echinata*
slash	*caribaea*
Virginia	*virginiana*
western white	*monticola*
western yellow	*ponderosa*
white	*strobus*
Pinegrass	*Calamagrostis rubescens*
Piñon (piñon pine)	*Pinus edulis*
Pinweed	*Lechea sp.*
Plantain	*Plantago sp.*
Plum	*Prunus sp.*
american (wild plum)	*americana*
Poisonivy	*Toxicodendron (Rhus) radicans*
Poisonoak	*diversiloba*
Poisonsumac	*vernix*
Pokeberry	*Phytolacca americana*
Popcorn flower	*Plagiobothrys nothofulvus*
Poplar	*Populus sp.*
California	*trichocarpa*
tulip (tuliptree)	*Liriodendron tulipifera*
Poppy, California	*Eschscholtzia californica*
Porcupinegrass	*Stipa spartea*
Potato	*Solanum tuberosum*
Povertygrass (oatgrass)	*Danthonia spicata*
Prickly pear	*Opuntia sp.*
nopal	*lindheimeri*
Primrose, evening	*Raimannia laciniata*
Privet, amur	*Ligustrum amurense*
California	*ovalifolium*
Prune	*Prunus sp.*
Pussytoes	*Antennaria sp.*

Q

Quackgrass	*Agropyron repens*
Quail brush	*Atriplex lentiformis; A. polycarpa*

R

Rabbitbrush	*Chrysothamnus sp.*
Ragweed, lesser	*Ambrosia artemisiifolia*
western	*psilostachya*
Rape	*Brassica napus*
Raspberry	*Rubus sp.*
trailing	*parvifolius*
Razorsedge (nutrush)	*Scleria sp.*
Britton's	*brittoni*
whip	*triglomerata*
Redcedar, eastern	*Juniperus virginiana*
Redtop	*Agrostis alba*
Redwood	*Sequoia sempervirens*
Rhynchosia	*Rhynchosia sp.*
Rice	*Oryza sativa*

Ricegrass, indian	*Oryzopsis hymenoides*
Rockdaisy	*Laphamia sp.*
Rose	*Rosa sp.*
multiflora	*multiflora*
prairie	*pratincola*
Ruellia	*Ruellia ciliosa*
Rush	*Juncus sp.*
Russianthistle	*Salsola kali*
Rye	*Secale cereale*
Ryegrass, Italian	*Lolium multiflorum*

S

Sacaton, alkali	*Sporobolus airoides*
Sage, black	*Salvia mellifera*
salt (saltbush)	*Atriplex sp.*
Sagebrush	*Artemisia sp.*
big	*tridentata*
bud	*spinescens*
coast	*californica*
silver	*cana*
Sagewort, cudweed	*gnaphalodes*
Sahuaro (giant cactus)	*Cereus giganteus*
Salal	*Gaultheria shallon*
Salmonberry	*Rubus spectabilis*
Salsify	*Tragopogon sp.*
Sassafras	*Sassafras albidum*
Saltbush (salt sage)	*Atriplex sp.*
Sawbrier	*Smilax glauca*
Sawpalmetto	*Serenoa repens*
Screwbean (mesquite)	*Prosopis pubescens*
Sedge	*Carex sp.*
Senna (cassia)	*Cassia sp.*
Sericea (sericea lespedeza)	*Lespedeza cuneata*
Serviceberry	*Amelanchier sp.*
western	*alnifolia; A. florida*
Shadscale	*Atriplex concertifolia*
Shepherdspurse	*Capsella bursa-pastoris*
Shinleaf	*Pyrola sp.*
Shinnery	*Quercus sp.*
Silene, sleepy	*Silene antirrhina*
Silktassel, Wright's	*Garrya wrighti*
Skunkcabbage	*Symplocarpus foetidus*
Sloughgrass (barestem paspalum; small-seeded paspalum)	*Paspalum longepedunculatum*
Smartweed	*Polygonum sp.*
Muhlenberg's	*muhlenbergi*
Pennsylvania	*pensylvanicum*
waterpepper	*hydropiper*
Snakeroot, white (boneset)	*Eupatorium rugosum*
Snakeweed	*Gutierrezia sp.*
Snapweed (touch-me-not)	*Impatiens sp.*
Snowberry	*Symphoricarpos albus*
mountain	*oreophilus*
roundleaf	*rotundifolius*
western (wolfberry)	*occidentalis*
Solomonplume, feather (false solomonseal)	*Smilacina racemosa*
Solomonseal	*Polygonatum sp.*
false	*Smilacina racemosa*
Sorghum	*Sorghum vulgare*
Sorrel (dock)	*Rumex sp.*
sheep	*acetosella*
wood (oxalis)	*Oxalis sp.*
Sotol	*Dasylirion sp.*
Soybean	*Soja max*

Spanish bayonet — *Yucca sp.; Y. elata*
Spiderling, Watson — *Boerhaavia watsoni*
Spirea — *Spiraea sp.*
Springbeauty — *Claytonia perfoliata*
Spruce — *Picea sp.*
  Engelmann — *engelmanni*
  Norway — *abies*
  red — *rubens*
  Sitka — *sitchensis*
  white — *glauca*
Spurge — *Euphorbia sp.*
  flowering — *corollata*
Squawberry — *Rhus microphylla*
Stargrass (goldstargrass) — *Hypoxis sp.*
Starwort, chickweed — *Stellaria media*
Strawberry — *Fragaria sp.*
Sudangrass — *Sorghum vulgare sudanense*
Sugarcane — *Saccharum officinarum*
Sumac — *Rhus sp.*
  dwarf (flameleaf sumac) — *copallina*
  lemonade (skunkbush sumac) — *trilobata*
  smooth — *glabra*
  staghorn — *typhina*
Sumpweed — *Iva sp.*
Sunflower (wirestem eriogonum) — *Eriogonum pharnaceoides*
  common — *Helianthus annuus*
  little — *Helianthella uniflora*
  prairie — *Helianthus petiolaris*
Sweetclover — *Melilotus sp.*
Sweetfern — *Comptonia peregrina*
Switchgrass — *Panicum virgatum*
Sycamore — *Platanus occidentalis*

T

Tamarack (larch) — *Larix laracina*
Tamarisk — *Tamarix gallica*
  evergreen — *articulata*
Tanoak — *Lithocarpus densiflorus*
Tansymustard, Menzie's — *Dascurainia menziesi*
Tarweed — *Hemizonia congesta; H. virgata; Microseris douglasi*
  Chile — *Madia sp.; M. sativa*
Tasajillo — *Opuntia leptocaulis*
Tea, New Jersey — *Ceanothus americana*
  mormon — *Ephedra sp.*
Teaberry (wintergreen) — *Gaultheria procumbens*
Thimbleberry — *Rubus parviflorus*
Thistle, napa — *Centaurea melitensis*
Thornapple (hawthorn) — *Crataegus sp.*
Three-awn (three-awngrass) — *Aristida sp.*
Tobacco — *Nicotiana tabacum*
Tobosa (tobosagrass) — *Hilaria mutica*
Tomato — *Lycopersicon esculentum*
Touch-me-not (jewelweed) — *Impatiens sp.*
Trefoil (deervetch) — *Lotus sp.*
  tick — *Desmodium sp.*
Triodea — *Triodea sp.*
Tuliptree (tulip poplar) — *Liriodendron tulipifera*
Turkeymullein — *Eremocarpus setigervus*

U

Uniola, spike — *Uniola laxa*

V

Velvetbean — *Stizolobium sp.*
Verbena (vervain) — *Verbena sp.*
  wooly — *stricta*
Vervain (verbena) — *sp.*
Vetch — *Vicia sp.*
  american — *americana*
  augusta (narrowleaf vetch) — *angustifolia*
  carolina — *caroliniana*
  hairy — *villosa*
  narrowleaf (augusta vetch) — *angustifolia*
  purple — *atropurpurea*
Viburnum — *Viburnum sp.*
  arrowwood (arrowwood) — *dentatum*
  blackhaw (blackhaw) — *prunifolium*
  cranberrybush (highbush cranberry) — *trilobum*
  mapleleaf — *acerifolium*
  nannyberry (nannyberry) — *lentago*
  witchhobble — *alnifolium*
  witherod — *cassinoides*
Violet — *Viola sp.*

W

Walnut — *Juglans sp.*
  black — *nigra*
Wedgescale — *Sphenopholis sp.*
Wheat — *Triticum aestivum*
Wheat grass, beardless — *Agropyron inerme*
  bluebunch (bunchgrass) — *spicatum*
  slender — *pauciflorum*
  western — *smithi*
Whitegrass — *Leersia virginica*
Whitethorn, mountain — *Ceanothus cordulatus*
Wildbean — *Strophostyles sp.*
  trailing — *helvola*
Wildlettuce, prickly — *Lactuca sp.*
Wildrye — *Elymus sp.*
  giant — *condensatus*
Willow — *Salix sp.*
  black — *nigra*
  purpleosier — *purpurea*
Winterberry (deciduous holly) — *Ilex verticillata*
  mountain — *montana*
Winterfat — *Eurotia lanata*
Wintergreen (teaberry) — *Gaultheria procumbens*
Wiregrass — *Aristida virgata*
Witchgrass, common — *Panicum capillare*
Witchhazel — *Hamamelis virginiana*
Wolfberry — *Lycium sp.*
Wolfberry (western snowberry) — *Symphoricarpos occidentalis*

Y

Yarrow — *Achillea lanulosc*
Yaupon — *Ilex vomitoria*

INDEX

⫷⫷⟨⟩⟩